HANDBOOK
of
THERMODYNAMIC
TABLES
Second Edited and Revised Edition

Kuzman Ražnjević

begell house, inc.
New York • Wallingford (U.K.)

Handbook of Thermodynamic Tables, Second Edited and Revised Edition

Library of Congress Cataloging-in-Publication Data

Raznjevic, Kuzman.
  [Termodinamicke tablice. English]
  Handbook of thermodynamic tables / Kuzman Raznjevic.-- 2nd edited and rev. ed.
        p.   cm.
  Includes bibliographical references and index.
  ISBN 1-56700-046-0 (hardcover)
  1. Thermodynamics--Tables.   I. Title.
QC311.3R3913   1995
536'.7'0212--dc20
                                                    95-44100
                                                      CIP

CONTENTS

3 Vapors

4 Gases

Instructions for Use of Tables

Each physical quantity is represented as the product of the numerical value and a unit of measurement. Thus, we can write some the unknown quantity X as:

$$X = \{X\}[X],\tag{1}$$

where $\{X\}$ is the numerical value and $[X]$ is the unit of measurement. Equation (1) could be written in the form of a fraction:

$$\{X\}=X/[X],\tag{2}$$

from which it follows that the numerical value $\{X\}$ is equal to the quotient of the physical quantity X and the unit of measurement, $[X]$. This is true for every physical quantity. For example, for the unknown physical quantity of length L, we can write:

$$L = \{L\}[L],\tag{3}$$

then the numerical value $\{L\}$ is equal to:

$$\{L\} = L/[L].\tag{4}$$

For a known quantity, for example, when the distance between two cities is 580 km, then according to equation (3), we will write:

$$L = 580 \text{ km},$$

where $580 = \{L\}$, the numerical value, and km = $[L]$ is the unit of length. According to equations (2) and (4) the numerical value 580 is equal to the quotient of quantity L and units of length, km, namely:

$$580 = L/km$$

Numerical values in the tables in this book are actually the numerical values of physical quantities, that is that the numerical values in the table column are quotients of the physical quantity and the unit of measurement in the column head of the table. For example, on page 10, table 1.8, in the column for the specific heat capacity, 0.314 is in the first row, that is the numerical value which is equal to the quotient of the quantity c and the unit of measurement kJ/(kg K) in the table head in the same row, namely:

$$0.314 = \frac{c}{\text{kJ(kg K)}}.$$

Hence it follows that the value of the specific heat capacity is:

$$c = 0.314 \text{ kJ/(kg K)}.$$

In the same way we can read any numerical values from the tables and determine the quantitative values of corresponding quantities.

This tabular way of representing physical quantities is the most suitable because there is no need to state separately the units to which the numerical values in the tables refer.

SOLIDS

Table 1-1 Thermal Properties of Solid Elements

Element		At a temperature of 20 °C		At a pressure $p = 1.013\ 25$ bar ($= 760$ mm Hg)			
Name	Symbol	Density ρ kg/m³	Linear expansion coefficient α 1/kK[1]	Melting point t_m °C	Heat of fusion q_f kJ/kg	Boiling point t_b °C	Heat of vaporization r kJ/kg
Aluminium	Al	2700	0.0237	658	355.878	2270	11723.040
Antimony	Sb	6690	0.0110	630.5	167.472	1640	1256.040
Arsenic	As	5720	0.0050	830	—	625	1674.720
Barium	Ba	3760	—	704	—	1700	1339.776
Beryllium	Be	1850	0.0130	1278	1427.699	3000	24827.724
Bismuth	Bi	9800	0.0135	271	54.428	1500	837.360
Boron	B	2340	0.008	2500	—	—	—
Cadmium	Cd	8640	0.030	320.9	54.428	767	1004.832
Calcium	Ca	1540	0.025	851	328.664	1400	4186.800
Carbon	C	—	—	3540	—	4000	5024.160
Cerium	Ce	6800	0.010	815	—	1400	—
Cesium	Cs	1870	0.097	28	15.910	670	502.416
Chromium	Cr	7100	0.008	1800	293.076	2400	6154.596
Cobalt	Co	8800	0.0123	1490	280.516	3200	6489.540
Copper	Cu	8930	0.0166	1083	209.340	2330	4647.348
Gallium	Ga	5900	0.018	29.78	79.968	2300	—
Gold	Au	19290	0.0142	1063	66.989	2700	1758.456
Iodine	J	4930	0.093	113.5	—	185	334.944
Iridium	Ir	22500	0.0065	2454	—	>4800	3893.724
Iron	Fe	7860	0.0123	1530	272.142	2500	6363.936
Lead	Pb	11340	0.029	327.3	23.865	1730	921.096
Lithium	Li	534	0.056	180	138.164	1400	21352.680
Magnesium	Mg	1740	0.026	650	209.340	1110	5652.180
Manganese	Mn	7300	0.023	1250	251.208	2100	4186.800
Mercury	Hg	—	—	−38.83	—	356.95	—
Molybdenum	Mo	10200	0.005	2600	—	3560	7117.560
Nickel	Ni	8900	0.013	1455	293.076	3000	6196.464
Osmium	Os	22480	0.0061	2500	—	—	—
Palladium	Pd	12000	0.0118	1555	150.725	—	3977.460
Phosphorus, white	P	1820	0.125	44.1	21.771	280	1674.720
Platinum	Pt	21450	0.009	1773	113.044	3800	2512.080
Potassium	K	862	0.083	63	54.428	760	2051.532
Rhenium	Re	20500	—	3150	—	—	—
Rhodium	Rh	12400	0.009	1966	—	—	—
Rubidium	Rb	1520	0.090	38.5	25.539	713	837.360
Selenium	Se	4400	0.037	220	68.664	688	1088.568
Silicon	Si	2330	0.0024	1410	—	2350	14067.648
Silver	Ag	10500	0.0189	960.5	104.670	1950	2177.136
Sodium	Na	971	0.072	97.7	113.044	880	4186.800
Strontium	Sr	—	—	757	—	1370	—
Sulfur (monoclinic)	S	1960	0.080	119	46.055	—	—
Sulfur (rhombic)	S	2060	0.074	112.8	39.356	444.60	293.076
Tantalum	Ta	16600	0.0065	3000	—	—	—
Tin	Sn	7280	0.027	231.9	58.615	2300	2595.816
Titanium	Ti	4530	0.0108	1800	—	—	—
Tungsten	W	19300	0.0043	3380	251.208	5000	4814.820
Vanadium	V	6000	0.0085	1720	—	—	—
Zinc	Zn	7130	0.029	419.4	112.206	907	1800.324
Zirconium	Zr	6530	—	1900	—	—	—

[1] kK = kilokelvin = 10^3 K

1 Btu = 1.055 06 kJ

Table 1-2 Thermal Properties of Solid Inorganic Compounds

Substance		At a temperature of 20 °C		At a pressure $p = 1.013\ 25$ bar (= 760 mm Hg)			
Name	Chemical formula	Density ρ kg/m^3	Cubic expansion coefficient α_V 1/K	Melting point t_m °C	Heat of fusion q_f kJ/kg	Boiling point t_b °C	Heat of vaporization r kJ/kg
Aluminium oxide	Al$_2$O$_3$	4000	0.000005	2050	—	2980	4731.084
Barium chloride	BaCl$_2$	3900	0.000060	955	116.393	1560	1214.172
Barium oxide	BaO	5700	—	1923	—	1880	2470.212
Barium sulphate	BaSO$_4$	4500	0.000075	1580	—	—	—
Calcium carbide	CaC$_2$	2210	—	2300	—	—	—
Calcium chloride	CaCl$_2$	2150	0.000067	772	—	<1600	—
Calcium oxide	CaO	3300	0.000060	2572	—	2850	—
Chromic oxide	Cr$_2$O$_3$	5200	—	2275	—	—	—
Cristobalite (silicon dioxide)	SiO$_2$	2300	—	1710	—	2590	—
Ferrous oxide	FeO	5900	—	1370	—	—	—
Hematite (ferric oxide)	FeO$_3$	5200	0.000008	1560	—	—	—
Lead monoxide	PbO	9300	0.000055	880	41.868	1480	962.964
Magnesium oxide	MgO	3600	0.000040	2800	—	—	—
Magnetite (ferroso-ferric oxide)	Fe$_3$O$_4$	5100	0.0000096	1550	—	—	—
Potassium chloride	KCl	1989	0.000115	770	—	1413	2512.080
Potassium hydroxide	KOH	2000	0.000188	360	—	1320	2320.740
Potassium nitrate	KNO$_3$	2100	0.000190	337	—	—	—
Potassium oxide	K$_2$O	2300	—	—	—	—	1632.852
Potassium sulphate	K$_2$SO$_4$	2660	0.000126	1067	—	—	—
Quartz (silicon dioxide)	SiO$_2$	2650	—	1470	—	—	—
Silver bromide	AgBr	6470	—	430	50.242	1330	962.964
Silver chloride	AgCl	5560	—	455	92.110	1554	1256.040
Sodium chloride	NaCl	2164	0.000106	802	519.163	1440	2847.024
Sodium hydroxide	NaOH	2130	0.000084	328	167.472	1390	3307.572
Sodium nitrate	NaNO$_3$	2260	0.000110	310	188.406	—	—
Sodium sulphate	Na$_2$SO$_4$	2700	0.000220	884	259.582	—	—
Tantalum carbide	TaC	14500	—	3800	—	—	—
Zinc oxide	ZnO	5700	0.000023	2000	—	—	—

1 Btu = 1.055 06 kJ

Table 1-3 Thermal Properties of Solid Organic Compounds

Substance		At a temperature of 20 °C		At a pressure $p = 1.013\ 25$ bar (= 760 mm Hg)			
Name	Chemical formula	Density ρ kg/m^3	Cubic expansion coefficient α_V 1/K	Melting point t_m °C	Heat of fusion q_f kJ/kg	Boiling point t_b °C	Heat of vaporization r kJ/kg
Anthracene	C$_{14}$H$_{10}$	1250	0.000210	216	167.472	340	—
Benzoic acid	C$_7$H$_6$O$_2$	1340	0.000520	122.4	138.164	250	703.382
Camphor	C$_{10}$H$_{16}$O	990	0.000485	179	41.868	209	—
Diphenyl	C$_{12}$H$_{10}$	1040	—	68.5	121.417	255	309.823
Diphenylamine	C$_{12}$H$_{11}$N	1160	—	54	100.483	302	—
Naphthalene	C$_{10}$H$_8$	1145	0.000283	80.1	150.725	217.9	314.010
Paraffin	—	—	—	54	146.538	300	—
Phenol	C$_6$H$_6$O	1070	—	41	121.417	182	510.790
Phthalic acid	C$_8$H$_6$O$_4$	1590	—	194	314.010	—	—
Picric acid	C$_6$H$_3$O$_7$N$_3$	1767	—	122	85.411	—	—
Resorcinol	C$_6$H$_6$O$_2$	1283	—	109	188.406	277	—
Stearic acid	C$_{18}$H$_{36}$O$_2$	941	—	70	200.966	380	234.461
Sugar, cane	—	—	—	160	56.103	—	—
Trinitrotoluene	C$_7$H$_5$O$_6$N$_3$	1750	—	81	87.923	—	—

1 Btu = 1.055 06 kJ

Table 1-4 Linear Thermal Expansion Coefficient α of Solids in the Temperature Range Between $0\,°C$ and t

Substance Name	Chemical composition and mass fractions of substances %	Temperature $\dfrac{t}{°C}$	Linear expansion coefficient $\dfrac{\alpha}{1/kK^{1)}}$
Aluminium	Al	−253	−0.0147
		−190	−0.0181
		−100	−0.0220
		−500	−0.0224
		+50	+0.0234
		100	0.0238
		200	0.0245
		300	0.0255
		400	0.0265
		500	0.0274
		600	0.0283
Aluminium alloy	Al, Mg, Mn	100	0.023
Aluminium alloy, Y-alloy	Al, Cu, Ni	100	0.023
Amber		50	0.05400
		75	0.05600
American alloy	G, Al, Cu	100	0.025
Anticorodal	Al, Mg, Si	100	0.022
Antimony ‖	Sb	50	0.0160
		100	0.0175
		200	0.0190
		300	0.0195
		400	0.0195
Antimony ⊥	Sb	50	0.0080
		100	0.0080
		200	0.0080
		300	0.0083
		400	0.0081
Bakelite		100	0.021...0.036
Basalt		100	0.009
Beryllium		100	0.123
Bismuth	Bi	100	0.124
Brass	62Cu, 38Zn	−253	−0.01403
		−190	−0.01637
		+100	+0.0184
		200	0.01925
		300	0.02010
		400	0.02298
Brick		100	0.0036...0.0058
Bronze	85Cu, 9Mn, 6Sn	−190	−0.01495
		+100	+0.01750
		200	0.01790
		300	0.01833
		400	0.01878
		500	0.01922
Bronze red (brass)		100	0.019
Cadmium	Cd	100	0.0308
Cement, Portland (concrete)		100	0.0140

Substance Name	Chemical composition and mass fractions of substances %	Temperature $\dfrac{t}{°C}$	Linear expansion coefficient $\dfrac{\alpha}{1/kK^{1)}}$
China		−190	−0.00168
		+100	+0.00300
		200	0.00330
		300	0.00343
		400	0.00353
		500	0.00364
		600	0.00373
		700	0.00376
		800	0.00388
		900	0.00440
		1000	0.00431
Chromium	Cr	−50	0.00940
		+100	0.00800
		200	0.00875
		300	0.00733
		400	0.00788
		500	0.00700
Clinker		100	0.0028...0.0048
Cobalt	Co	100	0.0123
Concrete, heaped concrete Blast furnace slag concrete		100	0.0058...0.0066
Constantan	60Cu, 40Ni	−190	−0.01189
		+100	+0.01520
		200	0.01560
		300	0.01603
		400	0.01643
		500	0.01682
Copper	Cu	−253	−0.01174
		−190	−0.01395
		−100	−0.01550
		+100	+0.01650
		200	0.01690
		300	0.01717
		400	0.01768
		500	0.01808
		600	0.01848
Duralumin	95Al, 4Cu+Mg, Mn, Si, Fe	100	0.02350
		200	0.02450
		300	0.02600
		400	0.02675
		500	0.02730
Ebonite		100	0.0170...0.0280
Electron and Magnevin alloys		100	0.025
German alloy	G Al, Zn, Cu	100	0.024
Glass, Jena 16 ‖‖		−253	−0.00478
		−190	−0.00595
		−80	−0.00713
		+100	+0.00810
		200	0.00835
		300	0.00867

1) kK = kilokelvin = 10^3 K

Substance				Substance			
Name	Chemical composition and mass fractions of substances	Tempe-rature	Linear expansion coefficient	Name	Chemical composition and mass fractions of substances	Tempe-rature	Linear expansion coefficient
	%	$\dfrac{t}{°C}$	$\dfrac{\alpha}{1/kK^{1)}}$		%	$\dfrac{t}{°C}$	$\dfrac{\alpha}{1/kK^{1)}}$
Glass, Jena 16 III		400	0.00898	Iridium	Ir	1000	0.00790
		500	0.00926			1500	0.00847
						1700	0.00871
Glass							
—Jena 59 III		−190	−0.00432	Iron, cast	Fe	−190	−0.008368
		+100	+0.00590			100	0.0104
		200	0.00600			200	0.011050
		300	0.00610			300	0.011633
		400	0.00618			400	0.012250
		500	0.00624			500	0.012880
						600	0.013483
—Jena 1565 III		100	0.00345			700	0.014100
		200	0.00360			800	0.014700
		300	0.00373	Iron, cast, gray	Fe	100	0.0104
		400	0.00390				
		500	0.00404	Iron, pure	Fe	100	0.012
—Jena 2594 III		−253	−0.00368	Lautal alloy	Al, Cu	100	0.023
		−190	−0.00447	Lead	Pb	−553	−0.02455
		−80	−0.00525			−190	−0.02674
		+100	+0.00630			+100	+0.02900
		200	0.00640			200	0.02965
		300	0.00657			300	0.03110
		400	0.00673				
		500	0.00686	Limestone		100	0.0070
Glass, quartz		−259	+0.00304	Lithium	Li	100	0.060
		−190	+0.00158				
		−190	−0.00150	Magnesium	Mg	−190	−0.02111
		−50	−0.00260			+100	+0.02600
		+50	+0.00044			200	0.02705
		100	0.00051			300	0.02787
		200	0.00585			400	0.02883
		300	0.00627			500	0.02966
		400	0.00635				
		500	0.00612	Mangal alloy	Al, Mn	100	0.022
		600	0.00600	Manganine	86Cu, 12Mn, 2Ni	100	0.01750
		700	0.00571			200	0.01825
		800	0.00563			300	0.01867
		900	0.00556			400	0.01888
		1000	0.00540			500	0.01940
						600	0.01983
Gold	Au	−235	−0.011739			700	0.02043
		−190	−0.013053			800	0.02100
		+100	+0.0142				
		200	0.014600	Marble		100	0.002...0.02
		300	0.014800	Mica		100	0.0135
		400	0.015025			200	0.01350
		500	0.015240			300	0.01383
		600	0.015583			400	0.01400
		700	0.015929			500	0.01380
		800	0.016250				
		900	0.016556				
Granite		100	0.0080...0.0118	Molybdenum	Mo	−190	−0.004158
						+100	0.005200
Hydronalium alloy	G Al-Mg	100	0.020			200	0.005350
						300	0.005467
Indium	In	100	0.044			400	0.005600
Invar (Invar steel)	36Ni	100	0.0015				
Iridium	Ir	−190	−0.00563	Monel metal		100	0.014
		−100	−0.00600				
		+100	+0.00650				

1) kK = kilokelvin = 10^3 K

Table 1-4 Linear Thermal Expansion Coefficient α of Solids in the Temperature Range Between 0 °C and t (continued)

Name	Chemical composition and mass fractions of substances %	Temperature t °C	Linear expansion coefficient α 1/kK[1)]
Mortar, cement		100	0.0085...0.0135
Mortar, lime		100	0.0073...0.0089
Nickel	Ni	−190	−0.00995
		+100	+0.01300
		200	0.01375
		300	0.01430
		400	0.01488
		500	0.01520
		600	0.01545
		700	0.01579
		800	0.01611
		900	0.01644
		1000	0.01180
Nickel silver		100	0.0180
Niobium		100	0.007
Osmium	Os	100	0.0067
Palladium	Pd	−190	−0.01016
		−100	−0.01070
		−50	−0.01120
		+100	+0.01190
		200	0.01210
		300	0.01233
		400	0.01255
		500	0.01276
		600	0.01288
		700	0.01320
		800	0.01333
		900	0.01363
		1000	0.01386
Plaster		100	0.025
Platinum	Pt	−190	−0.00795
		−100	−0.00840
		+100	−0.00860
		−50	+0.00900
		200	0.00915
		300	0.00927
		400	0.00940
		500	0.00954
		600	0.00967
		700	0.00980
		800	0.00992
		900	0.01006
		1000	0.01019
Platinum-iridium alloy	90Pt, 10Ir	−190	−0.00774
		+100	+0.00900
		200	0.00910
		300	0.00923
		400	0.00938
		500	0.00950
		600	0.00963
		700	0.00976
		800	0.00989
		900	0.01001
		1000	0.01015
		1100	0.01032
		1200	0.01042

Name	Chemical composition and mass fractions of substances %	Temperature t °C	Linear expansion coefficient α 1/kK[1)]
Platinum-iridium alloy	90Pt, 10Ir	1300	0.01055
		1400	0.01068
		1500	0.01080
	80Pt, 20Ir	−190	−0.00753
		+100	+0.00830
		200	0.00850
		300	0.00863
		400	0.00878
		500	0.00890
		600	0.00905
		700	0.00919
		800	0.00934
		900	0.00948
		1000	0.00962
		1100	0.00975
		1200	0.00990
		1300	0.01004
		1400	0.01019
		1500	0.01033
Platinum-rhodium alloy	80Pt, 20Rh	300	0.00927
		600	0.00975
		900	0.01023
		1000	0.01045
		1500	0.01121
Poly (vinylchloride) (PVC)	(C_2H_3Cl)	100	0.0781
Potassium	K	50	8.3
Rhodium	Rh	−190	−0.00684
		−100	−0.00780
		−50	−0.00780
		+50	+0.00900
Sandlime brick		100	0.0078
Sandstone		100	0.005...0.012
Silicon	Si	50	0.0078
Silumin	Al, Si	100	0.022
	G Al	100	0.019
Silver	Ag	−253	−0.01478
		−190	−0.01695
		+100	+0.01950
		200	0.02000
		300	0.02027
		400	0.02058
		500	0.02086
		600	0.02117
		700	0.02164
		800	0.02206
Sinter corundum		200	0.00650
		300	0.00667
		400	0.00668
		500	0.00720
		600	0.00742
		700	0.00757
		800	0.00781

[1)] kK = kilokelvin = 10^3 K

Name	Chemical composition and mass fractions of substances %	Temperature t °C	Linear expansion coefficient α 1/kK[1]
Sinter corundum		900	0.00794
		1000	0.00815
		1100	0.00832
		1200	0.00846
		1300	0.00858
		1400	0.00868
		1500	0.00877
Sinter magnesium		200	0.01225
		300	0.01200
		400	0.01225
		500	0.01260
		600	0.01292
		700	0.01329
		800	0.01350
		900	0.01352
		1000	0.01390
		1100	0.01409
		1200	0.01429
		1300	0.01450
		1400	0.01434
		1500	0.01507
		1800	0.01597
Sodium	Na	50	0.0720
Steel, carbon	0.1 C	100	0.012
	0.6 C	100	0.0117
Steel, chrome		100	0.010...0.014
Steel, hard		−190	−0.00863
		100	+0.01170
		200	0.01225
		300	0.01277
		400	0.01328
		500	0.01382
		600	0.91433
		700	0.91486
Steel, nickel	77Fe, 23Ni	300	0.00933
		400	0.01000
		500	0.01050
		600	0.01042
		700	0.01114
		800	0.01156
		900	0.01167
		1000	0.01185
	64Fe, 36Ni	100	0.00150
		200	0.00375
		300	0.00533
		400	0.00775
		500	0.00940
		600	0.01083
		700	0.01214
		800	0.01313
		900	0.01394
Steel, nickel chrome		100	0.0115
	18Cr, 8Ni	100	0.016
Steel, nickel chrome/ molybdenum	Cr, Ni, Mo	100	0.011
Steel, soft		−190	−0.00879
		+100	+0.01200
		200	0.01255
		300	0.01307
		400	0.01360
		500	0.01412
		600	0.01465
		700	0.01519
Steel, wrought		−253	−0.007115
		−190	−0.008842
		+100	+0.012200
		200	0.012650
		300	0.013100
		400	0.013575
		500	0.014040
		600	0.014517
		700	0.014986
Tantalum	Ta	100	0.0065
Tin	Sn	−190	−0.02232
		+100	+0.02670
Titanium	Ti	100	0.01080
Tungsten	W	−190	−0.003842
		+100	+0.004500
		200	0.004500
		300	0.004667
		400	0.004750
		500	0.004500
		600	0.004500
		700	0.004500
		800	0.004500
		900	0.004500
		1000	0.004600
		1100	0.004636
		1200	0.004708
		1300	0.004785
		1400	0.004871
		1500	0.004967
		1700	0.004765
		2000	0.005150
		3000	0.006500
Vanadium	V	100	0.00850
Vinidur plastic		100	0.0800
Widia		20	0.0053
Wood, fir ‖		100	0.0076
Wood, fir ⊥		100	0.0544
Wood, oak (with the grain) ‖		100	0.0030
Wood, oak (cross grain) ⊥		100	0.580
Zinc	Zn	−190	−0.00974
		+100	0.01650

[1] kK = kilokelvin = 10^3 K

Table 1-5 Melting Points of Alloys

Alloy	Mass fractions %	Melting point $\dfrac{t}{°C}$
Aluminium solder, hard	—	>540
Aluminium solder, soft	—	250...500
American alloy	G Al, Cu	544...640
Anticorrodal	Al, Mg, Li	630...650
Brass	—	900
Bronze	—	≈900
Copper solder	—	1160...1230
Delta metal	56Cu, 41Zn, 1Fe, Mn, Pb	≈950
Duralumin	Al, Cu, Mg	520...650
Electron and Magnevin alloys	—	625...650
German alloy	G Al, Zn, Cu	530...630
Hard solder	—	820...915
Hydronalium	Al, Mg	520...630
Invar (Invar steel)	—	1425
Iron, cast (gray)	—	≈1200
Iron, cast (white)	—	1130
Iron, wrought	—	1300...1500
Lautal	Al, Cu	650
Mangal	Al, Mn	650
Monel metal	—	1315...1350
Nickel silver	—	950...1180
Rose's metal	50Bi, 25Pb 25Sn	94
Silumin	Al, Si	570
Silver solder	—	720...855
Steel, hard	—	1460
Steel, high speed tool	—	1350
Steel, soft	—	1520
Tin-base solder[1]	25...90Sn, 75...10Pb	181...271
Wood's metal	50Bi, 12.5Cd, 25Pb, 12.5Sn	70

[1] All tin-base solder begin to soften at 181 °C. The temperature at which a tin melts completely, lies between 190 °C and 275 °C, depending upon its composition.

Table 1-6 Melting Points of Miscellaneous Solids

Substance	Melting point $\dfrac{t}{°C}$
Asbestos	1150
Bauxite	1820
Blast furnace slag	1300...1430
Blubber	44
Borax	878
Butter	31
China (porcelain)	1550
Chromite	≈2180
Clay, pure	2050
Enamel	≈960
Glass	1200
Glass, lead	1100
Glauber's salt	884
Ice (H_2O)	0
Mineral pitch	50...140
Naphthalene	80
Rubber	≈125
Shellac	≈150
Silicon carbide	2537
Silicon oxide	1470
Stearine	50
Tallow	40...50
Wax	64
Wax, bees'	60...65
Wax, mineral	7...195

Table 1-7 Melting Points of Salts for Salt Baths

Substance	Melting point $\dfrac{t}{°C}$
Aluminium chloride	190
Barium chloride	955
Barium fluoride	1300
Calcium carbonate	891
Calcium chloride	772
Calcium fluoride	1370
Calcium nitrate	337
Cupric chloride	630
Ferric chloride	302
Lead chloride	500
Lithium carbonate	733
Lithium chloride	606
Lithium fluoride	842
Magnesium chloride	718
Magnesium fluoride	1260
Potassium chloride	770
Potassium fluoride	846
Silver chloride	450
Sodium carbonate	850
Sodium chloride	802
Sodium nitrate	310
Sodium fluoride	995
Strontium fluoride	900
Zinc chloride	315

Table 1-8 Specific Heat Capacities c and $\bar{c}$ of Solid Elements

Element Name	Symbol	Temperature t °C	Specific heat capacity [1] c kJ/(kg K)	Mean specific heat capacity [2] $\bar{c}$ kJ/(kg K)	Element Name	Symbol	Temperature t °C	Specific heat capacity [1] c kJ/(kg K)	Mean specific heat capacity [2] $\bar{c}$ kJ/(kg K)
Aluminium	Al	−200	0.314	0.687	Carbon, graphite		1000	1.717	1.423
		−100	0.733	0.812	Cesium	Cs	20	0.230	—
		0	0.879	—	Chromium	Cr	−200	0.142	0.297
		20	0.896	0.888			−100	0.318	0.377
		100	0.938	0.909			0	0.427	—
		200	0.984	0.934			20	0.440	0.435
		300	1.009	0.955			100	0.473	0.452
		400	1.043	0.971			200	0.498	—
		500	1.089	0.992			300	0.523	0.486
Antimony	Sb	−100	0.193	0.201			600	—	0.523
		0	0.206	—			1000	—	0.565
		20	0.208	0.207	Cobalt	Co	−200	0.142	0.301
		100	0.212	0.209			−100	0.314	0.352
		300	0.226	0.216			0	0.381	—
Arsenic	As	−100	0.289	0.309			20	0.389	0.385
		0	0.326	—			100	0.423	0.402
		20	0.330	0.327			300	0.490	0.440
		100	0.339	0.333			600	0.586	0.490
Beryllium	Be	−100	0.837	1.277			900	0.687	0.540
		−50	1.340	1.499			1200	0.607	—
		0	1.658	—	Copper	Cu	−200	0.167	0.327
		20	1.750	1.704			−100	0.343	0.364
		100	2.010	1.851			0	0.379	—
		200	2.240	1.989			20	0.383	0.381
Bismuth	Bi	−200	0.100	0.113			100	0.396	0.388
		−100	0.116	0.120			200	0.406	0.397
		0	0.123	—			300	0.416	0.401
		20	0.124	0.123			400	0.427	0.406
		100	0.127	0.125			500	0.439	0.408
		200	0.134	0.127			800	0.469	0.427
Boron	B	−50	0.795	0.879	Gallium	Ga	−100	0.343	0.360
		0	0.963	—			0	0.373	—
		20	1.047	1.005			20	0.377	0.373
		100	1.214	1.089	Gold	Au	−200	0.088	0.117
Cadmium	Cd	−200	0.176	0.214			−100	0.122	0.126
		−100	0.218	0.224			0	0.129	—
		−50	0.224	0.227			20	0.129	0.129
		0	0.229	—			100	0.131	0.130
		20	0.231	0.230			300	0.135	0.132
		100	0.238	0.234			600	0.142	0.136
		200	0.245	0.238			1000	0.157	0.141
Calcium	Ca	−200	0.402	0.569	Iridium	Ir	−200	0.067	0.109
		−100	0.590	0.620			−100	0.113	0.126
		0	0.641	—			0	0.130	—
		20	0.649	0.645			20	0.134	0.132
		100	0.670	0.657			100	0.138	0.134
		200	0.712	0.670			1400	—	0.167
Carbon, amorphous	C	20	0.837	—	Iodine	J	−100	0.197	0.205
Carbon, diamond	C	20	0.502	—			0	0.214	—
Carbon, graphite		−200	0.084	0.335			20	0.218	0.218
		−100	0.335	0.481			100	0.234	0.226
		−50	0.481	0.561	Iron	Fe	−200	0.134	0.335
		0	0.641	—			−150	0.281	0.377
		20	0.708	0.674			−100	0.356	0.402
		100	0.934	0.795			−50	0.406	0.423
		200	1.176	0.929					
		300	1.411	1.055					
		500	1.633	1.256					

[1] Older name: Specific heat.
[2] Mean specific heat capacity $\bar{c}$ in the temperature range between 0 °C and t.
[2] Older name: Mean specific heat.

Element Name	Symbol	Temperature t °C	Specific heat capacity[1] c kJ/(kg K)	Mean specific heat capacity[2] $\bar{c}$ kJ/(kg K)
Iron	Fe	0	0.440	—
		20	0.452	0.444
		100	0.486	0.465
		200	0.532	0.486
		300	0.582	0.511
		400	0.628	0.532
		500	0.678	0.557
		600	0.754	0.582
		700	—	0.628
		800	—	0.670
		1000	—	0.703
		1400	—	0.691
Lead	Pb	−200	0.109	0.120
		−100	0.121	0.124
		0	0.128	—
		20	0.129	0.129
		100	0.134	0.131
		200	0.138	0.134
		300	0.142	0.136
Lithium	Li	−200	1.256	2.596
		−100	2.721	3.056
		0	3.308	—
		20	3.391	3.349
		100	3.768	3.559
Magnesium	Mg	−200	0.544	0.837
		−100	0.879	0.942
		0	1.001	—
		20	1.017	1.009
		100	1.068	1.034
		200	1.122	—
		300	1.156	1.089
		500	1.256	1.130
Manganese	Mn	−100	0.398	0.440
		0	0.473	—
		20	0.486	0.481
		100	0.515	0.498
		300	0.586	0.532
Mercury	Hg	−200	0.114	—
		−100	0.135	—
Molybdenum	Mo	−200	0.084	0.197
		−100	0.209	0.230
		0	0.247	—
		20	0.251	0.251
		100	0.260	0.255
		400	0.276	0.264
		1000	0.310	0.281
Nickel	Ni	−200	0.151	0.348
		−100	0.364	0.414
		−50	0.419	0.431
		0	0.422	—
		20	0.446	0.444
		100	0.467	0.452
		200	0.515	0.469
		300	0.569	0.494
		350	0.628	0.507
		400	0.544	0.515
		700	0.544	0.523
		1000	—	0.544
Niobium	Nb	0	0.269	—
		20	0.270	0.270

Element Name	Symbol	Temperature t °C	Specific heat capacity[1] c kJ/(kg K)	Mean specific heat capacity[2] $\bar{c}$ kJ/(kg K)
Niobium	Nb	100	0.273	0.271
		1000	0.310	0.289
Osmium	Os	0	0.129	—
		20	0.130	0.130
		100	0.131	0.131
		1000	0.151	0.138
Palladium	Pd	−100	0.209	0.230
		0	0.243	—
		20	0.247	0.243
		100	0.251	0.247
		500	0.272	0.260
		1000	0.310	0.276
Platinum	Pt	−200	0.075	0.105
		−100	0.117	0.128
		0	0.133	—
		20	0.133	0.133
		100	0.136	0.134
		200	0.136	—
		300	0.136	0.137
		500	0.146	0.139
		1000	0.147	—
		1200	0.165	0.149
Phosphorus	P	20	0.754	—
Potassium	K	−200	0.586	0.670
		−100	0.670	0.712
		0	0.733	—
		20	0.741	0.737
		50	0.758	0.745
Rhenium	Re	0	0.136	—
		20	0.137	0.136
		100	0.139	0.138
		1000	0.163	0.151
Rhodium	Rh	0	0.247	—
		20	0.248	0.247
		100	0.252	0.250
		500	0.289	0.268
		1200	0.339	0.293
Rubidium	Rb	20	0.348	—
Selenium	Se	20	0.335	—
Silicon	Si	−200	0.167	0.461
		−100	0.481	0.595
		0	0.678	—
		20	0.703	0.691
		100	0.791	0.741
		400	0.879	0.821
		900	0.963	0.879
Silver	Ag	−200	0.157	0.211
		−100	0.216	0.226
		0	0.233	—
		20	0.234	0.233
		100	0.238	0.235
		200	0.249	—
		300	0.247	0.239

[1] Older name: Specific heat.
[2] Mean specific heat capacity $\bar{c}$ in the temperature range between 0 °C and t.
[2] Older name: Mean specific heat.

Element		Tempe-rature	Specific heat capacity [1]	Mean specific heat capacity [2]
Name	Symbol	*t*	*c*	$\bar{c}$
		°C	kJ/(kg K)	kJ/(kg K)
Silver	Ag	500	0.264	—
		700	0.269	0.250
Sodium	Na	−200	0.879	1.089
		−100	1.089	1.139
		0	1.189	—
		20	1.206	1.181
		50	1.231	1.210
Sulfur (rhombic)	S	−100	0.586	0.649
		0	0.699	—
		20	0.720	0.708
		80	0.770	0.733
Tantalum	Ta	−200	0.084	0.121
		−100	0.126	0.132
		0	0.137	—
		20	0.138	0.138
		100	0.141	0.139
		400	0.147	0.142
		1000	0.159	0.147
Tellurium	Te	20	0.197	—
Thallium	Tl	−100	0.124	0.127
		0	0.131	—
		20	0.132	0.131
		100	0.139	0.135
		200	0.147	0.138
Thorium	Th	20	0.126	—
Tin	Sn	−100	0.209	0.218
		0	0.225	—
		20	0.227	0.226

Element		Tempe-rature	Specific heat capacity [1]	Mean specific heat capacity [2]
Name	Symbol	*t*	*c*	$\bar{c}$
		°C	kJ/(kg K)	kJ/(kg K)
Tin	Sn	100	0.234	0.230
		200	0.243	0.234
Titanium	Ti	20	0.611	—
		100	—	0.612
		200	—	0.629
		300	—	0.654
Tungsten	W	−200	0.067	0.109
		−100	0.109	0.126
		−50	0.126	0.130
		0	0.134	—
		20	0.134	0.134
		100	0.136	0.135
		500	0.144	0.139
		1000	0.154	0.144
		1500	0.163	0.149
Uranium	U	20	0.113	—
Vanadium	V	20	0.502	—
Zinc	Zn	−200	0.243	0.343
		−100	0.356	0.368
		0	0.381	—
		20	0.385	0.381
		100	0.398	0.389
		200	0.414	0.398
		300	0.420	—
		400	0.461	0.419
Zirconium	Zr	20	0.272	—

[1] Older name: Specific heat.
[2] Mean specific heat capacity $\bar{c}$ in the temperature range between 0 °C and *t*.
[2] Older name: Mean specific heat.

Table 1-9 Specific Heat Capacities c and $\bar{c}$ of Alloys

Alloy	Mass fractions %	Temperature t °C	Specific heat capacity [1] c kJ/(kg K)	Mean specific heat capacity [2] $\bar{c}$ kJ/(kg K)
Brass	40Zn	−100	0.335	0.356
		0	0.337	—
		20	0.381	0.379
		100	0.389	0.383
		200	0.414	0.394
		400	0.477	0.414
Bronze aluminium	12Al	20	0.419	—
Bronze phosphor	12Sn, 1P	20	0.360	—
Bronze, red	9Zn, 6Sn, 1Pb	20	0.377	—
Bronze, tin (Bell metal)	20Sn	20	0.352	—
Chromium nickel steel		20	0.477	—
		500	0.607	—
	18Cr, 8...36Ni	20	0.502	—
Constantan	60Cu, 40Ni	20	0.410	—
Copper-tin	3.9Sn	25	0.368	—
	7.9Sn	25	0.363	—
	13Sn	25	0.359	—
Duralumin	93.2Al, 3.9Cu, 1.3Mn, 0.7Mg, 0.5Si	20	0.913	—
Gold-copper		20	0.218	—
Iron, cast	93Fe, 4C, 1P, 1Si, 1Mn	0	0.532	—
		20	0.540	0.536
		100	0.557	0.544
		300	0.620	0.574
		500	0.699	0.607
		1000	—	0.729
Iron, cast (gray)		20	0.540	—
Iron transformer scheet	95Fe, 4Si, 1Mn	0	0.452	—
		20	0.456	0.452
		100	0.477	0.465
		300	0.553	0.502
		500	0.687	0.544
		1000	—	0.703
Manganese steel	80Fe, 19Mn, 1C	0	0.490	—
		20	0.502	0.498
		100	0.532	0.511
		300	0.590	0.540
		500	0.636	0.565
Manganine	12Mn, 4Ni	20	0.406	—
Monel metal	68Ni, 29Cu, 2Fe, 1Mn	−100	0.352	0.389
		0	0.419	—
		20	0.423	0.419
		100	0.440	0.427
		1200	—	0.528
Nickel silver	15Ni, 22Zn	20	0.394	—
Nickel steel	67Fe, 31Ni, 1Mn, 1C	20	0.507	—
Rose's metal	48.9Bi, 27.5Pb, 23.6Sn	20	0.167	—
Steel	98.5Fe, 1.3C, 0.1Si, 0.1Mn	0	0.465	—
		20	0.477	0.473
		100	0.519	0.494
		400	0.628	0.574
		800	—	0.657
		1200	—	0.691
	0.1...0.6C	20	0.461	—
	13Cr	20	0.461	—
Steel, V2A (chromium-nickel)	73Fe, 20Cr, 7Ni	0	0.465	—
		20	0.477	0.473
		100	0.507	0.486
		400	0.586	0.544
Steel, wrought		0	0.465	—
		400	0.628	—
Tin-based solder	64Pb, 36Sn	20	0.167	—
Wood's metal	52.4Bi, 25.9Pb, 14.7Zn, 7.0Cd	20	1.465	—

[1] Older name: Specific heat.
[2] Mean specific heat capacity $\bar{c}$ in the temperature range between 0 °C and t.
[2] Older name: Mean specific heat.

Table 1-10 Specific Heat Capacity c of Solid Organic Compounds

Organic compound	Chemical formula	Temperature t °C	Specific heat capacity [1] c kJ/(kg K)
Anthracene	$C_{14}H_{10}$	20	1.151
Benzoic acid	$C_7H_6O_2$	20	1.185
Benzophenone	$C_{13}H_{10}O$	20	1.591
Bromobenzene	C_6H_5Br	20	0.967
Bromonaphthalene	$C_{10}H_7Br$	20	1.047
Camphor	$C_{10}H_{16}O$	20	1.717
Diphenyl	$C_{12}H_{10}$	20	1.256
Diphenylamine	$C_{12}H_{11}N$	20	1.340
Diphenylmethane	$C_{13}H_{12}$	20	1.369
Lactose	$C_{12}H_{22}O_{11}$	20	1.214
Naphthalene	$C_{10}H_8$	20	1.298
Oxalic acid	$C_2H_2O_4$	20	1.151
Palmitic acid	$C_{16}H_{32}O_2$	20	2.093
Phenol	C_6H_6O	20	1.633
Phthalic acid	$C_8H_6O_4$	20	0.963
Picric acid	$C_6H_3O_7N_3$	20	1.047
Salicylic acid	$C_7H_6O_3$	20	1.172
Stearic acid	$C_{18}H_{36}O_2$	20	1.675
Succinic acid	$C_4H_4O_6$	20	1.298
Sugar, cane	$C_{12}H_{22}O_{11}$	20	1.256
Trinitrotoluene	$C_7H_5O_6N_3$	20	1.256
Urea	CH_4ON_2	20	1.549

[1] Older name: Specific heat.

Table 1-11 Specific Heat Capacities c and $\bar{c}$ of Solid Inorganic Compounds

Inorganic compound	Chemical formula	Temperature $\dfrac{t}{°C}$	Specific heat capacity[1] $\dfrac{c}{kJ/(kg\,K)}$	Mean specific heat capacity[2] $\dfrac{\bar{c}}{kJ/(kg\,K)}$
Aluminium oxide	Al$_2$O$_3$	0	0.670	—
		20	0.754	0.712
		100	0.921	0.795
		500	1.172	1.005
		1000	1.298	1.089
Ammonium chloride	NH$_4$Cl	0	1.507	—
		20	1.591	1.549
		100	1.842	1.675
		150	1.968	1.758
Barium chloride	BaCl$_2$	20	0.368	—
Calcium carbonate	CaCO$_3$	20	0.808	—
Calcium chloride	CaCl$_2$	20	0.628	—
Calcium oxide	CaO	0	0.754	—
		20	0.770	0.762
		100	0.808	0.783
		400	0.879	0.837
		1200	0.963	0.900
Calcium sulfate (gypsum)	CaSO$_4$,2H$_2$O	20	1.089	—
Cupric oxide	CuO	-100	0.377	0.461
		0	0.523	—
		20	0.540	0.532
		100	0.582	0.553
		500	0.687	0.620
Cupric sulfate	CuSO$_4$	20	0.628	—
Cuprous oxide	Cu$_2$O	0	0.419	—
		20	0.440	0.431
		100	0.494	0.465
		500	0.569	0.523
Ferrous oxide (III)	Fe$_2$O$_3$	20	0.666	—
Ferrous oxide (II, III)	Fe$_3$O$_4$	20	0.641	—
Ice	H$_2$O	-80	1.465	1.796
		-60	1.658	1.871
		-40	1.817	1.938
		-20	1.947	1.997
		0	2.039	—
Lead monoxide	PbO	-100	0.163	0.188
		0	0.209	—
		20	0.214	0.209
		100	0.222	0.218
Lead oxide, red (minium)	Pb$_3$O$_4$	20	0.921	—
Magnesium oxide	MgO	0	0.946	—
		20	0.963	0.955
		100	1.013	0.980
		500	1.185	1.080
		1000	1.290	1.172
		1500	1.344	1.227
Phosphorus pentoxide	P$_2$O$_5$	20	0.712	—
Potassium carbonate	K$_2$CO$_3$	20	0.879	—
Potassium chloride	KCl	-100	0.632	0.657
		0	0.678	—
		20	0.682	0.682
		100	0.699	0.691
		300	0.737	0.708
		600	0.800	0.737
Potassium nitrate	KNO$_3$	-100	0.754	0.837
		0	0.917	—
		20	0.242	0.929
		100	1.043	0.980
		200	1.172	1.340
Potassium sulfate	K$_2$SO$_4$	20	0.754	—
Silicon carbide (carborundum)	SiC	0	0.615	—
		20	0.678	0.641
		100	0.829	0.737
		500	1.130	0.921
		1000	1.298	1.089
Silicon dioxide —α-quartz	SiO$_2$	-200	0.167	0.469
		-100	0.067	0.607
		0	0.712	—
		20	0.745	0.729

[1] Older name: Specific heat.
[2] Mean specific heat capacity c in the temperature range between 0 °C and t.
[2] Older name: Mean specific heat.

Table 1-11 Specific Heat Capacities c and $\bar{c}$ of Solid Inorganic Compounds

Inorganic compound	Chemical formula	Temperature t/°C	Specific heat capacity[1] c / kJ/(kg K)	Mean specific heat capacity[2] $\bar{c}$ / kJ/(kg K)
Silicon dioxide		100	0.854	0.783
		300	1.055	0.904
		500	1.210	0.992
—β-quartz		700	1.143	1.063
—quartz glass		-200	0.180	0.469
		-100	0.486	0.599
		0	0.699	—
		20	0.729	0.712
		100	0.833	0.766
		300	1.022	0.879
		500	1.114	0.955
		1000	1.189	1.051
Silver bromide	AgBr	20	0.285	—
Silver chloride	AgCl	20	0.360	—
Silver nitrate	AgNO$_3$	20	0.586	—
Sodium carbonate	Na$_2$CO$_3$	-100	0.837	0.921
		0	1.017	—
		20	1.043	1.030
		100	1.130	1.089
Sodium chloride	NaCl	-100	0.775	0.816
		0	0.850	—
		20	0.862	0.854
		100	0.888	0.867
		300	0.950	0.904
		700	1.068	0.963
Sodium nitrate	NaNO$_3$	-100	0.837	0.929
		0	1.043	—
		20	1.084	1.063
		100	1.298	1.151
		200	1.591	1.298
Sodium sulfate	Na$_2$SO$_4$	20	0.921	—
Sodium tetraborate (borax)	Na$_2$B$_4$O$_7$	20	0.921	—
Thorium dioxide	ThO$_2$	20	0.226	0.226
		500	0.281	0.260
		1000	0.306	0.276
Zinc sulfate	ZnSO$_4$	20	0.712	—

[1] Older name: Specific heat.
[2] Mean specific heat capacity c in the temperature range between 0 °C and t.
[2] Older name: Mean specific heat.

Table 1-12 Specific Heat Capacity c of Miscellaneous Solid Substances

Substance	Temperature t °C	Specific heat capacity[1] c kg/(kgK)	Substance	Temperature t °C	Specific heat capacity[1] c kg/(kgK)
Asbestos	20	0.795	Colophony	20	1.214
Ashes	20	0.795	Concrete	20	0.879
Asphalt	20	0.921	Concrete, cellular	20	0.795
Bakelite	20	1.591	Cork	20	1.884
Basalt	20	0.795	— impregnated	20	1.382
	100	0.963	Cotton	20	1.298
Boiler incrustation (sulfate)	300	0.837	Crown	20	0.666
Brick	20	0.837	Dextrine	20	1.298
Brick masonry	20	1.047	Dolomite	20	0.879
Calcite	20	0.795	Dry ice (solid CO_2)	20	1.382
Cardboard, dry	20	1.340	Ebonite	20	1.424
Cellulose	20	1.549	Flax	32	1.340
Cement, Portland	20	0.779	Flint	20	0.481
	100	0.858	Gelatine	20	2.135
Cereals	20	2.093	Glass	20	0.837
Chamotte	20	0.837	— common Thüringia,	−50	0.662
	500	1.130	glass tubes	20	0.770
	1000	1.130		100	0.896
China, porcelain	20	0.795	— Jena 16 III	20	0.779
	100	0.879	— Jena 59 III	20	0.791
	500	1.089	— mirror	20	0.766
	1000	1.298	Glass wool	20	0.837
Clay	20	0.879	Granite	20	0.754
Coal			Graphite	20	0.712
— anthracite	100	1.089*	Gypsum	20	1.089
— briquettes	20	1.507	Ice	−20	2.135*
— brown (lignite), 60% water	20	3.140	Iporka	20	1.382
— brown (lignite), 47.6% water	100	2.587*	Kapok	—	1.357
— brown (lignite), 20% water	20	2.093	Kieselguhr	20	0.837
— brown (lignite), 12.1% water	100	1.507*	Leather	20	1.507
— brown (lignite), 3.4% water	100	1.243*	Light construction boards	20	1.675
— brown (lignite), no water	100	1.281*	Limestone	20	0.837
— channel, gas	100	1.118*	Marble	20	0.795
— charcoal	0	1.005	Mica	20	0.837
	100	1.005	Oil, frozen	20	1.465
	400	1.549	Paper	20	1.340
	1200	2.010			
— gas flame	100	1.306*			
— non-baking	100	1.172*			
— pit	100	1.193*			
Coal dust	30	1.298			
Coke	0	0.837			
	20	0.837			
	100	0.921			
	1000	1.465			
— blast furnace	100	0.862*			
— foundry	100	0.854*			
— gas	100	0.842*			
— low temperature	100	1.105*			

[1] Older name: Specific heat.
*) Mean specific heat capacity c in the temperature range between 0 °C and t.

Table 1-12 Specific Heat Capacity c of Miscellaneous Solid Substances   *(continued)*

Substance	Temperature t °C	Specific heat capacity[1] c kg/(kgK)	Substance	Temperature t °C	Specific heat capacity[1] c kg/(kgK)
Paraffin	−20	1.578	Slag wool	20	0.754
	0	2.240	Slate	20	0.754
	20	2.906	Snow	−40	1.805*
Peat	20	1.884	Soil	20	1.842
Plastering	20	0.837	Stone	20	0.879
Pumice stone	20	1.005	Stoneware	20	0.795
Pyrex	20	0.775	Styropore (polystyrene foam)	20	1.382
Quartz	20	0.754	Sugar	20	1.256
	20	0.729	Sulfur (rhombic)	20	0.712
Rubber	20	1.424	Tuff	100	1.386*
Salt, kitchen	20	0.879	Wax, yellow	20	2.931
Salt, rock	20	0.921	Wood	0	1.382
Sand (moist)	20	0.712		20	2.512
Sandstone	20	0.712		100	2.721
Sealing wax	20	1.047	Fir ⊥ fibers	20	2.721
Silica, brick	20	0.921	Oak ⊥ fibers	20	2.386
	25	0.795*	Pine ⊥ fibers	20	2.721
Silk	20	1.256	Spruce ⊥ fibers	34	1.206*
Slag	20	0.837	Wood resin, coniferous wood	20	1.842
Slag, blast furnace	20	0.837	Wool	20	1.884
	500	1.047		100	1.675*
	1000	1.172			

[1] Older name: Specific heat.
* Mean specific heat capacity c in the temperature range between 0 °C and t.

Table 1-13 Specific Heat Capacity c of Some Foods

| Food | Mass fraction | | Specific heat capacity [3] | | Heat of solidification or fusion |
	Water[1] %	Solids %	Before freezing c kJ/(kg K)	After freezing c kJ/(kg K)	q_f kJ/(kg K)
Apples	83	17	3.852	1.758	280.516
Asparagus	94	6	3.894	1.968	314.010
Bacon	—	—	2.303	1.298	71.176
Bananas	75	25	3.349	—	251.208
Beans, green	89	11	3.852	1.968	297.263
Beer	89...91	—	3.768	—	301.450
Berries	84...88	16...12	3.810	1.675...2.093	280.516...293.076
Butter	14...15	86...85	2.512...2.680	1.256	146.538+50.242[2]
Carrots	83	17	3.643	1.884	276.329
Caviar	50...60	50...40	2.931	1.298	167.472...209.340
Celery	88...95	12...5	3.936	1.968	293.076...318.097
Cheese, cream (cottage)	80	20	2.931	1.884	267.955
Cheese, fat	35...50	65...50	1.884...2.512	1.256	108.857...154.912
Cheese, skim	53	47	2.847	1.675	175.846
Cherries	82	18	3.643	1.842	276.329
Chocolate	1.6	98.4	3.182	—	—
Cocoa powder	0.5	99.5	2.093	—	83.736...125.604
Cream	59	41	3.559	1.507	196.780
Dough	—	—	1.884	—	—
Eel	62	38	2.931	1.633	209.340
Eggs	70	30	3.182	1.675	234.461
Fat, lard	0.7	99.3	2.512	1.675	121.417...146.538
Fat, vegetable	—	—	1.968...2.093	1.465	—
Fish, dried	—	—	2.261	1.424	150.725
Fish, fresh, fat	60	40	2.847	1.591	209.340
Fish, fresh, lean	73	27	3.433	1.800	255.395
Fish, smoked	—	—	3.182	—	—
Flour	12...13.5	88...86.5	1.800...1.884	—	—
Game	74	26	3.349	1.675	247.021
Gooseberries	90	10	3.852	1.926	301.450
Grape	81	19	3.684	1.884	263.768
Honey	19	81	1.465	1.089	58.615
Ice cream	60...65	40...35	3.266	1.884	217.714
Ice (water)	100	—	4.187	2.093	334.944
Kale	91	9	3.894	2.010	305.636
Leek	91	9	3.894	2.010	305.636
Lemons	83...89	17...11	3.852	1.926	276.329...297.263
Lobsters, crabs	77	23	3.391	1.800	259.582
Margarine	17...18	83...82	2.721...2.931	1.465	62.802+62.802
Meat, beef, fat	51	49	2.546	1.486	171.659
Meat, beef, lean	72	28	3.249	1.758	234.461
Meat, mutton, fat	50	50	2.512	1.465	167.472
Meat, mutton, lean	67	33	3.056	1.717	221.900
Meat, pork, fat	39...46	61...54	2.135	1.340	129.791...153.237
Meat, veal	63	37	2.948	1.675	209.340
Milk	88	12	3.936	2.512	293.076
Oil	—	—	1.675	1.465	—
Onion	80...89	20...11	3.810	1.926	267.955...297.263
Oranges	84	16	3.852	1.842	284.702
Oysters	80	20	3.517	1.842	263.768
Peaches	87	13	3.852	1.717	293.076
Pears	83	17	3.852	1.758	280.516
Peas, green	75	25	3.349	1.758	251.208
Potatoes	74	26	3.349	1.758	242.834
Poultry	74	26	2.931...3.182	1.675	247.021
Strawberries	90	10	3.852	1.968	299.775
Sugar	0.1	99.9	—	1.256	—
Tomatoes	94	6	3.894	2.052	314.010
Walnuts	7.2	94.8	1.047	0.921	37.681
Watermelons	89	11	3.852	1.926	297.263
Wine	—	—	3.768	—	—

[1] Water content of foods varies considerably with fat content; at the same time this causes differences in specific heat and solidification heat values.

[2] Solidification heat of fat + solidification heat of water.

[3] Older name: Specific heat.

Table 1-14 Thermal Conductivity λ of Metals

Substance	Chemical formula	Temperature t / °C	Density ρ / kg/m³	Thermal conductivity λ / W/(m K)
Aluminium, 99.75%	Al	-190 0 200 300 800	2700	255.860 229.111 229.11 222.133 125.604
—99%		-100 0 100 300	—	209.340 209.340 207.014 222.133
Antimony, very pure	Sb	-190 -100 0 100 300 500	6690	20.934 19.190 17.678 16.282 15.817 18.608
Beryllium, 99.5%	Be	-250 -100 0 100 200	1850	94.203 125.604 160.494 190.732 215.155
Bismuth	Bi	-190 -100 0 100 200	9800	25.586 12.095 8.374 7.211 7.211
Cadmium, pure	Cd	-190 -100 0 100 200 300	8620	104.670 96.529 93.040 91.877 91.296 87.807
Cobalt, 97.1%	Co	20	≈8900	69.780
Copper, pure 99.9 to 98%	Cu	-180 -100 0 100 200 400 600	8930	464.037 407.050 386.116 379.138 373.323 364.019 353.552
—commercial		20	8300	372.160

Substance	Chemical formula	Temperature t / °C	Density ρ / kg/m³	Thermal conductivity λ / W/(m K)
Copper, pure 99.9 to 98% —electrolytic, pure	Cu	-180 0 100 300 800	8900	488.460 395.420 391.931 381.464 367.508
Gold 99.999%	Au	-190 0 100 300	19290	327.966 310.521 310.521 304.706
—99.98%		0 100		294.239 294.239
Iridium, pure	Ir	0 100	22420	59.313 56.987
Iron (Armc) 99.92%	Fe	20 100 200 400 600 800	7850	73.169 67.454 61.639 48.846 38.379 29.075
—cast, 1% Ni		20 100 300 500	7280	50.009 49.428 46.520 37.216
—cast, 3% C		20	7280	55.824...63.965
—steel 99.2% Fe, 0.2% C		0 100 300 500 800	7800	45.357 45.357 43.031 37.216 30.238
—wrought, pure		0 100 200 400 600 800	7800	59.313 56.987 52.335 44.194 37.216 29.075
Lead, pure	Pb	-250 -200		48.846 40.705

1 Btu/(ft h °F) = 1.730 73 W/(m K)

Table 1-14 Thermal Conductivity λ of Metals

Substance	Chemical formula	Temperature t (°C)	Density ρ (kg/m³)	Thermal conductivity λ (W/(m K))
Lead, pure	Pb	-100		36.867
		0		35.123
		20	11340	34.774
		100		33.378
		300		29.773
		500		16.747
Lithium, pure	Li	0	530	70.943
		100		70.943
Magnesium, pure	Mg	-190	1740	186.080
		0		172.124
		200		162.820
-99.6%		0	≈1740	144.212
		100		139.560
		300		131.419
		500		131.419
Manganese	Mn	0	7300	50.242
Mercury	Hg	-190		48.846
		-100		36.053
		-50	13595	27.912
		0		8.141...10.467
Molybdenum 99.84%	Mo	-180		174.450
		-100		138.397
		0	10200	137.234
		100		137.234
		1000		98.855
Nickel 99.94%	Ni	-180		110.485
		0		93.040
		100		82.573
		200	8800	73.269
		300		63.965
		400		59.313
		500		61.639
-99.2%		0		67.454
		100		62.802
		200	—	58.150
		400		52.335
		600		56.987
		800		62.802
-97 to 99%		-100		55.824

(continued)

Substance	Chemical formula	Temperature t (°C)	Density ρ (kg/m³)	Thermal conductivity λ (W/(m K))
Nickel -97 to 99%	Ni	0		58.150
		100		56.987
		200		54.661
		400	—	48.846
		600		53.498
		800		58.150
Palladium, pure	Pd	-190		76.758
		0	—	68.617
		100		73.269
Platinum, pure	Pt	-190		77.921
		0		70.013
		100		71.408
		300	21400	75.595
		500		79.084
		800		86.062
		1000		89.551
Potassium, pure	K	0	860	136.071
		100		118.626
Rhodium, pure	Rh	-190		212.829
		0	12500	88.388
		100		80.247
Silver > 99.98%	Ag	-190		425.658
		0	10500	418.680
		100		416.354
		300		407.050
-99.9%		-100		419.843
		0		410.539
		100	10500	391.931
		300		361.693
		500		362.856
Sodium, pure	Na	-100		154.679
		0	970	100.018
		50		93.040
		100		83.736
Tantalum	Ta	0		54.661
		100	16650	54.080
		1000		63.965
		1400		72.106

1 Btu/(ft h °F) = 1.730 73 W/(m K)

Table 1-14 Thermal Conductivity λ of Metals

Substance	Chemical formula	Temperature $\frac{t}{°C}$	Density $\frac{\rho}{kg/m^3}$	Thermal conductivity $\frac{\lambda}{W/(m\,K)}$
Tantalum	Ta	1800		82.573
Thallium, pure	Tl	-190		62.802
		0	11840	51.172
		100		41.868
Tin, pure	Sn	-150		79.084
		-100		74.432
		0	7300	66.058
		100		59.313
		200		56.987
Tungsten	W	-190		217.481
		0	19300	166.309

Substance	Chemical formula	Temperature $\frac{t}{°C}$	Density $\frac{\rho}{kg/m^3}$	Thermal conductivity $\frac{\lambda}{W/(m\,K)}$
Tungsten	W	100		151.190
		500		119.789
		1000		98.855
		1500		113.974
		2000		136.071
		2400		146.538
Zinc, pure	Zn	-100		115.137
		0	7130	112.811
		100		109.904
		200		105.833
		300		101.181

1 Btu/(ft h °F) = 1.730 73 W/(m K)

(continued)

22

Table 1-15 Thermal Conductivity λ of Alloys

Alloy	Mass fraction %	Temperature t °C	Density ρ kg/m³	Thermal conductivity λ W/(m K)
Aluminium alloys	96Al, 1.8Cu, 0.9Fe, 0.9Cr, 0.4Si	20	—	104.670
Aluminium bronze	95Cu, 5Al	20	7800	82.573
Aluminium magnesium	92Al, 8Mg	−180	≈2600	75.595
		−100		84.899
		0		102.344
		20		105.833
		100		123.278
		200		147.701
Alusil	80Al, 20Si	−180	≈2650	122.115
		−100		141.886
		0		158.168
		20		160.494
		100		168.635
		200		174.450
Bismuth-antimony	80Bi, 20Sb	0	—	6.606
		100		8.618
	50Bi, 50Sb	0	—	8.327
		100		9.374
	30Bi, 70Sb	0	—	9.653
		100		11.660
Brass	90Cu, 10Zn	−100	≈8600	88.388
		0		102.344
		100		117.463
		200		133.745
		300		148.864
		400		166.309
		500		180.265
		600		195.384
	70Cu, 30Zn	0	≈8600	105.833
		100		109.322
		200		110.485
		300		113.974
		400		116.300
		500		119.789
		600		120.952
	66Cu, 33Zn	0	≈8600	100.018
		100		106.996
		200		112.811
Brass	66Cu, 33Zn	300	≈8600	120.952
		400		127.930
		500		134.908
		600		151.190
	60Cu, 40Zn	0	≈8600	105.833
		100		119.789
		200		137.234
		300		152.353
		400		168.635
		500		186.080
		600		200.036
	61.5Cu, 38.5Zn	20	—	79.084
		100		88.388
Bronze	90Cu, 10Sn	20	8766	41.868
	75Cu, 25Sn	20	≈8900	25.586
	88Cu, 10Sn, 2Zn	20	≈8800	47.683
	84Cu, 6Sn, 9Zn, 1Pb	20	—	58.150
Bronze (red bass)	86Cu, 7Zn, 6.4Sn	20	≈8600	60.476
		100		70.943
Chrome-nickel steel	0.8Cr, 3.5Ni, 0.4C	20	8100...8700	34.890
		100		36.053
		200		37.216
		400		37.216
		600		31.401
	Cr...Ni	20	7900	13.956
		200		17.445
		500		20.934
	17...19Cr, 8Ni, 0.1...0.2C	20	8100...9000	14.538
		100		15.701
		200		16.864
		300		18.608
		500		20.934
	10Cr, 34Ni	20	—	12.212
		100		13.375
		200		15.119

1 Btu/(ft h °F) = 1.730 73 W/(m K)

Table 1-15 Thermal Conductivity λ of Alloys

(continued)

Alloy	Mass fraction %	Temperature t °C	Density ρ kg/m³	Thermal conductivity λ W/(m K)
Chrome-nickel steel	10Cr, 34Ni	300 500		16.282 19.190
	15Cr, 27Ni, 3W, 0.5C	20 100 200 300 500	—	11.281 12.793 13.956 15.119 18.608
	15Cr, 13Ni, 2W, 0.5C	20 100 200 300 500 800		11.630 11.630 11.630 12.212 12.793 16.282
Chrome steel	0.8Cr, 0.2C	100 200 400 600	≈7850	39.542 37.216 31.401 26.749
	5Cr, 0.5Mn, 0.1C	20 100 200 500	8100...9000	37.216 31.635 31.053 33.727
	15Cr, 0.1C	20 500	8100...9000	25.586 25.586
	14Cr, 0.3C	20 100 200 300 500	8100...9000	24.423 25.005 25.586 25.586 25.586
	16Cr, 0.9C	100 200 300 500 800	8100...9000	23.842 23.260 23.260 23.260 23.260
	26Cr, 0.1C	20 100 200 300 500	8100...9000	19.771 20.934 22.097 22.911 24.423
Cobalt steel	5...10Co	20	≈7800	40.705

Alloy	Mass fraction %	Temperature t °C	Density ρ kg/m³	Thermal conductivity λ W/(m K)
Constantan	60Cu, 40Ni	−100 0 20 100	8800	20.934 22.213 22.679 25.586
Copper alloys	92Al, 8Cu	−180 −100 0 20 100 200	≈2800	89.551 109.322 127.930 131.419 143.049 152.353
Copper mangenese	70Cu, 30Mn	20	≈7800	12.793
Copper-nickel	90Cu, 10Ni	20 100	≈8800	58.150 75.595
	80Cu, 20Ni	20 100	≈8500	33.727 40.705
	40Cu,60Ni	20 100	≈8400	22.097 25.586
	18Cu, 82Ni	20 100		25.586 25.586
Duralumin	94...96Al, 3...5Cu, 0.5Mg	−180 −100 0 20 100 200	≈2800	90.714 125.604 159.331 165.146 181.428 194.221
Electron alloy	93Mg, 4Zn, 0.5Cu	20	1800	116.300
German alloy	88Al, 10Zn, 2Cu	0 20 100	2900	143.049 145.375 154.679
Gold-copper alloy	88Au,12Cu	0 100	—	55.824 67.454
	27Au, 73Cu	0 100	—	90.714 113.974
Invar	35Ni, 65Fe	20	8130	11.049

1 Btu/(ft h °F) = 1.730 73 W/(m K)

Table 1-15 Thermal Conductivity λ of Alloys

Alloy	Mass fraction %	Temperature t °C	Density ρ kg/m³	Thermal conductivity λ W/(m K)
Lautal	95Al, 4.5...5.5Cu, 0.3Si	20	—	139.560
Magnesium-aluminium	92Mg, 8Al	-180	≈1800	41.868
		-100		50.009
		0		60.476
		20		61.639
		100		69.780
		200		79.084
	2.5Al	20	—	85.597
	4.2Al	20	—	69.082
	6.2Al	20	—	55.591
	10.3Al	20	—	43.496
Magnesium-aluminium-silicone	88Mg, 10Al, 2Si	-180	≈1850	30.238
		-100		40.705
		0		55.824
		20		58.150
		100		68.617
		200		75.595
Magnesium-copper	92Mg, 8Cu	-180	≈2400	88.388
		-100		106.996
		0		124.441
		20		125.604
		100		130.256
		200		132.582
	93.7Mg, 6.3Cu	20		131.419
Manganese-nickel steel	12Mn, 3Ni, 0.75C	20	—	13.956
		100		14.770
		200		16.282
		300		17.445
		500		19.771
Manganese steel	1.6Mn, 0.5C	20	≈7850	40.705
		100		40.705
		300		37.216
		500		34.890
	2Mn	20	≈7850	32.564
	5Mn	20	≈7850	18.608

(continued)

Alloy	Mass fraction %	Temperature t °C	Density ρ kg/m³	Thermal conductivity λ W/(m K)
Manganine	84Cu, 4Ni, 12Mn	-100	8400	16.282
		0		20.934
		20		21.864
		100		26.400
Monel	29Cu, 67Ni, 2Fe	20	8710	22.097
		100		24.423
		200		27.563
		300		30.238
		400		33.727
New silver	62Cu, 15Ni, 22Zn	-150	8433	17.678
		-100		19.170
		+20		25.005
		100		31.401
		200		39.542
		300		45.357
		400		48.846
Nickel alloy	70Ni, 28Cu, 2Fe	20	≈8200	34.890
Nickel chrome	90Ni, 10Cr	0	≈8220	17.096
		20		17.445
		100		18.957
		200		20.934
		300		22.795
		400		24.656
	80Ni, 20Cr	0	≈8200	12.212
		20		12.560
		100		13.840
		200		15.584
		300		17.212
		400		18.957
		600		22.562
Nickel-chrome steel	61 Ni, 15Cr, 20Fe, 4Mn	20	≈8190	11.630
		100		11.863
		200		12.212
		300		12.444
		400		12.677
		600		13.142
		800		13.956
	6lNi, 16Cr, 23Fe	0	≈8190	11.863
		20		12.095

1 Btu/(ft h °F) = 1.730 73 W/(m K)

Table 1-15 Thermal Conductivity λ of Alloys

Alloy	Mass fraction %	Temperature t/°C	Density ρ/kg/m³	Thermal conductivity λ W/(m K)
Nickel-chrome steel	61Ni, 16Cr, 23Fe	100 200 300 400	8130	13.258 14.654 16.049 17.445
	70Ni, 18Cr, 12Fe	20	—	11.514
	62Ni, 12Cr, 26Fe	20	≈8100	13.491
Nickel silver	—	0 100	—	29.308 37.216
Nickel steel	5Ni 10Ni 15Ni 20Ni 25Ni 30Ni 35Ni 40Ni 50Ni 60Ni 70Ni 80Ni	20 20 20 20 20 20 20 20 20 20 20 20	8130	34.890 27.912 22.097 18.608 15.119 12.212 11.049 11.049 14.538 19.190 25.586 32.564
	30Ni, 1Mn, 0.25C	20 100	8190	12.095 13.607
	36Ni, 0.8Mn	20	—	12.095
	1.4Ni, 0.5Cr, 0.3C	20 100 300 500	≈7850	45.357 44.194 40.705 37.216
Phosphor bronze	92.8Cu, 5Sn, 2Zn, 0.15P	20	≈8766	79.084
	91.7Cu, 8Sn, 0.3P	20 100 200	8800	45.357 52.335 61.639
	87.8Cu, 10Sn, 2Zn, 0.2P	20		41.868
	87.2Cu, 12.4Sn, 0.4P	20	8700	36.053

Alloy	Mass fraction %	Temperature t/°C	Density ρ/kg/m³	Thermal conductivity λ W/(m K)
Piston alloy, cast	91.5Al, 4.6Cu, 1.8Ni, 1.5Mg	0 20 100 200	≈2800	143.049 144.212 151.190 158.168
	84Al, 12Si, 1.2Cu, 1Ni	0 20 100 200	≈2800	134.908 134.908 137.234 139.560
Platinum-iridium	90Pt, 10Ir	0 100	—	30.936 31.401
Platinum-rhodium	90Pt, 10Rh	0 100	—	30.238 30.587
Rose's metal	50Bi, 25Pb, 25Sn	20	—	16.282
Silumin	86...89Al, 11...14Si	0 20 100	2600	159.331 161.657 170.961
Steel	0.1C	0 100 200 300 400 600 900	7850	59.313 52.335 52.335 46.520 44.194 37.216 33.727
	0.2C	20	7850	50.009
	0.6C	20	7850	46.520
—Bessemer	0.52C, 0.34Si	20	7850	40.240
Tungsten steel	1W, 0.6Cr, 0.3C	20 100 300 500	7900	39.542 38.379 36.053 33.727
V 1 A steel	—	20	—	20.934
V 2 A steel	—	2	7860	15.119
Wood's metal	48Bi, 26Pb, 13Sn, 13Cd	20	—	12.793

1 Btu/(ft h °F) = 1.730 73 W/(m K)

(continued)

Table 1-16 Thermal Conductivity λ of Building Materials

Building material	Temperature t °C	Density ρ kg/m³	Thermal conductivity λ W/(m K)
Air brick masonry	20	800	0.349...0.523
	20	1600	0.523...0.756
Asbestos slate (Salonite), with high asbestos content	20	1800...1900	0.174...0.349
—10...50% asbestos, dry	20	1800	0.640...0.523
	20	2100	0.698
—30% asbestos, 10% moisture	20	2200	0.791
Asphalt	0	400	0.605
	20	600	0.698
	30		0.744
Bark	20	400	0.055
	20	600	0.074
Basalt	0	≈2900	1.651
	20		1.675
	100		1.768
Bituminous coal	20	1100	0.174
Brick	20	800	0.279
	20	1000	0.326
	20	1200	0.384
	20	1400	0.442
	20	1600	0.523
	20	1800	0.733
	20	2000	1.233
—dried	20	1600...1800	0.384...0.523
	100	1400...2000	0.442
	200		0.547
	600		0.965
	1000		1.291
—porous	20	600...800	0.116...0.174
—porous, normal moisture	20	—	0.233...0.349
Brick masonry, massive, inside	20	1600...1800	0.698
—outside	20		0.872
Brick masonry, porous, outside	20	800	0.395
	20	1200	0.558
Carborundum	20	—	0.212
Cement, hard	20	—	1.047
Cement, powdered	20	—	0.070
	100	—	0.477
Clay, 44.7% vol.moisture	23	1495	1.675
—dried	25	1500...1600	0.930
Clay (48.7% vol.moisture)	23	1545	1.256
Clinker brick	20	1800	0.954
	20	2000	1.128
Cob wall	20	1700	0.989
Concrete —air dried	20	500	0.186
	20	1000	0.361
	20	1500	0.593
	20	2000	0.896
	20	2250	1.105
—completely dry	20	500	0.128
	20	1000	0.233
	20	1500	0.407
	20	2000	0.663
	20	2250	0.837
—gas and foam, according to composition	20	600	0.174...0.349
	20	800	0.233...0.523
	20	1000	0.349...0.698
	20	1200	0.465...0.930
	20	1400	0.582...1.163
—gravel	20	1800	0.965
	20	2000	1.163
	20	2200	1.512
—gravel, reinforced	20	1600...1800	0.930
	20	1800...2200	1.279...1.512
—masonry, light concrete (slag blocks, cell concrete, Aerocrete, porous concrete and others)	20	800	0.314
	20	1000	0.419
	20	1200	0.535
	20	1600	0.814

1 Btu/(ft h °F) = 1.730 73 W/(m K)

Table 1-16 Thermal Conductivity λ of Building Materials

Building material	Temperature $\dfrac{t}{°C}$	Density $\dfrac{\rho}{kg/m^3}$	Thermal conductivity $\dfrac{\lambda}{W/(m\,K)}$
Concrete			
—pumice stone, boards	20	800	0.372
	20	1000	0.512
	20	1200	0.628
—pumice stone, inside	20	—	0.349
—pumice stone, outside	20	—	0.465
—pumice stone, rammed	20	800	0.372
	20	1000	0.500
	20	1200	0.628
—pumice stone, masonry, cell concrete, porous concrete, and others	20	800	0.465
	20	1000	0.558
	20	1200	0.651
	20	1400	0.744
	20	1600	0.814
—slag, inside	20	—	0.582
—slag, outside	20	—	0.698
—steel reinforced	20	—	1.512
—with 10% moisture	20	500	0.256
	20	1000	0.488
	20	1500	0.791
	20	2000	1.140
	20	2250	1.337
Earth, clayey, or clay	20	1500	1.512
—with 28% moisture	20	2000	2.559
Earth, sandy oil	20	1500	1.047
—with 8% moisture	20	2000	1.745
Feldspar	20	—	2.442
Fire clay, stones	100	1800...2200	0.465...1.163
	500		0.698...1.396
	1000		1.745
Glass, window	20	2400...3200	0.582...1.047
Granite	20	2600...2900	2.908...4.071
Gravel, as filling material	20	1500...1800	0.930

(continued)

Building material	Temperature $\dfrac{t}{°C}$	Density $\dfrac{\rho}{kg/m^3}$	Thermal conductivity $\dfrac{\lambda}{W/(m\,K)}$
Gypsum (plaster)	20	800	0.395
	20	1000	0.512
	20	1200	0.663
Light building sheets of mineralized wood fiber (Heraklite, Tekton, and others)	20	200	0.062
	20	400	0.083
	20	600	0.128
Lime	20	—	0.123
Limestone, amorphous	20	2550	1.221
Limestone, calcium carbonate	0	2650	2.268
	20		2.210
	100		1.919
Linoleum	20	535	0.081
	20	1180	0.186
Magnezite	1000	—	1.651
Marble	20	2500...2800	2.093...3.489
Metallurgical brick	20	1600	0.651
	20	1800	0.756
	20	2000	0.861
	20	2200	1.012
Mortar (plaster)	20	—	0.930
	20	1600	0.663
	20	1800	0.861
	20	2000	1.070
	20	2200	1.396
—with bricks	20	1600...1800	0.698...0.930
—with ligth concrete blocks	20	1600...1800	0.930...1.163
Natural stone, dense	20	—	2.908
Natural stone, porous	20	—	1.745
Onyx	20	—	2.326
Paving, flagstone	20	—	1.047
Paving plates	20	—	0.093...0.140

1 Btu/(ft h °F) = 1.730 73 W/(m K)

Table 1-16 Thermal Conductivity λ of Building Materials

Building material	Temperature t / °C	Density ρ / kg/m³	Thermal conductivity λ / W/(m K)
Plaster	20	1600	0.628
	20	1800	0.814
	20	2000	1.012
	20	2200	1.279
—inside	20	1600...1800	0.698...0.930
—outside	20		0.930...1.163
—supported, inside	20	—	0.698
—supported, outside	20		0.872
—unsupported, inside	20		0.465
—unsupported, outside	20		0.698
Plaster blocks	20	800	0.314
—for inner walls	20	—	0.291
—light	20	—	0.174
—for roofing	20	—	0.349
Porphyry, cross grain	20	2600	1.396
—parallel to grain	20	—	2.326
Pumice gravel or sand, as a filling material	20	600	0.326
Pumice stone	20	600	0.186...0.314
	20	800	0.267...0.407
	20	1000	0.349...0.465
	20	1400	0.582...0.663
Quarry stone masonry	20	—	1.512...2.442
Quartzite	20	2800	6.048
Rabitz wall, concrete	20	—	0.582
Rabitz wall, gypsum	20	—	0.291
Sand	0	1800...2000	1.745
—average value, mean value	20	1500...1800	0.930
—dry, heaped	20	—	0.582
—grown soil	20	—	2.326
—moist	20	1500	0.326
	20	1640	1.128

Building material	Temperature t / °C	Density ρ / kg/m³	Thermal conductivity λ / W/(m K)
Sand, bone dry, normally impure	20		0.326
—10% moisture, normally impure	20		0.965
—20% moisture, normally impure	20		1.326
—saturated with moisture, normally impure	20	—	1.884
Sandlime	20	400	0.105
	20	600	0.145
	20	800	0.198
	20	1000	0.273
	20	1200	0.337
	20	1600	0.989
	20	1800	1.163
	20	2000	1.396
Sandlime brick	20	1600	0.814
—inside	20		0.930
—outside	20		1.047
Sandstone	20	2200...2500	1.279...2.093
—dry	20		1.675
—moist	20	2250	1.291
Sawdust	0	215	0.070
	30		0.072
Sawdust, air-dried	20	190...215	0.058...0.070
Sawdust, as a filling material	20	190...215	0.116
Sea sand, bone dry	20	1600	0.314
—10% moisture	20		1.244
—20% moisture	20		1.756
—saturated with moisture	20		2.442
Shell lime	20	2680	2.442
—10% vol. moisture	20	2680	0.962
—20% vol. moisture	20		1.256
—30% vol. moisture	20		1.465
Silica brick	100	1800...2200	1.105
	500		1.047...1.279
	1000		1.105...1.396
Slag	20	—	0.186

1 Btu/(ft h °F) = 1.730 73 W/(m K)

(continued)

Table 1-16 Thermal Conductivity λ of Building Materials

Building material	Temperature t / °C	Density ρ / kg/m³	Thermal conductivity λ / W/(m K)
Slag			
—blast furnace slag	20	800	0.244...0.384
	20	1000	0.314...0.442
	20	1200	0.372...0.500
	20	1400	0.465...0.570
—blast furnace slag, as a filling material	20	1100...1300	0.582...0.814
—boiler slag	20	700...750	0.326
—boiler slag, as filling material	20	700...750	0.326
—slag concrete (blocks), masonry	20	300...400	0.221
State	20	—	1.396
—cross grain	20	2700	1.512...1.977
	100	2700	1.977
—parallel to grain	20	2700	2.326...3.373
Stone, gabbro	20	—	2.559
Stoneware, ceramics	20	2200...2500	1.047...1.570
Tar paper, roofing	20	1000...1200	0.140...0.349
—hard	20	790	0.151
Wood			
—ash	25	740	0.163
—ash ⊥ cross grain	25		0.174
—ash ‖ with grain	25		0.302
—beech, oak ⊥ cross grain	20	700...900	0.209...0.267
—beech, oak ‖ with grain	20		0.349...0.372
—bich, cross-grain	25	680	0.134
—boxwood	17	900	0.149
—dry, inside	20	—	0.140
—dry, outside	20	—	0.209
—hardwood	20	1200...1400	0.337

(continued)

Building material	Temperature t / °C	Density ρ / kg/m³	Thermal conductivity λ / W/(m K)
Wood			
—larch, cross-grain	25	620	0.140
—light, balsa, cross-grain	20	200...300	0.081...0.105
	25	100...200	0.047...0.066
—mahogany	17	550	0.213
—mahogany	25	700	0.151
—mahogany ⊥	25		0.151
—mahogany ‖	25		0.314
—maple ⊥	30	710	0.158
—maple ‖	30		0.419
—oak	17	650	0.243
—pine, fir, spruce	20	400...600	0.128...0.186
—pine, fir, spruce, with the grain	20		0.279
—plywood	0	588	0.109
	20		0.114
—teak	25	720	0.140
—teak ⊥	25		0.163
—veneer	0	600	0.151
—walnut	70	700	0.267
—wood fibre sheets (Celotex, Karok and others)	20	200	0.047
	20	337	0.074
	20	346	0.065
Wood cement	20	—	0.174
Wood felt	20	330	0.052
Wood shavings	30	140	0.058

1 Btu/(ft h °F) = 1.730 73 W/(m K)

Table 1-17 Thermal Conductivity λ of Miscellaneous Solids

Material	Temperature t / °C	Density ρ / kg/m³	Thermal conductivity λ / W/(m K)
Aluminium oxide, pulverized	20	—	0.675
Aluminium oxide, smelted	20	—	3.314
Amber	20	1050...1100	0.128
Aniline resin	20	1210	0.267
Bakelite	0	1270	0.244
	20		0.233
	100		0.267
Bauxite	600	—	0.558
Boiler incrustation:			
—rich in gypsum	20	2000...2700	0.698...2.326
—rich in lime	20	1000...2500	0.151...2.326
—rich in silicates	20	300...1200	0.081...0.233
Carbomide resin	20	1500	0.349
Carbon filament	1500	—	8.490
Cardboard	20	—	0.140...0.349
Cellon	20	1300...1400	0.209...0.256
Celluloid	20	1400	0.221
Chalk	50	2000	0.930
Coal:			
—amorphous	20	—	1.977
—anthracite	30	1370	0.238
—channel	30	1270	0.195...0.211
—charcoal	20	185...215	0.041...0.065
—gas	30	1260	0.217
—gas, long flame	30	1280	0.233
—lignite (brown) 47.6% H_2O	30	960	0.329
—lignite, dry, 12.1% H_2O	30	920	0.165
—lignite, dry, 3.4% H_2O	30	965	0.155
—non-baking	30	1280	0.212
—pit	20	1200...1350	0.244...0.267
Coal dust	20	730	0.116
Coke	20	1350	0.163
Coke			
—blast furnace	100	1400	2.908...3.489
—foundry	30	925	0.970
—gas	30	950	1.210
—low temperature	30	930	0.721
	30	680	0.151
Coke dust	20	1000	0.151
Compression molding compound, with inorganic filling material	20	1700...1900	0.582...0.930
Compression molding compound, with organic filling material	20	1310...1460	0.267...0.372
Earth, dry	20	—	0.134
Ebonite	20	1200	0.157...0.174
Fat	20	—	0.174
Feathers	20	109	0.076
Fiber (plastic)	20	—	0.233...0.349
Glass:			
—common, window	20	2400...3200	0.582...1.047
—crown	20	2300...2700	1.047
—Jena 16 III	20	2590	0.965
—lead	20	2600...4200	0.768...0.896
—mirror	20	2550	0.802
—plexi	20	—	0.186
—quartz	20	2600...4700	0.768
Graphite, strong (electr.)	20	—	11.630...174.450
Graphite powder	20	700	1.186
Guttapercha	20	—	0.200
Horn, artificial	20	1300...1400	0.163
Ice	-100	928	3.489
	-50	924	2.780
	-20	920	2.442
	0	917	2.210

1 Btu/(ft·h·°F) = 1.730 73 W/(m K)

Table 1-17 Thermal Conductivity λ of Miscellaneous Solids

Material	Temperature t / °C	Density ρ / kg/m³	Thermal conductivity λ / W/(m K)
Igelite	20	1390	0.151
Ivory	20	1800...1900	0.465...0.582
Kitchen salt, crystals	20	—	6.978
Lampblack	40	165	0.070...0.116
Lampblack, coal dust	20	100	0.029
	20	200	0.030
	20	400	0.041
	20	600	0.058
	20	800	0.078
	20	1000	0.010
	20	1200	0.123
Lava (volcanic)	20	—	0.849
Leather —excised	20	850...1000	0.140...0.174
	20		0.209
—fresh	20		0.209...0.419
Mica	20	2600...3200	0.465...0.582
	20	2900	0.523
Micanite	20	2480	0.238
—generally	20	—	0.209...0.407
Mipolan	20	1340	0.209
Paper —hard	20	700	0.140
	20	790	0.151
	20	1000	0.151
	20	1300	0.208
Paraffin	20	860...930	0.244...0.291
Phenolic resin	20	1320	0.262
Plexiglass	20	1180	0.195
Polystyrene	20	1050	0.157
Porcelain, Berlin	20	2290	1.047...1.279
—generally	20	2200...2500	0.814...1.861

(continued)

Material	Temperature t / °C	Density ρ / kg/m³	Thermal conductivity λ / W/(m K)
Press span, pressboard	20	1350	0.244...0.279
Pumice stone powder	20	600	0.128
	20	800	0.151
	20	1000	0.180
	20	1200	0.215
	20	1400	0.256
Rubber, Buna	20	1150	0.233
	20	1250	0.465
—crepe	20	50	0.040
	20	100	0.037
	20	200	0.044
	20	300	0.058
	20	400	0.070
	20	500	0.093
—hard (Ebonite)	20	1150	0.163
—hard, normal	−200		0.136
	−100		0.150
	0	1200	0.157
	100		0.160
—natural	20	1050	0.163
	20	1150	0.279
—Perbunan	20	1250	0.291
	20	1350	0.442
—spongy	20	224	0.055
—Thiokol	20	1650	0.291
—vulcanized, soft: 40% caoutchouc	20	1100	0.233
80% caoutchouc	20		0.151
100% caoutchouc	20		0.128
Rubber powder	20	134	0.050
Shellac	20	—	0.244
Snow, frost	0	150	0.116
	0	300	0.233

1 Btu/(ft h °F) = 1.730 73 W/(m K)

Table 1-17 Thermal Conductivity λ of Miscellaneous Solids

Material	Temperature $\dfrac{t}{°C}$	Density $\dfrac{\rho}{kg/m^3}$	Thermal conductivity $\dfrac{\lambda}{W/(m\,K)}$
Snow, frost	0 0	500 800	0.465 1.279
Soapstone	20	2850	3.256
Stoneware, majolica, semi-porcelain	20	2100...2400	1.047...1.628
Sugar	0	1600	0.582
Sulfur, rhombic	20	—	0.267
Textile, hard	20	1310...1330	0.326...0.349

(continued)

Material	Temperature $\dfrac{t}{°C}$	Density $\dfrac{\rho}{kg/m^3}$	Thermal conductivity $\dfrac{\lambda}{W/(m\,K)}$
Tuff stone	50	1550...2270	0.628...1.675
Vaseline	20	—	0.174
Vinidur	20	1350	0.151
Vulcano fibre	20	1100...1450	0.326...0.349
Wax, bees'	20	—	0.038
Xylolite	20	715	0.140

1 Btu/(ft h °F) = 1.730 73 W/(m K)

Table 1-18 Thermal Conductivity λ of Insulating Materials

Material	Temperature t / °C	Density ρ / kg/m³	Thermal conductivity λ / W/(m K)
Alfol (aluminium foil)	0	3.6	0.030
	20		0.033
	300		0.056
—(aluminium foil)	20	3.6	0.047
Aluminium wool	20	40	0.093
Asbestos	0	383	0.112
	50		0.115
	100		0.119
—fibrous (asbestos wool)	−200	470	0.084
	−150		0.117
	−100		0.137
	−50		0.149
	0		0.154
	20		0.156
	100		0.163
—fibrous	0	580	0.200
	20		0.202
	100		0.212
	200		0.221
—fibrous	−200	700	0.156
	−100		0.221
	0		0.233
	20		0.235
	100		0.244
Asbestos cotton	25	140	0.050
—wool	20	50	0.058
	20	100	0.058
	20	300	0.093
	20	500	0.160
	20	600	0.200
Asbestos felt (soft, flexible)	20	420	0.085
—paper	20	500	0.070
	20	1000	0.151
Asbestos plates	20	2000	0.698
Boiler slag	20	750	0.326

Material	Temperature t / °C	Density ρ / kg/m³	Thermal conductivity λ / W/(m K)
Cellular plastics	20	15	0.035
Coal slag	0	700	0.151
	20		0.163
—blast furnace slag	50	360	0.110
Copper file dust	20	3600	0.41
Cork, boards	20	150	0.042
	20	200	0.048
	20	300	0.059
—expanded (boards)	0	120	0.036
	20		0.038
	50		0.041
—expanded, granules, 3 mm	−200	45	0.009
	−100		0.021
	0		0.034
	100		0.047
—granulated	20	50	0.030
	20	100	0.035
	20	150	0.041
	20	200	0.045
	20	260	0.051
	20	300	0.056
		350	0.060
Cork —impregnated (boards)	0	155	0.041
	20		0.043
	50		0.045
—normal, granules, 1...3 mm	0	150	0.041
	100		0.053
	200		0.066
—roughly granulated, 6 mm	0	85	0.048
	100		0.063
Cotton	−200	81	0.033
	−100		0.044
	0		0.056
	20		0.058

1 Btu/(ft h °F) = 1.73073 W/(m K)

33

Table 1-18   Thermal Conductivity λ of Insulating Materials

Material	Temperature t °C	Density ρ kg/m³	Thermal conductivity λ W/(m K)
Cotton	100		0.067
—knitted	20	330	0.070
—surgical wool	20	10	0.041
	20	40	0.036
—woven	20	245	0.077
Diatomaceous earth (Diatomite)	200	466	0.126
	200	605	0.171
	200	790	0.185
Felt, hair	20	270	0.035...0.081
—rag	20	200	0.041
	20	600	0.087...0.093
Flax	20	160	0.055
Flax	20	19	0.051
	20	25	0.044
	20	50	0.040
	20	100	0.041
	20	150	0.043
	20	200	0.047
Flax, dried, fibers parallel with warm air stream	32	80	0.077
	32	154	0.120
—dried, fibers perpendicular to warm air stream	32	80	0.034
	32	154	0.038
Furnace dust	20	300	0.047
	20	400	0.055
	20	500	0.062
	20	600	0.070
	20	700	0.077
Glass fiber	0	220	0.035
	50		0.043
	100		0.050
	200		0.066
Glass fiber mat	20	100	0.038
	20	200	0.048

Material	Temperature t °C	Density ρ kg/m³	Thermal conductivity λ W/(m K)
Glass, perpendicular to the warm air stream	0	186	0.035
	50		0.044
	100		0.055
	200		0.079
	300		0.107
Glass wool	20	50	0.037
	20	100	0.036
	20	200	0.040
	100	200	0.052
	300	200	0.105
	20	300	0.043
	20	400	0.055
Gravel, as a filling material	20	1500...1800	0.930
Hair	20	90	0.042
—animal	20	176	0.037
—horse	20	172	0.052
	60		0.052
Hemp, dry	32	43	0.076
—manilla	20	45	0.049
Igelite	20	1390	0.151
Iporka	0	15	0.031
	50		0.043
	100		0.055
Jute	20	10	0.060
	32	15	0.053
	20	25	0.044
	20	50	0.036
	20	100	0.037
	20	200	0.041
	20	300	0.047
Kapok	20	5	0.036
	20	25	0.035
	20	50	0.038
	20	100	0.043
	20	150	0.048

(continued)

1 Btu/(ft h °F) = 1.73073 W/(m K)

Table 1-18   Thermal Conductivity λ of Insulating Materials

Material	Temperature $\dfrac{t}{°C}$	Density $\dfrac{\rho}{kg/m^3}$	Thermal conductivity $\dfrac{\lambda}{W/(m\,K)}$
Kieselguhr, powdered	−200	50	0.013
	0		0.035
	100		0.049
	0	200	0.042
	100		0.051
	300		0.070
	500		0.088
	700		0.108
	0	250	0.055
	100		0.064
	300		0.083
	0	350	0.065
	100		0.074
	300		0.095
	500		0.116
—burnt	20	200	0.060
	20	300	0.069
	20	400	0.081
	20	500	0.098
	20	600	0.117
	20	700	0.140
	20	800	0.163
	20	900	0.186
	20	1000	0.212
	20	1200	0.267
	20	1400	0.337
	20	1600	0.430
	20	1800	0.547
	20	2000	0.698
—burnt in forms	0	350...700	0.072...0.131
	50		0.081...0.140
	100		0.088...0.148
	200		0.105...0.164
	300		0.121...0.174
	500		0.140...0.198
Kieselguhr —and magnesia mass	100	200	0.055
	100	300	0.063
	100	400	0.073
	100	500	0.087
	100	600	0.106
	100	800	0.157
Kieselguhr —and magnesia mass	100	1000	0.221
Kieselguhr mass	50	450..840	0.072...0.170
	100		0.074...0.172
	200		0.080...0.176
	300		0.066...0.180
Light building blocks in masonry, slag blocks, porous concrete blocks etc.	20	200	0.062
	20	300	0.072
	20	400	0.083
	20	500	0.105
	20	600	0.128
Light building blocks, mineralized wood wool like Heraklite etc.	20	600	0.407
	20	800	0.477
	20	1000	0.570
	20	1200	0.663
	20	1400	0.779
Linen	25	265	0.066
	25	590	0.070
Magnesia, compressed	20	800	0.605
—powdered	0	200	0.073
Magnesium	−200	130	0.021
	−100		0.029
	0		0.038
	20		0.041
	100		0.049
Magnesium carbonate	20	250	0.055
	20	500	0.104
	100	—	0.097
Magnesium slag	50	270	0.073
	100		0.077
	200		0.084
Peat, lumps	20	120	0.047
—pressed, dry	20	—	0.035...0.070

1 Btu/(ft h °F) = 1.73073 W/(m K)

(continued)

35

Table 1-18 Thermal Conductivity λ of Insulating Materials

Material	Temperature t/°C	Density ρ/kg/m³	Thermal conductivity λ/W/(m K)
Peat dust	0 / 20 / 50	190	0.047 / 0.048 / 0.052
Peat moss	20	160	0.042
Peat plates	0 / 20 / 50 / 20	210 / 200...400	0.050 / 0.052 / 0.056 / 0.047...0.093
Pine and juniper bark	20	342	0.080
Plywood	0 / 20	590	0.109 / 0.114
Poresta	0 / 10 / 20	24	0.031 / 0.034 / 0.035
Pumice gravel, as a filling material	20	600	0.326
Pumice stone, natural	0 / 20 / 50	300...600	0.087...0.174 / 0.092...0.186 / 0.099...0.198
Sawdust	20	200	0.058
Sea grass	20	80	0.035
Silk, artificial	20 / 20 / 20	170 / 300 / 464	0.049 / 0.042 / 0.051
—fibrous	−200 / −150 / −100 / −50 / 0 / 50 / 100	58	0.013 / 0.016 / 0.022 / 0.028 / 0.034 / 0.041 / 0.048
—spun fiber	−200 / −100 / 0 / 100	100	0.024 / 0.037 / 0.050 / 0.060

Material	Temperature t/°C	Density ρ/kg/m³	Thermal conductivity λ/W/(m K)
Silk, artificial —woven	30	—	0.047
Sisal hemp	20	109	0.038
Slag wool	20	200	0.047
Slag, wool, stone wool (Silan)	20 / 20 / 20 / 20 / 20	100 / 200 / 300 / 400 / 500	0.034 / 0.040 / 0.047 / 0.055 / 0.058
Steel wool	20	104	0.058
Straw	0 / 20	140	0.045 / 0.050
Sugar cane	20 / 20 / 20 / 20 / 20 / 20	25 / 50 / 100 / 150 / 200 / 250	0.045 / 0.040 / 0.042 / 0.047 / 0.053 / 0.060
Tree bark	20	337	0.074
Wood felt	20 / 20	330 / 350	0.052 / 0.065
Wood fibre plates (Celotex, Kapak and others)	20 / 20 / 20 / 20 / 20	200 / 300 / 400 / 500 / 600	0.047 / 0.051 / 0.055 / 0.064 / 0.074
Wood shavings	20 / 20 / 20 / 20	150 / 200 / 250 / 300	0.058 / 0.059 / 0.062 / 0.065
Wood shavings (stuffing material)	20	100...140	0.093

1 Btu/(ft h °F) = 1.73073 W/(m K)

Table 1-18 Thermal Conductivity λ of Insulating Materials

Material	Temperature $\dfrac{t}{°C}$	Density $\dfrac{\rho}{kg/m^3}$	Thermal conductivity $\dfrac{\lambda}{W/(m\,K)}$
Wool	20	50	0.038
	20	100	0.036
	20	150	0.036
	20	200	0.038
	20	250	0.041
	20	300	0.043
	20	350	0.047
	20	400	0.050
—slag	-200		0.010

Material	Temperature $\dfrac{t}{°C}$	Density $\dfrac{\rho}{kg/m^3}$	Thermal conductivity $\dfrac{\lambda}{W/(m\,K)}$
Wool	-100		0.020
—slag	0	95	0.031
	20		0.034
	-200		0.012
	-100		0.021
	0	120	0.033
	20		0.035

1 Btu/(ft h °F) = 1.73073 W/(m K)

Table 1-19 Thermal Conductivity λ of Fire and Ceramic Bricks

Material	Mass fraction of basic materials %	Temperature t °C	Density ρ kg/m³	Thermal conductivity λ W/(m K)
Carbon brick	89 C	0	1200	0.698
		200		0.872
		400		1.047
		600		1.279
		800		1.454
		1000		1.628
Carborundum	50 SiC	0	2200	5.815
		200		5.234
		400		4.652
		600		4.303
		800		3.954
		1000		3.605
		1200		3.256
	75 SiC	0	2300	16.282
		200		13.026
		400		11.049
		600		9.886
		800		8.839
		1000		7.908
		1200		7.211
	100 SiC	0		72.106
		200	—	48.846
		400		37.216
		600		29.075
		800		23.412
		1000		19.771
		1200		16.864
Chamotte	50...75 SiO$_2$, 20...50 Al$_2$O$_3$	0	800	0.209
		200		0.244
		400		0.279
		600		0.314
		800		0.349
		1000		0.384
		1200		0.419
		0	1000	0.291
		200		0.326
		400		0.361
		600		0.407
		800		0.442
		1000		0.488
		1200		0.523
		0	1200	0.384
		200		0.407
		400		0.442
		600		0.477
		800		0.523
		1000		0.558
		1200		0.605
		0	2000	1.070
		200		1.128
		400		1.198
		600		1.256
		800		1.337
		1000		1.401
		1200		1.489
Chamotte		0	2200	1.558
		200		1.651
		400		1.745
		600		1.838
		800		1.942

Material	Mass fraction of basic materials %	Temperature t °C	Density ρ kg/m³	Thermal conductivity λ W/(m K)
Chamotte		1000		2.047
		1200		2.152
Chromite	40...45 Cr$_2$O$_3$	0	2750	1.279
		200		1.396
		400		1.512
		600		1.628
		800		1.628
		1000		1.686
		1200		1.686
Corundum	80 Al$_2$O$_3$	0	2700	2.326
		200		2.175
		400		2.093
		600		2.035
		800		2.000
		1000		1.977
		1200		1.954
	100 Al$_2$O$_3$	0	3750	20.934
		200		10.700
		400		7.908
		600		6.513
		800		5.699
		1000		5.117
		1200		4.768
Magnesite	50 MgO	0	2000	2.675
		200		2.559
		400		2.326
		600		2.093
		800		1.861
		1000		1.686
		1200		1.512
	75 MgO	0	2600	5.001
		200		4.536
		400		4.071
		600		3.605
		800		3.140
		1000		2.791
		1200		2.442
	100 MgO	0	3500	43.031
		200		25.586
		400		16.282
		600		11.630
		800		8.723
		1000		6.397
		1200		5.234
Porcelain	55 Al$_2$O$_3$ 45 SiO$_2$	0	2350	0.930
		200		1.396
		400		1.745
		600		2.035
		800		2.268
		1000		2.442
Silica	95 SiO$_2$	0	1900	1.070
		200		1.163
		400		1.279
		600		1.396
		800		1.535
		1000		1.686
		1200		1.861

1 Btu/(ft h °F) = 1.730 73 W/(m K)

Table 1-19 Thermal Conductivity λ of Fire and Ceramic Bricks *(continued)*

Material	Mass fraction of basic materials %	Temperature t °C	Density ρ kg/m³	Thermal conductivity λ W/(m K)	Material	Mass fraction of basic materials %	Temperature t °C	Density ρ kg/m³	Thermal conductivity λ W/(m K)
Silimanite	60...80 Al, O₃	0	1000	0.174	Silimanite	60...80 Al, O₃	800		1.105
		200		0.209			1000		1.105
		400		0.233			1200		1.105
		600		0.267					
		800		0.302			0	2500	2.152
		1000		0.337			200		2.047
		1200		0.372			400		1.954
							600		1.884
		0	1500	0.465			800		1.826
		200		0.488			1000		1.779
		400		0.523			1200		1.745
		600		0.558					
		800		0.593	Zircon bricks	62 ZrO₂	0	3600	2.442
		1000		0.628			200		2.326
		1200		0.663			400		2.210
							600		2.093
		0	2000	1.105			800		1.977
		200		1.105			1000		1.919
		400		1.105			1200		1.919
		600		1.105					

1 Btu/(ft h °F) = 1.73073 W/(m K)

Table 1-20 Thermal Conductivity λ of Burnt Kieselguhr (Diatomaceous Earth)

Temperature t °C	Density ρ kg/m³	Thermal conductivity λ W/(m K)	Temperature t °C	Density ρ kg/m³	Thermal conductivity λ W/(m K)
0	200	0.058	400	500	0.156
50		0.065	500		0.167
100		0.072	600		0.178
200		0.091	700		0.186
300		0.113			
400		0.135	0	600	0.114
500		0.156	50		0.124
600		0.177	100		0.135
700		0.199	200		0.151
			300		0.166
0	300	0.066	400		0.180
50		0.073	500		0.191
100		0.080	600		0.200
200		0.095	700		0.206
300		0.112			
400		0.128	0	700	0.135
500		0.144	50		0.147
600		0.159	100		0.159
700		0.174	200		0.177
			300		0.193
0	400	0.079	400		0.207
50		0.086	500		0.216
100		0.094	600		0.223
200		0.109	700		0.229
300		0.124			
400		0.138	0	800	0.158
500		0.151	50		0.172
600		0.162	100		0.185
700		0.171	200		0.205
			300		0.221
0	500	0.095	400		0.234
50		0.105	500		0.243
100		0.114	600		0.251
200		0.129	700		0.257
300		0.143			

1 Btu/(ft h °F) = 1.730 73 W/(m K)

Table 1-21 Thermal Conductivity λ of Lampblack

Temperature t °C	Density ρ kg/m³	Thermal conductivity λ W/(m K)	Temperature t °C	Density ρ kg/m³	Thermal conductivity λ W/(m K)
0	100	0.028	600	600	0.141
100		0.035	800		0.180
200		0.042	1000		0.221
400		0.058			
600		0.080	0	800	0.076
800		0.108	100		0.088
1000		0.140	200		0.101
			400		0.131
0	200	0.029	600		0.169
100		0.037	800		0.215
200		0.045	1000		0.267
400		0.064			
600		0.087	0	1000	0.098
800		0.116	100		0.112
1000		0.150	200		0.126
			400		0.160
0	400	0.040	600		0.204
100		0.049	800		0.256
200		0.058	1000		0.340
400		0.080			
600		0.112	0	1200	0.120
800		0.145	100		0.136
1000		0.183	200		0.151
			400		0.190
0	600	0.057	600		0.238
100		0.067	800		0.297
200		0.079	1000		0.361
400		0.107			

1 Btu/(ft h °F) = 1.730 73 W/(m K)

Table 1-22 Thermal Properties of Polymer Materials

Name	Density ρ kg/m³	Linear expansion coefficient α 1/kK	Specific heat capacity[2] c kJ/(kg K)	Thermal conductivity λ W/(m K)	Temperatura of constant use t °C	Melting point t_m °C
Low density polyethylene, LDPE	915...935	0.10...0.22	2.3	0.33	80	110...120
High density polyethylene, HDPE	940...970	0.11...0.13	2.3	0.46...0.50	120	130...140
Polypropylene	900...910	0.081...0.10	2	0.12	120...160	160...170
Polystyrene, PS	1050...1060	0.06...0.08	1.3	0.10...0.14	70	100...105
High impact polystyrene, HIPS	1050...1070	0.08...0.10	1.3	0.04...0.13	65	85...90
Styrene acrylonitrile copolymer (20...30% acrylonitrile), SAN	1080	0.06...0.08	—	0.32	85	110
Acrylonitrile-butadiene-styrene terpolymer, ABS	1030...1060	0.08...0.10	1.3...1.7	0.19...0.33	75...90	90...100
Polyvinyl chloride, rigid	1380...1550	0.05...0.10	0.8...1.1	0.15...0.20	65...85	—
Polyvinyl chloride, plasticized	1160...1350	0.07...0.25	1.3...2	0.13...0.17	50...70	—
Polytetrafluoroethylene, PTFE	2140...2200	0.16	0.9	0.24	−200...+250	320...340
Polychlorotrifluoroethylene, PCTFE	2100...2180	0.04...0.07	0.8	0.20	−200...+180	210
Polyvinyl fluoride, PVF	1380...1570	—	—	—	−70...+110	185...190
Polyvinylidene fluoride, PVDF	1750	0.12	—	—	30...+140	170
Polyoxymethylene, homopolymer	1425	0.10...0.14	1.47	—	do 85	175
Polyoxymethylene, copolymer	1410	—	—	—	—	163
Polyphenylene oxide	1060	0.033...0.06	—	0.22	—	260...270
Polysulfone	1240	0.052...0.056	1.3	0.12	150...180	—
Polymethyl methacrylate	1180	0.05...0.09	1.5	0.16...0.24	60...90	102...115
Polycarbonate	1200	0.068	1.3	0.20	120	170
Polyester (no fillers or reinforcements)	1200...1300	0.08...0.11	1.10...1.45	—	—	—
Polyurethane foams, rigid nith integrol lining	600	—	—	0.07	(80...120)[1]	—

[1] Temperature of stability of shape.
[2] Older name: specific heat.

1 Btu/(ft h °F) = 1.730 73 W/(m K)

40

Table 1-23 Emissivity ε_n of Metal Surfaces

Metal	Chemical formula and mass fraction %	State of surface	Temperature $\dfrac{t}{°C}$	Emissivity ε_n
Aluminum	Al	aluminium surfaced roofing	43	0.216
		colorized copper, heated to 600°C	200 / 600	0.180 / 0.190
		colorized steel, heated to 600°C	200 / 600	0.520 / 0.570
		oxidized to 600 °C	200 / 600	0.110 / 0.190
		polished plate	23 / 225 / 575	0.040 / 0.039 / 0.057
		rolled, polished	170	0.039
		rough plate	25	0.070
Bismuth	Bi	bright	80	0.340
Brass	Cu-Zn	burnished	—	0.42
		hard rolled	22	0.06
		oxidized	338	0.22
		oxidized at 600 °C	200 / 600	0.61 / 0.59
		polished	19 / 300	0.05 / 0.032
		rolled plate, rubbed with emery	22	0.20
		tarnished	56 / 338	0.202 / 0.221
		tube	—	0.208
Chromium	Cr	polished	150	0.058
Copper	Cu	black oxidized	20	0.780
		eletrolytic, carefully polished	80	0.018
		lightly tarnished	20	0.037
Copper	Cu	molten	1075 / 1275	0.160 / 0.130
		oxidized	130	0.760
		oxidized by heating to 600 °C	200 / 600	0.570 / 0.550
		polished	20 / 115	0.030 / 0.023
		scraped	20	0.070
		rolled	—	0.640
		tube	—	0.360
Cuprous oxide		—	800 / 1100	0.660 / 0.540
Gold	Au	highly polished	225 / 625	0.018 / 0.035
		not polished	20	0.47
		polished	20 / 130 / 400	0.025 / 0.018 / 0.022
Iron	Fe	completely rusty	20	0.85
		electrolytic, highly polished	175 / 225	0.052 / 0.064
		etched, bright	150	0.128
		fire proof, oxidized	80	0.613
		ground, bright	20	0.24
		molten, dull oxidized	20 / 360	0.94 / 0.94
		oxide	500 / 1200	0.85 / 0.89

1) ε_n (normal emissivity), emissivity coefficient for radiation normal to surface. Mean normal total emissivity (ε) can be calculated from: $\varepsilon = 1.2\,\varepsilon_n$ for bright metal surfaces; $\varepsilon = 0.95\,\varepsilon_n$ for other bodies with smooth surface; $\varepsilon = 0.98\,\varepsilon_n$ for other rough surfaces.

Table 1-23 Emissivity ε_n of Metal Surfaces

Metal	Chemical formula and mass fraction %	State of surface	Temperature t/°C	Emissivity ε_n
Iron	Fe	oxidized, smooth	125 525	0.78 0.82
		polished	425 1020	0.144 0.377
		rolled	20	0.77
		rubbed with emery	20	0.242
		rusty, red	20	0.61
		smooth	900 1040	0.55 0.60
		unwrought	925 1115	0.87 0.95
Iron castings		casting skin	100	0.80
		molten	1330	0.28
		oxidized at 600°C	200 600	0.64 0.78
		polished	200	0.21
		rough, strongly oxidized	40 250	0.95 0.95
		turned	22 830 990	0.435 0.60 0.70
Lead	Pb	gray oxidized	20	0.28
		oxidized at 200°C	200	0.63
		polished	130 230	0.056 0.074
Manganine		rolled, smooth	118	0.048
Mercury	Hg	—	20 100	0.09 0.12
Molybdenum	Mo	filament	725 2600	0.096 0.292
Nickel	Ni	dull	20 100	0.111 0.041
		oxidized	100	0.41
		oxidized at 600 °C	200 600	0.370 0.48
		(plated on iron sheet), polished	24	0.056
		plated on polished iron, polished	23	0.045
		plated on pickled iron, not polished	20	0.110
		polished	100 230 375	0.045 0.070 0.087
Nickel alloy (Chromenickel)		wire	185 1000	0.096 0.186
	18% Cr, 8% Ni	after 24 hr heating at 525 °C	225 525	0.62 0.73
	20% Ni, 25% Cr	brown, weathered	215 525	0.90 0.97
	Cr-Ni, 18...32% Ni, 95...68% Cr, 20% Zn	gray oxidized	20	0.262
	18% Cr, 8% Ni	lighly silvery, rough, brown after heating	215 490	0.44 0.36
	Ni-Cr	oxidized at 600 °C	200 600	0.41 0.46
	60% Ni, 12% Cr	smooth, black, firm oxide coat from weathering	270 560	0.89 0.82
Nickel-chrome	Cr-Ni	—	52 1035	0.64 0.76
Nickel oxide		—	650 1255	0.59 0.86

[1] ε_n (normal emissivity), emissivity coefficient for radiation normal to surface. Mean normal total emissivity (ε) can be calculated from: $\varepsilon = 1.2\ \varepsilon_n$ for bright metal surfaces; $\varepsilon = 0.95\ \varepsilon_n$ for other bodies with smooth surface; $\varepsilon = 0.98\ \varepsilon_n$ for other rough surfaces.

Table 1-23 Emissivity ε_n of Metal Surfaces

Metal	Chemical formula and mass fraction %	State of surface	Temperature $\frac{t}{°C}$	Emissivity ε_n
Platinum	Pt	filament	25 1230	0.036 0.192
		polished	225 625	0.054 0.104
		strip	925 1116	0.12 0.17
		wire	225 1375	0.073 0.182
Silumin, cast		polished	150	0.186
Silver	Ag	polished	20 38 370 630	0.025 0.0221 0.0312 0.0320
		polished, clean	225 625	0.0198 0.0342
Steel		dense shiny oxide layer	25	0.82
		ground sheet	940 1100	0.520 0.610
		mild, molten	1600 1800	0.28 0.28
		oxidized at 600°C	200 600	0.79 0.79
		oxidized, rough	40 370	0.94 0.97
		pipe	0 200	0.745 0.800
		rolled sheet	20	0.057

Metal	Chemical formula and mass fraction %	State of surface	Temperature $\frac{t}{°C}$	Emissivity ε_n
Steel		thick rough oxide layer	25	0.80
—tool		galvanized sheet	—	0.262
Steel, chrome		(sheet), oxidized	—	0.870
Steel casting		polished	770 1040	0.52 0.56
Tantalum	Ta	filament	1325 2525	0.193 0.31
Tin	Sn	bright	20	0.070
		tinned steel sheet	24	0.056 ... 0.086
Tungsten	W	—	230 2230	0.053 0.31
		filament	3300	0.39
		filament, used	25 3300	0.032 0.035
White metal		tinned, bright	— —	0.056 0.086
Zinc	Zn	galvanized sheet iron, bright galvanized sheet iron, gray oxidized	28 24	0.228 0.276
		oxidized by heating at 400°C	400	0.11
		polished	230 325	0.045 0.053
		tarnished	20 50 280	0.25 0.21 0.21

[1] ε_n (normal emissivity), emissivity coefficient for radiation normal to surface. Mean normal total emissivity (ε) can be calculated from: $\varepsilon = 1.2\,\varepsilon_n$ for bright metal surfaces; $\varepsilon = 0.95\,\varepsilon_n$ for other bodies with smooth surface; $\varepsilon = 0.98\,\varepsilon_n$ for other rough surfaces.

Table 1-24 Emissivity ε_n of Nonmetal Surfaces

Substance	State of surface	Temperature $\frac{t}{°C}$	Emissivity ε_n
Asbestos board	—	24	0.96
—paper	—	40 / 370	0.93 / 0.95
—slate	—	20	0.96
Brick	red, rough	20	0.93
Carbon filament	—	1040 / 1405	0.53 / 0.53
Chamotte	—	1200	0.60
Chamotte stone	glazed	1000 / 1220	0.75 / 0.60
Clay	burnt	70	0.91
Coal, pure	ground	125 / 625	0.81 / 0.79
Corundum powder on paper	rough	80	0.855
Cotton	—	—	0.78
Dinas brick	glazed, rough	1100	0.85
	unglazed, rough	1000	0.80
Enamel white	fused on iron	20	0.90
Glass	smooth	20 / 90	0.90 / 0.94
Granite	ground	—	0.427
Gypsum	—	0 / 200	0.90 / 0.90
Ice	smooth, water / rough	0 / 0	0.966 / 0.985
Lampblack	—	0 / 370	0.945 / 0.945
Linoleum	—	20	0.885
Magnezite stones	—	1390	0.39

Substance	State of surface	Temperature $\frac{t}{°C}$	Emissivity ε_n
Marble	light gray, polished	22	0.93
	ground smooth	—	0.545
Masonry	plastered	0 / 200	0.93 / 0.93
Paper	—	20 / 95	0.80 / 0.92
Plaster, lime	white, rough	20 / 200	0.93 / 0.93
Porcelain	glazed	20	0.93
Quartz	fused, rough	20	0.93
Refractory materials	high-emissive	500 / 600 / 1000	0.80 / 0.85 / 0.90
	low-emissive	500 / 600 / 1000	0.65 / 0.70 / 0.75
Roofing cardboard	—	20	0.93
Rubber, soft	gray	24	0.86
—hard	black, rough	24	0.95
Sandstone	ground smooth	—	0.576
Silicate stone	rough	1000 / 1220	0.80 / 0.66
Silimanite stone	—	1390	0.29
Silk cloth	—	20	0.77
Slate	ground	60 / 200	0.665 / 0.665

1) ε_n (normal emissivity), emissivity coefficient for radiation normal to surface. Mean normal total emissivity (ε) can be calculated from: $\varepsilon = 0.95\,\varepsilon_n$ for bright metal surfaces; $\varepsilon = 1.2\,\varepsilon_n$ for other bodies with smooth surface; $\varepsilon = 0.98\,\varepsilon_n$ for other rough surfaces.

Table 1-24 Emissivity ε_n of Nonmetal Surfaces

Substance	State of surface	Temperature $\frac{t}{°C}$	Emissivity ε_n
Wood	planed	20 70	0.90 0.925
—beech	planed	70	0.935
—oak	planed	21	0.885
Wool cloth	—	20	0.75

[1] ε_n (normal emissivity), emissivity coefficient for radiation normal to surface. Mean normal total emissivity (ε) can be calculated from: $\varepsilon = 1.2\,\varepsilon_n$ for bright metal surfaces; $\varepsilon = 0.95\,\varepsilon_n$ for other bodies with smooth surface; $\varepsilon = 0.98\,\varepsilon_n$ for other rough surfaces.

Table 1-25 Emissivity ε_n of Paints and Coatings

Substance	State of surface	Temperature $\frac{t}{°C}$	Emissivity ε_n
Aluminum bronze	—	100	0.20...0.40
Aluminum enamel	rough	20	0.39
Aluminum paint, after heating to 325°C	—	150...315	0.35
Aluminum paints, different	rough, smooth	100	0.27...0.67
Bakelite enamel	—	80	0.935
Enamel, white	—	40 95	0.80 0.95
—alcohol	black, bright	25	0.82
—black	bright	25	0.876
	dull	40 95	0.96 0.98
—for irradiators (heating bodies)	—	100	0.925
Oil	thick layer	—	0.82
Oil coating	smooth	—	0.78
Oil paint	—	0 200	0.885 0.885
Red lead primer	—	20 100	0.93 0.93
Shellack, black	bright	21	0.82
	dull	75 145	0.91 0.91
Water	—	—	0.8
Water glass-bound lampblack	—	20 100	0.96 0.96
White enamel, melted	white, rough	20	0.90

[1] ε_n (normal emissivity), emissivity coefficient for radiation normal to surface. Mean normal total emissivity (ε) can be calculated from: $\varepsilon = 1.2\,\varepsilon_n$ for bright metal surfaces; $\varepsilon = 0.95\,\varepsilon_n$ for other bodies with smooth surface; $\varepsilon = 0.98\,\varepsilon_n$ for other rough surfaces.

Table 1-26 Heating Values of Solid Fuels[1]

Fuel	Raw, air-dried fuel Composition, in %								Pure combustible matter (without moisture and ash) Composition, in %						
	Carbon C	Hydrogen H	Sulphur S	Oxygen O	Nitrogen N	Ash a	Moisture m	Heating value H_i kJ/kg	Carbon C	Hydrogen H	Sulphur S	Oxygen O	Nitrogen N	Volatile matter v	Heating value H_i kJ/kg
Anthracite	85.6	1.8	0.7	2.0	0.9	8	1	31192	94.0	2.0	0.8	2.2	1.0	5	34332
Brown coal															
—bright	58.4	4.0	2.4	14.4	0.8	12	8	23237	73.0	5.0	3.0	18.0	1.0	55	29308
—lignite	49.6	4.0	0.4	18.7	0.6	7	20	19678	68.0	5.1	0.5	25.6	0.7	65	27633
—ordinary	52.4	3.9	0.8	17.2	0.7	10	15	20725	70.0	5.2	1.0	22.9	0.9	60	28470
Brown coal coke (low-temperature)	68.9	1.7	0.8	3.0	0.6	20	5	24367	91.9	2.3	1.0	4.0	0.8	—	32657
Charcoal	79.0	3.1	—	11.9	—	1	5	28596	84.0	3.3	—	12.7	—	—	30564
Gas coke	86.0	0.5	0.9	0.9	0.6	9	2	29768	96.6	0.7	1.0	1.0	0.7	—	33494
Peat	40.3	3.8	—	22.1	0.8	8	25	14528	60.0	5.8	—	33.0	1.2	70	22609
Pit coal															
—coking, bituminous	82.0	4.1	0.7	4.2	1.0	6	2	32322	89.0	4.5	0.8	4.6	1.1	25	35169
—dry	75.2	4.6	0.9	8.8	0.5	8	2	28973	83.5	5.1	1.0	9.8	0.6	40	32238
—forge bituminous	77.4	4.7	0.7	5.3	0.9	8	3	31275	87.0	5.3	0.8	5.9	1.0	30	34750
—gas	74.8	4.8	0.7	6.6	1.1	10	2	29433	85.0	5.5	0.8	7.5	1.2	35	33494
—non-bituminous	83.8	2.7	0.7	2.9	0.9	7	2	32322	92.0	3.0	0.8	3.2	2.0	15	35588
Smelting coke	87.3	0.5	0.9	0.8	0.5	8	2	30103	97.0	0.5	1.0	0.9	0.6	—	33494
Wood	39.3	4.7	—	34.1	0.4	1.5	20	14277	50.0	6.0	—	43.5	0.5	75	18841

[1] Mean values of composition of some solid fuels.
1 Btu = 1.055 06 kJ.

LIQUIDS

Table 2-1 Thermal Properties of Liquids

Liquid Name	Chemical formula	At a temperature of 20 °C			At a pressure $p = 1.013\,25$ bar (= 760 mm Hg)			
		Molar mass M kg/kmol	Density ρ kg/m^3	Cubic expansion coefficient α_V 1/K	Melting point t_m °C	Heat of fusion q_f kJ/kg	Boiling point t_b °C	Heat of vaporization r kJ/kg
Acetaldehyde	C_2H_4O	44.05	783	—	−123.5	73.688	17.4	573.592
Acetic acid	$C_2H_4O_2$	60.05	1049	0.00107	16.7	194.268	118	406.120
Acetone	C_3H_6O	58.08	791	0.00143	−94.3	96.296	56.1	523.350
n-amyl alcohol	$C_5H_{12}O$	88.14	810	0.00088	−78	111.788	138	—
Amyl benzoate	$C_{12}H_{16}O_2$	176.24	1010	0.00085	—	—	260	—
Amyl bromide	$C_5H_{11}Br$	151.06	1223	—	−95	95.459	126	200.966
Amyl chloride	$C_5H_{11}Cl$	106.59	883	—	—	—	106	309.823
Aniline	C_6H_7N	93.12	1022	0.00085	−6.2	113.462	184	447.988
Arsenic trichloride	$AsCl_3$	181.28	2170	0.00102	−16	—	130.3	192.593
Benzene	C_6H_6	78.11	879	0.00106	5.5	127.279	80.1	395.653
Bromine	Br_2	159.83	3120	0.00113	−7.3	67.826	58.8	180.032
Bromobenzene	C_6H_5Br	157.02	1495	0.00092	−30.6	—	156	—
Bromoform	$CHBr_3$,	252.77	2890	0.00091	7.9	—	150	—
n-Butyl alcohol	$C_4H_{10}O$	74.12	810	—	−90	125.185	117.7	590.339
Carbon disulphide	CS_2	76.13	1263	0.00119	−112	74.106	46.3	372.625
Chloral	C_2HOCl_3	147.40	1512	0.00093	−57.5	—	98	226.087
Chlorobenzene	C_6H_5Cl	112.56	1106	0.00098	−45.2	66.570	132	324.896
Chloroform	$CHCl_3$	119.39	1489	0.00128	−63.5	79.549	61.20	247.021
m-Chlorotoluene	C_7H_7Cl	126.58	1072	—	−47.8	—	162.2	—
o-Chlorotoluene	C_7H_7Cl	126.58	1081	0.00089	−36.5	76.200	159	303.962
Cyclohexane	C_6H_{12}	84.15	778	0.00120	6.4	30.982	80.8	360.065
cis-Decalin	$C_{10}H_{18}$	138.24	900	—	−51	—	193	—
$trans$-Decalin	$C_{10}H_{18}$	138.24	870	—	−36	—	185	—
cis-Dichloroethylene	$C_2H_2Cl_2$	96.95	1265	—	−50	—	48.4	305.636
$trans$-Dichloroethylene	$C_2H_2Cl_2$	96.95	1283	—	−80	—	60	309.823
Dichlorotetrafluoroethane	$C_2F_4Cl_2$	170.93	—	—	—	—	3.5	127.697
Diethylamine	$C_4H_{11}N$	73.13	711	—	−39	—	56	380.999
Diethylene glycol	$C_4H_{10}O_3$	106.12	1120	—	−10.5	—	245	628.020
Dimethylamine	C_2H_7N	45.08	—	—	−93	—	7.0	586.152
Ethyl acetate	$C_4H_8O_2$	88.10	900	0.00138	−83.6	118.905	77.1	368.438
Ethyl alcohol	C_2H_6O	46.07	789.5	0.00110	−114.5	104.670	78.3	841.547
Ethylamine	C_2H_7N	45.08	—	—	−81	—	16.5	607.088
Ethylbenzene	C_8H_{10}	106.16	868	0.00096	−94	86.248	135.4	339.131
Ethyl benzoate	$C_9H_{10}O_2$	150.17	1047	0.00090	−34.6	—	213.2	267.955
Ethyl bromide	C_2H_5Br	108.98	1450	0.00142	−119	53.591	38.4	251.208
Ethyl chloride	C_2H_5Cl	64.52	—	—	−138.7	—	12.2	387.279
Ethyl ether	$C_4H_{10}O$	74.12	714	0.00162	−116.3	100.483	34.48	360.065
Ethyl iodide	C_2H_5J	155.98	1934	0.00117	−111	—	72.5	191.755
Ethyl mustard oil (Ethyl isothiocyanate)	C_4H_5NS	99.15	1018	—	−102.5	—	152.0	—
Ethylene glycol	$C_2H_6O_2$	62.07	1115	—	−12.3	188.406	197	812.239
Formic acid	CH_2O_2	46.03	1220	0.00102	8.4	276.329	100.7	494.042
Glycerol	$C_3H_8O_3$	92.09	1260	0.00050	18	200.548	290	—
n-Heptane	C_7H_{16}	100.19	684	0.00124	−90.6	141.514	98.4	318.197
n-Heptyl alcohol	$C_7H_{16}O$	116.19	823	—	−34.3	—	176	439.614
n-Hexane	C_6H_{14}	86.17	660	0.00135	−95.3	146.538	68.73	330.757
n-Hexyl alcohol	$C_6H_{14}O$	102.17	820	—	−50	150.724	157	—
n-Hexylene	C_6H_{12}	84.15	683	—	−98.5	—	64	388.535
Isoamyl acetate	$C_7H_{14}O_2$	130.18	873	0.00114	—	—	141	—
Isoamyl alcohol	$C_5H_{12}O$	88.14	810	0.00093	−117	—	131	—
Isobutyl alcohol	$C_4H_{10}O$	74.12	804	0.00094	−108	108	381.15	
Isopentane	C_5H_{12}	72.14	621	0.00154	−160.0	102.158	28.0	339.131
Isopropyl	C_3H_8O	60.09	786	—	−89	89.179	82.3	669.888
Lactic acid	$C_3H_6O_3$	90.08	1240	—	18	—	—	—

1 Btu = 1.055 06 kJ

Table 2-1   Thermal Properties of Liquids   (continued)

| Liquid | | Molar mass | At a temperature of 20 °C | | At a pressure $p = 1.013\,25$ bar (= 760 mm Hg) | | | |
Name	Chemical formula	M	Density ρ	Cubic expansion coefficient α_V	Melting point t_m	Heat of fusion q_f	Boiling point t_b	Heat of vaporization r
		kg/kmol	kg/m³	1/K	°C	kJ/kg	°C	kJ/kg
Mercury	Hg	200.61	13545.7	0.000181	−38.83	11.723	356.95	301.450
Methyl acetate	$C_3H_6O_2$	74.08	934	—	−98.1	—	57.1	410.306
Methyl alcohol	CH_4O	32.04	792	0.00119	−98	100.483	64.51	1101.128
Methyl benzoate	$C_8H_8O_2$	136.14	1100	0.00090	−12.5	—	199.6	—
Methyl bromide	CH_3Br	94.95	—	—	−93	—	4.0	259.582
Methyl formate	$C_2H_4O_2$	60.05	975	0.00124	−99.8	125.604	31.8	481.482
Methyl iodide	CH_3J	141.95	2279	—	−66.3	—	42.5	196.780
Methylene chloride	CH_2Cl_2	84.94	1336	—	−96.5	—	40	330.757
Methylene iodide	CH_2J_2	267.87	3325	0.00081	6.0	—	180	—
Nitric acid	HNO_3	63.015	1512	0.00124	−41	39.775	86	481.482
Nitrobenzene	$C_6H_5O_2N$	123.11	1203	0.00083	5.7	98.390	211	397.746
Nitroglycerol	$C_3H_5O_9N_3$	227.09	1600	—	13.2	96.296	—	—
n-Nonyl alcohol	$C_9H_{20}O$	144.25	828	—	−5	—	213.5	—
n-Octane	C_8H_{18}	114.22	720	0.00114	−57	180.032	125.7	297.263
n-Octyl alcohol	$C_8H_{18}O$	130.22	827	—	−16.5	—	195	410.306
Oleic acid	$C_{18}H_{34}O_2$	298.45	890	—	9	—	370	238.648
n-Pentane	C_5H_{12}	72.14	626	0.00160	−129.7	115.974	36.1	355.878
Phosphorus trichloride	PCl_3	137.39	1578	—	−91	—	76.0	215.202
Propionic acid	$C_3H_6O_2$	74.08	992	0.00109	−21.5	101.739	141.4	418.680
n-Propyl alcohol	C_3H_8O	60.09	804	0.00098	−126	86.667	97.2	682.448
n-Propyl chloride	C_3H_7Cl	78.54	892	—	−123	—	46	351.691
Pyridine	C_5H_5N	79.10	983	0.00112	−42.0	104.670	115.4	427.054
Quinoline	C_9H_7N	129.15	1093	—	−19.5	83.736	242	—
Sulphuric acid	H_2SO_4	98.08	1834	0.00057	10.5	108.857	—	—
Tetrachloromethane	CCl_4	153.84	1595	0.00122	−22.8	15.701	76.7	192.593
Tetralin	$C_{10}H_{12}$	132.19	975	—	−35	—	207	—
Toluene	C_7H_8	92.13	866	0.00108	−95	72.013	110.7	355.878
Trichloroethylene	C_2HCl_3	131.40	1464	0.00119	−86.4	—	86.8	238.648
Turpentine oil	$C_{10}H_{16}$	136.22	855	0.00097	−10	—	160	293.076
Vinyl bromide	C_2H_3Br	106.96	—	—	−138	—	16	—
Water	H_2O	18.0156	998.2	0.00018	0.00	332.432	100.00	2257.104
m-Xylene	C_8H_{10}	256.08	864	0.00099	−47.9	108.019	139.2	343.318
o-Xylene	C_8H_{10}	256.08	880	0.00097	−25.3	122.673	144	347.504
p-Xylene	C_8H_{10}	256.08	861	0.00102	13.3	159.517	138.4	339.431

1 Btu = 1.055 06 kJ

Table 2-2 Critical Constants of Liquids

Substance	Chemical formula	Critical temperature t_{cr} °C	Critical pressure p_{cr} bar	Critical density ρ_{cr} kg/m³
Acetaldehyde	C_2H_4O	188	—	—
Acetic acid	$C_2H_4O_2$	321.6	55.99597	351
Acetone	C_3H_6O	236	58.83990	252
n-Amyl alcohol	$C_5H_{12}O$	348	—	—
Amyl bromide	$C_5H_{11}Br$	307	—	—
Amyl chloride	$C_5H_{11}Cl$	279	—	—
Aniline	C_6H_7N	425.7	51.38685	—
Arsenic trichloride	$AsCl_3$	356	—	—
Benzene	C_6H_6	288.6	47.07192	305
Bromine	Br_2	310	100.02783	1180
Bromobenzene	C_6H_5Br	397	43.73766	485
n-Butyl alcohol	$C_4H_{10}O$	287	47.46419	—
Carbon disulphide	CS_2	277	73.54988	441
Chlorobenzene	C_6H_5Cl	360	43.73766	365
Chloroform	$CHCl_3$	260	53.83851	496
Cyclohexane	C_6H_{12}	281	39.81500	273
cis-Dichloroethylene	$C_2H_2Cl_2$	243	52.95591	—
trans-Dichloroethylene	$C_2H_2Cl_2$	74	—	—
Diethylamine	$C_4H_{11}N$	223	37.26527	243
Dimethylamine	C_2H_7N	164	52.95591	—
Ethyl acetate	$C_4H_8O_2$	250	37.26527	308
Ethyl alcohol	C_2H_6O	243	61.78190	280
Ethylamine	C_2H_7N	183.4	54.91724	248
Ethylbenzene	C_8H_{10}	346.4	37.36334	—
Ethyl bromide	C_2H_5Br	233	60.31090	507
Ethyl chloride	C_2H_5Cl	185	51.97525	330
Ethyl ether	$C_4H_{10}O$	194	35.59814	265
Ethyl iodide	C_2H_5J	281	—	—
n-Heptane	C_7H_{16}	266.8	26.37989	234
n-Heptyl alcohol	$C_7H_{16}O$	365.3	—	—
n-Hexane	C_6H_{14}	234.8	29.22382	234
n-Hexene	C_6H_{12}	244	—	—
Isoamyl acetate	$C_7H_{14}O_2$	326	—	—
Isoamyl alcohol	$C_5H_{12}O$	309	—	—
Isobutyl alcohol	$C_4H_{10}O$	272	47.36612	—
Mercury	Hg	1460	1021.85293	5000
Methyl acetate	$C_3H_6O_2$	234	46.09126	—
Methyl alcohol	CH_4O	240	97.08584	358
Methyl bromide	CH_3Br	194	—	—
Methyl formate	$C_2H_4O_2$	214	57.85924	349
Methyl iodide	CH_3J	255	—	—
Methylene chloride	CH_2Cl_2	245	99.43943	—
n-Octane	C_8H_{18}	296.2	24.22243	233
n-Octyl alcohol	$C_8H_{18}O$	385.5	—	—
i-Pentane	C_5H_{12}	188	32.36195	234
n-Pentane	C_5H_{12}	197	32.36195	232
Phosphorus trichloride	PCl_3	286	—	—
Propionic acid	$C_3H_6O_2$	339	51.87718	—
i-Propyl alcohol	C_3H_8O	240	51.97512	—
n-Propyl alcohol	C_3H_8O	264	49.03325	273
n-Propyl chloride	C_3H_7Cl	221	48.05259	—
Pyridine	C_5H_5N	344	58.83990	—
Turpentine oil	$C_{10}H_{16}$	376	—	—
Tetrachloromethane (Carbon tetrachloride)	CCl_4	283	44.12993	558
Toluene	C_7H_8	320.6	40.79566	—
Water	H_2O	374.15	221.28706	315
m-Xylene	C_8H_{10}	346	35.10781	—
o-Xylene	C_8H_{10}	359	36.18654	—
p-Xylene	C_8H_{10}	345	34.32328	—

Table 2-3   Cubic Expansion Coefficient $\alpha_V(\gamma)$ of Liquids in the Temperature Range between 0°C and t, at a Normal Pressure of 1.013 25 bar (760 mm Hg)

Liquid	Chemical formula	Temperature $\frac{t}{°C}$	Cubic expansion coefficient $\frac{\alpha_V}{1/K}$
Acetone	C_3H_6O	10	0.00135
		20	0.001375
		30	0.001433
		40	0.001463
		50	0.001500
Alcohol (absolute)		20	0.00115
Benzene	C_6H_6	10	0.00120
		20	0.00120
		30	0.00123
		40	0.00125
		50	0.00127
		60	0.00129
		70	0.00131
		80	0.00133
Glycerol	$C_3H_8O_3$	10	0.00050
		20	0.00050
		30	0.00050
		40	0.00051
		50	0.00052
Lubricating oil		20	9.000740
Mercury	Hg	10	0.0001819
		20	0.0001820
		30	0.0001820
		40	0.0001821
		50	0.0001822
		60	0.0001822
		70	0.0001823
		80	0.0001824
		90	0.0001825
Mercury	Hg	100	0.0001826
		150	0.0001832
		200	0.0001840
		250	0.0001851
		300	0.0001863
Mercury, at 20 at pressure	Hg	200	0.0001840
		250	0.0001851
		300	0.0001863
		350	0.0001878
		400	0.0001896
		450	0.0001916
		500	0.0001939
Olive oil		18	0.00072
Paraffin oil		10	0.00075
		20	0.00075
Petrol		20	0.00120
Petroleum		18	0.00092...0.0010
Toluene	C_7H_8	20	0.001075
		30	0.001073
		40	0.001100
		50	0.001112
		60	0.001133
		70	0.001150
		80	0.001171
		90	0.001189
		100	0.001205
Transformer oil		20	0.000690

Note: Cubic expansion coefficient of solids: $\alpha_V = 3\,\alpha$
Cubic expansion coefficient α_V of gases depends upon temperature.
Cubic expansion coefficient of ideal gases: $\alpha_V = (1/273.16)\ K^{-1}$.

Table 2-4 Specific Heat Capacity c of Liquids

Liquid	Chemical formula	Temperature t °C	Specific heat capacity [1] c kJ/(kg K)
Acetic acid	$C_2H_4O_2$	20	2.031
Acetone	C_3H_6O	−50	2.031
		0	2.119
		20	2.160
		50	2.248
Airplane motor oil		20	1.838
		40	1.922
		60	2.005
		80	2.089
		100	2.177
		120	2.269
		140	2.361
Ammonia	NH_3	−20	0.456
		0	0.461
		20	0.473
Aniline	C_6H_7N	0	2.018
		20	2.064
		50	2.144
		100	2.345
		150	2.931
Arsenic trichloride	As_2Cl_3	20	0.712
Beer		20	3.768
Benzene	C_6H_6	−100	0.963
		10	1.424
		20	1.738
		40	1.771
		50	1.800
		60	1.909
		65	2.018
Bromine	Br_2	20	0.461
Bromobenzene	C_6H_5Br	20	0.967
		40	0.976
		60	0.996
		80	1.026
Bromoform	$CHBr_2$	20	0.536
n-Butyl alcohol	$C_4H_{10}O$	−78	1.851
		21	2.366
		30	2.437
		114	2.885
Carbon dioxide	CO_2	20	3.643
Carbon disulphide	CS_2	−100	0.812
		0	0.996
		20	1.017
Castor oil		20	1.926
Chlorobenzene	C_6H_5Cl	20	1.298
		40	1.319
		60	1.365
		80	1.428
Chloroform	$CHCl_3$	20	0.967
		30	0.980

Liquid	Chemical formula	Temperature t °C	Specific heat capacity [1] c kJ/(kg K)
Chloroform	$CHCl_3$	40	0.996
		50	1.017
m-Chlorotoluene	C_7H_7Cl	20	1.214
o-Cresol	C_7H_8O	20	2.093
Crude oil		20	0.879
Dichlorodifluoromethane (Freon 12)	CF_2Cl_2	−150	0.8386
		−140	0.8411
		−130	0.8420
		−120	0.8432
		−110	0.8449
		−100	0.8474
		−90	0.8503
		−80	0.8541
		−70	0.8587
		−60	0.8646
		−50	0.8709
		−40	0.8788
		−30	0.8880
		−20	0.8989
		−10	0.9119
		0	0.9265
		10	0.9441
		20	0.9655
		30	0.9914
		40	1.0203
		50	1.0626
		60	1.1141
		70	1.1840
		80	1.2841
		90	1.4457
		100	1.7739
		110	3.6580
Diphenylmethane	$C_{13}H_{12}$	37.5	1.633
		49.4	1.645
Diphyl (mixture by vol. 26.5% diphenyl, $C_{12}H_{10}$ 73.5% diphenyl ether, $C_{12}H_{10}O$)		20	1.549
		30	1.604
		40	1.654
		50	1.700
		60	1.742
		70	1.779
		80	1.813
		90	1.842
		100	1.871
		110	1.897
		120	1.922
		130	1.943
		140	1.964
		150	1.985
		160	2.001
		170	2.018
		180	2.035
		190	2.052
		200	2.068
		210	2.085
		220	2.102
		230	2.119
		240	2.135
		250	2.156
		260	2.177

[1] Older name: Specific heat.
1 Btu = 1.055 06 kJ

Table 2-4 Specific Heat Capacity *c* of Liquids

Liquid	Chemical formula	Temperature *t* °C	Specific heat capacity [1] *c* kJ/(kg K)
Diphyl (mixture by vol. 26.5% diphenyl, $C_{12}H_{10}$ 73.5% diphenyl ether, $C_{12}H_{10}O$)		270	2.198
		280	2.219
		290	2.240
		300	2.265
		310	2.290
		320	2.315
		330	2.345
		340	2.374
		350	2.403
		360	2.433
		370	2.466
		380	2.500
		390	2.537
		400	2.575
Dowtherm (mixture by vol. 26.5% diphenyl, $C_{12}H_{10}$ 73.5% diphenyl ether, $C_{12}H_{10}O$)		20	1.549
Ethyl acetate	$C_4H_8O_2$	20	2.010
Ethyl alcohol	C_2H_6O	−100	1.884
		−50	2.010
		0	2.303
		20	2.470
		40	2.721
		50	2.805
		80	2.981
		120	3.806
		160	4.664
Ethylbenzene	C_8H_{10}	−50	1.507
		20	1.729
		50	1.884
Ethylbenzoate	$C_9H_{10}O_2$	20	1.612
Ethyl bromide	C_2H_5Br	20	0.879
Ethylene glycol	$C_2H_6O_2$	20	2.382
		40	2.474
		60	2.562
		80	2.650
		100	2.742
Ethyl ether	$C_4H_{10}O$	−100	2.022
		0	2.269
		20	2.328
Ethyl iodide	C_2H_5J	−30	0.656
		0	0.677
		20	0.690
		30	0.698
		60	0.718
Formic acid	CH_2O_2	20	3.177
Glue mass		20	4.187
Glycerol	$C_3H_8O_3$	0	2.261
		20	2.428
n-Heptane	C_7H_{16}	−50	2.056
		0	2.186
		20	2.219

Liquid	Chemical formula	Temperature *t* °C	Specific heat capacity [1] *c* kJ/(kg K)
n-Hexane	C_6H_{14}	20	1.884
HT-oil C		20	1.465
Hydrochloric acid, 17%	HCl	20	3.098
Isoamyl alcohol	$C_5H_{12}O$	20	2.345
Isobutyl alcohol	$C_4H_{10}O$	10	2.102
		20	2.303
		40	2.713
		85	3.521
Lubricating oil		20	1.851
		40	1.934
		60	2.018
		80	2.102
		100	2.186
		120	2.269
Magnesium chloride, 20%	$MgCl_2$	−20	2.989
		0	3.035
		20	3.081
Mercury	Hg	0	0.140
		20	0.139
		100	0.137
		200	0.136
Methyl acetate	$C_3H_6O_2$	20	2.135
Methyl alcohol	CH_4O	−50	2.303
		0	2.428
		20	2.470
		50	2.554
Methyl benzoate	$C_8H_8O_2$	20	1.549
Methyl chloride	CH_3Cl	−20	1.507
		0	1.570
		20	1.591
Methylene chloride	CH_2Cl_2	20	1.214
Milk		20	2.936
Mineral oil		20	1.884
Naphthalene	$C_{10}H_3$	90	1.775
		120	1.871
		190	2.093
Nitric acid (100%)	HNO_3	20	1.717
Nitrobenzene	$C_6H_5O_2N$	20	1.507
n-Octane	C_8H_{18}	20	2.177
Oleic acid	$C_{18}H_{34}O_2$	20	2.052
Olive oil		20	1.633
Oxygen	O_2	20	1.465
Paraffin oil		20	2.135

[1] Older name: Specific heat.
1 Btu = 1.055 06 kJ

Table 2-4   Specific Heat Capacity c of Liquids

Liquid	Chemical formula	Temperature t °C	Specific heat capacity [1] c kJ/(kg K)
n-Pentane	C_5H_{12}	−100	1.968
		0	2.135
		20	2.177
Petrol (gasoline)		20	2.093
Petroleum		20	2.135
Phosphorus trichloride	PCl_3	20	0.837
Pit coal tar		20	2.093
Propionic acid	$C_3H_6O_2$	20	2.177
n-Propyl alcohol	C_3H_8O	20	2.428
Pyridine	C_5H_5N	20	1.717
Quinoline	C_9H_7N	20	1.298
Rubber mass		20	3.433
Sodium hydroxide —20% salt		−10	3.056
—30% salt		−10	2.680
Sulfur dioxide	SO_2	−20	1.273
		0	1.357
		20	1.390
Sulfuric acid, 100%	H_2SO_4	20	1.382
Tetrachloromethane	CCl_4	20	0.846
Tetralin	$C_{10}H_{12}$	20	1.675
Toluene	C_7H_8	−50	1.507
		0	1.633
		20	1.675
		50	1.800

Liquid	Chemical formula	Temperature t °C	Specific heat capacity [1] c kJ/(kg K)
Toluene	C_7H_8	100	1.968
Transformer oil		20	1.892
		40	1.993
		60	2.093
		80	2.198
		100	2.294
Trichloroethylene	C_2HCl_3	20	0.950
Trimethylethylene	C_5H_{10}	−129.3	1.876
		−71.8	1.921
		−40.7	1.976
		2.2	2.085
		20.7	2.144
Turpentine oil	$C_{10}H_{16}$	0	1.717
		20	1.800
		50	1.926
		100	2.093
Water	H_2O	0	4.220
		20	4.183
		40	4.178
		60	4.191
		80	4.199
		100	4.216
		120	4.233
		140	4.258
		150	4.271
		160	4.283
		180	4.396
		200	4.501
		220	4.605
		240	4.731
		250	4.857
		260	4.982
		280	5.234
		300	5.694
Xylene	C_8H_{10}	20	1.717

[1] Older name: Specific heat.
   1 Btu = 1.055 06 kJ

Table 2-5 Specific Heat Capacity c of Water (H_2O) at a Pressure p = 0.980 665 bar (= 1 at)

Temperature t °C	Specific heat capacity [1] c kJ/(kg K)	Temperature t °C	Specific heat capacity [1] c kJ/(kg K)
0	4.2056	26	4.1776
1	4.2040	27	4.1772
2	4.2019	28	4.1768
3	4.2006	29	4.1763
4	4.1989	30	4.1763
5	4.1973		
		31	4.1763
6	4.1960	32	4.1759
7	4.1943	33	4.1759
8	4.1931	34	4.1759
9	4.1918	35	4.1759
10	4.1906		
		36	4.1763
11	4.1893	37	4.1763
12	4.1881	38	4.1768
13	4.1872	39	4.1768
14	4.1860	40	4.1772
15	4.1851		
		41	4.1776
16	4.1839	42	4.1780
17	4.1830	43	4.1784
18	4.1822	44	4.1788
19	4.1814	45	4.1797
20	4.1809		
		46	4.1801
21	4.1801	47	4.1809
22	4.1793	48	4.1818
23	4.1788	49	4.1826
24	4.1784	50	4.1835
25	4.1780		

[1] Older name: Specific heat.
1 Btu = 1.055 06 kJ

Table 2-6 Specific Heat Capacity c of Water (H_2O) at Higher Pressure

Pressure p=	49.033 250 bar (=50 at)	98.066 500 bar (=100 at)	147.099 750 bar (=150 at)	196.133 000 bar (=200 at)	245.166 250 bar (=250 at)	294.199 500 bar (=300 at)
Temperature t °C	Specific heat capacity [1]					
	c kJ/(kg K)	c kJ/(kg K)	c kJ/(kg K)	c kJ/(kg K)	c kJ/(kg K)	c kJ/(kg K)
0	4.204	4.195	4.187	4.178	4.170	4.162
20	4.170	4.162	4.153	4.141	4.132	4.120
40	4.162	4.153	4.141	4.128	4.120	4.107
60	4.166	4.153	4.141	4.128	4.116	4.103
80	4.183	4.166	4.153	4.141	4.124	4.111
100	4.204	4.187	4.174	4.157	4.141	4.128
120	4.233	4.216	4.199	4.183	4.166	4.149
140	4.266	4.250	4.224	4.212	4.195	4.174
160	4.325	4.304	4.283	4.262	4.241	4.220
180	4.396	4.371	4.346	4.321	4.300	4.275
200	4.484	4.455	4.425	4.396	4.367	4.342
220	4.593	4.555	4.522	4.488	4.455	4.421
240	4.739	4.693	4.647	4.605	4.564	4.526
260	4.945	4.882	4.823	4.769	4.719	4.664
280	—	5.154	5.074	4.999	4.928	4.861
300	—	5.661	5.443	5.300	5.200	5.120
310	—	—	5.744	5.518	5.372	5.263
320	—	—	6.196	5.824	5.673	5.434
330	—	—	6.921	6.284	5.899	5.661
340	—	—	8.118	7.013	6.402	5.966
350	—	—	—	8.219	7.088	6.431

[1] Older name: Specific heat.
1 Btu = 1.055 06 kJ

Table 2-7 Density ρ of Liquids

Liquid	Chemical formula	Temperature t °C	Density ρ kg/m³
Acetaldehyde	C_2H_4O	20	783
Acetic acid	$C_2H_4O_2$	0	1070
		10	1059
		20	1049
		30	1039
		40	1028
		50	1018
		60	1006
		70	995
		80	984
		90	972
		100	960
		110	948
		120	936
		130	924
		140	909
		150	896
		160	883
		170	869
		180	856
		190	841
		200	827
		210	811
		220	794
		230	776
		240	757
		250	736
		260	714
		270	690
		280	663
		290	633
		300	595
Acetone	C_3H_6O	20	791
Airplane motor oil		20	893
		40	881
		60	868
		80	856
		100	844
		120	832
		140	819
Ammonia	NH_3	−20	665
		0	639
		20	610
		100	452
n-Amyl alcohol	$C_5H_{12}O$	20	810
Amyl benzoate	$C_{12}H_{16}O_2$	20	1010
Amyl bromide	$C_5H_{11}Br$	20	1223
Amyl chloride	$C_5H_{11}Cl$	20	883
Amyl iodide	$C_5H_{11}J$	20	1524
Aniline	C_6H_7N	20	1022
Anisole	C_7H_8O	20	994
Benzene	C_6H_6	0	900
		20	879
		40	858
		60	836

Liquid	Chemical formula	Temperature t °C	Density ρ kg/m³
Benzene	C_6H_6	70	825
		80	815
		90	804
		100	793
		110	781
		120	769
		130	757
		140	744
		150	731
		160	719
		170	704
		180	691
		190	676
		200	661
		210	643
		220	626
		230	607
		240	585
		250	561
		260	533
		270	498
		280	451
Benzonitrile	C_7H_6N	15	1010
Bromine	Br_2	20	3120
Bromobenzene	C_6H_5Br	0	1522
		20	1495
		40	1468
		60	1441
		80	1414
		100	1386
		120	1358
		140	1329
		150	1315
		160	1299
		170	1285
		180	1270
		190	1253
		200	1239
		210	1221
		220	1204
		230	1188
		240	1169
		250	1151
		260	1131
		270	1110
Bromoform	$CHBr_3$	20	2890
i-Butane	C_4H_{10}	0	582
		8	573
		16	563
		24	553
		32	543
		40	533
		48	522
		56	511
n-Butane	C_4H_{10}	0	599
		8	591
		16	582
		24	573
		32	564
		40	554
		48	544

Table 2-7 Density ρ of Liquids

Liquid	Chemical formula	Temperature t °C	Density ρ kg/m³
n-Butane	C_4H_{10}	56	533
n-Butyl alcohol	$C_4H_{10}O$	20	810
n-Butyl bromide	C_4H_9Br	20	1275
n-Butyl chloride	C_4H_9Cl	20	886
n-Butyl iodide	C_4H_9J	20	1615
Carbon dioxide	CO_2	0	925
		20	771
		30	595
Carbon disulfide	CS_2	20	1263
Castor oil		20	960
Chlorine	Cl_2	−100	1717
		−90	1694
		−80	1673
		−70	1646
		−60	1622
		−50	1598
		−40	1574
		−30	1550
		−20	1524
		−10	1496
		0	1468
		10	1438
		20	1408
		30	1377
		40	1344
		50	1310
		60	1275
		70	1240
		80	1199
		90	1156
		100	1109
		110	1059
		120	998
		130	920
		140	750
Chlorobenzene	C_6H_5Cl	0	1128
		20	1106
		40	1085
		60	1064
		80	1042
		100	1019
		120	996
		130	984
		140	972
		150	960
		160	948
		170	935
		180	922
		190	909
		200	896
		210	882
		220	867
		230	852
		240	836
		250	820
		260	802
		270	783
Chloroform	$CHCl_3$	20	1489

Liquid	Chemical formula	Temperature t °C	Density ρ kg/m³
m-Cresol	C_7H_8O	20	1034
o-Cresol	C_7H_8O	41	1027
p-Cresol	C_7H_8O	41	1018
Cyclohexane	C_6H_{12}	7	791
		16	782
		20	779
		25	774
		40	759
		51	744
		79	722
Cyclohexanol	$C_6H_{10}O$	20	962
Cylinder oil		0	890
Dichlorodifluoromethane (Freon 12)	CF_2Cl_2	−150	1826
		−140	1798
		−130	1770
		−120	1743
		−110	1715
		−100	1688
		−90	1660
		−80	1632
		−70	1604
		−60	1575
		−50	1546
		−40	1517
		−30	1487
		−20	1456
		−10	1425
		0	1394
		10	1362
		20	1329
		30	1293
		40	1255
		50	1213
		60	1167
		70	1119
		80	1064
		90	999
		100	913
		110	742
Diethylene glycol	$C_4H_{10}O_3$	20	1120
Dimethylamine	C_2H_7N	−30	709
		−20	699
		−10	690
		0	680
		10	671
		20	662
		30	649
		40	641
Dimethylaniline	$C_8H_{11}N$	20	956
Diphyl (mixture by vol. 26.5% diphenyl, $C_{12}H_{10}$ 73.5% diphenyl ether, $C_{12}H_{10}O$)		20	1062
		30	1054
		40	1046
		50	1037
		60	1029
		70	1021
		80	1013
		90	1004

Table 2-7   Density ρ of Liquids

Liquid	Chemical formula	Temperature t °C	Density ρ kg/m³
Diphyl		100	996
(mixture by vol.		110	987
26.5% diphenyl, $C_{12}H_{10}$		120	979
73.5% diphenyl ether,		130	970
$C_{12}H_{10}O$)		140	962
		150	953
		160	945
		170	936
		180	927
		190	918
		200	909
		210	901
		220	892
		230	882
		240	873
		250	864
		260	855
		270	846
		280	836
		290	827
		300	818
		310	806
		320	798
		330	787
		340	779
		350	769
		360	759
		370	748
		380	738
		390	727
		400	717
Ethyl acetate	$C_4H_8O_2$	0	924
		20	901
		40	876
		60	851
		70	838
		80	825
		90	811
		100	797
		110	783
		120	768
		130	753
		140	738
		150	721
		160	703
		170	685
		180	665
		190	644
		200	621
		210	594
		220	565
		230	528
		240	478
Ethyl alcohol (ethanol)	C_2H_6O	0	806
		10	798
		20	789
		30	781
		40	772
		50	763
		60	754
		70	745
		80	735
		90	725
		100	716
		110	706
		120	693

Liquid	Chemical formula	Temperature t °C	Density ρ kg/m³
Ethyl alcohol (ethanol)	C_2H_6O	130	679
		140	663
		150	649
		160	633
		170	617
		180	598
		190	578
		200	557
		210	529
		220	496
		230	455
		240	383
Ethylamine	C_2H_7N	0	708
		10	695
		20	683
		30	671
		40	658
		50	646
		60	633
		70	620
		80	607
Ethylbenzene	C_8H_{10}	20	868
Ethyl benzoate	$C_9H_{10}O_2$	20	1047
Ethyl bromide	C_2H_5Br	20	1450
Ethyl chloride	C_2H_5Cl	−20	953
		−10	933
		0	919
		10	907
		20	892
		30	878
		40	862
		50	846
		60	829
		70	813
		80	796
Ethyl ether	$C_4H_{10}O$	0	736
		10	725
		20	714
		30	702
		40	689
		50	676
		60	666
		70	653
		80	640
		90	625
		100	611
		110	594
		120	576
		130	558
		140	539
		150	518
		160	495
		170	466
		180	427
		190	366
Ethyl formate	$C_3H_6O_2$	0	948
		20	923
		40	896
		50	883
		60	869
		70	855

Table 2-7   Density ρ of Liquids

(continued)

Liquid	Chemical formula	Temperature t °C	Density ρ kg/m³
Ethyl formate	$C_3H_6O_2$	80	841
		90	826
		100	811
		110	796
		120	780
		130	763
		140	745
		150	726
		160	706
		170	684
		180	661
		190	636
		200	607
		210	572
		220	529
		230	464
Ethyl iodide	C_2H_5J	20	1934
Ethylene chloride	$C_2H_4Cl_2$	20	1257
Ethylene glycol	$C_2H_6O_2$	20	1113
		40	1099
		60	1085
		80	1070
		100	1056
Fluorobenzene	C_6H_5F	0	1047
		20	1023
		40	999
		60	974
		80	950
		90	937
		100	923
		110	910
		120	896
		130	881
		140	867
		150	852
		160	836
		170	820
		180	804
		190	786
		200	767
		210	748
		220	727
		230	704
		240	679
		250	650
		260	616
		270	574
		280	513
Formamide	CH_3ON	20	1135
Formic acid	CH_2O_2	20	1220
Glycerol	$C_3H_8O_3$	20	1260
n-Heptane	C_7H_{16}	0	700
		10	692
		20	684
		30	675
		40	667
		50	658
		60	649
		70	640
		80	631

Liquid	Chemical formula	Temperature t °C	Density ρ kg/m³
n-Heptane	C_7H_{16}	90	622
		100	612
		110	603
		120	593
		130	582
		140	571
		150	560
		160	548
		170	536
		180	523
		190	510
		200	495
		210	479
		220	462
		230	441
		240	418
		250	388
		260	346
n-Heptyl alcohol	$C_7H_{16}O$	20	824
n-Hexane	C_6H_{14}	0	677
		10	668
		20	660
		30	651
		40	641
		50	632
		60	622
		70	612
		80	602
		90	592
		100	581
		110	570
		120	559
		130	547
		140	534
		150	521
		160	506
		170	491
		180	475
		190	457
		200	437
		210	412
		220	381
		230	333
n-Hexyl alcohol	$C_6H_{14}O$	15	822
Iodobenzene	C_6H_5J	0	1861
		20	1831
		40	1799
		60	1770
		80	1739
		100	1708
		120	1677
		140	1645
		160	1613
		180	1580
		190	1563
		200	1547
		210	1532
		220	1512
		230	1494
		240	1476
		250	1458
		260	1438
		270	1417

Table 2-7   Density ρ of Liquids

Liquid	Chemical formula	Temperature t °C	Density ρ kg/m³
Isoamyl acetate	$C_7H_{14}O_2$	20	873
Isoamyl alcohol	$C_5H_{12}O$	20	810
Isobutyl alcohol	$C_4H_{10}O$	20	804
Isobutyl bromide	C_4H_9Br	20	1264
Isobutyl chloride	C_4H_9Cl	20	884
Isobutyl iodide	C_4H_9J	20	1603
Isopentane	C_5H_{12}	0	639
		10	630
		20	620
		30	609
		40	599
		50	588
		60	577
		70	566
		80	554
		90	541
		100	528
		110	514
		120	499
		130	483
		140	464
		150	445
		160	421
		170	391
		180	350
Isoprene	C_5H_8	20	681
Isopropyl alcohol	C_3H_8O	20	786
Isopropyl bromide	C_3H_7Br	20	1310
Isopropyl chloride	C_3H_7Cl	20	859
Isopropyl iodide	C_3H_7J	15	1714
Lactic acid	$C_3H_6O_3$	20	1240
Lubricating oil		20	871
		40	858
		60	845
		80	832
		100	820
		120	807
Magnesium chloride, 20%	$MgCl_2$	−20	1184
		0	1184
		20	1184
Mercury	Hg	0	13595
		20	13546
Methyl acetate	$C_3H_6O_2$	0	959
		20	934
		40	908
		50	894
		60	880
		70	866
		80	852
		90	837
		100	822
		110	806

Liquid	Chemical formula	Temperature t °C	Density ρ kg/m³
Methyl acetate	$C_3H_6O_2$	120	789
		130	772
		140	753
		150	734
		160	713
		170	691
		180	667
		190	641
		200	610
		210	574
		220	528
		230	453
Methyl, alcohol (methanol)	CH_4O	0	810
		10	801
		20	792
		30	783
		40	774
		50	765
		60	756
		70	746
		80	736
		90	725
		100	714
		110	702
		120	690
		130	677
		140	664
		150	650
		160	634
		170	616
		180	598
		190	577
		200	553
		210	526
		220	490
		230	441
Methyl-aniline	C_7H_9N	20	986
Methyl benzoate	$C_8H_8O_2$	20	1100
Methyl bromide	CH_3Br	−50	1859
		−40	1839
		−30	1802
		−20	1783
		−10	1757
		0	1704
		10	1706
		20	1678
		30	1650
		40	1621
		50	1592
Methyl chloride	CH_3Cl	−40	1025
		−30	1008
		−20	997
		−10	972
		0	960
		10	940
		20	921
		30	894
		40	881
		50	859
		60	837
Methyl formate	$C_2H_4O_2$	0	1003

Table 2-7   Density ρ of Liquids

Liquid	Chemical formula	Temperature t °C	Density ρ kg/m³
Methyl formate	$C_2H_4O_2$	10	989
		30	960
		50	929
		60	913
		70	897
		80	880
		90	863
		100	845
		110	826
		120	807
		130	786
		140	764
		150	740
		160	714
		170	684
		180	652
		190	615
		200	566
		210	486
Methyl iodide	CH_3J	20	2279
Methylamine	CH_5N	−50	743
		−40	733
		−30	722
		−20	710
		−10	698
		0	687
		10	675
		20	660
		30	647
		40	633
		50	618
		60	603
		70	587
		80	571
Methylene chloride	CH_2Cl_2	20	1336
Nitrobenzene	$C_6H_5NO_2$	20	1203
Nitromethane	CH_3NO_2	25	1131
n-Nonane	C_9H_{20}	20	717
Nonyl alcohol	$C_9H_{20}O$	20	828
n-Octane	C_8H_{18}	0	718
		20	702
		40	686
		50	678
		60	669
		70	661
		80	653
		90	644
		100	635
		110	626
		120	617
		130	607
		140	597
		150	588
		160	577
		170	567
		180	556
		190	544
		200	532
		210	519
		220	505

Liquid	Chemical formula	Temperature t °C	Density ρ kg/m³
n-Octane	C_8H_{18}	230	490
		240	473
		250	455
		260	436
		270	412
		280	382
		290	337
n-Octyl alcohol	$C_8H_{18}O$	20	829
Olive oil		20	914
Paraffin		0	880
Paraffin oil		20	810
n-Pentane	C_5H_{12}	0	645
		10	636
		20	626
		30	617
		40	606
		50	596
		60	685
		70	574
		80	562
		90	550
		100	538
		110	525
		120	511
		130	496
		140	479
		150	460
		160	439
		170	416
		180	387
		190	345
Petrol, heavy		20	750
Petrol, light		20	700
Petroleum		20	760 … 860
Phenethyl alcohol	$C_8H_{10}O$	13	1019
Phenol	C_6H_6O	25	1071
		45	1054
Phenyl cyanide	C_7H_5N	15	978
Phenyl isothiocyanate	C_6H_5NS	15	1138
Propionic acid	$C_3H_6O_2$	20	993
		190	800
		200	786
Propionic anhydride	$C_6H_{10}O_3$	20	1012
Propyl acetate	$C_5H_{10}O_2$	0	910
		20	888
		40	866
		60	844
		80	820
		90	808
		100	796
		110	783
		120	770
		130	757

Table 2-7 Density ρ of Liquids
(continued)

Liquid	Chemical formula	Temperature t °C	Density ρ kg/m³
Propyl acetate	$C_5H_{10}O_2$	140	744
		150	730
		160	715
		170	684
		180	670
		190	667
		200	649
		210	630
		220	609
		230	586
		240	559
		250	529
		260	491
		270	433
n-Propyl alcohol	C_3H_8O	0	819
		20	804
		40	788
		60	770
		80	752
		90	743
		100	733
		110	722
		120	711
		130	670
		140	688
		150	674
		160	660
		170	645
		180	629
		190	611
		200	592
		210	572
		220	549
		230	523
		240	492
		250	453
		260	391
n-Propyl bromide	C_3H_7Br	20	1353
n-Propyl chloride	C_3H_7Cl	20	890
Propyl formate	$C_4H_8O_2$	0	929
		20	906
		40	883
		60	859
		70	847
		80	834
		90	821
		100	808
		110	795
		120	781
		130	767
		140	752
		150	737
		160	721
		170	705
		180	687
		190	669
		200	649
		210	626
		220	602
		230	576
		240	544
		250	503
		260	440

Liquid	Chemical formula	Temperature t °C	Density ρ kg/m³
n-Propyl iodide	C_3H_7J	20	1743
Pyridine	C_5H_5N	20	983
Sodium	Na	20	970
Stannic chloride	$SnCl_4$	0	2279
		20	2226
		40	2175
		60	2123
		80	2072
		100	2019
		110	1992
		120	1964
		130	1936
		140	1907
		150	1877
		160	1848
		170	1818
		180	1787
		190	1756
		200	1722
		210	1687
		220	1649
		230	1609
		240	1567
		250	1522
		260	1475
		270	1422
		280	1363
Stearic acid	$C_{18}H_{36}O_2$	69	847
Sulfur dioxide	SO_2	20	1485
		0	1435
		10	1409
		20	1383
Sulfuric acid	H_2SO_4	20	1834
Tar, brown coal		20	900
—gas		20	1000
—road tar		20	1220
Tetrachloromethane	CCl_4	0	1633
		20	1594
		40	1556
		60	1517
		70	1496
		80	1477
		90	1455
		100	1434
		110	1412
		120	1390
		130	1368
		140	1345
		150	1322
		160	1298
		170	1273
		180	1247
		190	1219
		200	1189
		210	1157
		220	1123
		230	1086
		240	1044
		250	998

Table 2-7 Density ρ of Liquids

Liquid	Chemical formula	Temperature t °C	Density ρ kg/m³
Tetrachloromethane	CCl_4	260	941
		270	867
		280	763
Thiophene	C_4H_4S	20	1064
Toluene	C_7H_8	20	866
		190	687
		200	672
n-Toluidine	C_7H_9N	20	989
o-Toluidine	C_7H_9N	20	999
p-Toluidine	C_7H_9N	20	1046
		50	962
Transformer oil		20	866
		40	852
		60	842
		80	830
		100	818
Trichloroethylene	C_2HCl_3	20	1464
Trichlorotrifluoroethane	$C_2F_3Cl_3$	20	1576
Turpentine oil	$C_{10}H_{16}$	20	855

Liquid	Chemical formula	Temperature t °C	Density ρ kg/m³
Water	H_2O	0	1000
		20	998
		40	992
		60	983
		80	972
		100	958
		120	944
		140	926
		160	908
		180	887
		200	863
		220	837
		240	809
		260	779
		280	750
		300	700
m-Xylene	C_8H_{10}	20	864
		190	690
		200	678
o-Xylene	C_8H_{10}	20	880
		190	716
		200	705
p-Xylene	C_8H_{10}	20	861
		190	620
		200	612

Table 2-8 Viscosity (Dynamic Viscosity) η of Liquids

Liquid	Chemical formula	Temperature t °C	Viscosity η mN s/m^2
Acetaldehyde	C_2H_4O	0	0.2797
		10	0.2557
		20	0.2220
Acetone	C_3H_6O	−80	1.487
		−70	1.220
		−60	0.984
		−50	0.807
		−40	0.681
		−30	0.575
		−20	0.507
		0	0.399
		10	0.362
		15	0.337
		20	0.331
		25	0.316
		30	0.295
		50	0.256
Airplane motor oil		20	796.2215
		40	204.0568
		60	71.2159
		80	31.5088
		100	16.6027
		120	9.9047
		140	6.5018
Ammonia	NH_3	−20	0.255
		0	0.240
		20	0.220
n-Amyl alcohol	$C_5H_{12}O$	15	4.65
		30	2.99
Aniline	C_6H_7N	−6	13.8
		0	10.2
		5	8.06
		10	6.50
		15	5.31
		20	4.43
		25	3.71
		30	3.23
		35	2.79
		40	2.37
		45	2.16
		50	1.85
		60	1.56
		70	1.27
		80	1.09
		90	0.935
		100	0.825
		110	0.729
		120	0.655
		125	0.492
Anisole	C_7H_8O	0	1.78
		10	1.51
		20	1.32
		30	1.21
		40	1.12
		50	1.04
		60	0.97
Benzene	C_6H_6	0	0.91
		10	0.76
		20	0.65
		30	0.56
		40	0.492

Liquid	Chemical formula	Temperature t °C	Viscosity η mN s/m^2
Benzene	C_6H_6	50	0.436
		60	0.390
		70	0.350
		80	0.316
		90	0.286
		100	0.261
		110	0.239
		120	0.219
		130	0.201
		140	0.189
		150	0.170
		160	0.156
		170	0.144
		180	0.132
		190	0.121
Benzonitrile	C_7H_5N	0	1.94
		20	1.28
		25	1.24
		40	1.00
		50	0.876
		55	0.826
		70	0.666
Bromine	Br_2	0	1.241
		7	1.140
		19	1.000
		27	0.925
		32	0.888
Bromobenzene	C_6H_5Br	0	1.52
		10	1.31
		20	1.13
		30	1.00
		40	0.89
		50	0.79
		60	0.72
		70	0.66
		80	0.60
		90	0.55
		100	0.52
		110	0.480
		130	0.420
		150	0.366
Bromoform	$CHBr_3$	15	2.152
		30	1.741
n-Butyl alcohol	$C_4H_{10}O$	−50	34.7
		−40	22.4
		−30	14.6
		−20	10.3
		−10	7.4
		0	5.19
		10	3.87
		20	2.95
		30	2.28
		40	1.78
		50	1.41
		60	1.14
		70	0.93
		80	0.76
		90	0.63
		100	0.54
		110	0.46
Carbon disulfide	CS_2	0	0.433
		10	0.396

Table 2-8 Viscosity (Dynamic Viscosity) η of Liquids

Liquid	Chemical formula	Temperature t °C	Viscosity η mN s/m²
Carbon disulfide	CS_2	20	0.366
		30	0.341
		40	0.319
Castor oil		10	2440
		20	987
		30	455
		40	233
		50	129
		60	77
		70	49
		80	32
Chlorine	Cl	−74	0.710
		−60	0.610
		−53	0.569
		−45	0.530
		−34	0.489
Chlorobenzene	C_6H_5Cl	0	1.06
		10	0.907
		20	0.799
		30	0.705
		40	0.631
		50	0.567
		60	0.515
		70	0.471
		80	0.431
		90	0.397
		100	0.367
		110	0.339
		120	0.313
		130	0.293
		140	0.274
		150	0.256
		160	0.239
		170	0.223
		180	0.209
		190	0.196
		200	0.185
		210	0.173
		220	0.163
		230	0.153
		240	0.144
Chloroform	$CHCl_3$	0	0.70
		10	0.63
		15	0.596
		20	0.580
		25	0.542
		30	0.514
		40	0.467
		50	0.426
		60	0.390
m-Cresol	C_7H_8O	0	95.0
		10	43.9
		20	20.8
		30	10.0
		40	6.18
		50	4.38
		60	3.37
		70	2.5
		80	2.1
		90	1.8
		100	1.6
o-Cresol	C_7H_8O	20	9.8

Liquid	Chemical formula	Temperature t °C	Viscosity η mN s/m²
o-Cresol	C_7H_8O	30	6.1
		35	4.75
		40	4.15
		50	3.24
		60	2.22
p-Cresol	C_5H_8O	20	20.2
		30	10.3
		35	8.06
		40	6.50
		45	5.75
		50	4.95
		55	4.29
		60	3.76
		65	3.33
		70	2.70
Cyclohexane	C_6H_{12}	15	1.056
		20	0.97
		30	0.82
		40	0.71
		50	0.61
		60	0.54
Cyclohexanol	$C_6H_{12}O$	15	97.0
		20	68.0
		25	49.0
		30	36.0
		35	27.0
		40	20.0
		50	12.0
		60	7.8
		70	5.0
		80	3.5
		90	2.5
Dichlorodifluoromethane (Frigen 12)	CF_2Cl_2	−150	0.97400
		−140	0.90486
		−130	0.84023
		−120	0.77933
		−110	0.72206
		−100	0.66832
		−90	0.61772
		−80	0.57026
		−70	0.52593
		−60	0.48415
		−50	0.44493
		−40	0.40992
		−30	0.37383
		−20	0.34147
		−10	0.31126
		0	0.28282
		10	0.25625
		20	0.23134
		30	0.20790
		40	0.18593
		50	0.16524
		60	0.14563
		70	0.12709
		80	0.10925
		90	0.09176
		100	0.07389
		110	0.05115
Dimethyl aniline	$C_8H_{11}N$	10	1.69
		20	1.41
		30	1.20
		40	1.04

Table 2-8 Viscosity (Dynamic Viscosity) η of Liquids

Liquid	Chemical formula	Temperature t °C	Viscosity η mN s/m²
Dimethyl aniline	$C_8H_{11}N$	50	0.91
		60	0.80
		70	0.71
		80	0.64
		90	0.58
		98	0.54
Diphyl (mixture by vol. 26.5% diphenyl, $C_{12}H_{10}$ 73.5% diphenyl ether, $C_{12}H_{10}O$)		20	4.295
		30	3.246
		40	2.520
		50	2.050
		60	1.726
		70	1.491
		80	1.285
		90	1.128
		100	0.990
		110	0.8806
		120	0.7826
		130	0.7012
		140	0.6345
		150	0.5796
		160	0.5305
		170	0.4894
		180	0.4521
		190	0.4197
		200	0.3913
		210	0.3638
		220	0.3403
		230	0.3177
		240	0.2981
		250	0.2805
		260	0.2648
		270	0.2491
		280	0.2334
		290	0.2187
		300	0.2059
		310	0.1951
		320	0.1853
		330	0.1765
		340	0.1687
		350	0.1608
		360	0.1559
		370	0.1520
		380	0.1481
		390	0.1442
		400	0.1402
Ethyl acetate	$C_4H_8O_2$	0	0.578
		10	0.507
		20	0.449
		30	0.401
		40	0.360
		50	0.326
		60	0.297
		70	0.270
		80	0.248
		90	0.228
		100	0.210
		110	0.193
		120	0.178
		130	0.165
		140	0.152
		150	0.140
		160	0.129
		170	0.119
		180	0.109
Ethyl alcohol (ethanol)	C_2H_6O	-100	47.0

Liquid	Chemical formula	Temperature t °C	Viscosity η mN s/m²
Ethyl alcohol (ethanol)	C_2H_6O	-90	28.3
		-80	18.1
		-70	12.4
		-60	8.7
		-50	6.4
		-40	4.79
		-30	3.65
		-20	2.83
		-10	2.23
		0	1.78
		10	1.47
		20	1.20
		30	0.991
		40	0.825
		50	0.701
		60	0.591
		70	0.503
		80	0.435
		90	0.376
		100	0.325
		110	0.283
		120	0.248
		130	0.217
		140	0.191
		150	0.166
Ethylbenzene	C_8H_{10}	0	0.874
		10	0.760
		20	0.666
		30	0.590
		40	0.527
		50	0.475
		60	0.432
		70	0.394
		80	0.360
		90	0.331
		100	0.305
		110	0.282
		120	0.262
Ethyl benzoate	$C_9H_{10}O_2$	10	2.88
		15	2.55
		20	2.24
		25	1.98
Ethyl bromide	C_2H_5Br	-120	5.60
		-110	3.86
		-100	2.89
		-90	2.25
		-80	1.81
		0	0.494
		15	0.418
		19	0.397
		30	0.348
		46	0.3037
		78	0.2336
		100	0.1980
		130	0.1613
		160	0.1253
Ethylene chloride	$C_2H_4Cl_2$	0	1.133
		15	0.887
		20	0.800
		25	0.785
		30	0.730
		50	0.584
Ethyl chloride	C_2H_5Cl	-20	0.392

Table 2-8   Viscosity (Dynamic Viscosity) η of Liquids

Liquid	Chemical formula	Temperature t °C	Viscosity η mN s/m²
Ethyl chloride	C_2H_5Cl	−10	0.354
		0	0.320
		10	0.291
		20	0.266
		30	0.244
		40	0.224
Ethyl ether	$C_4H_{10}O$	−120	4.25
		−110	2.54
		−100	1.71
		−90	1.24
		−80	0.97
		−70	0.79
		−60	0.65
		−50	0.55
		−40	0.470
		−30	0.410
		−20	0.364
		−10	0.328
		0	0.296
		10	0.268
		20	0.243
		30	0.220
		40	0.199
		60	0.166
		80	0.140
		100	0.118
Ethylene glycol	$C_2H_6O_2$	0	56.99
		20	19.9
		30	13.2
		40	9.13
		60	4.95
		80	3.02
		100	1.99
		120	1.40
		130	1.20
		140	1.04
Fluorobenzene	C_6H_5F	0	0.745
		10	0.646
		20	0.598
		30	0.532
		40	0.478
		50	0.428
		60	0.389
		70	0.357
		80	0.329
		90	0.300
		100	0.275
		110	0.250
		120	0.231
		130	0.214
		140	0.198
		150	0.182
		160	0.168
		170	0.156
		180	0.144
Formamide	CH_3ON	0	7.3
		10	5.0
		20	3.75
		30	2.94
		40	2.43
		50	2.04
		60	1.71
		70	1.42
		80	1.17

Liquid	Chemical formula	Temperature t °C	Viscosity η mN s/m²
Formamide	CH_3ON	90	0.98
		100	0.83
		110	0.72
		120	0.63
Formic acid	CH_2O_2	10	2.25
		20	1.78
		30	1.46
		40	1.22
		50	1.03
		60	0.89
		70	0.78
		80	0.68
		90	0.61
		100	0.54
Glycerol	$C_3H_8O_3$	0	12100.0
		5	7050.0
		10	3950.0
		15	2350.0
		20	1480.0
		25	439.7
		50	180.0
n-Heptane	C_7H_{16}	0	0.517
		10	0.458
		20	0.409
		30	0.367
		40	0.332
		50	0.301
		60	0.275
		70	0.252
		80	0.231
		90	0.213
n-Hexane	C_6H_{14}	0	0.397
		10	0.355
		20	0.320
		30	0.290
		40	0.264
		50	0.241
		60	0.221
Iodobenzene	C_6H_5J	10	1.97
		20	1.49
		30	1.45
		40	1.265
		50	1.12
		60	0.995
		80	0.815
		100	0.690
		120	0.585
		140	0.510
Isoamyl alcohol	$C_5H_{12}O$	0	8.83
		10	6.20
		80	0.887
Isoamyl alcohol (optically active)	$C_5H_{12}O$	0	11.1
		10	7.4
		20	5.1
		30	3.59
		40	2.61
		50	1.94
		60	1.47
		70	1.15
		80	0.91

Table 2-8   Viscosity (Dynamic Viscosity) η of Liquids

Liquid	Chemical formula	Temperature t °C	Viscosity η mN s/m²
Isoamyl alcohol (optically active)	$C_5H_{12}O$	90	0.74
		100	0.61
		110	0.51
		120	0.43
Isoamyl alcohol (optically inactive)	$C_5H_{12}O$	0	8.6
		10	6.1
		20	4.36
		30	3.20
		40	2.41
		50	1.85
		60	1.45
		70	1.15
		80	0.93
		90	0.76
		100	0.63
		110	0.53
		120	0.45
		130	0.39
Isobutyl alcohol	$C_4H_{10}O$	−40	51.3
		−30	29.9
		−20	18.4
		−10	12.3
		0	8.3
		10	5.65
		20	3.95
		30	2.85
		40	2.14
		50	1.61
		60	1.24
		70	0.97
		80	0.78
		90	0.63
		100	0.52
Isopentane	C_5H_{12}	0	0.272
		10	0.246
		20	0.223
		30	0.202
Isoprene	C_5H_8	0	0.260
		10	0.236
		20	0.216
		30	0.198
Isopropyl alcohol	C_3H_8O	−60	66.1
		−50	37.6
		−40	23.2
		−30	14.9
		−20	10.1
		−10	6.8
		0	4.60
		10	3.26
		20	2.39
		30	1.76
		40	1.33
		60	0.80
		80	0.52
Isopropyl bromide	C_3H_7Br	0	0.605
		10	0.538
		20	0.482
		30	0.435
		40	0.394
		50	0.359
Isopropyl chloride	C_3H_7Cl	0	0.402

Liquid	Chemical formula	Temperature t °C	Viscosity η mN s/m²
Isopropyl chloride	C_3H_7Cl	10	0.358
		20	0.322
		30	0.292
Isopropyl iodide	C_3H_7J	15	0.732
		30	0.620
Lactic acid	$C_3H_6O_3$	25	40.33
Lubricating oil		20	13.0527
		40	6.8058
		60	4.1776
		80	2.8341
		100	2.0006
		120	1.5396
Magnesium chloride, 20%	$MgCl_2$	−20	12.9546
		0	5.4917
		20	2.8537
Mercury	Hg	−20	1.855
		−10	1.764
		0	1.685
		10	1.615
		20	1.554
		30	1.499
		40	1.450
		50	1.407
		60	1.367
		70	1.331
		80	1.298
		90	1.268
		100	1.240
		110	1.214
		120	1.191
		130	1.169
		140	1.149
		150	1.130
		160	1.112
		170	1.096
		180	1.080
		190	1.066
		200	1.052
		210	1.039
		220	1.027
		230	1.016
		240	1.005
		250	0.995
		260	0.985
		270	0.975
		280	0.967
		290	0.958
		300	0.950
		310	0.942
		320	0.935
		330	0.928
		340	0.921
Methyl acetate	$C_3H_6O_2$	20	0.381
		30	0.344
		40	0.312
		50	0.284
		60	0.258
		70	0.237
		80	0.217
		90	0.198
		100	0.182
		110	0.166

Table 2-8 Viscosity (Dynamic Viscosity) η **of Liquids** *(continued)*

Liquid	Chemical formula	Temperature t °C	Viscosity η mN s/m^2
Methyl acetate	$C_3H_6O_2$	120	0.154
		130	0.142
		140	0.130
Methyl alcohol (methanol)	CH_4O	−100	16.0
		−90	8.8
		−80	5.7
		−70	4.02
		−60	2.98
		−50	2.26
		−40	1.75
		−30	1.39
		−20	1.16
		−10	0.970
		0	0.817
		20	0.584
		30	0.510
		40	0.450
		50	0.396
		60	0.351
		70	0.311
Methylamine	CH_3NH_2	0	0.236
Methyl aniline	C_7H_9N	25	2.00
		30	1.55
		50	1.48
Methyl benzoate	$C_8H_8O_2$	20	2.050
Methyl bromide	CH_3Br	15	0.109
		30	0.092
Methyl chloride	CH_3Cl	10	0.2023
		20	0.1834
		30	0.1661
		40	0.1521
		50	0.1400
		60	0.1289
		70	0.1183
		80	0.1084
		90	0.0987
		100	0.0896
		110	0.0807
		120	0.0720
		130	0.0634
Methyl formate	$C_2H_4O_2$	0	0.43
		10	0.38
		15	0.36
		20	0.345
		25	0.328
		30	0.315
Methyl iodide	CH_3J	0	0.6025
		20	0.4900
		40	0.4240
Methylene chloride	CH_2Cl_2	−20	0.68
		−10	0.602
		0	0.537
		10	0.481
		20	0.435
		30	0.396
		40	0.363
Naphthalene	$C_{10}H_8$	80	0.97
		90	0.86

Liquid	Chemical formula	Temperature t °C	Viscosity η mN s/m^2
Naphthalene	$C_{10}H_8$	100	0.78
		110	0.71
		120	0.65
		130	0.59
		140	0.54
		150	0.49
Nitric acid	HNO_3	0	2.275
		10	1.07
		20	0.913
		40	0.698
Nitrobenzene	$C_6H_5O_2N$	0	3.07
		10	2.51
		20	2.01
		30	1.68
		40	1.44
		50	1.25
		60	1.09
		70	0.97
		80	0.87
		90	0.78
		100	0.70
Nitromethane	CH_3O_2N	0	0.844
		10	0.742
		20	0.657
		30	0.595
		40	0.528
		50	0.478
		60	0.433
		70	0.392
		80	0.357
		85	0.343
n-Nonane	C_9H_{20}	0	0.969
		10	0.825
		20	0.711
		30	0.620
		40	0.548
		60	0.438
		80	0.360
		100	0.299
n-Octane	C_8H_{18}	0	0.70
		10	0.61
		20	0.54
		30	0.479
		40	0.428
		50	0.386
		60	0.350
		70	0.318
		80	0.291
		90	0.266
		100	0.245
		120	0.208
Olive oil		20	80.8
		30	55.7
		40	37.2
		50	25.3
		60	19.2
		70	14.5
		80	11.6
Paraffin oil		18	101.8
n-Pentane	C_5H_{12}	0	0.283

Table 2-8   Viscosity (Dynamic Viscosity) η of Liquids   *(continued)*

Liquid	Chemical formula	Temperature t °C	Viscosity η mN s/m²
n-Pentane	C_5H_{12}	10	0.254
		20	0.229
		30	0.208
Petrol (gasoline)		18	0.53
Phenethyl alcohol (phenyl ethanol)	$C_8H_{10}O$	0	44.2
		10	23.8
		20	14.3
		30	8.98
		40	6.11
		60	3.26
		80	2.01
		100	0.134
Phenol	C_6H_6O	20	11.6
		30	7.0
		40	4.77
		50	3.43
		60	2.56
		70	2.00
		80	1.59
		90	1.29
		100	1.05
		110	0.88
		120	0.78
		130	0.72
		140	0.69
Phenyl cyanide	C_7H_5N	0	1.96
		10	1.62
		20	1.33
		30	1.13
		40	0.984
		50	0.864
		60	0.767
		80	0.623
		100	0.515
Phenyl isothiocyanate	C_7H_5NS	0	2.29
		10	1.86
		20	1.56
		30	1.32
		40	1.14
		60	0.879
		80	0.713
		100	0.595
Phenyl propyl ketone		0	4.07
		10	3.03
		20	2.36
		30	1.89
		40	1.56
		60	1.13
		80	0.87
		100	0.69
Propionic acid	$C_3H_6O_2$	0	1.52
		10	1.29
		20	1.10
		30	0.96
		40	0.84
		50	0.75
		60	0.67
		70	0.602
		80	0.545
		90	0.495
		100	0.452

Liquid	Chemical formula	Temperature t °C	Viscosity η mN s/m²
Propionic acid	$C_3H_6O_2$	110	0.414
		120	0.380
		130	0.350
		140	0.322
Propionic anhydride	$C_6H_{10}O_3$	0	1.61
		10	1.33
		20	1.12
		30	0.96
		40	0.83
		50	0.73
		60	0.65
		70	0.58
		80	0.52
		90	0.472
		100	0.430
		110	0.399
		120	0.360
		130	0.331
		140	0.306
		150	0.284
		160	0.264
Propyl acetate	$C_5H_{10}O_2$	0	0.77
		10	0.67
		20	0.58
		30	0.51
		40	0.46
		50	0.41
		60	0.368
		70	0.334
		80	0.304
		100	0.250
n-Propyl alcohol	C_3H_8O	−70	54.6
		−60	31.6
		−50	20.2
		−40	13.5
		−30	9.5
		−20	6.9
		−10	5.1
		0	3.85
		10	2.89
		20	2.20
		30	1.72
		40	1.38
		60	0.92
		80	0.63
		90	0.53
n-Propyl bromide	C_3H_7Br	0	0.645
		10	0.575
		20	0.517
		30	0.467
		40	0.425
		50	0.388
		60	0.356
		70	0.328
n-Propyl chloride	C_3H_7Cl	0	0.436
		10	0.390
		20	0.352
		30	0.319
		40	0.291
Propylene glycol dinitrate (1.2-dinitro-1.2-propanediol)	$C_3H_6O_6N_2$	10	5.56
		20	4.07
		30	3.14

Table 2-8 Viscosity (Dynamic Viscosity) η of Liquids (*continued*)

Liquid	Chemical formula	Temperature t °C	Viscosity η mN s/m²
Propylene glycol dinitrate (1.2-dinitro-1.2-propanediol)	$C_3H_6O_6N_2$	40	2.46
		50	2.03
		60	1.71
n-Propyl iodide	C_3H_7J	15	0.837
		30	0.670
Pyridine	C_5H_5N	0	1.33
		10	1.12
		20	0.974
		30	0.835
		40	0.735
		50	0.651
		60	0.580
		70	0.528
		80	0.482
		90	0.443
Stannic chloride	$SnCl_4$	−10	1.37
		0	1.20
		10	1.07
		20	0.95
		30	0.85
		40	0.76
		50	0.68
Stearic acid	$C_{18}H_{36}O_2$	70	11.6
		80	7.95
		100	5.12
		120	3.37
		140	2.38
		160	1.78
		170	1.37
		200	1.09
Sulfur dioxide	SO_2	−20	0.476
		0	0.373
		20	0.310
Sulfuric acid	H_2SO_4	0	48.4
		10	35.2
		20	25.4
		30	15.7
		40	11.5
		50	8.82
		60	7.22
		70	6.09
		80	5.19
Tetrachloroethane	$C_2H_2Cl_4$	0	2.66
		10	2.15
		20	1.75
		30	1.48
		40	1.28
		50	1.13
		60	0.97
		70	0.85
		80	0.75
Tetrachloroethylene	C_2Cl_4	0	1.14
		10	1.00
		20	0.88
		30	0.80
		40	0.72
		50	0.66
		60	0.60
		70	0.56
		80	0.51

Liquid	Chemical formula	Temperature t °C	Viscosity η mN s/m²
Tetrachloroethylene	C_2Cl_4	90	0.475
		100	0.441
		110	0.411
		120	0.383
Tetrachloromethane	CCl_4	−10	1.680
		0	1.329
		10	0.130
		20	0.969
		30	0.843
		40	0.739
		50	0.651
		60	0.585
		70	0.524
		80	0.468
		90	0.426
		100	0.384
		110	0.352
		120	0.323
		130	0.299
		140	0.276
		150	0.255
		160	0.234
		170	0.217
		180	0.201
Thiophene	C_4H_4S	0	0.87
		10	0.75
		20	0.66
		30	0.58
		40	0.52
		50	0.468
		60	0.424
		70	0.386
		80	0.350
Toluene	C_7H_6	0	0.768
		10	0.667
		20	0.586
		30	0.522
		40	0.466
		50	0.420
		60	0.381
		70	0.348
		80	0.319
		90	0.294
		100	0.271
		110	0.249
		120	0.231
		130	0.214
		140	0.199
		160	0.172
		180	0.150
m-Toluidine	C_7H_9N	0	8.66
		10	5.51
		20	3.81
		30	2.79
		40	2.14
		60	1.40
		80	1.00
		100	0.77
o-Toluidine	C_7H_9N	0	10.2
		10	6.43
		20	4.39
		30	3.20
		40	2.44

Table 2-8　Viscosity (Dynamic Viscosity) η of Liquids

Liquid	Chemical formula	Temperature t °C	Viscosity η mN s/m²	Liquid	Chemical formula	Temperature t °C	Viscosity η mN s/m²
o-Toluidine	C_7H_9N	50	1.92	Tri-n-amylamine	$C_{15}H_{33}N$	40	1.67
		60	1.58			60	1.17
		70	1.30			80	0.87
		80	1.11			100	0.68
		90	0.95	Tri-n-butylamine	$C_{12}H_{27}N$	0	2.24
		100	0.83			10	1.74
p-Toluidine	C_7H_9N	50	1.80			20	1.41
		60	1.45			30	1.17
		70	1.20			40	0.99
		80	1.00			60	0.74
		90	0.85			80	0.57
		100	0.75			100	0.46
		110	0.65	Turpentine oil		0	2.248
		120	0.562			10	1.783
		130	0.532			20	1.487
		140	0.491			30	1.272
Transformer oil		20	31.5970			40	1.071
		40	14.2196			50	0.926
		60	7.3158			60	0.821
		80	4.3149			70	0.728
		100	3.0989			80	0.671
Trichloroethylene	C_2HCl_3	−10	0.79	Water	H_2O	0	1.7887
		0	0.71			5	1.5155
		10	0.64			10	1.3061
		20	0.58			15	1.1406
		30	0.53			20	1.0046
		40	0.48			25	0.8941
		50	0.45			30	0.8019
		60	0.41			35	0.7205
		70	0.38			40	0.6533
Trichloromonofluoroethane	$C_2H_2Cl_3F$	20	1.07			45	0.5958
		30	0.93			50	0.5497
		40	0.82			55	0.5072
		50	0.73			60	0.4701
		60	0.65			65	0.4359
Trichlorotrifluoroethane	$C_2F_3Cl_3$	0	0.925			70	0.4062
		10	0.805			75	0.3794
		20	0.711			80	0.3556
		30	0.627			85	0.3341
		40	0.559			90	0.3146
Triethylcarbinol	$C_7H_{16}O$	0	32.3			95	0.2981
		10	13.7			100	0.2821
		20	6.75	m-Xylene	C_8H_{10}	0	0.80
		30	3.75			10	0.70
		40	2.32			20	0.61
		60	1.13			30	0.55
		80	0.69			40	0.49
		100	0.47			50	0.443
Triisoamylamine	$C_{15}H_{33}N$	0	4.98			60	0.403
		10	3.58			70	0.369
		20	2.69			80	0.339
		30	2.10			90	0.313
		40	1.70			100	0.289
		60	1.17			110	0.269
		80	0.87			120	0.250
		100	0.67			130	0.233
Tri-n-amylamine	$C_{15}H_{33}N$	0	4.72	o-Xylene	C_8H_{10}	0	1.10
		10	3.43			10	0.93
		20	2.62			20	0.81
		30	2.06			30	0.71
						40	0.62
						50	0.56
						60	0.50

Table 2-8   Viscosity (Dynamic Viscosity) η of Liquids

Liquid	Chemical formula	Temperature t °C	Viscosity η mN s/m²	Liquid	Chemical formula	Temperature t °C	Viscosity η mN s/m²
o-Xylene	C_8H_{10}	70	0.453	*p*-Xylene	C_8H_{10}	30	0.57
		80	0.411			40	0.51
		90	0.376			50	0.456
		100	0.346			60	0.414
		110	0.318			70	0.377
		120	0.294			80	0.345
		130	0.273			90	0.317
		140	0.254			100	0.292
						110	0.270
p-Xylene	C_8H_{10}	10	0.74			120	0.251
		20	0.64			130	0.233

Table 2-9   Thermal Conductivity λ of Liquids

Liquid	Chemical formula	Temperature t °C	Thermal conductivity λ W/(m K)	Liquid	Chemical formula	Temperature t °C	Thermal conductivity λ W/(m K)
Acetic acid	$C_2H_4O_2$	0	0.177	Amyl iodide	$C_5H_{11}J$	12	0.0850
		12	0.198	Aniline	C_6H_7N	0	0.172
		20	0.193			20	0.172
		25	0.180			50	0.172
		75	0.162			100	0.167
Acetone	C_3H_6O	0	0.184			150	0.158
		20	0.180	Benzene	C_6H_6	20	0.154
		100	0.166			80	0.151
Airplane motor oil		20	0.145	Bromobenzene	C_6H_5Br	0	0.130
		40	0.143			12	0.111
		60	0.141			20	0.112
		80	0.140			100	0.121
		100	0.137	*n*-Butyl alcohol	$C_4H_{10}O$	0	0.170
		120	0.136			20	0.167
		140	0.134			100	0.159
Ammonia	NH_3	–20	0.585	Butyric acid (methyl ester)	$C_5H_{10}O_2$	12	0.142
		0	0.540	Carbon dioxide	CO_2	20	0.087
		20	0.494			30	0.071
		100	0.313	Carbon disulfide	CS_2	0	0.162
Amyl acetate	$C_7H_{14}O_2$	12	0.127			30	0.160
		33	0.105			75	0.151
Amyl alcohol	C_5H_2O	0	0.166	Castor oil		0	0.183
		20	0.164			20	0.181
		50	0.160			50	0.178
		100	0.154			100	0.173
Amyl benzoate	$C_{12}H_{16}O_2$	33	0.106			150	0.169
Amyl bromide	$C_5H_{11}Br$	12	0.0992	Chlorobenzene	C_6H_5Cl	0	0.151
		32	0.0847			12	0.127
Amyl chloride	$C_5H_{11}Cl$	12	0.119				

1 Btu/(ft h °F) = 1.730 73 W/(m K)

Table 2-9 Thermal Conductivity λ of Liquids

(continued)

Liquid	Chemical formula	Temperature t °C	Thermal conductivity λ W/(m K)
Chlorobenzene	C_6H_5Cl	75	0.138
Chloroform	$CHCl_3$	12	0.121
		20	0.129
		30	0.138
Cylinder oil		0	0.155
		50	0.151
		100	0.149
		200	0.142
Dichlorodifluoromethane (Freon 12)	CF_2Cl_2	−150	0.1429
		−140	0.1401
		−130	0.1374
		−120	0.1344
		−110	0.1315
		−100	0.1286
		−90	0.1256
		−80	0.1226
		−70	0.1196
		−60	0.1165
		−50	0.1134
		−40	0.1101
		−30	0.1069
		−20	0.1036
		−10	0.1003
		0	0.0969
		10	0.0933
		20	0.0897
		30	0.0858
		40	0.0820
		50	0.0779
		60	0.0736
		70	0.0691
		80	0.0642
		90	0.0586
		100	0.0521
		110	0.0420
Diethyl ether	$C_4H_{10}O$	0	0.141
		20	0.138
		50	0.136
		100	0.133
Diethylene glycol	$C_4H_{10}O_3$	0	0.202
		20	0.205
		100	0.214
Diphyl (mixture by vol.: 26.5% diphenyl, $C_{12}H_{10}$ 73.5% phenyl ether, $C_{12}H_{10}O$)		20	0.138
		30	0.137
		40	0.136
		50	0.134
		60	0.133
		70	0.131
		80	0.130
		90	0.128
		100	0.127
		110	0.126
		120	0.124
		130	0.122
		140	0.121
		150	0.120
		160	0.119
		170	0.116
		180	0.115
		190	0.114
		200	0.112

Liquid	Chemical formula	Temperature t °C	Thermal conductivity λ W/(m K)
Diphyl (mixture by vol.: 26.5% diphenyl, $C_{12}H_{10}$ 73.5% phenyl ether, $C_{12}H_{10}O$)		210	0.110
		220	0.109
		230	0.108
		240	0.106
		250	0.105
		260	0.104
		270	0.102
		280	0.100
		290	0.099
		300	0.098
		310	0.097
		320	0.094
		330	0.093
		340	0.092
		350	0.090
		360	0.088
		370	0.087
		380	0.086
		390	0.084
		400	0.083
Dodecane	$C_{12}H_{26}$	0	0.151
		75	0.142
		100	0.142
Ethyl acetate	$C_4H_8O_2$	12	0.145
		34	0.123
Ethyl alcohol	C_2H_6O	0	0.185
		20	0.182
		30	0.180
		50	0.178
		75	0.174
Ethyl benzoate	$C_9H_{10}O_2$	32	0.121
Ethyl bromide	C_2H_5Br	0	0.123
		20	0.121
		50	0.117
		100	0.112
Ethyl butyrate	$C_6H_{12}O_2$	12	0.134
Ethyl formate	$C_3H_6O_2$	12	0.158
Ethylene glycol	$C_2H_6O_2$	0	0.255
		20	0.258
		50	0.262
		100	0.269
Ethyl iodide	C_2H_5J	0	0.112
		20	0.112
		50	0.110
		100	0.108
Ethyl sulfide	$H_4H_{10}S$	12	0.138
Ethyl valerate	$C_7H_{14}O_2$	12	0.130
Formic acid	CH_2O_2	0	0.261
		20	0.257
		75	0.247
Glycerol	$C_3H_8O_3$	0	0.283
		20	0.285
		50	0.287
		100	0.291

1 Btu/(ft h °F) = 1.730 73 W/(m K)

Table 2-9 Thermal Conductivity λ of Liquids

(continued)

Liquid	Chemical formula	Temperature t °C	Thermal conductivity λ W/(m K)
n-Heptane	C_7H_{16}	0	0.141
		20	0.140
		60	0.137
n-Heptyl alcohol	$C_7H_{16}O$	0	0.166
		20	0.164
		30	0.163
		50	0.160
		75	0.157
		100	0.156
n-Hexane	C_6H_{14}	0	0.138
		20	0.137
		50	0.136
		100	0.135
n-Hexyl alcohol	$C_6H_{14}O$	20	0.163
		30	0.162
		50	0.159
		75	0.157
		100	0.154
Isoamyl alcohol	$C_5H_{12}O$	0	0.151
		20	0.150
		50	0.149
		100	0.147
Isobutyl alcohol	$C_4H_{10}O$	0	0.154
		12	0.142
Isobutyl bromide	C_4H_9Br	12	0.116
Isobutyl chloride	C_4H_9Cl	12	0.116
Isobutyl iodide	C_4H_9J	12	0.0871
Isopropyl alcohol	C_3H_8O	0	0.157
		20	0.156
		100	0.152
Kerosene		30	0.150
		75	0.141
Lubricating oil		0	0.144
		20	0.144
		40	0.143
		60	0.142
		80	0.141
		100	0.140
		120	0.138
Magnesium chloride, 20%	$MgCl_2$	−20	0.392
		0	0.452
Mercury	Hg	0	10.467
		20	9.304
Methyl acetate	$C_3H_6O_2$	12	0.161
		29	0.136
Methyl alcohol	CH_4O	0	0.214
		20	0.212
		30	0.212
		75	0.184
		100	0.204
Methyl chloride	CH_3Cl	−20	0.195

Liquid	Chemical formula	Temperature t °C	Thermal conductivity λ W/(m K)
Methyl chloride	CH_3Cl	−10	0.187
		0	0.179
		20	0.163
Methylene chloride	CH_2Cl_2	−20	0.162
		−10	0.159
		0	0.158
		20	0.155
Methyl valerate	$C_6H_{12}O_2$	12	0.134
Nitrobenzene	$C_6H_5NO_2$	0	0.154
		12	0.160
		20	0.151
		125	0.136
Nonyl alcohol	$C_9H_{20}O$	0	0.169
		20	0.169
		100	0.160
n-Octane	C_8H_{18}	0	0.149
		20	0.147
		100	0.137
n-Octyl alcohol	$C_8H_{18}O$	0	0.172
		20	0.167
		100	0.158
Olive oil		0	0.170
		20	0.169
		50	0.166
		100	0.164
		200	0.157
Paraffin oil		0	0.126
		20	0.124
		50	0.122
		100	0.119
Paraffine		0	0.126
		50	0.126
		100	0.126
		200	0.124
n-Pentane	C_5H_{12}	−200	0.170
		−150	0.163
		−100	0.155
		−50	0.148
		0	0.140
		20	0.136
		100	0.124
Petrol		0	0.145
		20	0.131
		50	0.110
Petrolether		0	0.134
		30	0.131
		50	0.129
		75	0.127
		100	0.124
Petroleum		0	0.156
		20	0.151
		50	0.145
		100	0.134

1 Btu/(ft h °F) = 1.730 73 W/(m K)

Table 2-9 Thermal Conductivity λ of Liquids *(continued)*

Liquid	Chemical formula	Temperature t °C	Thermal conductivity λ W/(m K)
Propionic acid	$C_3H_6O_2$	12	0.163
Propyl acetate	$C_5H_{10}O_2$	12	0.137
n-Propyl alcohol	C_3H_8O	0	0.174
		20	0.172
		100	0.162
Propyl bromide	C_3H_7Br	12	0.108
Propyl chloride	C_3H_7Cl	12	0.118
Propyl formate	$C_4H_8O_2$	12	0.150
Propyl iodide	C_3H_7J	12	0.092
Sodium	Na	100	84.783
		210	79.549
Sulfur dioxide	SO_2	−20	0.223
		−10	0.217
		0	0.212
		20	0.199
Sulfuric acid	H_2SO_4	20	0.314
Tar		20	0.140
Tetrachloromethane	CCl_4	0	0.109
		50	0.107
		100	0.105
Tetralin	$C_{10}H_{22}$	0	0.151
		75	0.142
		100	0.138
Toluene	C_7H_8	0	0.151

Liquid	Chemical formula	Temperature t °C	Thermal conductivity λ W/(m K)
Toluene	C_7H_8	20	0.151
		50	0.147
		100	0.137
Transformer oil		20	0.124
		40	0.123
		60	0.122
		80	0.120
		100	0.119
Trichloroethylene	C_2HCl_3	50	0.138
Turpentine		15	0.128
Valeric acid	$C_5H_{10}O_2$	12	0.138
Water	H_2O	0	0.555
		20	0.598
		40	0.627
		60	0.651
		80	0.669
		100	0.682
		120	0.685
		140	0.684
		150	0.683
		160	0.680
		180	0.673
		200	0.665
		220	0.652
		240	0.634
		250	0.624
		260	0.613
		280	0.588
		300	0.564
m-Xylene	C_8H_{10}	20	0.145
		125	0.113

1 Btu/(ft h °F) = 1.730 73 W/(m K)

Table 2-10 Thermal Properties of Water (H_2O) at Saturation Pressure

Temperature t °C	Density ρ kg/m³	Cubic expansion coefficient α_V 1/kK[2]	Specific heat capacity[1] c_p kJ/(kg K)	Thermal conductivity λ W/(m K)	Thermal diffusivity α mm²/s	Viscosity η μN s/m²	Kinematic viscosity ν mm²/s	Prandtl number Pr
0	999.9	−0.07	4.226	0.558	0.131	1793.636	1.789	13.7
5	1000.0	—	4.206	0.568	0.135	1534.741	1.535	11.4
10	999.7	0.095	4.195	0.577	0.137	1296.439	1.300	9.5
15	999.1	—	4.187	0.587	0.141	1135.610	1.146	8.1
20	998.2	0.21	4.182	0.597	0.143	993.414	1.006	7.0
25	997.1	—	4.178	0.606	0.146	880.637	0.884	6.1
30	995.7	0.30	4.176	0.615	0.149	792.377	0.805	5.4
35	994.1	—	4.175	0.624	0.150	719.808	0.725	4.8
40	992.2	0.39	4.175	0.633	0.151	658.026	0.658	4.3
45	990.2	—	4.176	0.640	0.155	605.070	0.611	3.9
50	988.1	0.46	4.178	0.647	0.157	555.056	0.556	3.55
55	985.7	—	4.179	0.652	0.158	509.946	0.517	3.27
60	983.2	0.53	4.181	0.658	0.159	471.670	0.478	3.00
65	980.6	—	4.184	0.663	0.161	435.415	0.444	2.76
70	977.8	0.58	4.187	0.668	0.163	404.034	0.415	2.55
75	974.9	—	4.190	0.671	0.164	376.575	0.366	2.23
80	971.8	0.63	4.194	0.673	0.165	352.059	0.364	2.21
85	968.7	—	4.198	0.676	0.166	328.523	0.339	2.04
90	965.3	0.70	4.202	0.678	0.167	308.909	0.326	1.95
95	961.9	—	4.206	0.680	0.168	292.238	0.310	1.84
100	958.4	0.75	4.211	0.682	0.169	277.528	0.294	1.75
110	951.0	0.80	4.224	0.684	0.170	254.973	0.268	1.57
120	943.5	0.85	4.232	0.685	0.171	235.360	0.244	1.43
130	934.8	0.91	4.250	0.686	0.172	211.824	0.226	1.32
140	926.3	0.97	4.257	0.684	0.172	201.036	0.212	1.23
150	916.9	1.03	4.270	0.684	0.173	185.346	0.201	1.17
160	907.6	1.08	4.285	0.680	0.173	171.616	0.191	1.10
170	897.3	1.15	4.396	0.679	0.172	162.290	0.181	1.05
180	886.6	1.21	4.396	0.673	0.172	152.003	0.173	1.01
190	876.0	1.28	4.480	0.670	0.171	145.138	0.166	0.97
200	862.8	1.35	4.501	0.665	0.170	139.254	0.160	0.95
210	852.8	1.43	4.560	0.655	0.168	131.409	0.154	0.92
220	837.0	1.52	4.605	0.652	0.167	124.544	0.149	0.90
230	827.3	1.62	4.690	0.637	0.164	119.641	0.145	0.88
240	809.0	1.72	4.731	0.634	0.162	113.757	0.141	0.86
250	799.2	1.86	4.857	0.618	0.160	109.834	0.137	0.86
260	779.0	2.00	4.982	0.613	0.156	104.931	0.135	0.86
270	767.9	2.17	5.030	0.590	0.152	101.989	0.133	0.87
280	750.0	2.38	5.234	0.588	0.147	98.067	0.131	0.89
290	732.3	2.65	5.445	0.558	0.140	94.144	0.129	0.92
300	712.5	2.95	5.694	0.564	0.132	92.182	0.128	0.98
310	690.6	3.35	6.155	0.519	0.122	88.260	0.128	1.05
320	667.1	3.80	6.610	0.494	0.112	85.318	0.128	1.13
325	650.0	—	6.699	0.471	0.108	83.357	0.127	1.18
330	640.2	4.25	7.245	0.468	0.101	81.395	0.127	1.25
340	609.4	4.75	8.160	0.437	0.088	77.473	0.127	1.45
350	572.0	—	9.295	0.400	0.076	72.569	0.127	1.67
360	524.0	—	9.850	0.356	0.067	66.685	0.127	1.91
370	448.0	—	11.690	0.293	0.058	56.879	0.127	2.18

[1] Older name: Specific heat.
[2] kK = kilokelvin = 10^3 K
1 Btu = 1.055 06 kJ
1 Btu/(ft h °F) = 1.730 73 W/(m K)

Table 2-11 Thermal Conductivity λ of Water (H_2O) at Various Pressures

Pressure p =	98.066 5 bar (= 100 bar)	196.133 0 bar (= 200 bar)	294.199 5 bar (= 300 bar)	392.266 0 bar (= 400 bar)
Temperature	Thermal conductivity			
t °C	$\dfrac{\lambda}{W/(m\ K)}$	$\dfrac{\lambda}{W/(m\ K)}$	$\dfrac{\lambda}{W/(m\ K)}$	$\dfrac{\lambda}{W/(m\ K)}$
0	0.555	0.558	0.563	0.568
20	0.604	0.608	0.614	0.620
40	0.638	0.644	0.650	0.656
60	0.664	0.669	0.675	0.680
80	0.679	0.685	0.691	0.697
100	0.690	0.695	0.701	0.707
120	0.693	0.700	0.707	0.714
140	0.693	0.700	0.707	0.715
160	0.690	0.697	0.705	0.713
180	0.683	0.690	0.698	0.708
200	O.672	0.679	0.690	0.700
220	0.656	0.665	0.677	0.687
240	0.636	0.648	0.659	0.671
260	0.612	0.623	0.636	0.649
280	0.582	0.595	0.612	0.626
300	0.542	0.561	0.508	0.597
320		0.516	0.538	0.561
340		0.456	0.491	0.520
360		0.365	0.423	0.466
370			0.379	0.437

1 Btu/(ft h °F) = 1.730 73 W/(m K)

Table 2-12 Composition and Heating Values H_s and H_i of Liquid Fuels

Fuel	Chemical formula	Density at 15°C ρ kg/m³	Boiling point t_b °C	Charac- teristic σ	Composition in % C	H	O + N₂	S	Heating value H_s kJ/kg	H_i kJ/kg	Cubic meters per 1 kg fuel required for combustion O_{min} m³/kg	L_{min} m³/kg	Combustion products of 1 kg fuel CO_2 m³	H_2O m³
Alcohol, 100%	C₂H₅OH	794	78.3	1.500	52	13	—	—	29726	26796	1.45	7.00	0.97	1.46
95%		809	78.5	1.500	—	—	—	—	28177	25246	1.39	6.54	0.92	1.45
90%		823	78.7	1.500	—	—	—	—	26586	23865	1.32	6.30	0.88	1.44
85%		836	78.9	1.500	—	—	—	—	25205	22316	1.24	5.98	0.83	1.43
Benzene		≈760	<120	1.530	80.7	14.2	5.1	—	45217	42035	2.43	11.6	1.59	1.68
Benzene	C₆H₆	875	80.5	1.250	91.7	7.8	—	0.5	42287	40403	2.16	10.3	1.72	0.86
—commercial, I (90)		882	—	1.260	92.1	7.9	—	—	41868	40193	2.17	10.4	1.71	0.88
—commercial, II (50)		876	—	1.300	91.6	8.4	—	—	42287	40403	2.20	10.6	1.70	0.98
—motor		870	—	—	91.7	8.3	—	—	42287	40403	—	—	—	—
Gas oil (Diesel oil)		≈870	<350	1.380	86.6	12.9	0.2	0.3	44715	41843	2.21	10.54	1.60	1.23
Heptane	C₇H₁₆	683	98	1.571	83.9	16.1	—	—	48023	44422	2.46	11.8	1.57	1.79
Hexane	C₆H₁₄	660	65	1.584	83.6	16.4	—	—	48148	44380	2.47	11.8	1.56	1.82
Liquid gas		2220	—	—	82.5	17.5	—	—	50911	46055	—	—	—	—
Methane, motor		920	—	—	77.4	20.6	2.0	—	50911	48567	—	—	—	—
Mineral oil		≈850	—	—	—	—	—	—	41868	40193	—	—	—	—
Naphthalene (boiling point 80 °C)	C₁₀H₈	977 (80 °C)	218	1.200	93.7	6.3	—	—	40528	39105	2.10	9.99	1.75	0.70
Octane	C₈H₁₈	700	125	1.562	84.1	15.9	—	—	47813	44254	2.46	11.8	1.57	1.78
Pentane	C₅H₁₂	626	37	1.600	83.2	16.8	—	—	48651	44882	2.49	11.9	1.55	1.87
Petroleum		≈810	—	—	85	15	—	—	41868	39775	—	—	—	—
Tetralin	C₁₀H₁₂	975	205	1.300	90.8	9.2	—	—	42496	40444	2.20	10.6	1.70	1.02
Toluene	C₇H₈	867	110	1.285	91.2	8.8	—	—	42496	40528	2.19	10.5	1.70	0.97
Xylene	C₈H₁₀	863	140	1.313	90.5	9.5	—	—	42831	40696	2.22	10.6	1.69	1.06

1 Btu = 1.055 06 kJ

Table 2-13 Composition and Heating Values H_s and H_i of Liquid Fuels

Fuel	Density $\dfrac{\rho}{kg/m^3}$	Composition by weight %				Heating value			$\dfrac{V_{min_{dry}}}{L_{min}}$	$CO_{2\,max}$ %
		C	H_2	$O_2 + N_2$	S	$\dfrac{H_s}{kJ/kg}$	$\dfrac{H_i}{kJ/kg}$	$\dfrac{L_{min}}{m^3/kg}$		
Fuel oils:										
—Californian	950	86.4	11.3	1.1	0.6	43543	41031	—	0.94	16.0
—heavy	950	85.0	11.7	1.2	2.1	43961	41784	10.670	0.939	15.90
—light	900	85.4	12.3	0.7	1.6	44799	42077	10.864	0.937	15.69
—Mexican	910	82.9	12.2	2.1	2.8	42998	40277	—	0.94	15.4
—Pennsylvanian	890	84.9	13.7	1.4	—	44673	41617	—	0.93	15.2
Tar oils:										
—lean tar oil	1120	90.4	6.0	3.2	0.4	38937	37597	9.519	0.966	18.28
—lighnite tar oil	925	84.0	11.0	4.3	0.7	42705	40235	10.246	0.942	16.21
—pit coal tar oil	1080	89.5	6.5	3.4	0.6	39272	37681	9.571	0.964	18.06

1 Btu = 1.055 06 kJ

VAPORS

Table 3-1 Properties of Saturated Steam (H₂O) (at a Given Temperature)

Temperature	Pressure	Specific volume		Density		Specific enthalpy		Heat of vaporization	Specific entropy	
		Liquid	Vapor	Liquid	Vapor	Liquid	Vapor		Liquid	Vapor
t	p	v'	v''	ρ'	ρ''	h'	h''	r	s'	s''
°C	bar	m³/kg	m³/kg	kg/m³	kg/m³	kJ/kg	kJ/kg	kJ/kg	kJ/(kg K)	kJ/(kg K)
0.01	0.006108	0.0010002	206.3	999.80	0.004847	0.00	2501	2501	0.0000	9.1544
1	0.006566	0.0010001	192.6	999.90	0.005192	4.22	2502	2498	0.0154	9.1281
2	0.007054	0.0010001	179.9	999.90	0.005559	8.42	2504	2496	0.0306	9.1018
3	0.007575	0.0010001	168.2	999.90	0.005945	12.63	2506	2493	0.0458	9.0757
4	0.008129	0.0010001	157.3	999.90	0.006357	16.84	2508	2491	0.0610	9.0498
5	0.008719	0.0010001	147.2	999.90	0.006793	21.05	2510	2489	0.0762	9.0241
6	0.009347	0.0010001	137.8	999.90	0.007257	25.25	2512	2489	0.0913	8.9978
7	0.010013	0.0010001	129.1	999.90	0.007746	29.45	2514	2485	0.1063	8.9736
8	0.010721	0.0010002	121.0	999.80	0.008264	33.55	2516	2482	0.1212	8.9485
9	0.011473	0.0010003	113.4	999.70	0.008818	37.85	2517	2479	0.1361	8.9238
10	0.012277	0.0010004	106.42	999.60	0.009398	42.04	2519	2477	0.1510	8.8994
11	0.013118	0.0010005	99.91	999.50	0.01001	46.22	2521	2475	0.1658	8.8752
12	0.014016	0.0010006	93.84	999.40	0.01066	50.41	2523	2473	0.1805	8.8513
13	0.014967	0.0010007	88.18	999.30	0.01134	54.60	2525	2470	0.1952	8.8276
14	0.015974	0.0010008	82.90	999.20	0.01206	58.78	2527	2468	0.2098	8.8040
15	0.017041	0.0010010	77.97	999.00	0.01282	62.97	2528	2465	0.2244	8.7806
16	0.018170	0.0010011	73.39	998.90	0.01363	67.16	2530	2463	0.2389	8.7574
17	0.019364	0.0010013	69.10	998.70	0.01447	71.34	2532	2461	0.2534	8.7344
18	0.02062	0.0010015	65.09	998.50	0.01536	75.53	2534	2458	0.2678	8.7116
19	0.02196	0.0010016	61.34	998.40	0.01630	79.72	2536	2456	0.2821	8.6890
20	0.02337	0.0010018	57.84	998.20	0.01729	83.90	2537	2454	0.2964	8.6665
21	0.02486	0.0010021	54.56	997.90	0.01833	88.09	2539	2451	0.3107	8.6442
22	0.02643	0.0010023	51.50	997.71	0.01942	92.27	2541	2449	0.3249	8.6220
23	0.02808	0.0010025	48.62	997.51	0.02057	96.46	2543	2447	0.3391	8.6001
24	0.02982	0.0010028	45.93	997.21	0.02177	100.63	2545	2444	0.3532	8.5785
25	0.03166	0.0010030	43.40	997.01	0.02304	104.81	2547	2442	0.3672	8.5570
26	0.03360	0.0010033	41.04	996.71	0.02437	108.99	2548	2440	0.3812	8.5358
27	0.03564	0.0010036	38.82	996.41	0.02576	113.17	2550	2437	0.3951	8.5147
28	0.03779	0.0010038	36.73	996.21	0.02723	117.35	2552	2435	0.4090	8.4938
29	0.04004	0.0010041	34.77	995.92	0.02876	121.53	2554	2432	0.4228	8.4730
30	0.04241	0.0010044	32.93	995.62	0.03037	125.71	2556	2430	0.4366	8.4523
31	0.04491	0.0010047	31.20	995.32	0.03205	129.89	2558	2428	0.4503	8.4319
32	0.04753	0.0010051	29.57	994.93	0.03382	134.07	2559	2425	0.4640	8.4117
33	0.05029	0.0010054	28.04	994.63	0.03566	138.25	2561	2423	0.4777	8.3916
34	0.05318	0.0010057	26.60	994.33	0.03759	142.42	2563	2421	0.4913	8.3716
35	0.05622	0.0010061	25.24	993.94	0.03962	146.60	2565	2418	0.5049	8.3519
36	0.05940	0.0010064	23.97	993.64	0.04172	150.78	2567	2416	0.5185	8.3323
37	0.06274	0.0010068	22.77	993.25	0.04392	154.96	2569	2414	0.5320	8.3129
38	0.06624	0.0010071	21.63	992.95	0.04623	159.14	2570	2411	0.5455	8.2938
39	0.06991	0.0010075	20.56	992.56	0.04864	163.32	2572	2409	0.5589	8.2748
40	0.07375	0.0010079	19.55	992.16	0.05115	167.50	2574	2406	0.5723	8.2559
41	0.07777	0.0010083	18.59	991.77	0.05379	171.67	2575	2403	0.5856	8.2372
42	0.08198	0.0010087	17.69	991.38	0.05653	175.86	2577	2401	0.5988	8.2187
43	0.08639	0.0010091	16.84	990.98	0.05938	180.04	2579	2399	0.6120	8.2003
44	0.09101	0.0010095	16.04	990.59	0.06234	184.22	2581	2397	0.6252	8.1820
45	0.09584	0.0010099	15.28	990.20	0.06544	188.40	2582	2394	0.6384	8.1638
46	0.10088	0.0010103	14.56	989.81	0.06868	192.58	2584	2391	0.6516	8.1458
47	0.10614	0.0010108	13.88	989.32	0.07205	196.76	2586	2389	0.6647	8.1279
48	0.11163	0.0010112	13.23	988.92	0.07559	200.93	2588	2387	0.6778	8.1102
49	0.11736	0.0010116	12.62	988.53	0.07924	205.11	2590	2385	0.6908	8.0927
50	0.12335	0.0010121	12.04	988.04	0.08306	209.3	2592	2383	0.7038	8.0753
51	0.12960	0.0010126	11.50	987.56	0.08696	213.5	2593	2380	0.7167	8.0579
52	0.13612	0.0010130	10.98	987.17	0.09107	217.7	2595	2377	0.7295	8.0407
53	0.14292	0.0010135	10.49	986.68	0.09533	221.9	2597	2375	0.7423	8.0236
54	0.15001	0.0010140	10.02	986.19	0.09980	226.0	2599	2373	0.7551	8.0068

Table 3-1 Properties of Saturated Steam (H₂O) (at a Given Temperature) (continued)

Temperature	Pressure	Specific volume		Density		Specific enthalpy		Heat of vaporization	Specific entropy	
		Liquid	Vapor	Liquid	Vapor	Liquid	Vapor		Liquid	Vapor
t	p	v'	v''	ρ'	ρ''	h'	h''	r	s'	s''
°C	bar	m³/kg	m³/kg	kg/m³	kg/m³	kJ/kg	kJ/kg	kJ/kg	kJ/(kg K)	kJ/(kg K)
55	0.15740	0.0010145	9.578	985.71	0.1044	230.2	2600	2370	0.7679	7.9901
56	0.16510	0.0010150	9.158	985.22	0.1092	234.4	2602	2368	0.7806	7.9736
57	0.17312	0.0010155	8.757	984.74	0.1142	238.6	2604	2365	0.7933	7.9571
58	0.18146	0.0010160	8.380	984.25	0.1193	242.8	2606	2363	0.8059	7.9407
59	0.19014	0.0010166	8.020	983.67	0.1247	246.9	2608	2361	0.8185	7.9245
60	0.19917	0.0010171	7.678	983.19	0.1302	251.1	2609	2358	0.8311	7.9084
61	0.2086	0.0010177	7.353	982.61	0.1360	255.3	2611	2355	0.8436	7.8925
62	0.2184	0.0010182	7.043	982.13	0.1420	259.5	2613	2353	0.8561	7.8767
63	0.2285	0.0010188	6.749	981.55	0.1482	263.7	2614	2350	0.8686	7.8609
64	0.2391	0.0010193	6.468	981.07	0.1546	267.9	2616	2348	0.8810	7.8452
65	0.2501	0.0010199	6.201	980.49	0.1613	272.1	2617	2345	0.8934	7.8297
66	0.2615	0.0010205	5.947	979.91	0.1681	276.2	2619	2343	0.9057	7.8144
67	0.2733	0.0010210	5.705	979.43	0.1753	280.4	2621	2341	0.9180	7.7992
68	0.2856	0.0010216	5.475	978.86	0.1826	284.6	2623	2338	0.9303	7.7841
69	0.2984	0.0010222	5.255	978.28	0.1903	288.8	2625	2336	0.9426	7.7692
70	0.3117	0.0010228	5.045	977.71	0.1982	293.0	2626	2333	0.9549	7.7544
71	0.3254	0.0010234	4.846	977.14	0.2064	297.2	2628	2331	0.9672	7.7396
72	0.3396	0.0010240	4.655	976.56	0.2148	301.4	2630	2329	0.9794	7.7249
73	0.3543	0.0010246	4.473	975.99	0.2236	305.6	2631	2326	0.9916	7.7103
74	0.3696	0.0010252	4.299	975.42	0.2326	309.8	2633	2323	1.0037	7.6958
75	0.3855	0.0010258	4.133	974.85	0.2420	314.0	2635	2321	1.0157	7.6815
76	0.4019	0.0010264	3.975	974.28	0.2516	318.2	2636	2318	1.0277	7.6673
77	0.4189	0.0010270	3.824	973.71	0.2615	322.4	2638	2316	1.0396	7.6533
78	0.4365	0.0010277	3.679	973.05	0.2718	326.4	2639	2313	1.0515	7.6393
79	0.4547	0.0010283	3.540	972.48	0.2825	330.6	2641	2310	1.0634	7.6254
80	0.4736	0.0010290	3.408	971.82	0.2934	334.9	2643	2308	1.0753	7.6116
81	0.4931	0.0010297	3.282	971.16	0.3047	339.1	2645	2306	1.0872	7.5979
82	0.5133	0.0010304	3.161	970.50	0.3164	343.3	2646	2303	1.0990	7.5843
83	0.5342	0.0010310	3.045	969.93	0.3284	347.5	2648	2300	1.1107	7.5707
84	0.5558	0.0010317	2.934	969.27	0.3408	351.7	2650	2298	1.1225	7.5572
85	0.5781	0.0010324	2.828	968.62	0.3536	355.9	2651	2295	1.1342	7.5438
86	0.6011	0.0010331	2.727	967.96	0.3667	360.1	5653	2293	1.1459	7.5305
87	0.6249	0.0010338	2.629	967.31	0.3804	364.3	2655	2291	1.1576	7.5174
88	0.6495	0.0010345	2.536	966.65	0.3943	368.5	2656	2288	1.1693	7.5044
89	0.6749	0.0010352	2.447	966.00	0.4087	372.7	2658	2285	1.1809	7.4915
90	0.7011	0.0010359	2.361	965.34	0.4235	377.0	2659	2282	1.1925	7.4787
91	0.7281	0.0010366	2.279	964.69	0.4388	381.2	2661	2280	1.2041	7.4660
92	0.7560	0.0010373	2.200	964.04	0.4545	385.4	2662	2277	1.2157	7.4533
93	0.7848	0.0010381	2.124	963.30	0.4708	389.6	2664	2274	1.2272	7.4407
94	0.8145	0.0010388	2.052	962.65	0.4873	393.8	2666	2272	1.2387	7.4281
95	0.8451	0.0010396	1.982	961.91	0.5045	398.0	2668	2270	1.2502	7.4155
96	0.8767	0.0010404	1.915	961.17	0.5222	402.2	2669	2267	1.2617	7.4030
97	0.9093	0.0010412	1.851	960.43	0.5402	406.4	2671	2265	1.2731	7.3907
98	0.9429	0.0010420	1.789	959.69	0.5590	410.7	2673	2262	1.2845	7.3786
99	0.9775	0.0010427	1.730	959.05	0.5780	414.9	2674	2259	1.2958	7.3666
100	1.0131	0.0010435	1.673	958.31	0.5977	419.1	2676	2257	1.3071	7.3547
101	1.0498	0.0010443	1.618	957.58	0.6181	423.3	2677	2254	1.3184	7.3429
102	1.0876	0.0010450	1.566	956.94	0.6386	427.5	2679	2251	1.3297	7.3311
103	1.1265	0.0010458	1.515	956.21	0.6601	431.7	2680	2248	1.3409	7.3193
104	1.1666	0.0010466	1.466	955.47	0.6821	436.0	2681	2245	1.3521	7.3076
105	1.2079	0.0010474	1.419	954.75	0.7047	440.2	2683	2243	1.3632	7.2959
106	1.2504	0.0010482	1.374	954.02	0.7278	444.4	2685	2241	1.3743	7.2843
107	1.2941	0.0010490	1.331	953.29	0.7513	448.6	2687	2238	1.3854	7.2728
108	1.3390	0.0010498	1.289	952.56	0.7758	452.9	2688	2235	1.3964	7.2614
109	1.3852	0.0010507	1.249	951.75	0.8006	457.1	2689	2232	1.4074	7.2500

Table 3-1 Properties of Saturated Steam (H₂O) (at a Given Temperature) *(continued)*

Temperature	Pressure	Specific volume		Density		Specific enthalpy		Heat of vaporization	Specific entropy	
		Liquid	Vapor	Liquid	Vapor	Liquid	Vapor		Liquid	Vapor
t	p	v'	v''	ρ'	ρ''	h'	h''	r	s'	s''
°C	bar	m³/kg	m³/kg	kg/m³	kg/m³	kJ/kg	kJ/kg	kJ/kg	kJ/(kg K)	kJ/(kg K)
110	1.4326	0.0010515	1.210	951.02	0.8264	461.3	2691	2230	1.4184	7.2387
111	1.4814	0.0010523	1.173	950.30	0.8525	465.6	2693	2272	1.4294	7.2274
112	1.5316	0.0010532	1.137	949.49	0.8795	469.8	2694	2224	1.4404	7.2162
113	1.5831	0.0010540	1.102	948.77	0.9074	474.0	2696	2222	1.4514	7.2051
114	1.6361	0.0010549	1.069	947.96	0.9354	478.2	2697	2219	1.4624	7.1941
115	1.6905	0.0010559	1.036	947.15	0.9652	482.5	2698	2216	1.4733	7.1832
116	1.7464	0.0010567	1.005	946.34	0.9950	486.7	2700	2213	1.4842	7.1724
117	1.8038	0.0010576	0.9754	945.54	1.025	491.0	2702	2211	1.4951	7.1616
118	1.8628	0.0010585	0.9465	944.73	1.056	495.2	2703	2208	1.5060	7.1509
119	1.9233	0.0010594	0.9186	943.93	1.089	499.5	2705	2205	1.5169	7.1403
120	1.9854	0.0010603	0.8917	943.13	1.121	503.7	2706	2202	1.5277	7.1298
121	2.0491	0.0010612	0.8657	942.33	1.155	507.9	2708	2200	1.5385	7.1193
122	2.1144	0.0010621	0.8407	941.53	1.189	512.2	2709	2197	1.5492	7.1089
123	2.1814	0.0010630	0.8164	940.73	1.225	516.5	2710	2194	1.5599	7.0985
124	2.2502	0.0010640	0.7930	939.85	1.261	520.8	2712	2191	1.5706	7.0881
125	2.3208	0.0010649	0.7704	939.06	1.298	525.0	2713	2188	1.5814	7.0777
126	2.3932	0.0010658	0.7486	938.26	1.336	529.2	2715	2186	1.5922	7.0674
127	2.4674	0.0010668	0.7276	937.38	1.374	533.4	2716	2183	1.6029	7.0573
128	2.5434	0.0010677	0.7074	936.59	1.414	537.7	2718	2180	1.6135	7.0472
129	2.6213	0.0010687	0.6880	935.72	1.454	542.0	2719	2177	1.6240	7.0372
130	2.7011	0.0010697	0.6683	934.84	1.496	546.3	2721	2174	1.6354	7.0272
131	2.7829	0.0010707	0.6499	933.97	1.539	550.5	2722	2171	1.6450	7.0173
132	2.8668	0.0010717	0.6321	933.10	1.582	554.8	2723	2168	1.6555	7.0074
133	2.9528	0.0010727	0.6148	932.23	1.626	559.0	2724	2165	1.6659	6.9976
134	3.041	0.0010737	0.5981	931.36	1.672	563.2	2725	2162	1.6764	6.9878
135	3.130	0.0010747	0.5820	930.49	1.718	567.5	2727	2159	1.6869	6.9781
136	3.222	0.0010757	0.5664	929.63	1.765	571.8	2728	2156	1.6973	6.9685
137	3.317	0.0010767	0.5512	928.76	1.814	576.1	2730	2154	1.7078	6.9589
138	3.414	0.0010777	0.5366	927.90	1.864	580.4	2731	2151	1.7183	6.9493
139	3.513	0.0010788	0.5224	926.96	1.914	584.7	2733	2148	1.7278	6.9398
140	3.614	0.0010798	0.5087	926.10	1.966	589.0	2734	2145	1.7392	6.9304
141	3.717	0.0010808	0.4953	925.24	2.019	593.3	2735	2142	1.7496	6.9211
142	3.823	0.0010819	0.4824	924.30	2.073	597.6	2737	2139	1.7599	6.9117
143	3.931	0.0010829	0.4699	923.45	2.128	601.9	2738	2136	1.7702	6.9024
144	4.042	0.0010840	0.4579	922.51	2.184	606.2	2739	2133	1.7804	6.8932
145	4.155	0.0010851	0.4461	921.57	2.242	610.5	2740	2130	1.7907	6.8839
146	4.271	0.0010862	0.4347	920.64	2.300	614.8	2742	2127	1.8009	6.8747
147	4.389	0.0010873	0.4237	919.71	2.360	619.1	2743	2124	1.8112	6.8655
148	4.510	0.0010884	0.4130	918.78	2.421	623.4	2744	2121	1.8214	6.8564
149	4.634	0.0010895	0.4026	917.85	2.484	627.8	2745	2117	1.8316	6.8473
150	4.760	0.0010906	0.3926	916.93	2.547	632.2	2746	2114	1.8418	6.8383
151	4.889	0.0010917	0.3827	916.00	2.612	636.6	2748	2111	1.8520	6.8293
152	5.020	0.0010928	0.3733	915.08	2.679	641.0	2749	2108	1.8622	6.8204
153	5.155	0.0010939	0.3641	914.16	2.746	645.3	2750	2105	1.8723	6.8115
154	5.293	0.0010950	0.3552	913.24	2.815	649.6	2752	2102	1.8824	6.8027
155	5.433	0.0010962	0.3466	912.24	2.885	653.9	2753	2099	1.8924	6.7940
156	5.576	0.0010974	0.3381	911.24	2.958	658.2	2754	2096	1.9025	6.7854
157	5.723	0.0010986	0.3299	910.25	3.030	662.5	2755	2092	1.9125	6.7768
158	5.872	0.0010998	0.3220	909.26	3.106	666.9	2756	2089	1.9226	6.7681
159	6.024	0.0011009	0.3143	908.35	3.182	671.2	2757	2086	1.9326	6.7595
160	6.180	0.0011021	0.3068	907.36	3.258	675.6	2758	2082	1.9427	6.7508
161	6.339	0.0011033	0.2996	906.37	3.338	679.9	2759	2079	1.9527	6.7421
162	6.502	0.0011044	0.2925	905.47	3.419	684.2	2760	5076	1.9657	6.7335
163	6.667	0.0011056	0.2856	904.49	3.500	688.6	2761	2072	1.9726	6.7250
164	6.836	0.0011069	0.2790	903.42	3.584	692.9	2762	2069	1.9825	6.7165

Table 3-1   Properties of Saturated Steam (H₂O) (at a Given Temperature)   (*continued*)

Temperature	Pressure	Specific volume		Density		Specific enthalpy		Heat of vaporization	Specific entropy	
		Liquid	Vapor	Liquid	Vapor	Liquid	Vapor		Liquid	Vapor
t	p	v'	v''	ρ'	ρ''	h'	h''	r	s'	s''
°C	bar	m³/kg	m³/kg	kg/m³	kg/m³	kJ/kg	kJ/kg	kJ/kg	kJ/(kg K)	kJ/(kg K)
165	7.008	0.0011081	0.2725	902.45	3.670	697.3	2763	2066	1.9924	6.7081
166	7.183	0.0011094	0.2662	901.39	3.757	701.7	2764	2062	2.0023	6.6998
167	7.362	0.0011106	0.2600	900.41	3.846	706.1	2765	2059	2.0122	6.6915
168	7.545	0.0011119	0.2541	899.36	3.935	710.5	2667	2056	2.0221	6.6832
169	7.731	0.0011131	0.2483	898.39	4.027	714.8	2768	2053	2.0319	6.6749
170	7.920	0.0011144	0.2426	897.34	4.122	719.2	2769	2050	2.0417	6.6666
171	8.114	0.0011156	0.2371	896.38	4.218	723.5	2770	2046	2.0515	6.6583
172	8.311	0.0011169	0.2318	895.34	4.314	727.9	2771	2043	2.0614	6.6500
173	8.511	0.0011182	0.2266	894.29	4.413	732.3	2772	2040	2.0712	6.6418
174	8.176	0.0011195	0.2215	893.26	4.515	736.7	2773	2036	2.0811	6.6336
175	8.925	0.0011208	0.2166	892.22	4.617	741.1	2773	2032	2.0909	6.6256
176	9.137	0.0011221	0.2118	891.19	4.721	745.5	2774	2029	2.1006	6.6177
177	9.354	0.0011234	0.2071	890.15	4.829	749.9	2775	2025	2.1103	6.6097
178	9.574	0.0011248	0.2026	889.05	4.936	754.3	2776	2022	2.1201	6.6017
179	9.799	0.0011261	0.1982	888.02	5.045	758.7	2777	2018	2.1298	6.5938
180	10.027	0.0011275	0.1939	886.92	5.157	763.1	2778	2015	2.1395	6.5858
181	10.260	0.0011289	0.1897	885.82	5.271	767.5	2779	2011	2.1491	6.5779
182	10.497	0.0011303	0.1856	884.72	5.388	771.9	2780	2008	2.1587	6.5700
183	10.728	0.0011316	0.1816	883.70	5.507	776.3	2780	2004	2.1683	6.5622
184	10.984	0.0011330	0.1777	882.61	5.627	780.7	2781	2000	2.1780	6.5344
185	11.234	0.0011344	0.1739	881.52	5.750	785.2	2782	1997	2.1876	6.5465
186	11.488	0.0011358	0.1702	880.44	5.875	789.6	2783	1993	2.1972	6.5386
187	11.747	0.0011372	0.1666	879.35	6.002	794.0	2784	1990	2.2069	6.5307
188	12.011	0.0011386	0.1631	878.27	6.131	798.5	2784	1986	2.2165	6.5229
189	12.280	0.0011401	0.1597	877.12	6.262	803.0	2785	1982	2.2261	6.5151
190	12.553	0.0011415	0.1564	876.04	6.394	807.5	2786	1979	2.2357	6.5074
191	12.830	0.0011430	0.1531	874.89	6.532	811.9	2787	1975	2.2453	6.4998
192	13.112	0.0011445	0.1499	873.74	6.671	816.4	2787	1971	2.2584	6.4921
193	13.400	0.0011459	0.1468	872.68	6.812	820.9	2788	1967	2.2643	6.4845
194	13.692	0.0011474	0.1438	871.54	6.954	825.4	2789	1964	2.2739	6.4770
195	13.989	0.0011489	0.1409	870.40	7.097	829.9	2790	1960	2.2834	6.4694
196	14.291	0.0011504	0.1380	869.26	7.246	834.4	2790	1956	2.2929	6.4619
197	14.598	0.0011519	0.1352	868.13	7.396	838.9	2791	1952	2.3024	6.4544
198	14.910	0.0011534	0.1325	867.00	7.547	843.4	2792	1949	2.3119	6.4468
199	15.228	0.0011550	0.1298	865.80	7.704	847.9	2793	1945	2.3214	6.4393
200	15.551	0.0011565	0.1272	864.68	7.862	852.4	2793	1941	2.3308	6.4318
201	15.879	0.0011581	0.1246	863.48	8.026	856.9	2793	1936	2.3402	6.4243
202	16.212	0.0011596	0.1221	862.37	8.190	861.5	2794	1932	2.3496	6.4168
203	16.551	0.0011612	0.1197	861.18	8.354	866.0	2794	1928	2.3590	6.4094
204	16.895	0.0011628	0.1174	859.99	8.518	870.5	2795	1924	2.3684	6.4020
205	17.245	0.0011644	0.1151	858.81	8.688	875.0	2796	1921	2.3777	6.3945
206	17.601	0.0011660	0.1128	857.63	8.865	879.6	2797	1917	2.3870	6.3871
207	17.962	0.0011676	0.1106	856.46	9.042	884.2	2797	1913	2.3964	6.3797
208	18.329	0.0011693	0.1084	855.21	9.225	888.7	2797	1908	2.4058	6.3723
209	18.701	0.0011709	0.1063	854.04	9.407	893.2	2798	1905	2.4152	6.3650
210	19.080	0.0011726	0.1043	852.81	9.588	897.7	2798	1900	2.4246	6.3577
211	19.464	0.0011743	0.1023	851.57	9.775	902.3	2798	1896	2.4340	6.3504
212	19.855	0.0011760	0.1003	850.34	9.970	906.9	2799	1892	2.4434	6.3431
213	20.252	0.0011778	0.09836	849.04	10.17	911.5	2799	1888	2.4528	6.3358
214	20.654	0.0011795	0.09649	847.82	10.36	916.1	2800	1884	2.4622	6.3285
215	21.062	0.0011812	0.09465	846.60	10.56	920.7	2800	1879	2.4751	6.3212
216	21.477	0.0011829	0.09285	845.38	10.77	925.3	2800	1875	2.4808	6.3140
217	21.899	0.0011846	0.09110	844.17	10.98	929.9	2801	1871	2.4901	6.3067
218	22.327	0.0011864	0.08938	842.89	11.19	934.5	2801	1867	2.4994	6.2994
219	22.761	0.0011882	0.08770	841.61	11.40	939.1	2801	1862	2.5087	6.2921

Temperature	Pressure	Specific volume		Density		Specific enthalpy		Heat of vaporization	Specific entropy	
		Liquid	Vapor	Liquid	Vapor	Liquid	Vapor		Liquid	Vapor
t	p	v'	v''	ρ'	ρ''	h'	h''	r	s'	s''
°C	bar	m³/kg	m³/kg	kg/m³	kg/m³	kJ/kg	kJ/kg	kJ/kg	kJ/(kg K)	kJ/(kg K)
220	23.201	0.0011900	0.08606	840.34	11.62	943.7	2802	1858	2.5179	6.2849
221	23.649	0.0011918	0.08446	839.07	11.84	948.3	2802	1854	2.5272	6.2776
222	24.103	0.0011937	0.08288	837.73	12.06	952.9	2802	1849	2.5364	6.2704
223	24.563	0.0011955	0.08135	836.47	12.29	957.5	2802	1845	2.5456	6.2632
224	25.030	0.0011973	0.07984	835.21	12.52	962.2	2802	1840	2.5548	6.2560
225	25.504	0.0011992	0.07837	833.89	12.76	966.9	2802	1835	2.5640	6.2488
226	25.985	0.0012011	0.07693	832.57	13.00	971.6	2803	1831	2.5732	6.2417
227	26.473	0.0012029	0.07552	831.32	13.24	976.3	2803	1826	2.5824	6.2346
228	26.967	0.0012048	0.07414	830.01	13.49	981.0	2803	1822	2.5916	6.2275
229	27.469	0.0012068	0.07279	828.64	13.74	985.7	2803	1817	2.6008	6.2204
230	27.979	0.0012087	0.07147	827.34	13.99	990.4	2803	1813	2.6101	6.2133
231	28.495	0.0012107	0.07018	825.97	14.25	995.1	2804	1809	2.6193	6.2063
232	29.019	0.0012126	0.06891	824.67	14.51	999.8	2804	1804	2.6285	6.1993
233	29.550	0.0012146	0.06767	823.32	14.78	1004.5	2804	1800	2.6377	6.1922
234	30.089	0.0012167	0.06646	821.90	15.05	1009.2	2804	1795	2.6469	6.1851
235	30.635	0.0012187	0.06527	820.35	15.32	1013.9	2804	1790	2.6561	6.1780
236	31.188	0.0012208	0.06410	819.13	15.60	1018.6	2804	1785	2.6653	6.1709
237	31.749	0.0012228	0.06296	817.80	15.88	1023.3	2804	1781	2.6745	6.1638
238	32.318	0.0012249	0.06184	816.39	16.17	1028.1	2804	1776	2.6837	6.1567
239	32.895	0.0012270	0.06075	815.00	16.46	1032.8	2804	1771	2.6929	6.1496
240	33.480	0.0012291	0.05967	813.60	16.76	1037.5	2803	1766	2.7021	6.1425
241	34.073	0.0012312	0.05862	812.22	17.06	1042.3	2803	1761	2.7113	6.1354
242	34.673	0.0012334	0.05759	810.77	17.36	1047.1	2803	1756	2.7205	6.1283
243	35.282	0.0012355	0.05658	809.39	17.67	1051.9	2803	1751	2.7296	6.1213
244	35.899	0.0012377	0.05559	807.95	17.99	1056.7	2803	1746	2.7387	6.1143
245	36.524	0.0012399	0.05462	806.52	18.30	1061.6	2803	1741	2.7478	6.1073
246	37.157	0.0012421	0.05367	805.09	18.63	1066.4	2802	1736	2.7569	6.1003
247	37.799	0.0012443	0.05274	803.66	18.96	1071.3	2802	1731	2.7660	6.0933
248	38.450	0.0012466	0.05183	802.18	19.29	1076.1	2802	1726	2.7751	6.0863
249	39.109	0.0012489	0.05093	800.70	19.63	1080.9	2802	1721	2.7842	6.0792
250	39.776	0.0012512	0.05006	799.23	19.28	1085.7	2801	1715	2.7934	6.0721
251	40.45	0.0012536	0.04919	797.70	20.33	1090.6	2801	1710	2.8026	6.0650
252	41.14	0.0012559	0.04835	796.24	20.68	1095.5	2801	1705	2.8118	6.0579
253	41.84	0.0012583	0.04752	794.72	21.04	1100.4	2800	1700	2.8210	6.0508
254	42.54	0.0012607	0.04671	793.21	21.41	1105.3	2799	1694	2.8302	6.0437
255	43.25	0.0012631	0.04591	791.70	21.78	1110.2	2799	1689	2.8394	6.0366
256	43.97	0.0012655	0.04513	790.20	22.16	1115.2	2798	1683	2.8486	6.0295
257	44.70	0.0012680	0.04436	788.64	22.54	1120.1	2798	1678	2.8577	6.0224
258	45.43	0.0012705	0.04361	787.09	22.93	1125.1	2797	1672	2.8668	6.0154
259	46.18	0.0012730	0.04287	785.55	23.33	1130.1	2797	1667	2.8759	6.0084
260	46.94	0.0012755	0.04215	784.01	23.72	1135.1	2796	1661	2.8851	6.0013
261	47.71	0.0012781	0.04144	782.41	24.13	1140.1	2796	1656	2.8942	5.9942
262	48.48	0.0012807	0.04074	780.82	24.55	1145.1	2795	1650	2.9034	5.9871
265	49.27	0.0012833	0.04005	779.24	24.96	1150.1	2795	1645	2.9125	5.9800
264	50.06	0.0012859	0.03938	777.67	25.39	1155.1	2795	1640	2.9216	5.9729
265	50.87	0.0012886	0.03872	776.04	25.83	1160.2	2794	1634	2.9307	5.9657
266	51.69	0.0012913	0.03807	774.41	26.26	1165.2	2793	1628	2.9398	5.9585
267	52.51	0.0012940	0.03744	772.80	26.71	1170.2	2792	1622	2.9489	5.9513
268	53.35	0.0012967	0.03681	771.19	27.16	1175.2	2791	1616	2.9580	5.9441
269	54.19	0.0012995	0.03620	769.53	27.62	1180.3	2790	1610	2.9672	5.9369
270	55.05	0.0013023	0.03560	767.87	28.09	1185.3	2790	1605	2.9764	5.9297
271	55.92	0.0013051	0.03501	766.22	28.56	1190.3	2789	1598.7	2.9856	5.9225
272	56.79	0.0013080	0.03443	764.53	29.04	1195.4	2788	1592.7	2.9948	5.9153
273	57.68	0.0013109	0.03386	762.83	29.53	1200.5	2787	1586.6	3.0040	5.9082
274	58.58	0.0013138	0.03330	761.15	30.03	1205.6	2786	1580.4	3.0132	5.9010

Table 3-1 Properties of Saturated Steam (H₂O) (at a Given Temperature)   *(continued)*

Temperature	Pressure	Specific volume		Density		Specific enthalpy		Heat of vaporization	Specific entropy	
		Liquid	Vapor	Liquid	Vapor	Liquid	Vapor		Liquid	Vapor
t	p	v'	v''	ρ'	ρ''	h'	h''	r	s'	s''
°C	bar	m³/kg	m³/kg	kg/m³	kg/m³	kJ/kg	kJ/kg	kJ/kg	kJ/(kg K)	kJ/(kg K)
275	59.49	0.0013168	0.03274	759.42	30.53	1210.7	2785	1574.2	3.0223	5.8938
276	60.41	0.0013198	0.03220	757.69	31.06	1215.9	2784	1568.0	3.0314	5.8865
277	61.34	0.0013228	0.03167	755.97	31.58	1221.1	2783	1561.7	3.0405	5.8792
278	62.28	0.0013259	0.03115	754.20	32.10	1226.3	2782	1555.5	3.0497	5.8719
279	63.23	0.0013290	0.03064	752.45	32.64	1231.6	2781	1549.2	3.0589	5.8646
280	64.19	0.0013321	0.03013	750.69	33.19	1236.9	2780	1542.9	3.0681	5.8573
281	65.17	0.0013353	0.02964	748.90	33.74	1242.1	2779	1536.5	3.0774	5.8500
282	66.16	0.0013385	0.02915	747.10	34.30	1247.3	2777	1530.0	3.0867	5.8427
283	67.15	0.0013417	0.02867	745.32	34.88	1252.5	2776	1523.5	3.0960	5.8353
284	68.16	0.0013450	0.02820	743.49	35.46	1257.8	2775	1516.9	3.1053	5.8279
285	69.18	0.0013483	0.02773	741.67	36.05	1263.1	2773	1510.2	3.1146	5.8205
286	70.21	0.0013516	0.02728	739.86	36.66	1268.4	2772	1503.5	3.1239	5.8130
287	71.25	0.0013550	0.02684	738.01	37.26	1273.7	2771	1496.8	3.1331	5.8054
288	72.30	0.0013585	0.02640	736.11	37.88	1279.1	2769	1490.0	3.1424	5.7979
289	73.37	0.0013620	0.02596	734.12	38.52	1284.5	2768	1483.2	3.1517	5.7903
290	74.45	0.0013655	0.02554	732.33	39.15	1290.0	2766	1476.3	3.1611	5.7827
291	75.54	0.0013691	0.02512	730.41	39.81	1295.5	2765	1469.4	3.1705	5.7751
292	76.64	0.0013727	0.02471	728.49	40.47	1300.9	2763	1462.4	3.1798	5.7674
293	77.76	0.0013764	0.02430	726.53	41.15	1306.3	2761	1455.3	3.1892	5.7597
294	78.88	0.0013801	0.02390	724.59	31.84	1311.7	2760	1448.2	3.1986	5.7520
295	80.02	0.0013839	0.02351	722.60	42.53	1317.2	2758	1441.0	3.2079	5.7443
296	81.18	0.0013877	0.02312	720.62	43.23	1322.7	2757	1433.8	3.2172	5.7365
297	82.35	0.0013916	0.02275	718.60	43.96	1328.3	2755	1426.6	3.2265	5.7287
298	83.52	0.0013956	0.02237	716.54	44.70	1333.8	2753	1419.3	3.2359	5.7208
299	84.71	0.0013996	0.02200	714.49	45.43	1339.3	2751	1411.8	3.2453	5.7129
300	85.92	0.0014036	0.02164	712.45	46.21	1344.9	2749	1404.3	3.2548	5.7049
301	87.14	0.001407	0.02129	710.73	46.97	1350.5	2747	1396.6	3.2644	5.6969
302	88.37	0.001412	0.02094	708.22	47.75	1356.2	2745	1389.0	3.2739	5.6889
303	89.61	0.001416	0.02059	706.21	48.57	1361.9	2744	1381.3	3.2834	5.6809
304	90.87	0.001420	0.02025	704.23	49.38	1367.5	2741	1373.5	3.2930	5.6728
305	92.14	0.001425	0.01992	701.75	50.20	1373.1	2739	1365.6	3.3026	5.6647
306	93.42	0.001429	0.01959	699.79	51.05	1378.8	2737	1357.6	3.3122	5.6565
307	94.72	0.001434	0.01926	697.35	51.92	1384.5	2734	1349.6	3.3218	5.6483
308	96.03	0.001438	0.01894	695.41	52.80	1390.3	2732	1341.6	3.3314	5.6400
309	97.36	0.001443	0.01863	693.00	53.68	1396.2	2730	1333.5	3.3411	5.6317
310	98.70	0.001447	0.01832	691.09	54.58	1402.1	2727	1325.2	3.3508	5.6233
311	100.05	0.001452	0.01801	688.71	55.52	1408.0	2725	1316.7	3.3605	5.6148
312	101.42	0.001457	0.01771	686.34	56.46	1413.9	2722	1308.2	3.3702	5.6063
313	102.80	0.001462	0.01741	683.99	57.44	1419.8	2720	1299.6	3.3800	5.5977
314	104.20	0.001467	0.01712	681.66	58.41	1425.7	2717	1291.0	3.3898	5.5890
315	105.61	0.001472	0.01683	679.35	59.42	1431.7	2714	1282.3	3.3996	5.5802
316	107.04	0.001477	0.01655	677.05	60.42	1437.7	2711	1273.4	3.4095	5.5714
317	108.48	0.001483	0.01627	674.31	61.46	1443.8	2709	1264.6	3.4194	5.5625
318	109.94	0.001488	0.01599	672.04	62.54	1449.9	2706	1255.8	3.4294	5.5535
319	111.41	0.001494	0.01572	669.34	63.61	1456.0	2703	1246.8	3.4395	5.5444
320	112.90	0.001499	0.01545	667.11	64.72	1462.1	2700	1237.8	3.4495	5.5353
321	114.40	0.001505	0.01519	664.45	65.83	1468.3	2697	1228.7	3.4596	5.5261
322	115.92	0.001511	0.01493	661.81	66.98	1474.6	2694	1219.4	3.4697	5.5169
323	117.15	0.001517	0.01467	659.20	68.17	1480.9	2691	1209.9	3.4798	5.5077
324	119.00	0.001523	0.01442	656.60	69.35	1487.2	2687	1200.2	3.4900	5.4984
325	120.57	0.001529	0.01417	654.02	70.57	1493.6	2684	1190.3	3.5002	5.4891
326	122.15	0.001535	0.01392	651.47	71.84	1500.0	2680	1180.3	3.5104	5.4797
327	123.75	0.001542	0.01368	648.51	73.10	1506.4	2676	1170.2	3.5207	3.4702
328	125.37	0.001548	0.01344	645.99	74.40	1512.9	2673	1160.1	3.5311	5.4607
329	127.00	0.001555	0.01320	643.09	75.76	1519.4	2669	1149.9	3.5416	5.4510

Table 3-1 Properties of Saturated Steam (H₂O) (at a Given Temperature) *(continued)*

Temperature	Pressure	Specific volume		Density		Specific enthalpy		Heat of vaporization	Specific entropy	
		Liquid	Vapor	Liquid	Vapor	Liquid	Vapor		Liquid	Vapor
t	p	v'	v''	ρ'	ρ''	h'	h''	r	s'	s''
°C	bar	m³/kg	m³/kg	kg/m³	kg/m³	kJ/kg	kJ/kg	kJ/kg	kJ/(kg K)	kJ/(kg K)
330	128.65	0.001562	0.01297	640.20	77.10	1526.1	2666	1139.6	3.5522	5.4412
331	130.31	0.001569	0.01274	637.35	78.49	1532.8	2662	1129.1	3.5628	5.4313
332	131.99	0.001577	0.01251	634.12	79.94	1539.5	2658	1118.6	3.5735	5.4213
333	133.69	0.001584	0.01228	631.31	81.43	1546.2	2654	1107.9	3.5842	5.4112
334	135.41	0.001591	0.01206	628.54	82.92	1553.0	2650	1096.9	3.5949	5.4009
335	137.14	0.001599	0.01184	625.39	84.46	1559.8	2646	1085.7	3.6056	5.3905
336	138.89	0.001607	0.01162	622.28	86.06	1566.6	2641	1074.3	3.6163	5.3799
337	140.66	0.001615	0.01141	619.20	87.64	1573.4	2636	1062.7	3.6272	5.3692
338	142.45	0.001623	0.01120	616.14	89.29	1580.4	2631	1050.9	3.6381	5.3583
339	144.26	0.001631	0.01099	613.12	90.99	1587.6	2627	1039.0	3.6492	5.3473
340	146.08	0.001639	0.01078	610.13	92.76	1594.7	2622	1027.0	3.6605	5.3361
341	147.92	0.001648	0.01057	606.80	94.60	1602	2617	1014.8	3.6720	5.3247
342	149.78	0.001658	0.01037	603.14	96.43	1609	2612	1002.4	3.6835	5.3131
343	151.66	0.001667	0.01017	599.88	98.33	1616	2606	989.7	3.6950	5.3013
344	153.56	0.001676	0.09969	596.66	100.31	1624	2601	976.7	3.7067	5.2892
345	155.48	0.001686	0.009771	593.12	102.34	1632	2595	963.5	3.7184	5.2769
346	157.42	0.001696	0.009574	589.62	104.45	1640	2590	950.2	3.7302	5.2644
347	159.38	0.001707	0.009379	585.82	106.62	1647	2584	936.6	3.7420	5.2517
348	161.35	0.001718	0.009186	582.07	108.86	1655	2578	922.7	3.7540	5.2387
349	163.35	0.001729	0.008995	578.37	111.17	1663	2571	908.3	3.7662	5.2253
350	165.37	0.001741	0.008803	574.38	113.6	1671	2565	893.5	3.7786	5.2117
351	167.41	0.001752	0.008613	570.78	116.1	1679	2558	878.5	3.7912	5.1979
352	169.47	0.001764	0.008425	566.89	118.7	1688	2551	863.0	3.8040	5.1837
353	171.55	0.001777	0.008238	562.75	121.4	1696	2543	847.0	3.8170	5.1690
354	173.65	0.001792	0.008053	558.04	124.2	1705	2535	830.3	3.8303	5.1539
355	175.77	0.001807	0.007869	553.40	127.1	1714	2527	813.0	3.8439	5.1385
356	177.92	0.001823	0.007684	548.55	130.0	1723	2518	795.1	3.8577	5.1225
357	180.09	0.001840	0.007499	543.48	133.2	1732	2509	776.7	3.8718	5.1058
358	182.28	0.001857	0.007314	538.50	136.6	1742	2500	758.0	3.8862	5.0886
359	184.50	0.001875	0.007130	533.33	140.2	1752	2491	738.9	3.9010	5.0710
360	186.74	0.001894	0.006943	527.98	144.0	1762	2481	719.3	3.9162	5.0530
361	189.00	0.001918	0.00675	521.38	148.1	1772	2471	698.8	3.9320	5.0342
362	191.29	0.001943	0.00656	514.67	152.4	1783	2460	677.1	3.9482	5.0145
363	193.60	0.001968	0.00637	508.13	157.0	1794	2448	654.0	3.9649	4.9940
364	195.94	0.00199	0.00618	502.51	161.8	1805	2435	629.5	3.9825	4.9706
365	198.30	0.00202	0.00599	495.05	166.8	1817	2421	603.5	4.0009	4.9463
366	200.69	0.00205	0.00580	487.80	172.5	1830	2406	575.9	4.0202	4.9212
367	203.11	0.00208	0.00559	480.77	178.8	1844	2390	546.2	4.0413	4.8939
368	205.56	0.00212	0.00538	471.70	185.8	1859	2372	513.4	4.0629	4.8646
369	208.03	0.00217	0.00516	460.83	193.6	1875	2353	478.1	4.0870	4.8320
370	210.53	0.00222	0.00493	450.45	203	1893	2331	438.4	4.1137	4.7951
371	213.06	0.00229	0.00468	436.68	214	1913	2305	392.3	4.1441	4.7529
372	215.63	0.00328	0.00440	420.17	227	1937	2273	336.2	4.1809	4.7018
373	218.23	0.00251	0.00405	398.41	247	1969	2230	261.3	4.2295	4.6335
374	220.87	0.00280	0.00347	357.14	288	2032	2147	114.7	4.3258	4.5029
374.15	221.297	0.00326	0.00326	306.75	306.75	2100	2100	0.0	4.4296	4.4296

Table 3-2 Properties of Saturated Steam (H₂O) (at a Given Pressure)

Temperature	Pressure	Specific volume		Density		Specific enthalpy		Heat of vaporization	Specific entropy	
		Liquid	Vapor	Liquid	Vapor	Liquid	Vapor		Liquid	Vapor
t	p	v'	v''	ρ'	ρ''	h'	h''	r	s'	s''
°C	bar	m³/kg	m³/kg	kg/m³	kg/m³	kJ/kg	kJ/kg	kJ/kg	kJ/(kg K)	kJ/(kg K)
0.010	6.92	0.0010001	129.9	999.9	0.00770	29.32	2513	2484	0.1054	8.975
0.015	13.038	0.0010007	87.90	999.3	0.01138	54.75	2525	2470	0.1958	8.827
0.020	17.514	0.0010014	66.97	998.6	0.01493	73.52	2533	2459	0.2609	8.722
0.025	21.094	0.0010021	54.24	997.9	0.01843	88.50	2539	2451	0.3124	8.642
0.030	24.097	0.0010028	45.66	997.2	0.02190	101.04	2545	2444	0.3546	8.576
0.035	26.692	0.0010035	39.48	996.5	0.02533	111.86	2550	2438	0.3908	8.521
0.040	28.979	0.0010041	34.81	995.9	0.02873	121.42	2554	2433	0.4225	8.473
0.045	31.033	0.0010047	31.13	995.3	0.03211	130.00	2557	2427	0.4507	8.431
0.050	32.88	0.0010053	28.19	994.7	0.03547	137.83	2561	2423	0.4761	8.393
0.055	34.59	0.0010059	25.77	994.1	0.03880	144.95	2564	2419	0.4993	8.359
0.060	36.18	0.0010064	23.74	993.6	0.04212	151.50	2567	2415	0.5207	8.328
0.065	37.65	0.0010070	22.02	993.0	0.04542	157.68	2570	2412	0.5406	8.300
0.070	39.03	0.0010075	20.53	992.6	0.04871	163.43	2572	2409	0.5591	8.274
0.075	40.32	0.0010080	19.23	992.1	0.05198	168.8	2574	2405	0.5764	8.250
0.080	41.54	0.0010085	18.10	991.6	0.05525	173.9	2576	2402	0.5927	8.227
0.085	42.69	0.0010090	17.10	991.1	0.05849	178.7	2578	2399	0.6080	8.206
0.090	43.79	0.0010094	16.20	990.7	0.06172	183.3	2580	2397	0.6225	8.186
0.095	44.84	0.0010098	15.40	990.3	0.06493	187.7	2582	2394	0.6362	8.167
0.10	45.84	0.0010103	14.68	989.8	0.06812	191.9	2584	2392	0.6492	8.149
0.11	47.72	0.0010111	13.40	989.0	0.07462	199.7	2588	2388	0.6740	8.116
0.12	49.45	0.0010119	12.35	988.2	0.08097	207.0	2591	2384	0.6966	8.085
0.13	51.07	0.0010126	11.46	987.6	0.08726	213.8	2594	2380	0.7174	8.057
0.14	52.58	0.0010133	10.69	986.9	0.09354	220.1	2596	2376	0.7368	8.031
0.15	54.00	0.0010140	10.02	986.2	0.09980	226.1	2599	2373	0.7550	8.007
0.16	55.34	0.0010147	9.429	985.5	0.10600	231.7	2601	2369	0.7722	7.984
0.17	56.61	0.0010153	8.909	984.9	0.1123	236.9	2603	2366	0.7884	7.963
0.18	57.82	0.0010159	8.444	984.3	0.1185	241.9	2605	2363	0.8038	7.944
0.19	58.98	0.0010165	8.025	983.8	0.1247	246.7	2607	2360	0.8183	7.925
0.20	60.08	0.0010171	7.647	983.2	0.1308	251.4	2609	2358	0.8321	7.907
0.21	61.14	0.0010177	7.304	982.6	0.1369	255.9	2611	2355	0.8453	7.890
0.22	62.16	0.0010183	6.992	982.0	0.1430	260.2	2613	2353	0.8581	7.874
0.23	63.14	0.0010188	6.708	981.5	0.1491	264.3	2614	2350	0.8703	7.859
0.24	64.08	0.0010193	6.445	981.1	0.1551	268.2	2616	2348	0.8821	7.884
0.25	64.99	0.0010199	6.202	980.5	0.1612	272.0	2618	2346	0.8934	7.830
0.26	65.88	0.0010204	5.977	980.0	0.1673	275.7	2620	2344	0.9043	7.816
0.27	66.73	0.0010209	5.769	979.5	0.1733	279.3	2621	2342	0.9147	7.803
0.28	67.55	0.0010214	5.576	979.0	0.1793	282.7	2623	2340	0.9248	7.791
0.29	68.35	0.0010218	5.395	978.7	0.1853	286.0	2624	2338	0.9346	7.779
0.30	69.12	0.0010222	5.226	978.3	0.1913	289.3	2625	2336	0.9441	7.769
0.32	70.60	0.0010232	4.922	977.3	0.2032	295.5	2627	2332	0.9625	7.745
0.34	72.02	0.0010240	4.650	976.6	0.2151	301.5	2630	2328	0.9796	7.724
0.36	73.36	0.0010248	4.407	975.8	0.2269	307.1	2632	2325	0.9958	7.705
0.38	74.64	0.0010256	4.189	975.0	0.2387	312.5	2634	2322	1.0113	7.687
0.40	75.88	0.0010264	3.994	974.3	0.2504	317.7	2636	2318	1.0261	7.670
0.45	78.75	0.0010282	3.574	972.6	0.2797	329.6	2641	2311	1.0601	7.629
0.50	81.35	0.0010299	3.239	971.0	0.3087	340.6	2645	2304	1.0910	7.593
0.55	83.74	0.0010315	2.963	969.5	0.3375	350.7	2649	2298	1.1193	7.561
0.60	85.95	0.0010330	2.732	968.1	0.3661	360.0	2653	2293	1.1453	7.531
0.65	88.02	0.0010345	2.534	966.7	0.3946	368.6	2657	2288	1.1693	7.504
0.70	89.97	0.0010359	2.364	965.3	0.4230	376.8	2660	2283	1.1918	7.479
0.75	91.80	0.0010372	2.216	964.1	0.4512	384.5	2663	2278	1.2130	7.456
0.80	93.52	0.0010385	2.087	962.9	0.4792	391.8	2665	2273	1.2330	7.434
0.85	95.16	0.0010397	1.972	961.8	0.5071	398.7	2668	2269	1.2518	7.414
0.90	96.72	0.0010409	1.869	960.7	0.5350	405.3	2670	2265	1.2696	7.394
0.95	98.21	0.0010421	1.777	959.6	0.5627	411.5	2673	2261	1.2865	7.376

Table 3-2   Properties of Saturated Steam (H_2O) (at a Given Pressure)   *(continued)*

Temperature	Pressure	Specific volume		Density		Specific enthalpy		Heat of vaporization	Specific entropy	
		Liquid	Vapor	Liquid	Vapor	Liquid	Vapor		Liquid	Vapor
t	p	v'	v''	ρ'	ρ''	h'	h''	r	s'	s''
°C	bar	m³/kg	m³/kg	kg/m³	kg/m³	kJ/kg	kJ/kg	kJ/kg	kJ/(kg K)	kJ/(kg K)
1.0	99.64	0.0010432	1.694	958.6	0.5903	417.4	2675	2258	1.3026	7.360
1.1	102.32	0.0010452	1.550	956.8	0.6453	428.9	2679	2250	1.3327	7.328
1.2	104.81	0.0010472	1.429	954.9	0.6999	439.4	2683	2244	1.3606	7.298
1.3	107.14	0.0010492	1.325	953.1	0.7545	449.2	2687	2238	1.3866	7.271
1.4	109.33	0.0010510	1.236	951.5	0.8088	458.5	2690	2232	1.4109	7.246
1.5	111.38	0.0010527	1.159	949.9	0.8627	467.2	2693	2226	1.4336	7.223
1.6	113.32	0.0010543	1.091	948.5	0.9164	475.4	2696	2221	1.4550	7.202
1.7	115.17	0.0010559	1.031	947.1	0.9699	483.2	2699	2216	1.4752	7.182
1.8	116.94	0.0010575	0.9773	945.6	1.023	490.7	2702	2211	1.4943	7.163
1.9	118.62	0.0010591	0.9290	944.2	1.076	497.9	2704	2206	1.5126	7.145
2.0	120.23	0.0010605	0.8854	943.0	1.129	504.8	2707	2202	1.5302	7.127
2.1	121.78	0.0010619	0.8459	941.7	1.182	511.4	2709	2198	1.5470	7.111
2.2	123.27	0.0010633	0.8098	940.5	1.235	517.8	2711	2193	1.5630	7.096
2.3	124.71	0.0010646	0.7768	939.3	1.287	524.0	2713	2189	1.5783	7.081
2.4	126.09	0.0010659	0.7465	938.2	1.340	529.8	2715	2185	1.5929	7.067
2.5	127.43	0.0010672	0.7185	937.0	1.393	535.4	2717	2182	1.6071	7.053
2.6	128.73	0.0010685	0.6925	935.9	1.444	540.9	2719	2178	1.621	7.040
2.7	129.98	0.0010697	0.6684	934.8	1.496	546.2	2721	2175	1.634	7.027
2.8	131.20	0.0010709	0.6461	933.8	1.548	551.4	2722	2171	1.647	7.015
2.9	132.39	0.0010721	0.6253	932.7	1.599	556.5	2724	2167	1.660	7.003
3.0	133.54	0.0010733	0.6057	931.7	1.651	561.4	2725	2164	1.672	6.992
3.1	134.66	0.0010744	0.5873	930.8	1.703	556.3	2727	2161	1.683	6.981
3.2	135.75	0.0010754	0.5701	929.9	1.754	571.1	2728	2157	1.695	6.971
3.3	136.82	0.0010765	0.5539	928.9	1.805	575.7	2730	2154	1.706	6.961
3.4	137.86	0.0010776	0.5386	928.0	1.857	580.2	2731	2151	1.717	6.951
3.5	138.88	0.0010786	0.5241	971.1	1.908	584.5	2732	2148	1.728	6.941
3.6	139.87	0.0010797	0.5104	926.2	1.959	588.7	2734	2145	1.738	6.932
3.7	140.84	0.0010807	0.4975	925.3	2.010	592.8	2735	2142	1.748	6.923
3.8	141.79	0.0010817	0.4852	924.5	2.061	596.8	2736	2139	1.758	6.914
3.9	142.71	0.0010827	0.4735	923.6	2.112	600.8	2737	2136	1.768	6.905
4.0	143.62	0.0010836	0.4624	922.8	2.163	604.7	2738	2133	1.777	6.897
4.1	144.51	0.0010845	0.4518	922.1	2.213	608.5	2740	2131	1.786	6.889
4.2	145.39	0.0010855	0.4416	921.2	2.264	612.3	2741	2129	1.795	6.881
4.3	146.25	0.0010865	0.4391	920.4	2.315	616.1	2742	2126	1.804	6.873
4.4	147.09	0.0010874	0.4227	919.6	2.366	619.8	2743	2123	1.812	6.865
4.5	147.92	0.0010883	0.4139	918.9	2.416	623.4	2744	2121	1.821	6.857
4.6	148.73	0.0010892	0.4054	918.1	2.467	626.9	2745	2118	1.829	6.850
4.7	149.53	0.0010901	0.3973	917.3	2.517	630.3	2746	2116	1.837	6.843
4.8	150.41	0.0010910	0.3895	916.6	2.568	633.7	2747	2113	1.845	6.835
4.9	151.08	0.0010918	0.3819	915.9	2.618	639.9	2748	2111	1.853	6.828
5.0	151.84	0.0010927	0.3747	915.2	2.669	640.1	2749	2109	1.860	6.822
5.2	153.32	0.0010943	0.3612	913.8	2.769	646.5	2750	2104	1.875	6.809
5.4	154.76	0.0010960	0.3485	912.4	2.869	652.7	2752	2099	1.890	6.796
5.6	156.16	0.0010976	0.3368	911.1	2.969	658.8	2754	2095	1.904	6.784
5.8	157.52	0.0010992	0.3258	909.8	3.069	664.7	2755	2090	1.918	6.772
6.0	158.84	0.0011007	0.3156	908.5	3.169	670.5	2757	2086	1.931	6.761
6.2	160.12	0.0011022	0.3060	907.3	3.268	676.0	2758	2082	1.944	6.750
6.4	161.37	0.0011037	0.2970	906.0	3.367	681.5	2760	2078	1.956	6.739
6.6	162.59	0.0011052	0.2885	904.8	3.467	686.9	2761	2074	1.968	6.729
6.8	163.79	0.0011066	0.2804	903.7	3.566	692.1	2762	2070	1.980	6.719
7.0	164.96	0.0011081	0.2728	902.4	3.666	697.2	2764	2067	1.992	6.709
7.2	166.10	0.0011095	0.2656	901.3	3.765	702.2	2765	2063	2.003	6.699
7.4	167.21	0.0011109	0.2588	900.2	3.864	707.1	2766	2059	2.014	6.690
7.6	168.30	0.0011123	0.2523	899.0	3.963	711.8	2767	2055	2.025	6.681
7.8	169.37	0.0011136	0.2462	898.0	4.062	716.4	2768	2052	2.036	6.672

Table 3-2 Properties of Saturated Steam (H₂O) (at a Given Pressure) *(continued)*

Temperature	Pressure	Specific volume		Density		Specific enthalpy		Heat of vaporization	Specific entropy	
		Liquid	Vapor	Liquid	Vapor	Liquid	Vapor		Liquid	Vapor
t	p	v'	v''	ρ'	ρ''	h'	h''	r	s'	s''
°C	bar	m³/kg	m³/kg	kg/m³	kg/m³	kJ/kg	kJ/kg	kJ/kg	kJ/(kg K)	kJ/(kg K)
8.0	170.42	0.0011149	0.2403	896.9	4.161	720.9	2769	2048	2.046	6.663
8.2	171.44	0.0011162	0.2347	895.9	4.260	725.4	2770	2045	2.056	6.655
8.4	172.44	0.0011175	0.2294	894.9	4.359	729.8	2771	2041	2.066	6.647
8.6	173.43	0.0011187	0.2243	893.9	4.458	734.2	2772	2038	2.076	6.639
8.8	174.40	0.0011200	0.2195	892.9	4.556	738.6	2773	2034	2.085	6.631
9.0	175.35	0.0011213	0.2149	891.8	4.654	742.8	2774	2031	2.094	6.623
9.2	176.29	0.0011225	0.2104	890.9	4.753	746.9	2775	2028	2.103	6.615
9.4	177.21	0.0011237	0.2061	889.9	4.852	750.9	2776	2025	2.112	6.608
9.6	178.12	0.0011249	0.2020	889.0	4.949	754.8	2777	2022	2.121	6.601
9.8	179.01	0.0011261	0.1982	888.0	5.045	758.8	2778	2019	2.130	6.594
10.0	179.88	0.0011273	0.1946	887.1	5.139	762.7	2778	2015	2.138	6.587
10.5	182.00	0.0011303	0.1856	884.7	5.388	772.1	2779	2007	2.159	6.570
11.0	184.05	0.0011331	0.1775	882.5	5.634	781.1	2781	2000	2.179	6.554
11.5	186.04	0.0011358	0.1701	880.4	5.879	789.8	2783	1993	2.198	6.538
12.0	187.95	0.0011385	0.1633	878.3	6.124	798.3	2785	1987	2.216	6.523
12.5	189.80	0.0011412	0.1570	876.3	6.369	806.5	2786	1980	2.234	6.509
13.0	191.60	0.0011438	0.1512	874.3	6.614	814.5	2787	1973	2.251	6.495
13.5	193.34	0.0011464	0.1458	872.3	6.859	822.3	2789	1967	2.268	6.482
14.0	195.04	0.0011490	0.1408	870.3	7.103	830.0	2790	1960	2.284	6.469
14.5	196.68	0.0011515	0.1361	868.4	7.348	837.4	2791	1954	2.299	6.457
15.0	198.28	0.0011539	0.1317	866.6	7.593	844.6	2792	1947	2.314	6.445
15.5	199.84	9.0011563	0.1276	864.8	7.837	851.5	2793	1941	2.329	6.433
16.0	201.36	0.0011586	0.1238	863.1	8.080	858.3	2793	1935	2.344	6.422
16.5	202.85	0.0011609	0.1201	861.4	8.325	865.0	2794	1929	2.358	6.411
17.0	204.30	0.0011632	0.1167	859.7	8.569	871.6	2795	1923	2.371	6.400
17.5	205.72	0.0011655	0.1135	858.0	8.812	878.1	2796	1918	2.384	6.389
18.0	207.10	0.0011678	0.1104	856.3	9.058	884.4	2796	1912	2.397	6.379
18.5	208.45	0.0011700	0.1075	854.7	9.303	890.6	2797	1907	2.410	6.369
19.0	209.78	0.0011722	0.1047	853.1	9.549	896.6	2798	1901	2.422	6.359
19.5	211.09	0.0011744	0.1021	851.5	9.795	902.6	2799	1896	2.435	6.350
20.0	212.37	0.0011766	0.09958	849.9	10.041	908.5	2799	1891	2.447	6.340
20.5	213.62	0.0011788	0.09719	848.3	10.29	914.2	2800	1886	2.458	6.331
21.0	214.84	0.0011809	0.09492	846.8	10.54	919.8	2800	1880	2.470	6.322
21.5	216.05	0.0011830	0.09276	845.3	10.78	925.4	2800	1875	2.481	6.314
22.0	217.24	0.0011851	0.09068	843.8	11.03	930.9	2801	1870	2.492	6.305
22.5	218.41	0.0011872	0.08869	842.3	11.28	936.4	2801	1865	2.503	6.297
23.0	219.55	0.0011892	0.08679	840.9	11.52	941.5	2801	1860	2.514	6.288
23.5	220.67	0.0011912	0.08498	839.5	11.77	946.7	2802	1855	2.524	6.280
24.0	221.77	0.0011932	0.08324	838.1	12.01	951.8	2802	1850	2.534	6.272
24.5	222.85	0.0011952	0.08156	836.7	12.26	956.8	2802	1845	2.544	6.264
25.0	223.93	0.0011972	0.07993	835.3	12.51	961.8	2802	1840	2.554	6.256
25.5	224.99	0.0011992	0.07837	833.9	12.76	966.8	2803	1836	2.564	6.249
26.0	226.03	0.0012012	0.07688	835.2	13.01	971.7	2803	1831	2.573	6.242
26.5	227.05	0.0012031	0.07545	831.2	13.25	976.6	2803	1826	2.582	6.234
27.0	228.06	0.0012050	0.07406	829.9	13.50	981.3	2803	1822	2.592	6.227
27.5	239.06	0.0012069	0.07271	828.6	13.75	985.9	2803	1817	2.602	6.220
28.0	230.04	0.0012088	0.07141	827.3	14.00	990.4	2803	1813	2.611	6.213
28.5	231.01	0.0012107	0.07016	826.0	14.25	994.9	2803	1808	2.620	6.206
29.0	231.96	0.0012126	0.06895	824.7	14.50	999.4	2803	1804	2.628	6.199
29.5	232.90	0.0012145	0.06778	823.4	14.75	1003.8	2804	1800	2.637	6.193
30	233.83	0.0012163	0.06665	822.2	15.00	1008.3	2804	1796	2.646	6.186
31	235.66	0.0012201	0.06450	819.6	15.50	1016.9	2804	1787	2.662	6.173
32	237.44	0.0012238	0.06246	817.1	16.01	1025.3	2803	1778	2.679	6.161
33	239.18	0.0012274	0.06055	814.7	16.52	1033.7	2803	1769	2.695	6.149
34	240.88	0.0012310	0.05875	812.3	17.02	1041.9	2803	1761	2.710	6.137

Temperature	Pressure	Specific volume		Density		Specific enthalpy		Heat of vaporization	Specific entropy	
		Liquid	Vapor	Liquid	Vapor	Liquid	Vapor		Liquid	Vapor
t	p	v'	v''	ρ'	ρ''	h'	h''	r	s'	s''
°C	bar	m³/kg	m³/kg	kg/m³	kg/m³	kJ/kg	kJ/kg	kJ/kg	kJ/(kg K)	kJ/(kg K)
35	242.54	0.0012345	0.05704	810.0	17.53	1049.8	2803	1753	2.725	6.125
36	244.16	0.0012380	0.05543	807.8	18.04	1057.5	2802	1745	2.740	6.113
37	245.75	0.0012415	0.05391	805.5	18.55	1065.2	2802	1737	2.757	6.102
38	247.31	0.0012450	0.05246	803.2	19.06	1072.7	2802	1729	2.769	6.091
39	248.84	0.0012485	0.05108	801.0	19.58	1080.2	2801	1721	2.783	6.081
40	250.33	0.0012520	0.04977	798.7	20.09	1087.5	2801	1713	2.796	6.070
41	251.80	0.0012554	0.04852	796.6	20.61	1094.7	2800	1705	2.810	6.059
42	253.24	0.0012588	0.04732	794.4	21.13	1101.7	2800	1698	2.823	6.049
43	254.66	0.0012622	0.04617	792.3	21.66	1108.5	2799	1691	2.836	6.039
44	256.05	0.0012656	0.04508	790.1	22.18	1115.3	2798	1683	2.849	6.029
45	257.41	0.0012690	0.04404	788.0	22.71	1122.1	2798	1676	2.862	6.020
46	258.75	0.0012724	0.04305	785.9	23.23	1128.8	2797	1668	2.874	6.010
47	260.07	0.0012757	0.04210	783.9	23.76	1135.4	2796	1661	2.886	6.001
48	261.37	0.0012790	0.04118	781.9	24.29	1141.8	2796	1654	2.898	5.991
49	262.65	0.0012824	0.04029	779.8	24.82	1148.2	2795	1647	2.909	5.982
50	263.91	0.0012857	0.03944	777.8	25.35	1154.4	2794	1640	2.921	5.973
51	265.15	0.0012890	0.03863	775.8	25.89	1160.6	2793	1632	2.932	5.964
52	266.38	0.0012923	0.03784	773.8	26.43	1166.8	2792	1625	2.943	5.956
53	267.58	0.0012955	0.03708	771.9	26.97	1172.9	2791	1618	2.954	5.947
54	268.77	0.0012988	0.03635	769.9	27.51	1179.0	2791	1612	2.965	5.939
55	269.94	0.0013021	0.03564	768.0	28.06	1184.9	2790	1604.6	2.976	5.930
56	271.10	0.0013054	0.03495	766.0	28.61	1190.8	2789	1597.7	2.987	5.922
57	272.24	0.0013087	0.03429	764.1	29.16	1196.6	2788	1591.0	2.997	5.914
58	273.36	0.0013120	0.03365	762.2	29.72	1202.4	2786	1584.3	3.007	5.906
59	274.47	0.0013152	0.03303	760.3	30.28	1208.2	2786	1577.6	3.017	5.898
60	275.56	0.0013185	0.03243	758.4	30.84	1213.9	2785	1570.8	3.027	5.890
61	276.64	0.0013217	0.03185	756.6	31.40	1219.6	2784	1564.1	3.037	5.882
62	277.71	0.0013250	0.03130	754.7	31.95	1225.1	2782	1557.4	3.047	5.874
63	278.76	0.0013282	0.03076	752.9	32.51	1230.6	2781	1550.7	3.057	5.866
64	279.80	0.0013314	0.03024	751.1	33.07	1236.0	2780	1544.1	3.066	5.859
65	280.83	0.0013347	0.02973	749.2	33.64	1241.3	2779	1537.5	3.076	5.851
66	281.85	0.0013380	0.02923	747.4	34.21	1246.6	2778	1530.9	3.085	5.844
67	282.86	0.0013412	0.02874	745.6	34.79	1251.8	2776	1524.4	3.095	5.836
68	283.85	0.0013445	0.02827	743.8	35.37	1257.0	2775	1517.9	3.104	5.829
69	284.83	0.0013478	0.02782	741.9	35.95	1262.2	2773	1511.4	3.113	5.822
70	285.80	0.0013510	0.02737	740.2	36.54	1267.4	2772	1504.9	3.122	5.814
71	286.76	0.0013542	0.02694	738.4	37.12	1272.5	2771	1498.4	3.131	5.807
72	287.71	0.0013574	0.02652	736.7	37.71	1277.6	2769	1492.0	3.140	5.800
73	288.65	0.0013607	0.02611	734.9	38.30	1282.6	2768	1485.6	3.149	5.793
74	289.58	0.0013640	0.02571	733.1	38.89	1287.6	2767	1479.2	3.158	5.786
75	290.50	0.0013673	0.02532	713.4	39.49	1292.7	2766	1472.8	3.166	5.779
76	291.41	0.0013706	0.02494	729.6	40.09	1297.7	2764	1466.4	3.174	5.772
77	292.32	0.0013739	0.02457	727.8	40.70	1302.6	2763	1460.0	3.183	5.765
78	293.22	0.0013772	0.02421	726.1	41.30	1307.4	2761	1453.7	3.192	5.758
79	294.10	0.0013805	0.02386	724.4	41.91	1312.2	2759	1447.4	3.200	5.751
80	294.98	0.0013838	0.02352	722.6	42.52	1317.0	2758	1441.1	3.208	5.745
81	295.85	0.0013872	0.02318	720.9	43.14	1321.8	2757	1434.8	3.216	5.738
82	296.71	0.0013905	0.02285	719.2	43.76	1326.6	2755	1428.5	3.224	5.731
83	297.56	0.0013938	0.02253	717.5	44.38	1331.4	2753	1422.2	3.232	5.724
84	298.40	0.0013972	0.02222	715.7	45.00	1336.1	2752	1416.0	3.240	5.717
85	299.24	0.0014005	0.02192	714.0	45.62	1340.8	2751	1409.8	3.248	5.711
86	300.07	0.0014039	0.02162	712.3	46.25	1345.4	2749	1403.7	3.255	5.704
87	300.89	0.0014073	0.02132	710.6	46.90	1350.1	2747	1397.6	3.263	5.698
88	301.71	0.0014106	0.02103	708.9	47.55	1354.7	2746	1391.5	3.271	5.691
89	302.52	0.0014140	0.02075	707.2	48.19	1359.2	2744	1385.4	3.279	5.685

Table 3-2 Properties of Saturated Steam (H₂O) (at a Given Pressure)   *(continued)*

Temperature	Pressure	Specific volume		Density		Specific enthalpy		Heat of vaporization	Specific entropy	
		Liquid	Vapor	Liquid	Vapor	Liquid	Vapor		Liquid	Vapor
t	p	v'	v''	ρ'	ρ''	h'	h''	r	s'	s''
°C	bar	m³/kg	m³/kg	kg/m³	kg/m³	kJ/kg	kJ/kg	kJ/kg	kJ/(kg K)	kJ/(kg K)
90	303.32	0.0014174	0.02048	705.5	48.83	1363.7	2743	1379.3	3.287	5.678
91	304.11	0.0014208	0.02021	703.8	49.48	1368.2	2741	1373.2	3.294	5.672
92	304.90	0.0014242	0.01995	702.1	50.13	1372.7	2740	1367.0	3.301	5.665
93	305.67	0.0014276	0.01969	700.5	50.79	1377.1	2738	1360.9	3.309	5.659
94	306.45	0.0014310	0.01944	698.8	51.45	1381.5	2736	1354.7	3.316	5.653
95	307.22	0.0014345	0.01919	697.1	52.11	1385.9	2734	1348.4	3.324	5.646
96	307.98	0.0014380	0.01895	695.4	52.77	1390.2	2732	1342.1	3.331	5.640
97	308.74	0.0014415	0.01871	693.7	53.44	1394.2	2730	1335.8	3.338	5.634
98	309.49	0.0014450	0.01848	692.0	54.11	1398.9	2728	1329.5	3.346	5.628
99	310.23	0.0014486	0.01825	690.3	54.79	1403.3	2726	1323.2	3.353	5.621
100	310.96	0.0014521	0.01803	688.7	55.46	1407.7	2725	1317.0	3.360	5.615
102	312.42	0.0014592	0.01759	685.3	56.85	1416.4	2721	1304.6	3.374	5.602
104	313.86	0.0014664	0.01716	681.9	58.27	1425.0	2717	1292.3	3.388	5.590
106	315.28	0.0014736	0.01675	678.6	59.70	1433.5	2713	1280.0	3.402	5.578
108	316.67	0.0014808	0.01636	675.3	61.13	1441.9	2709	1267.3	3.416	5.565
110	318.04	0.001489	0.01598	671.6	62.58	1450.2	2705	1255.4	3.430	5.553
112	319.39	0.001496	0.01561	668.4	64.05	1458.4	2701	1243.0	3.443	5.541
114	320.73	0.001503	0.01526	665.3	65.54	1466.6	2697	1230.6	3.457	5.528
116	322.05	0.001511	0.01491	661.8	67.06	1474.8	2693	1218.3	3.470	5.516
118	323.35	0.001519	0.01458	658.3	68.59	1483.0	2689	1205.9	3.483	5.504
120	324.63	0.001527	0.01426	654.9	70.13	1491.1	2685	1193.5	3.496	5.492
122	325.90	0.001535	0.01395	651.5	71.70	1499.2	2680	1181.0	3.509	5.480
124	327.15	0.001543	0.01364	648.1	73.30	1507.3	2676	1168.5	3.522	5.468
126	328.39	0.001551	0.01334	644.7	74.94	1515.4	2671	1156.0	3.535	5.456
128	329.61	0.001559	0.01305	641.4	76.61	1523.5	2667	1143.4	3.548	5.444
130	330.81	0.001567	0.01277	638.2	78.30	1531.5	2662	1130.8	3.561	5.432
132	332.00	0.001576	0.01250	634.5	80.00	1539.5	2658	1118.2	3.573	5.420
134	333.18	0.001585	0.01224	630.9	81.72	1547.3	2653	1105.5	3.586	5.408
136	334.34	0.001594	0.01198	627.4	83.47	1555.1	2648	1092.7	3.598	5.396
138	335.49	0.001602	0.01173	624.2	85.25	1562.9	2643	1079.9	3.610	5.384
140	336.63	0.001611	0.01149	620.7	87.03	1570.8	2638	1066.9	3.623	5.372
142	337.75	0.001620	0.01125	617.3	88.89	1578.7	2633	1053.8	3.636	5.360
144	338.86	0.001629	0.01101	613.9	90.83	1586.6	2628	1040.7	3.648	5.348
146	339.96	0.001638	0.01078	610.5	92.76	1594.5	2622	1027.6	3.660	5.336
148	341.04	0.001648	0.01056	606.8	94.69	1602	2617	1014.5	3.672	5.323
150	342.11	0.001658	0.01035	603.1	92.62	1610	2611	1001.1	3.684	5.310
152	343.18	0.001668	0.01014	599.5	98.62	1618	2606	987.5	3.697	5.297
154	344.23	0.001678	0.009928	595.9	100.72	1626	2600	973.8	3.709	5.285
156	345.27	0.001688	0.009720	592.4	102.9	1634	2594	960.0	3.721	5.273
158	346.30	0.001699	0.009517	588.6	105.1	1642	2588	946.1	3.733	5.260
160	347.32	0.001710	0.009318	584.8	107.3	1650	2582	932.0	3.746	5.247
162	348.33	0.001721	0.009124	581.1	109.6	1658	2576	917.7	3.758	5.233
164	349.32	0.001732	0.008934	577.4	111.9	1666	2569	903.2	3.770	5.219
166	350.31	0.001744	0.008747	573.4	114.3	1674	2562	888.4	3.783	5.205
168	351.29	0.001756	0.008563	569.5	116.8	1682	2555	873.4	3.795	5.191
170	352.26	0.001768	0.008382	565.6	119.3	1690	2548	848.3	3.807	5.177
172	353.21	0.001781	0.008203	561.5	121.9	1698	2541	843.0	3.820	5.163
174	354.17	0.001794	0.008025	557.4	124.6	1707	2534	827.4	3.832	5.149
176	355.11	0.001808	0.007848	553.1	127.4	1715	2526	811.4	3.845	5.135
178	356.04	0.001822	0.007674	548.8	130.3	1723	2518	795.0	3.858	5.121
180	356.96	0.001837	0.007504	544.4	133.2	1732	2510	778.2	3.871	5.107
182	357.87	0.001853	0.007336	539.7	136.3	1741	2502	761.2	3.884	5.092
184	358.78	0.001870	0.007169	534.8	139.5	1749	2493	743.9	3.898	5.076
186	359.67	0.001887	0.007003	529.9	142.8	1758	2484	726.4	3.911	5.060
188	360.56	0.001904	0.00684	525.2	146.2	1767	2475	708.5	3.925	5.044

Table 3-2 Properties of Saturated Steam (H₂O) (at a Given Pressure)   *(continued)*

Temperature	Pressure	Specific volume		Density		Specific enthalpy		Heat of vaporization	Specific entropy	
		Liquid	Vapor	Liquid	Vapor	Liquid	Vapor		Liquid	Vapor
t	p	v'	v''	ρ'	ρ''	h'	h''	r	s'	s''
°C	bar	m³/kg	m³/kg	kg/m³	kg/m³	kJ/kg	kJ/kg	kJ/kg	kJ/(kg K)	kJ/(kg K)
190	361.44	0.001921	0.00668	520.6	149.7	1776	2466	690	3.938	5.027
192	362.31	0.001940	0.00652	515.5	153.4	1785	2456	671	3.952	5.009
194	363.17	0.001961	0.00636	509.9	157.3	1795	2446	651	3.967	4.990
196	364.02	0.001985	0.00619	503.8	161.6	1805	2435	630	3.982	4.970
198	364.87	0.00201	0.00602	497.5	166.1	1816	2423	607	3.998	4.949
200	365.71	0.00204	0.00585	490.2	170.9	1827	2410	583	4.015	4.928
202	366.54	0.00207	0.00568	483.1	176.0	1838	2397	559	4.032	4.906
204	367.37	0.00210	0.00551	476.2	181.4	1849	2383	534	4.049	4.883
206	368.18	0.00213	0.00534	469.5	187.2	1861	2369	508	4.067	4.858
208	368.99	0.00217	0.00516	460.8	193.6	1874	2353	479	4.087	4.832
210	369.79	0.00221	0.00498	452.5	200.7	1888	2336	448	4.108	4.803
212	370.58	0.00226	0.00480	442.5	208.5	1903	2316	413	4.131	4.771
214	371.4	0.00232	0.00460	431.0	217.4	1920	2294	374	4.157	4.734
216	372.2	0.00239	0.00436	418.4	229.3	1940	2269	329	4.188	4.692
218	372.9	0.00249	0.00402	401.6	248.7	1965	2233	268	4.223	4.645
220	373.7	0.00273	0.00367	366.3	272.5	2016	2168	152	4.303	4.591
221.29	374.15	0.00326	0.00326	306.75	306.75	2100	2100	0	4.430	4.430

Table 3-3 Critical Constants of Water (H₂O)

Temperature	Pressure	Specific volume	Density	Specific enthalpy	Specific entropy
t_{cr}	p_{cr}	v_{cr}	ρ_{cr}	h_{cr}	s_{cr}
°C	bar	m³/kg	kg/m³	kJ/kg	kJ/(kg K)
374.15	221.29	0.00326	306.75	2100	4.430

Table 3-4 Properties of Superheated Steam (H_2O)

Pressure $p=$	0.01 bar			0.04 bar			0.05 bar			0.06 bar		
Tempera-ture	t_s = 6.92 °C h'' = 2 513 kJ/kg v'' = 129.9 m³/kg s'' = 8.975 kJ/(kg K)			t_s = 28.979 °C h'' = 2 554 kJ/kg v'' = 34.81 m³/kg s'' = 8.473 kJ/(kg K)			t_s = 32.88 °C h'' = 2 561 kJ/kg v'' = 28.19 m³/kg s'' = 8.393 kJ/(kg K)			t_s = 36.18 °C h'' = 2 567 kJ/kg v'' = 23.74 m³/kg s'' = 8.328 kJ/(kg K)		
t	v	h	s	v	h	s	v	h	s	v	h	s
°C	m³/kg	kJ/kg	kJ/(kg K)	m³/kg	kJ/kg	kJ/(kg K)	m³/kg	kJ/kg	kJ/(kg K)	m³/kg	kJ/kg	kJ/(kg K)
0	0.0010002	0.0	0.0000	0.0010002	0.0	0.0000	0.0010002	0.0	0.0000	0.0010002	0.0	0.0000
10	131.3	2518	8.995	0.0010003	41.9	0.1511	0.0010003	41.9	0.1511	0.0010003	41.9	0.1511
20	136.0	2537	9.056	0.0010018	83.7	0.2964	0.0010018	83.7	0.2964	0.0010018	83.7	0.2964
30	140.7	2556	9.117	34.95	2556	8.470	0.0010044	125.6	0.4363	0.0010044	125.6	0.4363
40	145.4	2575	9.178	36.12	2574	8.537	28.87	2574	8.434	24.72	2574	8.350
50	150.0	2594	9.238	37.29	2593	8.595	29.80	2593	8.492	24.82	2593	8.407
60	154.7	2613	9.296	38.45	2612	8.651	30.73	2612	8.549	25.59	2612	8.464
70	159.4	2632	9.352	39.60	2631	8.707	31.65	2631	8.605	26.36	2631	8.520
80	164.0	2651	9.406	40.75	2650	8.762	32.58	2650	8.659	27.13	2650	8.574
90	168.7	2669	9.459	41.91	2669	8.815	33.50	2669	8.712	27.91	2669	8.627
100	173.3	2688	9.510	43.07	2668	8.867	34.43	2688	8.764	28.68	2688	8.679
110	177.9	2707	9.560	44.23	2707	8.917	35.35	2707	8.814	29.45	2707	8.729
120	182.6	2726	9.609	45.39	2726	8.966	36.28	2726	8.863	30.22	2726	8.778
130	187.2	2745	9.656	46.54	2745	9.014	37.20	2745	8.911	30.99	2745	8.826
140	191.9	2764	9.703	47.69	2764	9.060	38.13	2764	8.957	31.76	2764	8.873
150	196.5	2783	9.748	48.85	2783	9.105	39.05	2783	9.002	32.53	2783	8.918
160	201.1	2803	9.793	50.01	2803	9.150	39.98	2803	9.047	33.30	2803	8.963
170	205.8	2822	9.837	51.16	2822	9.195	40.90	2822	9.092	34.07	2822	9.007
180	210.4	2841	9.880	52.31	2841	9.238	41.83	2841	9.135	34.84	2841	9.050
190	215.1	2860	9.922	53.47	2860	9.280	42.75	2860	9.177	35.61	2860	9.092
200	219.8	2880	9.963	54.63	2880	9.321	43.68	2880	9.219	36.38	2880	9.134
210	224.4	2899	10.004	55.78	2899	9.362	44.60	2899	9.259	37.15	2899	9.175
220	229.1	2918	10.044	56.93	2918	9.402	45.53	2918	9.299	37.92	2918	9.215
230	233.7	2938	10.083	58.09	2938	9.441	46.45	2938	9.338	38.69	2938	9.254
240	238.3	2958	10.121	59.24	2958	9.479	47.37	2958	9.376	39.46	2958	9.292
250	243.0	2977	10.159	60.40	2977	9.517	48.30	2977	9.414	40.23	2977	9.330
260	247.6	2997	10.196	61.56	2997	9.554	49.22	2997	9.451	41.00	2997	9.367
280	256.9	3037	10.269	63.87	3037	9.627	51.07	3037	9.524	42.54	3037	9.440
300	266.2	3077	10.340	66.18	3077	9.698	52.92	3077	9.595	44.08	3077	9.511
310	270.8	3097	10.374	67.33	3097	9.732	53.84	3097	9.630	44.85	3097	9.545
320	275.4	3117	10.408	68.49	3117	9.766	54.77	3117	9.664	45.62	3117	9.579
330	280.1	3137	10.441	69.64	3137	9.800	55.69	3137	9.697	46.39	3137	9.613
340	284.8	3157	10.474	70.80	3157	9.833	56.62	3157	9.730	47.16	3157	9.646
350	289.5	3177	10.507	71.96	3177	9.866	57.74	3177	9.763	47.93	3177	9.679
360	294.1	3198	10.539	73.11	3198	9.899	58.47	3198	9.796	48.70	3198	9.711
380	303.4	3238	10.603	75.42	3238	9.962	60.32	3238	9.859	50.24	3238	9.775
400	312.6	3280	10.665	77.73	3280	10.024	62.16	3280	9.921	51.78	3280	9.837
410	317.3	3301	10.696	78.89	3301	10.055	63.08	3301	9.952	52.55	3301	9.868
420	321.9	3321	10.726	80.04	3321	10.085	64.00	3321	9.982	53.32	3321	9.898
430	326.6	3342	10.756	81.20	3342	10.115	64.92	3342	10.012	54.09	3342	9.928
440	331.2	3363	10.786	82.35	3363	10.145	65.85	3363	10.042	54.86	3363	9.958
450	335.8	3384	10.815	83.51	3384	10.174	66.77	3384	10.071	55.63	3384	9.987
460	340.5	3405	10.844	84.66	3405	10.203	67.70	3405	10.100	56.40	3405	10.016
480	349.8	3448	10.902	86.97	3448	10.261	69.54	3448	10.158	57.94	3448	10.074
500	359.0	3490	10.958	89.28	3490	10.317	71.39	3490	10.214	59.84	3490	10.130
510	363.7	3512	10.986	90.44	3512	10.345	72.31	3512	10.242	60.25	3512	10.158
520	368.3	3533	11.014	91.59	3533	10.373	73.24	3533	10.270	61.02	3533	10.186
530	372.9	3555	11.041	92.75	3555	10.400	74.16	3555	10.297	61.79	3555	10.213
540	377.6	3576	11.068	93.90	3576	10.427	75.09	3576	10.324	62.56	3576	10.240
550	382.2	3598	11.095	95.06	3598	10.454	76.01	3598	10.351	63.34	3598	10.267
560	386.9	3619	11.122	96.22	3619	10.481	76.94	3619	10.378	64.11	3619	10.294
580	396.2	3663	11.174	98.53	3663	10.533	78.79	3663	10.430	65.65	3663	10.346
600	405.6	3707	11.226	100.84	3707	10.585	80.64	3707	10.482	67.19	3707	10.398
610	410.2	3729	11.251	102.00	3729	10.610	81.57	3729	10.507	67.96	3729	10.423
620	414.8	3751	11.276	103.15	3751	10.635	82.49	3751	10.532	68.73	3751	10.448
630	419.4	3773	11.301	104.31	3773	10.660	83.42	3773	10.557	69.50	3773	10.473
640	424.1	3796	11.325	105.46	3796	10.684	84.34	3796	10.581	70.27	3796	10.497
650	428.7	3818	11.349	106.62	3818	10.709	85.27	3818	10.605	71.04	3818	10.521
660	433.4	3841	11.373	107.77	3841	10.733	86.19	3841	10.629	71.81	3841	10.545
680	442.6	3886	11.421	110.08	3886	10.781	88.04	3886	10.677	73.35	3886	10.593
700	451.9	3931	11.468	112.39	3931	10.828	89.88	3931	10.725	74.89	3931	10.640

Table 3-4   Properties of Superheated Steam (H₂O)   (continued)

Pressure $p=$	0.07 bar			0.08 bar			0.09 bar			0.10 bar		
Tempera-ture	$t_s = 39.03\ ^\circ C$ $h'' = 2\ 572\ kJ/kg$ $v'' = 20.53\ m^3/kg$ $s'' = 8.274\ kJ/(kg\ K)$			$t_s = 41.54\ ^\circ C$ $h'' = 2\ 576\ kJ/kg$ $v'' = 18.10\ m^3/kg$ $s'' = 8.227\ kJ/(kg\ K)$			$t_s = 43.79\ ^\circ C$ $h'' = 2\ 580\ kJ/kg$ $v'' = 16.20\ m^3/kg$ $s'' = 8.186\ kJ/(kg\ K)$			$t_s = 45.84\ ^\circ C$ $h'' = 2\ 584\ kJ/kg$ $v'' = 14.68\ m^3/kg$ $s'' = 8.149\ kJ/(kg\ K)$		
t	v	h	s	v	h	s	v	h	s	v	h	s
°C	m³/kg	kJ/kg	kJ/(kg K)	m³/kg	kJ/kg	kJ/(kg K)	m³/kg	kJ/kg	kJ/(kg K)	m³/kg	kJ/kg	kJ/(kg K)
0	0.0010002	0.0	0.0000	0.0010002	0.0	0.0000	0.0010002	0.0	0.0000	0.0010002	0.0	0.0000
10	0.0010003	41.9	0.1511	0.0010003	41.9	0.1511	0.0010003	41.9	0.1511	0.0010003	41.9	0.1511
20	0.0010018	83.7	0.2964	0.0010018	83.7	0.2964	0.0010018	83.7	0.2964	0.0010018	83.7	0.2964
30	0.0010044	125.6	0.4363	0.0010044	125.6	0.4363	0.0010044	125.6	0.4363	0.0010044	125.6	0.4363
40	20.94	2574	8.279	0.0010079	167.5	0.5715	0.0010079	167.5	0.5715	0.0010079	167.5	0.5715
50	21.27	2593	8.336	18.61	2593	8.274	16.57	2593	8.220	15.00	2592	8.170
60	21.94	2612	8.393	19.19	2612	8.331	17.09	2612	8.277	15.35	2611	8.227
70	22.60	2631	8.449	19.76	2631	8.387	17.61	2631	8.333	15.81	2630	8.283
80	23.26	2650	8.503	20.34	2650	8.441	18.12	2650	8.387	16.27	2649	8.337
90	23.92	2669	8.556	20.92	2669	8.494	18.64	2669	8.440	16.74	2669	8.390
100	24.58	2688	8.608	21.50	2688	8.546	19.16	2688	8.492	17.20	2688	8.442
110	25.24	2707	8.658	22.08	2707	8.596	19.67	2707	8.542	17.67	2707	8.493
120	25.90	2726	8.707	22.26	2726	8.645	20.19	2726	8.591	18.13	2726	8.542
130	26.26	2745	8.755	23.24	2745	8.693	20.70	2745	8.639	18.59	2745	8.589
140	27.22	2764	8.802	23.82	2764	8.740	21.22	2764	8.686	19.06	2764	8.636
150	27.88	2783	8.847	24.40	2783	8.785	21.73	2783	8.731	19.52	2783	8.682
160	28.54	2802	8.892	24.97	2802	8.830	22.25	2802	8.776	19.98	2802	8.727
170	29.20	2822	8.936	25.55	2822	8.874	22.76	2822	8.820	20.44	2822	8.771
180	29.86	2841	8.979	26.13	2841	8.917	23.28	2841	8.863	20.90	2841	8.814
190	30.52	2860	9.021	26.71	2860	8.959	23.79	2860	8.905	21.36	2860	8.856
200	31.18	2880	9.062	27.29	2880	9.000	24.31	2879	8.946	21.83	2879	8.897
210	31.84	2899	9.103	27.86	2899	9.041	24.83	2899	8.987	22.30	2899	8.938
220	32.50	2918	9.143	28.44	2918	9.081	25.34	2918	9.027	22.76	2918	8.978
230	33.16	2938	9.182	29.02	2938	9.120	25.86	2938	9.066	23.22	2938	9.017
240	33.82	2957	9.221	29.60	2957	9.159	26.37	2957	9.105	23.68	2957	9.056
250	34.48	2977	9.258	30.18	2977	9.197	26.89	2977	9.143	24.14	2977	9.094
260	35.14	2997	9.295	30.75	2997	9.234	27.40	2997	9.180	24.60	2997	9.131
280	36.46	3037	9.368	31.90	3037	9.306	28.43	3037	9.252	25.53	3037	9.203
300	37.78	3077	9.439	33.06	3077	9.377	29.46	3077	9.323	26.46	3077	9.274
310	38.44	3097	9.474	33.64	3097	9.412	29.98	3097	9.358	26.92	3097	9.309
320	39.10	3117	9.508	34.22	3117	9.446	30.49	3117	9.392	27.38	3117	9.343
330	39.76	3137	9.541	34.79	3137	9.480	31.00	3137	9.426	27.84	3137	9.377
340	40.42	3157	9.574	35.37	3157	9.513	31.51	3157	9.459	28.30	3157	9.410
350	41.08	3177	9.607	35.94	3177	9.546	32.03	3177	9.492	28.76	3177	9.443
360	41.74	3198	9.640	36.52	3198	9.578	32.54	3198	9.524	29.23	3198	9.475
380	43.06	3238	9.703	37.68	3238	9.641	33.57	3238	9.587	30.15	3238	9.539
400	44.38	3280	9.765	38.84	3280	9.704	34.60	3280	9.650	31.08	3280	9.601
410	45.04	3301	9.796	39.41	3301	9.735	35.12	3301	9.681	31.54	3301	9.632
420	45.70	3321	9.826	39.98	3321	9.765	35.63	3321	9.711	32.00	3321	9.662
430	46.36	3342	9.856	40.56	3342	9.795	36.15	3342	9.741	32.46	3342	9.692
440	47.02	3363	9.886	41.14	3363	9.825	36.66	3363	9.771	32.93	3363	9.722
450	47.68	3384	9.916	41.72	3384	9.854	37.18	3384	9.800	33.39	3384	9.751
460	48.45	3405	9.945	42.30	3405	9.883	37.69	3405	9.829	33.85	3405	9.780
480	49.66	3448	10.002	43.46	3448	9.941	38.72	3448	9.887	34.77	3448	9.838
500	50.98	3490	10.059	44.61	3490	9.997	39.75	3490	9.943	35.70	3490	9.895
510	51.64	3512	10.086	45.18	3512	10.025	40.27	3512	9.971	36.16	3512	9.922
520	52.30	3533	10.114	45.76	3533	10.053	40.78	3533	9.999	36.63	3533	9.950
530	52.96	3555	10.142	46.34	3555	10.080	41.30	3555	10.026	37.09	3555	9.977
540	53.62	3576	10.169	46.91	3576	10.107	41.81	3576	10.053	37.55	3576	10.004
550	54.28	3598	10.196	47.49	3598	10.134	42.32	3598	10.080	38.01	3598	10.031
560	54.94	3619	10.223	48.07	3619	10.161	42.83	3619	10.107	38.47	3619	10.058
580	56.26	3663	10.275	49.23	3663	10.213	43.86	3663	10.159	39.40	3663	10.110
600	57.58	3707	10.327	50.38	3707	10.265	44.89	3707	10.211	40.32	3707	10.162
610	58.24	3729	10.352	50.95	3729	10.290	45.40	3729	10.236	40.78	3729	10.187
620	58.90	3751	10.377	51.53	3751	10.315	45.92	3751	10.261	41.24	3751	10.212
630	59.56	3773	10.402	52.11	3773	10.340	46.43	3773	10.286	41.70	3773	10.237
640	60.22	3796	10.426	52.69	3796	10.365	46.95	3796	10.311	42.17	3796	10.262
650	60.88	3818	10.450	53.27	3818	10.389	47.46	3818	10.335	42.63	3818	10.286
660	61.54	3841	10.474	53.84	3841	10.413	47.98	3841	10.359	43.10	3841	10.310
680	62.86	3886	10.522	54.99	3886	10.461	49.01	3886	10.407	44.02	3886	10.358
700	64.17	3931	10.569	56.15	3931	10.508	50.04	3931	10.454	44.94	3931	10.405

Table 3-4 Properties of Superheated Steam (H₂O) *(continued)*

Pressure $p=$	0.12 bar			0.14 bar			0.16 bar			0.18 bar		
Tempera-ture	$t_s = 49.45\,°C$ $h'' = 2\,591$ kJ/kg $v'' = 12.35$ m³/kg $s'' = 8.085$ kJ/(kg K)			$t_s = 52.58\,°C$ $h'' = 2\,596$ kJ/kg $v'' = 10.69$ m³/kg $s'' = 8.031$ kJ/(kg K)			$t_s = 55.34\,°C$ $h'' = 2\,601$ kJ/kg $v'' = 9.429$ m³/kg $s'' = 7.984$ kJ/(kg K)			$t_s = 57.82\,°C$ $h'' = 2\,605$ kJ/kg $v'' = 8.444$ m³/kg $s'' = 7.944$ kJ/(kg K)		
t	v	h	s	v	h	s	v	h	s	v	h	s
°C	m³/kg	kJ/kg	kJ/(kg K)	m³/kg	kJ/kg	kJ/(kg K)	m³/kg	kJ/kg	kJ/(kg K)	m³/kg	kJ/kg	kJ/(kg K)
0	0.0010002	0.0	0.0000	0.0010002	0.0	0.0000	0.0010002	0.0	0.0000	0.0010002	0.0	0.0000
10	0.0010003	41.9	0.1511	0.0010003	41.9	0.1511	0.0010003	41.9	0.1511	0.0010003	41.9	0.1511
20	0.0010018	83.7	0.2964	0.0010018	83.7	0.2964	0.0010018	83.7	0.2964	0.0010018	83.7	0.2964
30	0.0010044	125.6	0.4363	0.0010044	125.6	0.4363	0.0010044	125.6	0.4363	0.0010044	125.6	0.4363
40	0.0010079	167.5	0.5715	0.0010079	167.5	0.5715	0.0010079	167.5	0.5715	0.0010079	167.5	0.5715
50	12.44	2592	8.086	0.0010121	209.3	0.7030	0.0010121	209.3	0.7030	0.0010121	209.3	0.7030
60	12.78	2611	8.143	10.95	2611	8.071	9.573	2610	8.009	8.497	2610	7.954
70	13.17	2630	8.199	11.28	2630	8.127	9.867	2629	8.065	8.764	2629	8.010
80	13.55	2649	8.253	11.61	2649	8.181	10.160	2649	8.120	9.024	2648	8.064
90	13.94	2668	8.306	11.94	2668	8.235	10.450	2668	8.173	9.283	2667	8.117
100	14.33	2687	8.358	12.27	2687	8.287	10.740	2687	8.225	9.542	2687	8.169
110	14.72	2706	8.408	12.61	2706	8.337	11.030	2706	8.275	9.800	2706	8.220
120	15.10	2725	8.457	12.94	2725	8.386	11.320	2725	8.324	10.058	2725	8.269
130	15.49	2744	8.505	13.27	2744	8.434	11.610	2744	8.372	10.316	2744	8.317
140	15.87	2764	8.552	13.60	2763	8.481	11.899	2763	8.419	10.574	2763	8.364
150	16.26	2783	8.598	13.93	2782	8.527	12.189	2782	8.465	10.832	2782	8.410
160	16.64	2802	8.643	14.26	2802	8.572	12.478	2802	8.510	11.090	2802	8.455
170	17.03	2822	8.687	14.59	2821	8.616	12.768	2821	8.554	11.347	2821	8.499
180	17.42	2841	8.730	14.92	2840	8.659	13.057	2840	8.597	11.605	2840	8.542
190	17.80	2860	8.772	15.25	2860	8.701	13.346	2860	8.639	11.862	2860	8.584
200	18.19	2879	8.813	15.58	2879	8.742	13.635	2879	8.680	12.120	2879	8.625
210	18.57	2898	8.854	15.91	2898	8.783	13.924	2898	8.721	12.377	2898	8.666
220	18.96	2918	8.894	16.24	2918	8.823	14.213	2918	8.761	12.634	2918	8.706
230	19.34	2937	8.933	16.57	2937	8.862	14.502	2937	8.800	12.892	2937	8.745
240	19.73	2957	8.972	16.90	2957	8.900	14.790	2957	8.838	13.149	2957	8.784
250	20.11	2977	9.010	17.23	2977	8.938	15.079	2977	8.876	13.406	2976	8.822
260	20.50	2996	9.047	17.56	2997	8.975	15.367	2997	8.913	13.663	2997	8.859
280	21.27	3036	9.119	18.22	3037	9.048	15.943	3037	8.986	14.177	3037	8.932
300	22.04	3077	9.190	18.88	3077	9.119	16.52	3077	9.057	14.690	3077	9.003
310	22.42	3097	9.225	19.21	3097	9.154	16.81	3097	9.092	14.947	3097	9.038
320	22.81	3117	9.259	19.54	3117	9.188	17.10	3117	9.126	15.204	3117	9.072
330	23.19	3137	9.292	19.87	3137	9.221	17.39	3137	9.160	15.460	3137	9.106
340	23.58	3157	9.326	20.20	3157	9.255	17.68	3157	9.193	15.716	3157	9.139
350	23.96	3177	9.359	20.53	3177	9.288	17.96	3177	9.226	15.971	3177	9.171
360	24.35	3198	9.391	20.86	3198	9.320	18.25	3198	9.258	16.23	3198	9.204
380	25.12	3238	9.455	21.52	3238	9.383	18.83	3238	9.322	16.74	3238	9.268
400	25.89	3280	9.517	22.18	3280	9.446	19.41	3280	9.384	17.26	3280	9.330
410	26.28	3301	9.548	22.51	3301	9.476	19.70	3301	9.415	17.51	3301	9.361
420	26.66	3321	9.578	22.84	3321	9.506	19.99	3321	9.445	17.76	3321	9.391
430	27.04	3342	9.608	23.17	3342	9.536	20.28	3342	9.475	18.02	3342	9.421
440	27.43	3363	9.638	23.50	3363	9.566	20.56	3363	9.504	18.27	3363	9.450
450	27.82	3384	9.667	23.83	3384	9.596	20.85	3384	9.534	18.53	3384	9.480
460	28.20	3405	9.696	24.16	3405	9.625	21.13	3405	9.563	18.78	3405	9.509
480	28.96	3448	9.754	24.82	3448	9.683	21.71	3448	9.621	19.29	3448	9.567
500	29.74	3490	9.810	25.49	3490	9.739	22.29	3490	9.678	19.80	3490	9.624
510	30.13	3512	9.838	25.82	3512	9.767	22.58	3512	9.706	20.06	3512	9.652
520	30.52	3533	9.866	26.15	3533	9.795	22.87	3533	9.734	20.32	3533	9.680
530	30.90	3555	8.894	26.48	3555	9.823	23.16	3555	9.762	20.58	3555	9.708
540	31.29	3576	9.921	26.81	3576	9.850	23.45	3576	9.789	20.83	3576	9.735
550	31.67	3598	9.948	27.14	3598	9.877	23.74	3598	9.816	21.09	3598	9.762
560	32.06	3619	9.974	27.47	3619	9.903	24.03	3619	9.842	21.35	3619	9.788
580	32.83	3663	10.026	28.13	3663	9.955	24.60	3663	9.894	21.87	3663	9.840
600	33.60	3707	10.078	28.79	3707	10.007	25.18	3707	9.945	22.39	3707	9.891
610	33.98	3729	10.103	29.12	3729	10.032	25.47	3729	9.970	22.64	3729	9.916
620	34.37	3751	10.128	29.45	3751	10.057	25.76	3751	9.995	22.90	3751	9.941
630	34.75	3773	10.153	29.78	3773	10.082	26.05	3773	10.020	23.16	3773	9.966
640	35.14	3796	10.178	30.11	3796	10.106	26.34	3796	10.045	23.41	3796	9.991
650	35.52	3818	10.202	30.44	3818	10.130	26.63	3818	10.069	23.67	3818	10.015
660	35.91	3841	10.226	30.77	3841	10.154	26.92	3841	10.093	23.92	3841	10.039
680	36.68	3886	10.274	31.42	3886	10.202	27.50	3886	10.141	24.44	3886	10.087
700	37.44	3931	10.321	32.08	3931	10.249	28.08	3931	10.188	24.95	3931	10.133

Table 3-4 Properties of Superheated Steam (H₂O) *(continued)*

Pressure p=	0.20 bar			0.30 bar			0.40 bar			0.50 bar		
Temperature	t_s = 60.08 °C h'' = 2 609 kJ/kg v'' = 7.647 m³/kg s'' = 7.907 kJ/(kg K)			t_s = 69.12 °C h'' = 2 625 kJ/kg v'' = 5.226 m³/kg s'' = 7.769 kJ/(kg K)			t_s = 75.88 °C h'' = 2 636 kJ/kg v'' = 3.994 m³/kg s'' = 7.760 kJ/(kg K)			t_s = 81.35 °C h'' = 2 645 kJ/kg v'' = 3.239 m³/kg s'' = 7.593 kJ/(kg K)		
t °C	v m³/kg	h kJ/kg	s kJ/(kg K)	v m³/kg	h kJ/kg	s kJ/(kg K)	v m³/kg	h kJ/kg	s kJ/(kg K)	v m³/kg	h kJ/kg	s kJ/(kg K)
	0.0010002	0.0	0.0000	0.0010002	0.0	0.0000	0.0010002	0.0	0.0000	0.0010002	0.1	0.0000
10	0.0010003	41.9	0.1511	0.0010003	41.9	0.1511	0.0010003	41.9	0.1511	0.0010003	42.0	0.1511
20	0.0010018	83.7	0.2964	0.0010018	83.7	0.2964	0.0010018	83.7	0.2964	0.0010018	83.8	0.2964
30	0.0010044	125.6	0.4363	0.0010044	125.6	0.4363	0.0010044	125.6	0.4363	0.0010044	125.6	0.4363
40	0.0010079	167.5	0.5715	0.0010079	167.5	0.5715	0.0010079	167.5	0.5715	0.0010079	167.5	0.5715
50	0.0010121	209.3	0.7030	0.0010121	209.3	0.7030	0.0010121	209.3	0.7031	0.0010121	209.3	0.7031
60	0.0010171	251.1	0.8307	0.0010171	251.1	0.8307	0.0010171	251.1	0.8307	0.0010171	251.1	0.8307
70	7.887	2629	7.961	5.268	2627	7.770	0.0010228	293.0	0.9546	0.0010228	293.0	0.9546
80	8.119	2648	8.015	5.400	2646	7.825	4.088	2645	7.690	0.0010290	334.9	1.0748
90	8.351	2667	8.068	5.557	2666	7.879	4.163	2665	7.745	3.324	2663	7.640
100	8.584	2687	8.120	5.713	2685	7.931	4.282	2684	7.798	3.420	2683	7.693
110	8.816	2706	8.171	5.869	2705	7.982	4.399	2703	7.849	3.514	2703	7.745
120	9.049	2725	8.220	6.025	2724	8.031	4.516	2723	7.899	3.608	2722	7.795
130	9.281	2744	8.268	6.180	2743	8.079	4.633	2742	7.947	3.702	2741	7.843
140	9.513	2763	8.315	6.335	2762	8.126	4.750	2761	7.995	3.795	2761	7.890
150	9.745	2782	8.361	6.490	2782	8.172	4.866	2781	8.041	3.889	2780	7.936
160	9.977	2801	8.406	6.645	2801	8.217	4.892	2800	8.086	3.982	2799	7.981
170	10.209	2821	8.450	6.800	2820	8.261	5.099	2819	8.130	4.075	2819	8.025
180	10.441	2840	8.493	6.955	2839	8.304	5.215	2838	8.173	4.169	2838	8.069
190	10.673	2859	8.535	7.110	2859	8.346	5.331	2858	8.215	4.262	2858	8.111
200	10.905	2879	8.576	7.264	2878	8.388	5.447	2878	8.256	4.355	2877	8.152
210	11.137	2898	8.617	7.419	2898	8.429	5.564	2897	8.297	4.448	2897	8.193
220	11.369	2918	8.657	7.573	2917	8.469	5.680	2917	8.337	4.540	2916	8.233
230	11.600	2937	8.696	7.728	2937	8.508	5.796	2937	8.376	4.633	2936	8.272
240	11.832	2957	8.735	7.882	2956	8.547	5.912	2956	8.415	4.726	2956	8.311
250	12.064	2976	8.773	8.037	2976	8.585	6.028	2976	8.453	4.819	2975	8.349
260	12.295	2996	8.810	8.191	2996	8.622	6.144	2995	8.490	4.912	2995	8.386
280	12.758	3036	8.883	8.500	3036	8.695	6.376	3035	8.564	5.098	3035	8.460
300	13.220	3077	8.954	8.809	3076	8.766	6.608	3076	8.635	5.284	3076	8.531
310	13.452	3097	8.989	8.964	3096	8.801	6.723	3096	8.669	5.377	3096	8.565
320	13.683	3117	9.023	9.118	3116	8.835	6.839	3116	8.703	5.470	3116	8.599
330	13.914	3137	9.057	9.272	3136	8.869	6.954	3136	8.737	5.563	3136	8.633
340	14.145	3157	9.090	9.426	3157	8.902	7.070	3156	8.770	5.656	3156	8.666
350	14.376	3177	9.123	9.580	3177	8.935	7.186	3177	8.803	5.749	3176	8.699
360	14.606	3198	9.155	9.734	3198	8.967	7.301	3197	8.835	5.841	3197	8.731
380	15.068	3238	9.219	10.042	3238	9.031	7.533	3238	8.899	6.027	3237	8.795
400	15.530	3280	9.281	10.351	3280	9.093	7.765	3279	8.962	6.212	3279	8.858
410	15.761	3301	9.312	10.505	3300	9.124	7.880	3300	8.992	6.304	3300	8.889
420	15.992	3321	9.342	10.659	3321	9.155	7.996	3321	9.022	6.397	3320	8.919
430	16.220	3342	9.372	10.813	3342	9.185	8.112	3341	9.053	6.489	3341	8.949
440	16.45	3363	9.402	10.967	3363	9.215	8.228	3362	8.083	6.582	3362	8.979
450	16.68	3384	9.431	11.121	3384	9.244	8.343	3383	9.112	6.674	3383	9.008
460	16.90	3405	9.460	11.275	3405	9.273	8.459	3404	9.141	6.766	3404	9.037
480	17.36	3448	9.518	11.583	3447	9.331	8.690	3447	9.199	6.951	3447	9.095
500	17.82	3490	9.575	11.891	3490	9.388	8.921	3490	9.256	7.136	3489	9.152
510	18.05	3512	9.603	12.045	3512	9.416	9.036	3511	9.284	7.229	3511	9.180
520	18.28	3533	9.631	12.199	3533	9.444	9.152	3532	9.311	7.321	3532	9.208
530	18.52	3555	9.659	12.353	3555	9.472	9.267	3554	9.339	7.413	3554	9.236
540	18.75	3576	9.686	12.507	3576	9.499	9.382	3576	9.366	7.506	3576	9.263
550	18.99	3598	9.713	12.661	3598	9.526	9.498	3598	9.393	7.598	3597	9.290
560	19.22	3619	9.739	12.815	3619	9.552	9.613	3619	9.419	7.690	3619	9.316
580	19.69	3663	9.791	13.123	3663	9.604	9.843	3663	9.471	7.874	3663	9.368
600	20.15	3707	9.842	13.430	3707	9.655	10.074	3707	9.522	8.058	3707	9.419
610	20.38	3729	9.867	13.584	3729	9.680	10.190	3729	9.547	8.150	3729	9.444
620	20.61	3751	9.892	13.738	3751	9.705	10.305	3751	9.572	8.242	3741	9.469
630	20.84	3773	9.917	13.892	3773	9.730	10.420	3773	9.597	8.335	3773	9.494
640	21.07	3796	9.942	14.046	3796	9.755	10.536	3795	9.622	8.427	3795	9.519
650	21.30	3818	9.966	14.200	3818	9.779	10.651	3818	9.646	8.520	3818	9.543
660	21.53	3841	9.990	14.353	3841	9.803	10.767	3840	9.670	8.612	3840	9.567
680	21.99	3886	10.038	14.661	3886	9.851	10.998	3885	9.718	8.797	3885	9.615
700	22.45	3931	10.085	14.969	3931	9.898	11.228	3930	9.765	8.982	3930	9.662

Table 3-4 Properties of Superheated Steam (H₂O) *(continued)*

Pressure $p=$	0.60 bar			0.70 bar			0.80 bar			0.90 bar		
Tempera-ture	t_s = 85.95 °C h'' = 2 653 kJ/kg v'' = 2.732 m³/kg s'' = 7.531 kJ/(kg K)			t_s = 89.97 °C h'' = 2 660 kJ/kg v'' = 2.364 m³/kg s'' = 7.479 kJ/(kg K)			t_s = 93.52 °C h'' = 2 665 kJ/kg v'' = 2.087 m³/kg s'' = 7.434 kJ/(kg K)			t_s = 96.72 °C h'' = 2 670 kJ/kg v'' = 1.869 m³/kg s'' = 7.394 kJ/(kg K)		
t °C	v m³/kg	h kJ/kg	s kJ/(kg K)	v m³/kg	h kJ/kg	s kJ/(kg K)	v m³/kg	h kJ/kg	s kJ/(kg K)	v m³/kg	h kJ/kg	s kJ/(kg K)
	0.0010002	0.1	0.0000	0.0010002	0.1	0.0000	0.0010002	0.1	0.0000	0.0010001	0.1	0.0000
10	0.0010003	42.0	0.1511	0.0010003	42.0	0.1511	0.0010003	42.0	0.1511	0.0010003	42.0	0.1511
20	0.0010018	83.8	0.2964	0.0010018	83.9	0.2964	0.0010018	83.9	0.2964	0.0010018	83.9	0.2964
30	0.0010044	125.6	0.4363	0.0010044	125.7	0.4363	0.0010044	125.7	0.4363	0.0010044	125.7	0.4363
40	0.0010079	167.5	0.5715	0.0010079	167.5	0.5715	0.0010079	167.5	0.5715	0.0010079	167.5	0.5715
50	0.0010121	209.3	0.7031	0.0010121	209.3	0.7031	0.0010121	209.3	0.7031	0.0010121	209.3	0.7031
60	0.0010171	251.1	0.8307	0.0010171	251.1	0.8307	0.0010171	251.1	0.8307	0.0010171	251.1	0.8307
70	0.0010228	293.0	0.9546	0.0010228	293.0	0.9546	0.0010227	293.0	0.9546	0.0010227	293.0	0.9546
80	0.0010289	334.9	1.0748	0.0010290	334.9	1.0748	0.0010289	334.9	1.0748	0.0010289	334.9	1.0748
90	2.765	2661	7.551	2.366	2659	7.479	0.0010359	376.9	1.1924	0.0010359	376.8	1.1924
100	2.846	2681	7.604	2.436	2680	7.532	2.127	2679	7.468	1.887	2677	7.411
110	2.925	2701	7.657	2.504	2700	7.584	2.187	2699	7.520	1.941	2698	7.464
120	3.004	2721	7.708	2.572	2720	7.635	2.247	2719	7.572	1.995	2718	7.515
130	3.082	2740	7.757	2.640	2739	7.684	2.307	2739	7.621	2.048	2738	7.565
140	3.160	2760	7.804	2.707	2759	7.731	2.366	2758	7.669	2.101	2757	7.613
150	2.328	2780	7.850	2.773	2779	7.778	2.424	2778	7.715	2.153	2777	7.660
160	3.316	2799	7.895	2.840	2798	7.823	2.483	2797	7.761	2.205	2797	7.705
170	3.394	2818	7.939	2.907	2818	7.867	2.542	2817	7.805	2.258	2816	7.750
180	3.472	2837	7.983	2.974	2837	7.911	2.600	2836	7.849	2.310	2836	7.794
190	3.550	2857	8.025	3.041	2857	7.954	2.659	2856	7.892	2.362	2855	7.836
200	3.628	2877	8.067	3.107	2876	7.995	2.717	2876	7.934	2.414	2875	7.878
210	3.706	2897	8.108	3.174	2896	8.036	2.775	2896	7.975	2.466	2895	7.919
220	3.784	2916	8.148	3.240	2916	8.076	2.834	2915	8.015	2.518	2914	7.960
230	3.861	2936	8.187	3.307	2935	8.116	2.892	2935	8.054	2.570	2934	7.999
240	3.939	2956	8.226	3.374	2955	8.155	2.951	2955	8.093	2.621	2954	8.037
250	4.016	2975	8.264	3.440	2975	8.193	3.009	2974	8.131	2.673	2974	8.075
260	4.093	2995	8.302	3.507	2995	8.230	3.067	2994	8.168	2.725	2994	8.133
280	4.247	3035	8.375	3.639	3035	8.303	3.183	3034	8.242	2.828	3034	8.186
300	4.401	3075	8.446	3.772	3075	8.374	3.299	3075	8.313	2.931	3074	8.257
310	4.479	3095	8.481	3.839	3095	8.409	3.357	3095	8.347	2.983	3094	8.292
320	4.556	3115	8.515	3.905	3115	8.443	3.415	3115	8.381	3.035	3114	8.326
330	4.634	3136	8.549	3.971	3135	8.477	3.474	3135	8.415	3.087	3134	8.360
340	4.711	3156	8.582	4.038	3156	8.510	3.532	3156	8.448	3.138	3155	8.393
350	4.788	3176	8.615	4.104	3176	8.543	3.590	3176	8.481	3.190	3175	8.426
360	4.865	3197	8.647	4.170	3197	8.575	3.648	3196	8.513	3.242	3196	8.458
380	5.020	3237	8.711	4.303	3237	8.639	3.764	3237	8.577	3.345	3237	8.522
400	5.175	3279	8.773	4.435	3279	8.702	3.880	3279	8.640	3.448	3278	8.585
410	5.252	3300	8.804	4.501	3300	8.733	3.937	3299	8.671	3.499	3299	8.616
420	5.330	3320	8.834	4.567	3320	8.763	3.995	3320	8.701	3.551	3320	8.646
430	5.407	3341	8.864	4.634	3341	8.793	4.052	3341	8.731	3.602	3341	8.675
440	5.484	3362	8.894	4.700	3362	8.823	4.110	3362	8.761	3.654	3362	8.705
450	5.562	3383	8.924	4.766	3383	8.852	4.168	3383	8.790	3.705	3383	8.734
460	5.639	3404	8.953	4.832	3404	8.881	4.226	3404	8.819	3.757	3404	8.763
480	5.793	3447	9.011	4.964	3447	8.939	4.342	3446	8.887	3.860	3446	8.821
500	5.947	3489	9.067	5.096	3489	8.996	4.458	3489	8.934	3.962	3489	8.879
510	6.024	3511	9.095	5.162	3511	9.024	4.515	3510	8.962	4.013	3510	8.907
520	6.101	3532	9.123	5.228	3532	9.052	4.573	3532	8.990	4.065	3532	8.935
530	6.177	3554	9.151	5.294	3554	9.079	4.631	3554	9.018	4.116	3553	8.963
540	6.254	3576	9.178	5.360	3576	9.106	4.689	3576	9.045	4.167	3575	8.990
550	6.331	3597	9.205	5.246	3597	9.133	4.747	3597	9.072	4.219	3597	9.017
560	6.407	3619	9.232	5.491	3619	9.160	4.804	3619	9.099	4.270	3619	9.044
580	6.560	3663	9.284	5.623	3663	9.213	4.919	3663	9.151	4.372	3662	9.097
600	6.714	3707	9.335	5.754	3707	9.264	5.035	3707	9.202	4.475	3706	9.147
610	6.791	3729	9.360	5.820	3729	9.289	5.093	3729	9.227	4.526	3728	9.172
620	6.868	3751	9.385	5.886	3751	9.314	5.150	3751	9.252	4.578	3750	9.197
630	6.945	3773	9.410	5.952	3773	9.339	5.208	3773	9.277	4.629	3772	9.222
640	7.022	3795	9.435	6.018	3795	9.364	5.266	3795	9.302	4.680	3795	9.274
650	7.099	3818	9.459	6.084	3818	9.388	5.324	3818	9.326	4.732	3817	9.271
660	7.176	3840	9.483	6.150	3840	9.412	5.381	3840	9.350	4.783	3840	9.295
680	7.330	3885	9.531	6.282	3885	9.460	5.496	3885	9.398	4.885	3885	9.343
700	7.484	3930	9.578	6.414	3930	9.507	5.612	3930	9.445	4.988	3930	9.390

Table 3-4   Properties of Superheated Steam (H₂O) *(continued)*

Pressure p=	1.0 bar			1.2 bar			1.3 bar			1.4 bar		
Temperature	t_s = 99.64 °C h'' = 2 675 kJ/kg v'' = 1.694 m³/kg s'' = 7.360 kJ/(kg K)			t_s = 104.81 °C h'' = 2 683 kJ/kg v'' = 1.429 m³/kg s'' = 7.298 kJ/(kg K)			t_s = 107.14 °C h'' = 2 687 kJ/kg v'' = 1.325 m³/kg s'' = 7.271 kJ/(kg K)			t_s = 109.33 °C h'' = 2 690 kJ/kg v'' = 1.236 m³/kg s'' = 7.246 kJ/(kg K)		
t	v	h	s	v	h	s	v	h	s	v	h	s
°C	m³/kg	kJ/kg	kJ/(kg K)	m³/kg	kJ/kg	kJ/(kg K)	m³/kg	kJ/kg	kJ/(kg K)	m³/kg	kJ/kg	kJ/(kg K)
0	0.0010001	0.1	0.0000	0.0010001	0.1	0.0000	0.0010001	0.1	0.0000	0.0010000	0.1	0.0000
20	0.0010018	83.9	0.2964	0.0010018	83.9	0.2964	0.0010017	83.9	0.2964	0.0010017	83.9	0.2964
40	0.0010079	167.5	0.5715	0.0010079	167.5	0.5715	0.0010078	167.5	0.5715	0.0010078	167.5	0.5715
50	0.0010121	209.3	0.7031	0.0010121	209.3	0.7031	0.0010120	209.3	0.7032	0.0010120	209.3	0.7032
60	0.0010171	251.1	0.8307	0.0010171	251.1	0.8307	0.0010170	251.1	0.8307	0.0010170	251.1	0.8307
80	0.0010289	334.9	1.0748	0.0010289	334.9	1.0748	0.0010289	334.9	1.0748	0.0010289	334.9	1.0748
100	1.695	2676	7.361	0.0010434	419.0	1.3067	0.0010434	419.0	1.3067	0.0010434	419.0	1.3067
120	1.795	2717	7.465	1.491	2715	7.376	1.376	2714	7.337	1.275	2713	7.301
140	1.889	2757	7.562	1.572	2755	7.475	1.449	2754	7.437	1.344	2753	7.401
150	1.937	2776	7.608	1.611	2775	7.522	1.486	2774	7.484	1.378	2773	7.449
160	1.984	2796	7.654	1.650	2795	7.568	1.522	2794	7.530	1.412	2793	7.495
180	2.078	2835	7.743	1.729	2834	7.657	1.594	2834	7.619	1.480	2833	7.584
200	2.172	2875	7.828	1.807	2874	7.742	1.667	2873	7.704	1.547	2873	7.669
220	2.266	2914	7.910	1.886	2913	7.824	1.740	2913	7.787	1.615	2912	7.752
240	2.359	2954	7.988	1.964	2953	7.903	1.812	2952	7.865	1.682	2952	7.831
250	2.405	2974	8.026	2.003	2973	7.941	1.848	2972	7.904	1.715	2972	7.870
260	2.452	2993	8.064	2.042	2993	7.979	1.884	2992	7.942	1.749	2992	7.908
280	2.545	3033	8.139	2.120	3033	8.053	1.956	3032	8.016	1.815	3032	7.982
300	2.638	3074	8.211	2.197	3073	8.126	2.028	3072	8.088	1.882	3072	8.054
320	2.731	3114	8.281	2.275	3113	8.196	2.100	3113	8.159	1.949	3113	8.124
340	2.825	3155	8.348	2.352	3154	8.263	2.172	3154	8.226	2.016	3154	8.191
350	2.871	3175	8.381	2.391	3174	8.296	2.208	3174	8.259	2.049	3174	8.224
360	2.918	3195	8.414	2.430	3195	8.329	2.243	3195	8.292	2.082	3194	8.257
380	3.010	3236	8.478	2.507	3236	8.393	2.314	3236	8.356	2.148	3235	8.322
400	3.102	3278	8.541	2.584	3278	8.456	2.385	3278	8.419	2.124	3277	8.385
420	3.195	3319	8.602	2.661	3319	8.517	2.456	3319	8.480	2.280	3318	8.446
440	3.288	3361	8.661	2.738	3361	8.577	2.527	3361	8.540	2.346	3360	8.506
450	3.334	3382	8.690	2.777	3382	8.606	2.563	3382	8.569	2.379	3381	8.535
460	3.380	3403	8.719	2.816	3403	8.635	2.599	3403	8.598	2.413	3402	8.564
480	3.472	3446	8.777	2.893	3445	8.693	2.670	3445	8.656	2.479	3445	8.621
500	3.565	3488	8.833	2.970	3488	8.749	2.741	3488	8.712	2.545	3488	8.677
520	3.658	3531	8.888	3.048	3531	8.804	2.813	3531	8.767	2.611	3531	8.732
540	3.751	3575	8.942	3.125	3574	8.858	2.884	3574	8.821	2.678	3574	8.787
550	3.797	3596	8.969	3.164	3596	8.885	2.920	3596	8.848	2.711	3596	8.814
560	3.843	3618	8.995	3.202	3618	8.911	2.955	3618	8.874	2.744	3618	8.840
580	3.935	3662	9.047	3.279	3662	8.963	3.026	3661	8.926	2.810	3661	8.891
600	4.028	3706	9.097	3.357	3705	9.013	3.098	3705	8.976	2.876	3705	8.941
620	4.121	3750	9.146	3.435	3749	9.062	3.170	3749	9.025	2.943	3749	8.990
640	4.214	3795	9.195	3.512	3794	9.111	3.242	3794	9.074	3.010	3794	9.039
650	4.260	3817	9.219	3.551	3816	9.135	3.278	3816	9.098	3.043	3816	9.063
660	4.306	3840	9.243	3.589	3839	9.159	3.313	3839	9.122	3.076	3839	9.087
680	4.398	3885	9.291	3.665	3884	9.207	3.384	3884	9.170	3.142	3884	9.135
700	4.491	3929	9.338	3.742	3928	9.255	3.454	3928	9.217	3.207	3928	9.182
720	4.583	3974	9.384	3.820	3973	9.301	3.525	3973	9.264	3.273	3973	9.229
740	4.676	4019	9.430	3.897	4019	9.347	3.596	4019	9.310	3.340	4018	9.275
750	4.722	4042	9.453	3.935	4042	9.370	3.632	4042	9.333	3.373	4041	9.298
760	4.768	4065	9.475	3.974	4065	9.392	3.667	4065	9.355	3.406	4064	9.320
780	4.860	4111	9.519	4.050	4111	9.436	3.738	4111	9.399	3.471	4110	9.364
800	4.952	4175	9.563	4.127	4157	9.480	3.809	4157	9.443	3.537	4157	9.408
820	5.045	4205	9.606	4.204	4205	9.524	3.881	4204	9.486	3.603	4204	9.451
840	5.137	4252	9.649	4.280	4252	9.567	3.952	4252	9.529	3.668	4252	9.494
850	5.183	4276	9.670	4.319	4276	9.588	3.987	4276	9.550	3.701	4276	9.515
860	5.229	4300	9.691	4.358	4300	9.606	4.022	4300	9.571	3.734	4300	9.536
880	5.321	4348	9.733	4.435	4348	9.650	4.093	4348	9.613	3.801	4347	9.578
900	5.413	4395	9.774	4.511	4395	9.691	4.164	4395	9.654	3.867	4395	9.619
920	5.505	4443	9.815	4.589	4443	9.732	4.236	4443	9.695	3.933	4443	9.660
940	5.598	4491	9.855	4.666	4491	9.773	4.307	4491	9.375	4.000	4491	9.700
950	5.644	4515	9.875	4.704	4515	9.793	4.342	4515	9.755	4.033	4515	9.720
960	5.690	4539	9.895	4.743	4539	9.812	4.378	4539	9.775	4.066	4539	9.740
980	5.782	4587	9.934	4.819	4587	9.852	4.448	4587	9.814	4.131	4587	9.779
1000	5.874	4636	9.973	4.896	4636	9.890	4.518	4636	9.853	4.196	4636	9.818

Table 3-4   Properties of Superheated Steam (H₂O)   *(continued)*

Pressure p=	1.5 bar			1.6 bar			1.8 bar			2.0 bar		
Tempera-ture	t_s = 111.38 °C h'' = 2 693 kJ/kg v'' = 1.159 m³/kg s'' = 7.223 kJ/(kg K)			t_s = 113.32 °C h'' = 2 696 kJ/kg v'' = 1.091 m³/kg s'' = 7.202 kJ/(kg K)			t_s = 116.94 °C h'' = 2 702 kJ/kg v'' = 0.9773 m³/kg s'' = 7.163 kJ/(kg K)			t_s = 120.23 °C h'' = 2 707 kJ/kg v'' = 0.8854 m³/kg s'' = 7.127 kJ/(kg K)		
t °C	v m³/kg	h kJ/kg	s kJ/(kg K)	v m³/kg	h kJ/kg	s kJ/(kg K)	v m³/kg	h kJ/kg	s kJ/(kg K)	v m³/kg	h kJ/kg	s kJ/(kg K)
0	0.0010000	0.1	0.0000	0.0010000	0.2	0.0000	0.0010000	0.2	0.0000	0.0010000	0.2	0.0000
20	0.0010017	83.9	0.2964	0.0010017	84.0	0.2964	0.0010017	84.0	0.2964	0.0010017	84.0	0.2964
40	0.0010078	167.5	0.5715	0.0010078	167.6	0.5715	0.0010078	167.6	0.5716	0.0010078	167.6	0.5716
50	0.0010120	209.3	0.7032	0.0010120	209.4	0.7032	0.0010120	209.4	0.7033	0.0010120	209.4	0.7033
60	0.0010170	251.1	0.8307	0.0010170	251.2	0.8307	0.0010170	251.2	0.8307	0.0010170	251.2	0.8307
80	0.0010289	334.9	1.0748	0.0010289	335.0	1.0748	0.0010289	335.0	1.0748	0.0010289	335.0	1.0748
100	0.0010434	419.0	1.3067	0.0010434	419.0	1.3067	0.0010434	419.0	1.3067	0.0010434	419.0	1.3067
120	1.188	2712	7.268	1.113	2711	7.236	0.986	2708	7.177	0.0010603	503.7	1.5269
140	1.253	2753	7.368	1.173	2752	7.337	1.041	2750	7.279	0.9357	2749	7.227
150	1.285	2773	7.416	1.203	2772	7.385	1.068	2771	7.328	0.9603	2769	7.276
160	1.317	2793	7.462	1.233	2792	7.431	1.095	2791	7.375	0.9840	2790	7.324
180	1.380	2833	7.551	1.293	2832	7.520	1.148	2831	7.465	1.032	2830	7.415
200	1.443	2872	7.636	1.352	2872	7.606	1.201	2871	7.550	1.080	2870	7.501
220	1.506	2912	7.719	1.411	2912	7.689	1.253	2911	7.633	1.128	2910	7.583
240	1.569	2952	7.799	1.470	2951	7.768	1.306	2950	7.712	1.175	2950	7.663
250	1.600	2972	7.837	1.500	2971	7.807	1.332	2970	7.751	1.198	2970	7.702
260	1.632	2992	7.875	1.529	2991	7.845	1.358	2990	7.789	1.222	2990	7.740
280	1.694	3032	7.950	1.587	3031	7.919	1.410	3030	7.864	1.269	3030	7.815
300	1.756	3072	8.022	1.646	3071	7.991	1.462	3071	7.936	1.316	3071	7.887
320	1.819	3112	8.092	1.705	3112	8.061	1.514	3112	8.006	1.363	3111	7.957
340	1.881	3154	8.159	1.763	3153	8.129	1.566	3153	8.075	1.410	3153	8.025
350	1.912	3174	8.192	1.792	3174	8.162	1.592	3173	8.108	1.433	3173	8.059
360	1.943	3194	8.225	1.821	3194	8.195	1.618	3194	8.141	1.457	3194	8.092
380	2.004	3235	8.290	1.879	3235	8.259	1.669	3235	8.205	1.503	3235	8.156
400	2.066	3277	8.353	1.937	3277	8.322	1.721	3277	8.268	1.549	3276	8.219
420	2.128	3318	8.414	1.995	3318	8.384	1.772	3318	8.329	1.595	3318	8.280
440	2.190	3360	8.474	2.054	3360	8.444	1.824	3360	8.389	1.641	3360	8.340
450	2.221	3381	8.503	2.082	3381	8.473	1.850	3381	8.418	1.664	3381	8.369
460	2.252	3402	8.532	2.111	3402	8.502	1.876	3402	8.447	1.687	3402	8.398
480	2.313	3445	8.589	2.169	3445	8.559	1.928	3445	8.505	1.734	3445	8.456
500	2.375	3488	8.645	2.227	3488	8.615	1.979	3488	8.561	1.781	3487	8.512
520	2.437	3530	8.700	2.285	3530	8.670	2.031	3530	8.616	1.828	3530	8.567
540	2.499	3574	8.754	2.343	3574	8.724	2.083	3574	8.670	1.874	3574	8.621
550	2.530	3596	8.781	2.372	3596	8.751	2.109	3596	8.697	1.897	3595	8.648
560	2.561	3617	8.807	2.401	3617	8.777	2.134	3617	8.723	1.920	3617	8.674
580	2.623	3661	8.859	2.459	3661	8.829	2.185	3661	8.775	1.967	3661	8.726
600	2.685	3705	8.909	2.517	3705	8.879	2.237	3705	8.825	2.013	3705	8.776
620	2.747	3749	8.958	2.575	3749	8.928	2.289	3749	8.874	2.060	3749	8.825
640	2.810	3794	9.007	2.633	3794	8.977	2.340	3794	8.922	2.107	2794	8.874
650	2.841	3816	9.031	2.662	3816	9.001	2.366	3816	8.947	2.130	3816	8.898
660	2.871	3839	9.055	2.691	3839	9.025	2.391	3839	8.971	2.153	3839	8.922
680	2.932	3884	9.103	2.749	3884	9.073	2.443	3884	9.019	2.199	3884	8.970
700	2.993	3928	9.150	2.807	3928	9.120	2.494	3928	9.066	2.245	3928	9.018
720	3.055	3973	9.197	2.865	3973	9.167	2.545	3973	9.112	2.291	3973	9.064
740	3.118	4018	9.243	2.923	4018	9.213	2.596	4018	9.158	2.338	4018	9.110
750	3.149	4041	9.266	2.952	4041	9.235	2.622	4041	9.181	2.361	4041	9.133
760	3.179	4064	9.288	2.981	4064	9.258	2.648	4064	9.203	2.384	4064	9.155
780	3.240	4110	9.332	3.038	4110	9.302	2.699	4110	9.247	2.430	4110	9.199
800	3.301	4157	9.376	3.094	4157	9.346	2.750	4157	9.291	2.476	4157	9.242
820	3.363	4204	9.419	3.152	4204	9.389	2.802	4204	9.334	2.522	4204	9.286
840	3.423	4252	9.462	3.210	4252	9.432	2.854	4252	9.378	2.568	4252	9.329
850	3.454	4276	9.483	3.239	4276	9.453	2.879	4276	9.399	2.591	4276	9.351
860	3.485	4300	9.504	3.268	4300	9.474	2.905	4300	9.420	2.614	4299	9.372
880	3.547	4347	9.546	3.326	4347	9.516	2.956	4347	9.462	2.661	4347	9.414
900	3.609	4395	9.587	3.383	4395	9.557	3.007	4395	9.503	2.706	4395	9.455
920	3.671	4443	9.628	3.441	4443	9.598	3.059	4443	9.544	2.753	4443	9.495
940	3.733	4491	9.668	3.499	4491	9.638	3.110	4491	9.584	2.800	4491	9.535
950	3.764	4515	9.688	3.528	4515	9.658	3.136	4515	9.604	2.823	4515	9.555
960	3.794	4539	9.708	3.557	4539	9.678	3.162	4539	9.624	2.846	4539	9.575
980	3.855	4587	9.747	3.614	4587	9.717	3.214	4587	9.663	2.891	4587	9.615
1000	3.916	4636	9.786	3.671	4636	9.756	3.264	4636	9.702	2.937	4635	9.653

Table 3-4 Properties of Superheated Steam (H_2O) *(continued)*

Pressure p=	2.5 bar			3.0 bar			4.0 bar			5.0 bar		
Temperature	t_s = 127.43 °C h'' = 2 717 kJ/kg v'' = 0.7185 m³/kg s'' = 7.053 kJ/(kg K)			t_s = 133.54 °C h'' = 2 725 kJ/kg v'' = 0.6057 m³/kg s'' = 6.992 kJ/(kg K)			t_s = 143.62 °C h'' = 2 738 kJ/kg v'' = 0.4624 m³/kg s'' = 6.897 kJ/(kg K)			t_s = 151.84 °C h'' = 2 749 kJ/kg v'' = 0.3747 m³/kg s'' = 6.822 kJ/(kg K)		
t	v	h	s	v	h	s	v	h	s	v	h	s
°C	m³/kg	kJ/kg	kJ/(kg K)	m³/kg	kJ/kg	kJ/(kg K)	m³/kg	kJ/kg	kJ/(kg K)	m³/kg	kJ/kg	kJ/(kg K)
0	0.0010000	0.2	0.0000	0.0010000	0.3	0.0000	0.0010000	0.5	0.0000	0.0009999	0.6	0.0000
20	0.0010017	84.0	0.2964	0.0010017	84.1	0.2964	0.0010017	84.1	0.2964	0.0010016	84.2	0.2964
40	0.0010078	167.6	0.5716	0.0010078	167.7	0.5716	0.0010078	167.7	0.5716	0.0010077	167.8	0.5716
50	0.0010120	209.4	0.7032	0.0010120	209.5	0.7031	0.0010120	209.5	0.7030	0.0010119	209.6	0.7029
60	0.0010170	251.2	0.8305	0.0010170	251.3	0.8304	0.0010170	251.3	0.8303	0.0010169	251.4	0.8302
80	0.0010289	335.0	1.0747	0.0010288	335.1	1.0746	0.0010288	335.1	1.0745	0.0010287	335.1	1.0744
100	0.0010434	419.0	1.3067	0.0010434	419.1	1.3066	0.0010433	419.1	1.3063	0.0010433	419.1	1.3063
120	0.0010603	503.7	1.5269	0.0010602	503.7	1.5268	0.0010602	503.7	1.5265	0.0010601	503.7	1.5265
140	0.7445	2745	7.118	0.6171	2740	7.025	0.0010798	589.1	1.738	0.0010797	589.1	1.738
150	0.7647	2766	7.168	0.6344	2762	7.077	0.4709	2745	6.928	0.0010906	632.1	1.840
160	0.7845	2787	7.216	0.6512	2783	7.126	0.4840	2776	6.980	0.3839	2767	6.864
180	0.8234	2827	7.308	0.6838	2824	7.218	0.5094	2818	7.077	0.4047	2812	6.965
200	0.8618	2867	7.395	0.7161	2864	7.306	0.5341	2859	7.166	0.4249	2854	7.056
220	0.9000	2908	7.478	0.7482	2905	7.389	0.5585	2900	7.251	0.4448	2896	7.141
240	0.9380	2948	7.557	0.7802	2946	7.470	0.5827	2941	7.332	0.4644	2937	7.224
250	0.9570	2968	7.596	0.7961	2966	7.509	0.5948	2962	7.371	0.4742	2958	7.264
260	0.9758	2988	7.634	0.8120	2986	7.547	0.6068	2982	7.410	0.4839	2979	7.304
280	1.0133	3029	7.709	0.8436	3027	7.623	0.6307	3023	7.486	0.5031	3020	7.380
300	1.051	3069	7.781	0.8750	3068	7.695	0.6545	3065	7.560	0.5224	3062	7.454
320	1.089	3110	7.852	0.9064	3109	7.766	0.6782	3106	7.631	0.5414	3104	7.525
340	1.126	3152	7.920	0.9377	3150	7.835	0.7019	3148	7.700	0.5605	3146	7.595
350	1.145	3172	7.954	0.9434	3171	7.869	0.7137	3169	7.734	0.5700	3167	7.629
360	1.164	3193	7.987	0.9690	3192	7.902	0.7254	3190	7.767	0.5794	3188	7.662
380	1.201	3234	8.052	1.000	3233	7.967	0.7488	3231	7.832	0.5984	3230	7.727
400	1.238	3276	8.115	1.032	3275	8.030	0.7723	3273	7.895	0.6173	3272	7.791
420	1.275	3318	8.176	1.063	3317	8.091	0.7957	3315	7.957	0.6361	3314	7.853
440	1.312	3360	8.236	1.094	3359	8.151	0.8190	3358	8.017	0.6548	3356	7.913
450	1.330	3381	8.266	1.110	3380	8.181	0.8307	3379	8.047	0.6642	3377	7.943
460	1.349	3402	8.295	1.125	3401	8.210	0.8424	3400	8.076	0.6735	3398	7.792
480	1.386	3444	8.353	1.156	3444	8.268	0.8657	3443	8.134	0.6922	3441	8.030
500	1.421	3487	8.409	1.187	3486	8.324	0.8890	3485	8.190	0.7109	3484	8.086
520	1.461	3529	8.464	1.218	3529	8.379	0.9123	3528	8.245	0.7296	3527	8.141
540	1.498	3573	8.518	1.248	3573	8.433	0.9357	3572	8.299	0.7483	3571	8.196
550	1.517	3594	8.545	1.264	3594	8.460	0.9473	3593	8.326	0.7576	3592	8.223
560	1.536	3616	8.571	1.279	3616	8.486	0.9590	3615	8.352	0.7669	3614	8.249
580	1.573	3660	8.622	1.310	3660	8.538	0.9822	3659	8.404	0.7855	3658	8.301
600	1.610	3704	8.672	1.341	3704	8.588	1.0054	3703	8.455	0.8041	3702	8.351
620	1.648	3748	8.722	1.372	3748	8.638	1.0287	3747	8.504	0.8228	3746	8.401
640	1.685	3793	8.771	1.403	3793	8.686	1.0519	3792	8.553	0.8414	3791	8.450
650	1.703	3815	8.795	1.418	3815	8.711	1.0636	3814	8.578	0.8507	3813	8.474
660	1.722	3838	8.819	1.434	3838	8.735	1.0752	3837	8.602	0.8600	3836	8.498
680	1.759	3883	8.867	1.465	3883	8.783	1.0983	3882	8.650	0.8785	3881	8.546
700	1.795	3927	8.914	1.496	3927	8.830	1.1214	3926	8.697	0.8969	3925	8.594
720	1.833	3972	8.961	1.527	3972	8.876	1.1446	3971	8.744	0.9155	3971	8.640
740	1.870	4018	9.007	1.558	4018	8.922	1.1677	4017	8.790	0.9342	4017	8.686
750	1.888	4041	9.030	1.573	4041	8.945	1.1793	4040	8.812	0.9434	4040	8.709
760	1.907	4064	9.052	1.588	4064	8.968	1.1909	4063	8.835	0.9526	4063	8.731
780	1.944	4110	9.096	1.619	4110	9.012	1.2141	4109	8.879	0.9711	4109	8.775
800	1.980	4157	9.140	1.650	4157	9.056	1.2372	4156	8.923	0.9895	4156	8.819
820	2.017	4204	9.183	1.681	4204	9.099	1.2604	4203	8.966	1.0080	4203	8.862
840	2.054	4252	9.226	1.713	4251	9.142	1.2835	4251	9.009	1.0266	4250	8.905
850	2.072	4275	9.247	1.728	4275	9.163	1.2950	4275	9.030	1.0358	4274	8.926
860	2.091	4299	9.268	1.743	4299	9.184	1.3065	4299	9.051	1.0451	4298	8.948
880	2.128	4347	9.310	1.774	4347	9.226	1.3295	4346	9.093	1.0636	4346	8.990
900	2.164	4395	9.351	1.804	4395	9.267	1.3525	4394	9.134	1.0821	4394	9.031
920	2.202	4442	9.392	1.835	4442	9.308	1.3756	4442	9.175	1.1006	4441	9.072
940	2.239	4490	9.432	1.866	4490	9.348	1.3987	4490	9.215	1.1192	4489	9.112
950	2.257	4514	9.452	1.882	4514	9.368	1.4103	4514	9.235	1.1284	4513	9.132
960	2.276	4538	9.472	1.898	4538	9.388	1.4218	4538	9.255	1.1377	4537	9.152
980	2.313	4587	9.511	1.928	4587	9.427	1.4448	4586	9.294	1.1562	4586	9.192
1000	2.349	4635	9.550	1.958	4635	9.466	1.4679	4635	9.333	1.1746	4635	9.230

Table 3-4 Properties of Superheated Steam (H₂O) *(continued)*

Pressure p=	6 bar			7 bar			8 bar			9 bar		
Tempera-ture	t_s = 158.84 °C h'' = 2 757 kJ/kg v'' = 0.3156 m³/kg s'' = 6.761 kJ/(kg K)			t_s = 164.96 °C h'' = 2 764 kJ/kg v'' = 0.2728 m³/kg s'' = 6.709 kJ/(kg K)			t_s = 170.42 °C h'' = 2 769 kJ/kg v'' = 0.2403 m³/kg s'' = 6.663 kJ/(kg K)			t_s = 175.35 °C h'' = 2 774 kJ/kg v'' = 0.2149 m³/kg s'' = 6.623 kJ/(kg K)		
t	v	h	s	v	h	s	v	h	s	v	h	s
°C	m³/kg	kJ/kg	kJ/(kg K)	m³/kg	kJ/kg	kJ/(kg K)	m³/kg	kJ/kg	kJ/(kg K)	m³/kg	kJ/kg	kJ/(kg K)
0	0.0009998	0.7	0.0000	0.0009998	0.8	0.0000	0.0009997	0.9	0.0000	0.0009997	1.0	0.0000
10	0.0010015	84.3	0.2964	0.0010015	84.4	0.2963	0.0010015	84.5	0.2962	0.0010015	84.6	0.2961
40	0.0010076	167.9	0.5716	0.0010076	168.0	0.5715	0.0010076	168.1	0.5714	0.0010076	168.2	0.5713
50	0.0010118	209.7	0.7028	0.0010118	209.8	0.7027	0.0010118	209.9	0.7026	0.0010118	210.0	0.7025
60	0.0010168	251.5	0.8302	0.0010168	251.6	0.8301	0.0010167	251.7	0.8300	0.0010167	251.8	0.8299
80	0.0010287	335.2	1.0744	0.0010286	335.2	1.0743	0.0010286	335.3	1.0742	0.0010285	335.4	1.0741
100	0.0010432	419.1	1.3062	0.0010432	419.1	1.3061	0.0010431	419.2	1.3060	0.0010431	419.3	1.3059
120	0.0010601	503.7	1.5265	0.0010600	503.7	1.5264	0.0010600	503.8	1.5263	0.0010599	503.9	1.5262
140	0.0010797	589.1	1.738	0.0010796	589.1	1.738	0.0010795	589.1	1.737	0.0010795	589.2	1.737
150	0.0010906	632.1	1.840	0.0010904	632.1	1.840	0.0010904	632.1	1.840	0.0010903	632.1	1.840
160	0.3176	2759	6.767	0.0011020	765.3	1.941	0.0011020	675.3	1.941	0.0011019	675.7	1.941
180	0.3348	2805	6.869	0.2847	2799	6.787	0.2473	2792	6.715	0.2180	2785	6.648
200	0.3520	2849	6.963	0.2998	2844	6.884	0.2609	2839	6.814	0.2304	2833	6.750
220	0.3688	2891	7.051	0.3145	2887	6.973	0.2739	2883	6.905	0.2422	2878	6.844
240	0.3855	2933	7.135	0.3290	2929	7.058	0.2867	2926	6.991	0.2537	2922	6.931
250	0.3937	2954	7.175	0.3361	2951	7.099	0.2930	2947	7.032	0.2594	2944	6.973
260	0.4019	2975	7.215	0.3432	2972	7.139	0.2993	2969	7.073	0.2651	2965	7.014
280	0.4181	3017	7.292	0.3572	3014	7.216	0.3118	3011	7.151	0.2762	3008	7.093
300	0.4342	3059	7.366	0.3711	3056	7.291	0.3240	3054	7.226	0.2872	3051	7.168
320	0.4502	3101	7.437	0.3850	3099	7.363	0.3362	3096	7.299	0.2980	3093	7.241
340	0.4661	3143	7.507	0.3987	3141	7.433	0.3482	3139	7.369	0.3088	3136	7.312
350	0.4741	3164	7.451	0.4055	3162	7.468	0.3542	3160	7.404	0.3142	3158	7.347
360	0.4820	3185	7.575	0.4124	3183	7.502	0.3602	3181	7.438	0.3196	3179	7.381
380	0.4979	3228	7.640	0.4261	3236	7.568	0.3722	3224	7.504	0.3303	3222	7.447
400	0.5136	3270	7.704	0.4396	3268	7.632	0.3842	3267	7.568	0.3409	3265	7.511
420	0.5293	3312	7.766	0.4531	3311	7.694	0.3960	3309	7.631	0.3516	3308	7.574
440	0.5450	3355	7.827	0.4667	3353	7.755	0.4097	3352	7.692	0.3621	3351	7.635
450	0.5528	3376	7.857	0.4734	3375	7.785	0.4137	3373	7.722	0.3674	3372	7.665
460	0.5607	3397	7.886	0.4801	3396	7.814	0.4196	3395	7.751	0.3726	3393	7.695
480	0.5763	3440	7.944	0.4935	3439	7.872	0.4315	3437	7.809	0.3831	3436	7.753
500	0.5919	3483	8.001	0.5069	3482	7.929	0.4432	3481	7.866	0.3936	3480	7.810
520	0.6075	3526	8.056	0.5203	3525	7.984	0.4549	3524	7.921	0.4041	3523	7.866
540	0.6230	3570	8.110	0.5337	3569	8.038	0.4667	3568	7.975	0.4145	3567	7.920
550	0.6308	3592	8.137	0.5403	3591	8.065	0.4725	3590	8.002	0.4197	3589	7.947
560	0.6387	3613	8.163	0.5470	3612	8.092	0.4784	3611	8.029	0.4250	3610	7.974
580	0.6442	3657	8.215	0.5605	3656	8.144	0.4901	3655	8.081	0.4355	3654	8.026
600	0.6697	3701	8.266	0.5738	3700	8.195	0.5018	3699	8.132	0.4458	4698	8.077
620	0.6852	3745	8.316	0.5872	3745	8.245	0.5135	3744	8.182	0.4561	3743	8.127
640	0.7007	3790	8.365	0.6005	3789	8.294	0.5253	3788	8.232	0.4665	3787	8.177
650	0.7085	3812	8.389	0.6071	3811	8.318	0.5311	3810	8.256	0.4717	3809	8.201
660	0.7162	3835	8.413	0.6138	3834	8.342	0.5369	3833	8.280	0.4769	3832	8.225
680	0.7317	3880	8.461	0.6270	3879	8.390	0.5485	3878	8.328	0.4873	3877	8.273
700	0.7472	3925	8.508	0.6402	3924	8.437	0.5601	3924	8.375	0.4976	3923	8.321
720	0.7627	3970	8.555	0.6535	3970	8.484	0.5718	3969	8.422	0.5079	3969	8.367
740	0.7782	4016	8.601	0.6668	4016	8.530	0.5834	4015	8.468	0.5183	4015	8.413
750	0.7859	4039	8.624	0.6735	4039	8.552	0.5893	4038	8.490	0.5235	4038	8.436
760	0.7937	4062	8.646	0.6802	4062	8.575	0.5951	4061	8.513	0.5287	4061	8.458
780	0.8091	4108	8.690	0.6933	4108	8.619	0.6066	4108	8.557	0.5390	4108	8.503
800	0.8245	4155	8.734	0.7065	4155	8.663	0.6182	4155	8.601	0.5493	4154	8.547
820	0.8400	4202	8.777	0.7199	4202	8.706	0.6298	4202	8.645	0.5597	4201	8.590
840	0.8554	4250	8.820	0.7331	4249	8.749	0.6413	4249	8.688	0.5700	4249	8.633
850	0.8631	4274	8.842	0.7397	4273	8.771	0.6471	4273	8.709	0.5751	4273	8.655
860	0.8708	4298	8.863	0.7463	4297	8.792	0.6529	4297	8.730	0.5802	4297	8.676
880	0.8862	4345	8.905	0.7595	4345	8.834	0.6645	4345	8.772	0.5906	4344	8.718
900	0.9016	4393	8.946	0.7727	4393	8.875	0.6761	4392	8.814	0.6009	4392	8.759
920	0.9171	4441	8.987	0.7860	4441	8.916	0.6877	4440	8.855	0.6112	4440	8.800
940	0.9326	4489	9.028	0.7992	4489	8.957	0.6993	4488	8.895	0.6216	4488	8.840
950	0.9403	4513	9.048	0.8058	4513	8.977	0.7051	4512	8.915	0.6268	4512	8.860
960	0.9480	4537	9.067	0.8124	4537	8.996	0.7109	4536	8.935	0.6319	4536	8.880
980	0.9633	4586	9.107	0.8256	4585	9.036	0.7224	4585	8.974	0.6421	4585	8.919
1000	0.9786	4634	9.145	0.8388	4634	9.074	0.7338	4634	9.013	0.6523	4633	8.958

Table 3-4 Properties of Superheated Steam (H_2O) *(continued)*

Pressure $p=$	10 bar			12 bar			14 bar			16 bar		
Temperature	t_s = 179.88 °C h'' = 2 778 kJ/kg v'' = 0.1946 m3/kg s'' = 6.587 kJ/(kg K)			t_s = 187.95 °C h'' = 2 785 kJ/kg v'' = 0.1633 m3/kg s'' = 6.523 kJ/(kg K)			t_s = 195.04 °C h'' = 2 790 kJ/kg v'' = 0.1408 m3/kg s'' = 6.469 kJ/(kg K)			t_s = 201.36 °C h'' = 2 793 kJ/kg v'' = 0.1238 m3/kg s'' = 6.422 kJ/(kg K)		
t	v	h	s	v	h	s	v	h	s	v	h	s
°C	m³/kg	kJ/kg	kJ/(kg K)	m³/kg	kJ/kg	kJ/(kg K)	m³/kg	kJ/kg	kJ/(kg K)	m³/kg	kJ/kg	kJ/(kg K)
0	0.0009996	1.1	0.0000	0.0009995	1.3	0.0000	0.0009994	1.5	0.0000	0.0009994	1.7	0.0000
20	0.0010014	84.7	0.2960	0.0010013	84.9	0.2959	0.0010012	85.1	0.2958	0.0010011	85.3	0.2958
40	0.0010075	168.3	0.5712	0.0010074	168.5	0.5711	0.0010073	168.7	0.5710	0.0010072	168.8	0.5710
50	0.0010117	210.1	0.7024	0.0010116	210.2	0.7023	0.0010115	210.4	0.7022	0.0010114	210.5	0.7022
60	0.0010166	251.8	0.8298	0.0010165	251.9	0.8297	0.0010164	252.1	0.8296	0.0010163	252.2	0.8296
80	0.0010285	335.4	1.0740	0.0010284	335.5	1.0738	0.0010282	335.7	1.0736	0.0010282	335.8	1.0735
100	0.0010430	419.3	1.3058	0.0010429	419.4	1.3056	0.0010427	419.6	1.3054	0.0010426	419.7	1.3052
120	0.0010598	503.9	1.5261	0.0010597	504.0	1.5259	0.0010596	504.2	1.5257	0.0010595	504.3	1.5256
140	0.0010794	589.2	1.737	0.0010793	589.3	1.737	0.0010792	589.5	1.736	0.0010790	589.6	1.736
150	0.0010902	632.1	1.840	0.0010901	632.2	1.839	0.0010900	632.4	1.839	0.0010898	632.5	1.839
160	0.0011018	675.4	1.941	0.0011016	675.5	1.940	0.0011015	675.7	1.940	0.0011013	675.7	1.940
180	0.1949	2778	6.588	0.0011273	763.2	2.138	0.0011271	763.2	1.137	0.0011270	763.2	2.137
200	0.2060	2827	6.692	0.1693	2816	6.588	0.1429	2803	6.497	0.0011565	852.4	2.329
220	0.2169	2874	6.788	0.1788	2865	6.688	0.1515	2855	6.602	0.1309	2844	6.524
240	0.2274	2918	6.877	0.1879	2911	6.780	0.1596	2902	6.697	0.1382	2893	6.622
250	0.2326	2940	6.920	0.1924	2933	6.824	0.1635	2925	6.741	0.1417	2917	6.667
260	0.2377	2962	6.961	0.1967	2955	6.866	0.1673	2948	6.784	0.1452	2940	6.711
280	0.2478	3005	7.040	0.2054	2999	6.947	0.1748	2992	6.867	0.1519	2986	6.796
300	0.2578	3048	7.116	0.2139	3042	7.025	0.1823	3036	6.945	0.1585	3030	6.877
320	0.2677	3091	7.189	0.2221	3086	7.099	0.1894	3080	7.021	0.1649	3075	6.953
340	0.2774	3134	7.261	0.2302	3129	7.171	0.1965	3125	7.094	0.1712	3120	7.027
350	0.2822	3156	7.296	0.2343	3151	7.206	0.2001	3147	7.130	0.1743	3142	7.063
360	0.2871	3177	7.330	0.2384	3173	7.241	0.2036	3169	7.164	0.1775	3164	7.098
380	0.2968	3220	7.397	0.2466	3216	7.308	0.2107	3213	7.232	0.1838	3209	7.166
400	0.3065	3253	7.461	0.2547	3260	7.373	0.2176	3256	7.299	0.1899	3253	7.233
420	0.3160	3306	7.524	0.2627	3302	7.437	0.2246	3300	7.363	0.1960	3297	7.298
440	0.3255	3349	7.585	0.2707	3346	7.499	0.2315	3344	7.425	0.2021	3341	7.360
450	0.3303	3370	7.615	0.2747	3368	7.529	0.2349	3365	7.455	0.2051	3363	7.390
460	0.3351	3392	7.645	0.2786	3390	7.559	0.2383	3387	7.485	0.2082	3384	7.420
480	0.3445	3435	7.703	0.2865	3433	7.617	0.2452	3431	7.543	0.2141	3428	7.479
500	0.3539	3479	7.761	0.2944	3477	6.674	0.2520	3474	7.601	0.2201	3472	7.537
520	0.3634	3522	7.817	0.3023	3520	7.730	0.2588	3518	7.657	0.2261	3516	7.593
540	0.3729	3566	7.871	0.3103	3564	7.784	0.2656	3561	7.712	0.2320	3560	7.648
550	0.3776	3588	7.898	0.3143	3586	7.811	0.2690	3584	7.739	0.2350	3582	7.675
560	0.3824	3609	7.924	0.3182	3608	7.838	0.2725	3606	7.766	0.2381	3604	7.702
580	0.3917	3653	7.976	0.3261	3652	7.890	0.2793	3650	7.818	0.2441	3648	7.754
600	0.4010	3698	8.027	0.3339	3696	7.942	0.2858	3695	7.870	0.2490	3693	7.806
620	0.4104	3742	8.077	0.3417	3740	7.992	0.2925	3739	7.920	0.2558	3737	7.857
640	0.4199	3787	8.127	0.3495	3785	8.042	0.2993	3784	7.970	0.2617	3782	7.907
650	0.4246	3809	8.152	0.3534	3808	8.067	0.3026	3806	7.994	0.2646	3805	7.932
660	0.4292	3832	8.176	0.3573	3830	8.091	0.3060	3829	8.018	0.2676	3828	7.956
680	0.4384	3877	8.224	0.3651	3875	8.139	0.3127	3874	8.066	0.2735	3873	8.004
700	0.4477	3923	8.272	0.3728	3921	8.187	0.3194	3920	8.114	0.2783	3919	8.052
720	0.4571	3968	9.318	0.3807	3967	8.233	0.3261	3966	8.161	0.2852	3965	8.099
740	0.4664	4014	8.364	0.3884	4013	8.279	0.3327	4012	8.207	0.2911	4011	8.145
750	0.4711	4037	8.387	0.3923	4036	8.302	0.3361	4035	8.230	0.2940	4034	8.168
760	0.4757	4060	8.409	0.3962	4059	8.325	0.3394	4058	8.253	0.2969	4057	8.191
780	0.4850	4107	8.454	0.4040	4106	8.369	0.3461	4105	8.297	0.3028	4105	8.235
800	0.4942	4154	8.498	0.4117	4153	8.413	0.3527	4152	8.341	0.3086	4151	8.279
820	0.5036	4201	8.542	0.4195	4200	8.457	0.3594	4199	8.385	0.3144	4199	8.323
840	0.5128	4249	9.584	0.4272	4248	8.499	0.3660	4247	8.428	0.3202	4246	8.366
850	0.5174	4272	8.606	0.4310	4272	8.521	0.3693	4271	8.449	0.3231	4270	8.387
860	0.5221	4296	8.627	0.4349	4296	8.542	0.3727	4295	8.470	0.3260	4294	8.408
880	0.5314	4344	8.669	0.4427	4343	8.584	0.3793	4343	8.512	0.3318	4342	8.451
900	0.5406	4392	8.710	0.4504	4391	8.626	0.3860	4391	8.554	0.3377	4390	8.492
920	0.5500	4440	8.751	0.4582	4432	8.667	0.3927	4439	8.595	0.3435	4438	8.533
940	0.5592	4488	8.791	0.4660	4487	8.707	0.3994	4487	8.635	0.3493	4486	8.574
950	0.5638	4512	8.811	0.4699	4511	7.727	0.4027	4511	8.655	0.3522	4510	8.594
960	0.5685	4536	8.831	0.4737	4535	8.747	0.4061	4535	8.675	0.3551	4534	8.614
980	0.5777	4584	8.870	0.4814	4584	8.786	9.4127	4584	8.714	0.3609	4583	8.653
1000	0.5870	4633	8.909	0.4890	4632	8.825	0.4192	4632	8.753	0.3666	4632	8.691

Table 3-4   Properties of Superheated Steam (H₂O)   *(continued)*

Pressure p=	18 bar			20 bar			25 bar			30 bar		
Temperature	t_s = 207.10 °C h'' = 2 796 kJ/kg v'' = 0.1104 m3/kg s'' = 6.379 kJ/(kg K)			t_s = 212.37 °C h'' = 2 799 kJ/kg v'' = 0.09958 m3/kg s'' = 6.340 kJ/(kg K)			t_s = 223.93 °C h'' = 2 802 kJ/kg v'' = 0.07993 m3/kg s'' = 6.256 kJ/(kg K)			t_s = 233.83 °C h'' = 2 804 kJ/kg v'' = 0.06665 m3/kg s'' = 6.186 kJ/(kg K)		
t °C	v m³/kg	h kJ/kg	s kJ/(kg K)	v m³/kg	h kJ/kg	s kJ/(kg K)	v m³/kg	h kJ/kg	s kJ/(kg K)	v m³/kg	h kJ/kg	s kJ/(kg K)
0	0.0009992	1.9	0.0000	0.0009991	2.1	0.0000	0.0009989	2.6	0.0000	0.0009986	3.1	0.0000
20	0.0010010	85.5	0.2957	0.0010009	85.7	0.2957	0.0010007	86.2	0.2975	0.0010004	86.7	0.2956
40	0.0010071	169.0	0.5709	0.0010070	169.2	0.5709	0.0010068	169.7	0.5708	0.0010065	170.1	0.5707
50	0.0010113	210.7	0.7021	0.0010112	210.9	0.7020	0.0010110	211.4	0.7019	0.0010107	211.8	0.7018
60	0.0010162	252.4	0.8295	0.0010161	252.6	0.8294	0.0010159	253.1	0.8292	0.0010157	253.5	0.8290
80	0.0010281	336.0	1.0733	0.0010280	336.2	1.0731	0.0010277	336.6	1.0728	0.0010275	337.0	1.0726
100	0.0010425	419.9	1.3050	0.0010424	420.1	1.3048	0.0010422	420.5	1.3043	0.0010419	420.9	1.3038
120	0.0010594	504.5	1.5254	0.0010593	504.7	1.5252	0.0010590	505.1	1.5247	0.0010587	505.4	1.5244
140	0.0010789	589.8	1.736	0.0010787	589.9	1.736	0.0010785	590.3	1.735	0.0010782	590.6	1.735
150	0.0010897	632.7	1.838	0.0010895	632.8	1.838	0.0010892	633.1	1.838	0.0010889	633.4	1.837
160	0.0011012	675.8	1.939	0.0011011	675.9	1.939	0.0011007	676.2	1.938	0.0011004	676.4	1.938
180	0.0011268	763.2	2.136	0.0011267	763.2	2.136	0.0011262	763.5	2.135	0.0011258	763.7	2.134
200	0.0011562	852.4	2.328	0.0011561	852.4	2.328	0.0011556	852.5	2.327	0.0011551	852.6	2.326
220	0.1149	2822	6.452	0.1021	2821	6.385	0.0011898	943.6	2.516	0.0011891	943.5	2.514
240	0.1216	2884	6.554	0.1084	2875	6.491	0.08453	2850	6.351	0.06826	2823	6.225
250	0.1248	2908	6.601	0.1114	2900	6.539	0.08713	2878	6.404	0.07067	2853	6.283
260	0.1280	2932	6.646	0.1143	2924	6.585	0.08962	2904	6.454	0.07294	2882	6.337
280	0.1341	2979	6.732	0.1200	2972	6.674	0.09437	2955	6.547	0.07720	2937	6.438
300	0.1401	3025	6.814	0.1255	3019	6.757	0.09891	3004	6.635	0.08119	2988	6.530
320	0.1460	3071	6.892	0.1308	3065	6.837	0.1033	3052	6.717	0.08500	3038	6.615
340	0.1516	3116	6.966	0.1358	3111	6.913	0.1075	3099	6.795	0.08870	3087	6.696
350	0.1545	3138	7.003	0.1384	3134	6.949	0.1096	3123	6.833	0.09051	3111	6.735
360	0.1573	3160	7.039	0.1410	3156	6.985	0.1117	3146	6.870	0.09230	3135	6.773
380	0.1629	3205	7.108	0.1461	3201	7.055	0.1159	3192	6.941	0.09582	3182	6.847
400	0.1683	3249	7.175	0.1511	3246	7.122	0.1201	3238	7.010	0.09929	3229	6.916
420	0.1738	3294	7.240	0.1560	3291	7.187	0.1241	3283	7.076	0.1027	3275	6.984
440	0.1792	3338	7.303	0.1609	3335	7.251	0.1281	3328	7.140	0.1061	3321	7.048
450	0.1819	3360	7.333	0.1634	3357	7.282	0.1301	3350	7.172	0.1078	3343	7.080
460	0.1847	3381	7.363	0.1659	3379	7.312	0.1321	3373	7.202	0.1095	3366	7.111
480	0.1900	3425	7.422	0.1707	3423	7.371	0.1360	3417	7.262	0.1128	3411	7.172
500	0.1953	3470	7.480	0.1755	3468	7.429	0.1399	3462	7.321	0.1161	3456	7.231
520	0.2007	3514	7.537	0.1804	3512	7.486	0.1438	3507	7.378	0.1194	3501	7.289
540	0.2061	3558	7.592	0.1851	3556	7.542	0.1477	3552	7.434	0.1227	3547	7.345
550	0.2088	3580	7.619	0.1875	3578	7.569	0.1497	3574	7.461	0.1243	3569	7.373
560	0.2115	3602	7.646	0.1900	3600	7.596	0.1516	3597	7.488	0.1260	3592	7.400
580	0.2167	3647	7.698	0.1948	3645	7.649	0.1555	3641	7.542	0.1292	3637	7.454
600	0.2219	3691	7.750	0.1995	3690	7.701	0.1593	3686	7.594	0.1325	3682	7.506
620	0.2272	3736	7.801	0.2043	3735	7.752	0.1631	3732	7.646	0.1357	3728	7.558
640	0.2325	3781	7.851	0.2090	3780	7.802	0.1670	3777	7.696	0.1389	3773	7.608
650	0.2351	3803	7.876	0.2114	3802	7.827	0.1689	3799	7.721	0.1405	3796	7.633
660	0.2377	3826	7.900	0.2137	3825	7.851	0.1708	3822	7.746	0.1421	3819	7.658
680	0.2429	3871	7.948	0.2185	3871	7.899	0.1746	3868	7.794	0.1453	3865	7.707
700	0.2481	3917	7.996	0.2232	3917	7.947	0.1784	3914	7.842	0.1484	3911	7.755
720	0.2534	3963	8.043	0.2279	3963	7.994	0.1822	3960	7.889	0.1516	3957	7.803
740	0.2586	4009	8.089	0.2326	4009	8.040	0.1860	4006	7.935	0.1548	4004	7.849
750	0.2613	4033	8.112	0.2350	4032	8.063	0.1879	4030	7.958	0.1564	4027	7.872
760	0.2639	4056	8.135	0.2373	4055	8.086	0.1897	4053	7.981	0.1580	4050	7.895
780	0.2691	4103	8.180	0.2421	4102	8.130	0.1934	4100	8.026	0.1610	4097	7.940
800	0.2742	4150	8.224	0.2467	4150	8.174	0.1971	4147	8.070	0.1641	4145	7.984
820	0.2794	4198	8.268	0.2514	4197	8.218	0.2009	4195	8.114	0.1673	4193	8.028
840	0.2845	4245	8.311	0.2560	4245	8.262	0.2046	4243	8.158	0.1704	4241	8.072
850	0.2871	4269	8.332	0.2583	4269	8.283	0.2065	4267	8.179	0.1720	4265	8.093
860	0.2897	4293	8.354	0.2606	4293	8.304	0.2084	4291	8.200	0.1735	4289	8.115
880	0.2949	4341	8.396	0.2654	4340	8.346	0.2121	4339	8.242	0.1767	4337	8.157
900	0.3001	4389	8.438	0.2700	4388	8.388	0.2158	4387	8.284	0.1798	4386	8.199
920	0.3053	4437	8.478	0.2747	4437	8.429	0.2196	4435	8.325	0.1830	4434	8.240
940	0.3105	4485	8.519	0.2794	4485	8.469	0.2234	4484	8.365	0.1861	4482	8.280
950	0.3131	4510	8.539	0.2817	4509	8.489	0.2252	4508	8.385	0.1877	4506	8.300
960	0.3157	4534	8.559	0.2841	4533	8.509	0.2271	4532	8.403	0.1892	4331	8.320
980	0.3208	4582	8.598	0.2887	4582	8.549	0.2308	4581	8.445	0.1923	4579	8.360
1000	0.3258	4631	8.637	0.2933	4630	8.588	0.2345	4629	8.484	0.1953	4628	8.399

Table 3-4 Properties of Superheated Steam (H₂O) *(continued)*

Pressure p=	35 bar			40 bar			45 bar			50 bar		
Temperature	t_s = 242.54 °C h'' = 2 803 kJ/kg v'' = 0.05704 m3/kg s'' = 6.125 kJ/(kg K)			t_s = 250.33 °C h'' = 2 801 kJ/kg v'' = 0.04977 m3/kg s'' = 6.070 kJ/(kg K)			t_s = 257.41 °C h'' = 2 798 kJ/kg v'' = 0.04404 m3/kg s'' = 6.020 kJ/(kg K)			t_s = 263.91 °C h'' = 2 794 kJ/kg v'' = 0.03944 m3/kg s'' = 5.973 kJ/(kg K)		
t	v	h	s	v	h	s	v	h	s	v	h	s
°C	m³/kg	kJ/kg	kJ/(kg K)	m³/kg	kJ/kg	kJ/(kg K)	m³/kg	kJ/kg	kJ/(kg K)	m³/kg	kJ/kg	kJ/(kg K)
0	0.0009983	3.7	0.0001	0.0009981	4.2	0.0002	0.0009978	4.7	0.0003	0.0009976	5.2	0.0004
20	0.0001002	87.2	0.2955	0.0010000	87.6	0.2953	0.0009979	88.1	0.2952	0.0009995	88.5	0.2951
40	0.0010063	170.6	0.5706	0.0010061	171.0	0.5704	0.0010059	171.5	0.5702	0.0010056	171.9	0.5699
50	0.0010105	212.3	0.7015	0.0010103	212.7	0.7012	0.0010101	213.2	0.7008	0.0010098	213.6	0.7005
60	0.0010154	254.0	0.8286	0.0010152	254.4	0.8282	0.0010150	254.9	0.8277	0.0010147	255.3	0.8273
80	0.0010272	337.4	1.0722	0.0010270	337.8	1.0718	0.0010268	338.3	1.0713	0.0010265	338.7	1.0709
100	0.0010416	421.3	1.3034	0.0010414	421.7	1.3030	0.0010411	422.1	1.3025	0.0010408	422.5	1.3020
120	0.0010584	505.8	1.5240	0.0010582	506.2	1.5236	0.0010579	506.6	1.5230	0.0010576	506.9	1.5223
140	0.0010778	590.9	1.735	0.0010776	591.2	1.734	0.0010772	591.6	1.734	0.0010769	591.9	1.733
150	0.0010885	633.7	1.837	0.0010883	634.0	1.836	0.0010879	634.4	1.836	0.0010876	634.7	1.835
160	0.0011000	676.7	1.937	0.0010997	677.0	1.936	0.0010993	677.4	1.936	0.0010990	677.7	1.935
180	0.0011254	764.0	2.133	0.0011250	764.2	2.133	0.0011246	764.6	2.132	0.0011242	764.9	2.131
200	0.0011546	852.9	2.325	0.0011541	853.0	2.324	0.0011536	853.4	2.323	0.0011530	853.6	2.322
220	0.0011885	943.7	2.513	0.0011879	943.8	2.512	0.0011873	944.0	2.511	0.0011867	944.1	2.510
240	0.0012288	1037.4	2.699	0.0012280	1037.4	2.698	0.0012273	1037.4	2.697	0.0012264	1037.4	2.696
250	0.05877	2828	6.173	0.0012511	1085.7	2.791	0.0012502	1085.7	2.790	0.0012492	1085.7	2.789
260	0.06089	2859	6.232	0.05174	2834	6.133	0.04451	2808	6.038	0.0012749	1135.1	2.822
280	0.06482	2918	6.339	0.05550	2898	6.249	0.04818	2876	6.164	0.04224	2854	6.083
300	0.06847	2972	6.437	0.05888	2955	6.352	0.05142	2938	6.273	0.04539	2920	6.200
320	0.07188	3024	6.526	0.06201	3010	6.446	0.05434	2995	6.372	0.04817	2980	6.304
340	0.07514	3075	6.610	0.06496	3062	6.532	0.05705	3049	6.462	0.05071	3036	6.397
350	0.07674	3100	6.649	0.06639	3087	6.573	0.05837	3075	6.504	0.05195	3063	6.440
360	0.07832	3124	6.688	0.06781	3113	6.613	0.05967	3101	6.545	0.05316	3090	6.483
380	0.08143	3172	6.763	0.07062	3162	6.690	0.06223	3152	6.624	0.05553	3142	6.564
400	0.08448	3220	6.835	0.07337	3211	6.762	0.06474	3202	6.699	0.05781	3193	6.640
420	0.08748	3267	6.904	0.07606	3259	6.832	0.06717	3250	6.770	0.06004	3242	6.712
440	0.09043	3313	6.970	0.07870	3306	6.900	0.06955	3298	6.838	0.06224	3291	6.781
450	0.09190	3336	7.002	0.08001	3329	6.933	0.07073	3322	6.871	0.06332	3315	6.815
460	0.09336	3559	7.033	0.08130	3353	6.965	0.07190	3346	6.903	0.06439	3339	6.848
480	0.09625	3405	7.095	0.08388	3399	7.027	0.07421	3393	6.966	0.06650	3386	6.912
500	0.09910	3451	7.155	0.08642	3445	7.087	0.07649	3439	7.028	0.06858	3433	6.974
520	0.1019	3496	7.213	0.08895	3491	7.146	0.07877	3486	7.088	0.07064	3480	7.033
540	0.1048	3542	7.270	0.09145	3537	7.203	0.08103	3532	7.145	0.07268	3527	7.091
550	0.1062	3564	7.298	0.09270	3560	7.231	0.08215	3555	7.173	0.07370	3550	7.120
560	0.1076	3587	7.325	0.09394	3583	7.259	0.08326	3578	7.201	0.07471	3574	7.148
580	0.1105	3633	7.379	0.09640	3629	7.313	0.08546	3624	7.255	0.07672	3620	7.203
600	0.1132	3678	7.432	0.09885	3674	7.367	0.08766	3670	7.309	0.07870	3666	7.257
620	0.1160	3724	7.484	0.1013	3720	7.419	0.08982	3716	7.361	0.08065	3713	7.310
640	0.1188	3770	7.534	0.1037	3766	7.470	0.09198	3762	7.413	0.08260	3759	7.362
650	0.1202	3793	7.559	0.1049	3789	7.495	0.09305	3785	7.438	0.08357	3782	7.387
660	0.1215	3816	7.584	0.1061	3812	7.520	0.09412	3808	7.463	0.08454	3805	7.412
680	0.1243	3862	7.633	0.1085	3858	7.570	0.09626	3855	7.513	0.08648	3852	7.462
700	0.1269	3908	7.681	0.1109	3905	7.618	0.09841	3902	7.561	0.08842	3899	7.510
720	0.1297	3954	7.729	0.1133	3952	7.666	0.1006	3949	7.609	0.09035	3946	7.558
740	0.1325	4001	7.776	0.1157	3998	7.712	0.1027	3996	7.656	0.09227	3993	7.606
750	0.1339	4024	7.799	0.1169	4022	7.735	0.1038	4019	7.679	0.09323	4017	7.629
760	0.1352	4048	7.822	0.1181	4045	7.758	0.1048	4043	7.702	0.09419	4041	7.652
780	0.1379	4095	7.868	0.1205	4093	7.804	0.1070	4091	7.748	0.09612	4088	7.698
800	0.1405	4143	7.912	0.1228	4141	7.848	0.1091	4138	7.792	0.09803	4136	7.742
820	0.1432	4191	7.956	0.1252	4188	7.892	0.1113	4186	7.836	0.09993	4184	7.786
840	0.1459	4239	8.000	0.1276	4236	7.936	0.1134	4235	7.880	0.1018	4232	7.830
850	0.1473	4263	8.021	0.1288	4261	7.958	0.1145	4259	7.902	0.1027	4257	7.852
860	0.1487	4287	8.042	0.1300	4285	7.979	0.1156	4283	7.924	0.1037	4281	7.874
880	0.1513	4335	8.085	0.1324	4333	8.022	0.1176	4332	7.966	0.1057	4329	7.916
900	0.1540	4384	8.127	0.1346	4382	8.064	0.1196	4380	8.008	0.1075	4387	7.958
920	0.1568	4432	8.168	0.1370	4430	8.105	0.1218	4429	8.050	0.1094	4427	8.000
940	0.1595	4480	8.208	0.1394	4479	8.146	0.1240	4477	8.090	0.1114	4475	8.040
950	0.1608	4505	8.228	0.1405	4503	8.166	0.1250	4502	8.110	0.1123	4500	8.060
960	0.1621	4529	8.248	0.1417	4527	8.186	0.1260	4526	8.130	0.1132	4524	8.080
980	0.1647	4578	8.288	0.1441	4576	8.226	0.1280	4575	8.170	0.1150	4573	8.120
1000	0.1673	4626	8.327	0.1464	4625	8.265	0.1300	4623	8.208	0.1170	4622	8.159

Table 3-4 Properties of Superheated Steam (H₂O) (continued)

Pressure $p=$	60 bar			70 bar			80 bar			90 bar		
Tempera-ture	t_s = 275.56 °C h'' = 2 785 kJ/kg v'' = 0.03243 m3/kg s'' = 5.890 kJ/(kg K)			t_s = 285.80 °C h'' = 2 772 kJ/kg v'' = 0.02737 m3/kg s'' = 5.814 kJ/(kg K)			t_s = 294.98 °C h'' = 2 758 kJ/kg v'' = 0.02352 m3/kg s'' = 5.745 kJ/(kg K)			t_s = 303.32 °C h'' = 2 743 kJ/kg v'' = 0.02048 m3/kg s'' = 5.678 kJ/(kg K)		
t	v	h	s	v	h	s	v	h	s	v	h	s
°C	m³/kg	kJ/kg	kJ/(kg K)	m³/kg	kJ/kg	kJ/(kg K)	m³/kg	kJ/kg	kJ/(kg K)	m³/kg	kJ/kg	kJ/(kg K)
0	0.0009971	6.2	0.0004	0.0009966	7.2	0.0004	0.0009961	8.2	0.0004	0.0009956	9.2	0.0004
20	0.0009991	89.4	0.2948	0.0009987	90.4	0.2945	0.0009983	91.3	0.2943	0.0009978	92.3	0.2941
40	0.0010052	172.8	0.5694	0.0010048	173.7	0.5689	0.0010043	174.6	0.5686	0.0010038	175.5	0.5681
50	0.0010094	214.4	0.7000	0.0010090	215.3	0.6995	0.0010085	216.2	0.6992	0.0010080	217.1	0.6986
60	0.0010143	256.1	0.8268	0.0010139	256.9	0.8263	0.0010134	257.8	0.8260	0.0010129	258.7	0.8253
80	0.0010261	339.5	1.0702	0.0010257	340.3	1.0694	0.0010254	341.2	1.0689	0.0010249	342.1	1.0682
100	0.0010403	423.3	1.3012	0.0010400	424.1	1.3003	0.0010398	424.9	1.2996	0.0010393	425.7	1.2988
120	0.0010571	507.7	1.5215	0.0010567	508.4	1.5205	0.0010564	509.1	1.5198	0.0010559	509.8	1.5189
140	0.0010763	592.6	1.732	0.0010758	593.2	1.731	0.0010754	593.9	1.730	0.0010749	594.6	1.729
150	0.0010869	635.4	1.834	0.0010864	636.0	1.833	0.0010859	636.6	1.832	0.0010854	637.3	1.831
160	0.0010938	678.4	1.934	0.0010977	679.0	1.933	0.0010972	679.6	1.931	0.0010966	680.3	1.930
180	0.0011234	765.5	2.119	0.0011226	766.1	2.128	0.0011220	766.7	2.126	0.0011213	767.4	2.125
200	0.0011522	854.0	2.320	0.0011512	854.5	2.319	0.0011504	855.0	2.317	0.0011496	855.5	2.316
220	0.0011955	944.5	2.508	0.0011845	944.8	2.506	0.0011833	945.1	2.504	0.0011822	945.5	2.502
240	0.0012249	1037.6	2.693	0.0012235	1037.8	2.691	0.0012221	1037.9	2.688	0.0012207	1038.1	2.686
250	0.0012476	1085.7	2.786	0.0012459	1085.7	2.783	0.0012443	1085.7	2.781	0.0012427	1085.7	2.778
260	0.0012727	1134.8	2.879	0.0012706	1134.6	2.876	0.0012689	1134.4	2.873	0.0012669	1134.2	2.870
280	0.03315	2803	5.923	0.0013304	1235.9	3.063	0.0013275	1235.4	3.059	0.0013246	1234.9	3.056
300	0.03620	2800	6.060	0.02948	2835	5.925	0.02429	2784	5.788	0.0014016	1344.3	3.249
320	0.03884	2948	6.177	0.03206	2913	6.058	0.02687	2874	5.943	0.02272	2829	5.827
340	0.04118	3010	6.279	0.03430	2981	6.171	0.02904	2951	6.070	0.02488	2916	5.972
350	0.04227	3039	6.326	0.03532	3012	6.222	0.03003	2985	6.126	0.02586	2954	6.033
360	0.04334	3067	6.371	0.03630	3042	6.270	0.03098	3017	6.177	0.02678	2989	6.089
380	0.04542	3121	6.456	0.03819	3099	6.360	0.03274	3077	6.272	0.02847	3054	6.189
400	0.04742	3174	6.535	0.03997	3155	6.442	0.03438	3135	6.358	0.03001	3114	6.280
420	0.04935	3225	6.610	0.04170	3208	6.520	0.03595	3190	6.439	0.03147	3172	6.364
440	0.05124	3275	6.681	0.04338	3259	6.593	0.03746	3244	6.515	0.03286	3227	6.443
450	0.05217	3299	6.716	0.04420	3285	6.628	0.03821	3270	6.552	0.03354	3254	6.481
460	0.05309	3324	6.750	0.04501	3310	6.663	0.03894	3296	6.588	0.03421	3281	6.518
480	0.05490	3373	6.815	0.04661	3360	6.731	0.04037	3347	6.657	0.03552	3334	6.589
500	0.05667	3421	6.878	0.04817	3409	6.795	0.04177	3397	6.722	0.03680	3386	6.656
520	0.05842	3469	6.939	0.04970	3458	6.858	0.04315	3447	6.785	0.03805	3436	6.720
540	0.06016	3517	6.999	0.05122	3506	6.918	0.04449	3496	6.846	0.03927	3485	6.783
550	0.06103	3540	7.028	0.05197	3530	6.947	0.04516	3520	6.876	0.03988	3510	6.813
560	0.06189	3564	7.056	0.05272	3554	6.976	0.04583	3544	6.905	0.04049	3534	6.843
580	0.06358	3611	7.111	0.05421	3602	7.032	0.04716	3592	6.963	0.04169	3582	6.901
600	0.06525	3658	7.165	0.05556	3649	7.087	0.04844	3640	7.019	0.04285	3631	6.957
620	0.06691	3705	7.219	0.05708	3697	7.141	0.04972	3688	7.073	0.04399	3679	7.012
640	0.06855	3751	7.271	0.05851	3744	7.194	0.05098	3736	7.126	0.04513	3728	7.066
650	0.06937	3775	7.297	0.05923	3768	7.220	0.05161	3760	7.152	0.04570	3752	7.092
660	0.07019	3798	7.322	0.05995	3791	7.246	0.05225	3784	7.178	0.04627	3776	7.118
680	0.07183	3846	8.372	0.06137	3839	7.296	0.05350	3832	7.230	0.04739	3825	7.170
700	0.07347	3893	7.422	0.06277	3887	7.346	0.05475	3881	7.280	0.04851	3874	7.220
720	0.07509	3940	7.471	0.06417	3935	7.395	0.05599	3929	7.329	0.04963	3922	7.270
740	0.07670	3988	7.519	0.06557	3983	7.443	0.05723	3977	7.377	0.05075	3971	7.319
750	0.07751	4012	7.542	0.06627	4007	7.467	0.05785	4002	7.401	0.05130	3996	7.343
760	0.07831	4036	7.565	0.06697	4031	7.490	0.05847	4026	7.425	0.05185	4020	6.367
780	0.07992	4084	7.610	0.06836	4079	7.535	0.05970	4074	7.470	0.05295	4069	7.413
800	0.08153	4132	7.655	0.06975	4127	7.580	0.06092	4122	7.515	0.05405	4117	7.459
820	0.08314	4180	7.699	0.07114	4176	7.624	0.06214	4171	7.559	0.05515	4166	7.504
840	0.08474	4229	7.743	0.07252	4225	7.668	0.06337	4221	7.603	0.05623	4216	7.548
850	0.08554	4253	7.765	0.07321	4249	7.690	0.06398	4245	7.625	0.05677	4240	7.570
860	0.08634	4277	7.787	0.07390	4273	7.712	0.06459	4269	7.647	0.05732	4264	7.592
880	0.08794	4326	7.830	0.07527	4322	7.755	0.06579	4318	7.690	0.05840	4314	7.635
900	0.08953	4375	7.872	0.07665	4371	7.797	0.06700	4367	7.732	0.05949	4363	7.677
920	0.09111	4424	7.914	0.07802	4420	7.839	0.06819	4416	7.774	0.06056	4413	7.719
940	0.09269	4472	7.954	0.07938	4469	7.879	0.06939	4466	7.816	0.06162	4462	7.761
950	0.09348	4496	7.974	0.08005	4493	7.899	0.06998	4490	7.836	0.06215	4487	7.781
960	0.09427	4521	7.994	0.08073	4518	7.919	0.07058	4515	7.856	0.06268	4512	7.801
980	0.09584	4570	8.034	0.08208	4567	7.959	0.07176	4565	7.896	0.06374	4561	7.841
1000	0.09740	4619	8.073	0.08343	4617	7.999	0.07295	4614	7.936	0.06480	4611	7.881

Table 3-4   Properties of Superheated Steam (H₂O)   (continued)

Pressure p=	100 bar			110 bar			120 bar			130 bar		
Tempera-ture	t_s = 310.96 °C h'' = 2 725 kJ/kg v'' = 0.01803 m3/kg s'' = 5.615 kJ/(kg K)			t_s = 318.04 °C h'' = 2 705 kJ/kg v'' = 0.01598 m3/kg s'' = 5.553 kJ/(kg K)			t_s = 324.63 °C h'' = 2 685 kJ/kg v'' = 0.01426 m3/kg s'' = 5.492 kJ/(kg K)			t_s = 330.81 °C h'' = 2 662 kJ/kg v'' = 0.01277 m3/kg s'' = 5.432 kJ/(kg K)		
t °C	v m³/kg	h kJ/kg	s kJ/(kg K)	v m³/kg	h kJ/kg	s kJ/(kg K)	v m³/kg	h kJ/kg	s kJ/(kg K)	v m³/kg	h kJ/kg	s kJ/(kg K)
0	0.0009951	10.2	0.0004	0.0009946	11.2	0.0005	0.0009941	12.2	0.0006	0.0009936	13.2	0.0007
20	0.0009975	93.2	0.2939	0.0009970	94.1	0.2937	0.0009965	95.1	0.2935	0.0009961	96.0	0.2931
40	0.0010033	176.4	0.5677	0.0010028	177.3	0.5672	0.0010024	178.2	0.5668	0.0010020	179.0	0.5664
50	0.0010075	218.0	0.6980	0.0010070	219.9	0.6975	0.0010066	219.8	0.6970	0.0010062	220.6	0.6965
60	0.0010125	259.6	0.8247	0.0010120	260.5	0.8241	0.0010116	216.4	0.8236	0.0010112	262.2	0.8230
80	0.0010245	342.9	1.0676	0.0010240	343.8	1.0669	0.0010236	344.6	1.0662	0.0010231	345.4	1.0654
100	0.0010386	426.5	1.2982	0.0010384	427.3	1.2974	0.0010379	428.1	1.2967	0.0010373	428.9	1.2959
120	0.0010552	510.5	1.5182	0.0010549	511.3	1.5173	0.0010544	512.0	1.5165	0.0010538	512.7	1.5156
140	0.0010741	595.3	1.728	0.0010738	596.0	1.728	0.0010732	596.7	1.727	0.0010725	597.4	1.726
150	0.0010845	638.0	1.830	0.0010841	638.7	1.829	0.0010835	639.4	1.828	0.0010828	610.1	1.827
160	0.0010956	681.0	1.929	0.0010952	681.7	1.928	0.0010946	682.4	1.927	0.0010939	683.0	1.926
180	0.0011201	768.0	2.123	0.0011197	768.6	2.123	0.0011189	769.1	2.121	0.0011182	769.7	2.119
200	0.0011482	856.0	2.314	0.0011477	856.5	2.312	0.0011468	857.0	2.311	0.0011458	857.4	2.309
220	0.0011805	945.8	2.500	0.0011799	946.2	2.498	0.0011788	946.6	2.497	0.0011777	946.9	2.495
240	0.0012185	1038.3	2.684	0.0012178	1038.5	2.682	0.0012164	1038.7	2.680	0.0012150	1038.9	2.678
250	0.0012402	1085.7	2.776	0.0012394	1085.8	2.774	0.0012377	1085.8	2.772	0.0012361	1085.9	2.769
260	0.0012650	1134.1	2.868	0.0012630	1134.0	2.865	0.0012612	1133.9	2.863	0.0012593	1133.8	2.860
280	0.0013217	1234.5	3.053	0.0013190	1234.1	3.049	0.0013164	1233.7	3.046	0.0013137	1233.3	3.043
300	0.0013970	1342.2	3.244	0.0013928	1341.1	3.239	0.0013886	1340.0	3.235	0.0013847	1339.0	3.230
320	0.01926	2778	5.705	0.01629	2719	5.579	0.001493	1459.3	3.441	0.001485	1456.5	3.433
340	0.02150	2878	5.872	0.01868	2836	5.770	0.01624	2789	5.667	0.01403	2737	5.555
350	0.02247	2920	5.940	0.01967	2884	5.849	0.01726	2844	5.755	0.01514	2799	5.657
360	0.02337	2958	6.002	0.02056	2927	5.918	0.01816	2892	5.832	0.01610	2853	5.744
380	0.02498	3028	6.111	0.02214	3002	6.037	0.01973	2974	5.963	0.01767	2945	5.888
400	0.02646	3093	6.207	0.02356	3071	6.138	0.02113	3049	6.071	0.01905	3026	6.006
420	0.02784	3154	6.294	0.02476	3135	6.230	0.02239	3116	6.168	0.02028	3097	6.108
440	0.02915	3211	6.377	0.02612	3194	6.315	0.02357	3177	6.256	0.02143	3159	6.200
450	0.02979	3239	6.416	0.02672	3222	6.355	0.02414	3206	6.298	0.02197	3189	6.243
460	0.03042	3266	6.454	0.02731	3250	6.394	0.02471	3235	6.338	0.02250	3219	6.285
480	0.03163	3320	6.527	0.02844	3305	6.469	0.02578	3291	6.415	0.02352	3277	6.364
500	0.03281	3372	6.596	0.02954	3360	6.540	0.02681	3347	6.487	0.02450	3334	6.438
520	0.03397	3424	6.662	0.03061	3412	6.607	0.02782	3400	6.556	0.02546	3388	6.507
540	0.03510	3474	6.725	0.03167	3463	6.671	0.02880	3452	6.621	0.02638	3441	6.574
550	0.03566	3499	6.756	0.03218	3488	6.702	0.02928	3478	6.653	0.02683	3467	6.606
560	0.03621	3524	6.786	0.03269	3513	6.733	0.02976	3503	6.684	0.02728	3493	6.638
580	0.03730	3572	6.845	0.03370	3563	6.793	0.03070	3553	6.744	0.02817	3543	6.698
600	0.03837	3621	6.901	0.03469	3612	6.850	0.03163	3603	6.803	0.02903	3594	6.758
620	0.03941	3670	6.957	0.03565	3662	6.906	0.03253	3653	6.859	0.02988	3645	6.816
640	0.04045	3719	7.011	0.03661	3711	6.961	0.03342	3703	6.915	0.03071	3696	6.872
650	0.04097	3744	7.038	0.03709	3736	6.988	0.03387	3728	6.942	0.03113	3721	6.899
660	0.04149	3768	7.064	0.03757	3761	7.015	0.03431	3753	6.969	0.03155	3746	6.926
680	0.04252	3818	7.166	0.03851	3811	7.067	0.03519	3804	7.021	0.03236	3797	6.980
700	0.04354	3867	7.167	0.03945	3860	7.118	0.03605	3853	7.073	0.03317	3847	7.032
720	0.04456	3915	7.217	0.04038	3909	7.168	0.03691	3903	7.123	0.03398	3897	7.082
740	0.04556	3964	7.265	0.04130	3958	7.216	0.03777	3952	7.172	0.03478	3947	7.132
750	0.04606	3989	7.289	0.04176	3983	7.240	0.03820	3977	7.196	0.03517	3972	7.156
760	0.04656	4013	7.313	0.04222	4007	7.264	0.03863	4002	7.220	0.03557	3997	7.180
780	0.04756	4062	7.360	0.04314	4057	7.311	0.03947	4052	7.268	0.03635	4047	7.228
800	0.04856	4111	7.406	0.04406	4106	7.357	0.04031	4102	7.314	0.03714	4097	7.274
820	0.04956	4160	7.452	0.04497	4156	7.403	0.04115	4151	7.360	0.03792	4147	7.320
840	0.05054	4210	7.497	0.04587	4205	7.448	0.04199	4201	7.405	0.03969	4197	7.365
850	0.05103	4235	7.519	0.04643	4230	7.470	0.04240	4226	7.427	0.03908	4222	7.388
860	0.05152	4259	7.541	0.04677	4255	7.492	0.04282	4251	7.449	0.03947	4247	7.410
880	0.05250	4309	7.585	0.04767	4305	7.536	0.04363	4301	7.493	0.04023	4297	7.454
900	0.05347	4358	7.627	0.04856	4354	7.579	0.04446	4351	7.536	0.04100	4347	7.498
920	0.05445	4408	7.669	0.04944	4404	7.621	0.04528	4400	7.578	0.04175	4397	7.540
940	0.05541	4457	7.711	0.05032	4454	7.663	0.04609	4450	7.620	0.04250	4447	7.582
950	0.05589	4482	7.732	0.05076	4479	7.684	0.04649	4475	7.641	0.04287	4472	7.603
960	0.05637	4507	7.752	0.05120	4504	7.704	0.04690	4500	7.661	0.04324	4497	7.623
980	0.05733	4557	7.792	0.05206	4553	7.744	0.04770	4550	7.701	0.04400	4547	7.663
1000	0.05829	4606	7.832	0.05294	4603	7.784	0.04850	4600	7.741	0.04475	4597	7.703

Table 3-4   Properties of Superheated Steam (H_2O) *(continued)*

Pressure $p=$	140 bar			150 bar			160 bar			170 bar		
Temperature	t_s = 336.63 °C h'' = 2 638 kJ/kg v'' = 0.01149 m3/kg s'' = 5.372 kJ/(kg K)			t_s = 342.11 °C h'' = 2 611 kJ/kg v'' = 0.01035 m3/kg s'' = 5.310 kJ/(kg K)			t_s = 347.32 °C h'' = 2 582 kJ/kg v'' = 0.009318 m3/kg s'' = 5.247 kJ/(kg K)			t_s = 352.26 °C h'' = 2 548 kJ/kg v'' = 0.008382 m3/kg s'' = 5.177 kJ/(kg K)		
t	v	h	s	v	h	s	v	h	s	v	h	s
°C	m³/kg	kJ/kg	kJ/(kg K)	m³/kg	kJ/kg	kJ/(kg K)	m³/kg	kJ/kg	kJ/(kg K)	m³/kg	kJ/kg	kJ/(kg K)
0	0.0009931	14.2	0.0008	0.0009927	15.2	0.0008	0.0009922	16.2	0.0009	0.0009917	17.2	0.0010
20	0.0009957	96.9	0.2930	0.0009953	97.9	0.2927	0.0009948	98.9	0.2925	0.0009943	99.8	0.2923
40	0.0010016	179.9	0.5660	0.0010012	180.8	0.5656	0.0010007	181.7	0.5653	0.0010003	182.6	0.5650
50	0.0010058	421.4	0.6960	0.0010054	222.3	0.6955	0.0010049	223.2	0.6951	0.0010045	224.1	0.6947
60	0.0010108	263.0	0.8224	0.0010104	263.8	0.8218	0.0010099	264.7	0.8212	0.0010095	265.6	0.8206
80	0.0010226	346.2	1.0648	0.0010222	347.0	1.0641	0.0010217	347.9	1.0634	0.0010213	348.7	1.0627
100	0.0010368	429.6	1.2951	0.0010363	430.4	1.2944	0.0010359	431.2	1.2937	0.0020354	431.9	1.2930
120	0.0010533	513.4	1.5148	0.0010527	514.1	1.5139	0.0010522	514.9	1.5131	0.0010517	515.6	1.5123
140	0.0010719	598.0	1.724	0.0010713	598.7	1.723	0.0010707	599.4	1.722	0.0010701	600.1	1.722
150	0.0010822	640.7	1.826	0.0010815	641.3	1.824	0.0010809	642.0	1.823	0.0010802	642.7	1.823
160	0.0010932	683.6	1.925	0.0010925	684.2	1.923	0.0010918	684.9	1.922	0.0010911	685.5	1.922
180	0.0011174	770.4	2.118	0.0011166	770.8	2.117	0.0011157	771.3	2.116	0.0011149	771.9	2.115
200	0.0011448	857.9	2.308	0.0011439	858.3	2.306	0.0011430	858.8	2.305	0.0011420	859.3	2.303
220	0.0011766	947.3	2.493	0.0011755	947.6	2.491	0.0011744	948.0	2.489	0.0011732	948.4	2.488
240	0.0012136	1039.1	2.676	0.0012123	1039.2	2.674	0.0012109	1039.5	2.672	0.0012095	1039.7	2.670
250	0.0012345	1086.0	2.767	0.0012330	1086.0	2.775	0.0012316	1086.2	2.762	0.0012301	1086.3	2.760
260	0.0012575	1133.8	2.858	0.0012557	1133.7	2.885	0.0012539	1133.7	2.853	0.0012521	1133.7	2.850
280	0.0013111	1232.9	3.040	0.0013086	1232.5	3.007	0.0013061	1232.2	3.035	0.0013037	1231.9	3.031
300	0.0013808	1338.0	3.226	0.0013771	1337.0	3.222	0.0013735	1336.2	3.128	0.001370	1335.4	3.214
320	0.001479	1454.1	3.427	0.001472	1451.7	3.420	0.001466	1449.8	3.414	0.001461	1448.1	3.409
340	0.01197	2672	5.436	0.001633	1592.2	3.654	0.001616	1586.3	3.642	0.001604	1581.1	3.631
350	0.01325	2750	5.556	0.01150	2690	5.442	0.00978	2612	5.302	0.001732	1668	3.770
360	0.01425	2812	5.654	0.01260	2765	5.559	0.01106	2711	5.457	0.00956	2649	5.342
380	0.01588	2914	5.813	0.01430	2880	5.739	0.01289	2843	5.662	0.01161	2803	5.582
400	0.01726	3000	5.942	0.01568	2973	5.878	0.01429	2945	5.816	0.01306	2915	5.753
420	0.01847	3077	6.051	0.01688	3055	5.997	0.01549	3031	5.941	0.01426	3006	5.885
440	0.01957	3141	6.146	0.01796	3123	6.093	0.01655	3103	6.042	0.01531	3083	5.992
450	0.02010	3172	6.190	0.01847	3155	6.139	0.01704	3137	6.090	0.01579	3118	6.042
460	0.02061	3203	6.233	0.01896	3186	6.183	0.01752	3169	6.136	0.01625	3152	6.090
480	0.02158	3262	6.314	0.01991	3248	6.268	0.01844	3233	6.233	0.01714	3218	6.179
500	0.02252	3321	6.390	0.02080	3308	6.346	0.01930	3294	6.303	0.01798	3281	6.261
520	0.02342	3387	6.461	0.02166	3364	6.419	0.02012	3352	6.377	0.01876	3340	6.337
540	0.02431	3430	6.529	0.02250	3418	6.488	0.02092	3407	6.448	0.01952	3396	6.410
550	0.02474	3456	6.562	0.02291	3445	6.521	0.02132	3434	6.482	0.01991	3423	6.444
560	0.02516	3482	6.594	0.02331	3472	6.554	0.02171	3461	6.515	0.02029	3450	6.477
580	0.02600	3534	6.656	0.02411	3524	6.616	0.02249	3514	6.578	0.02104	3504	6.542
600	0.02683	3585	6.716	0.02490	3576	6.677	0.02322	3567	6.640	0.02174	3558	6.604
620	0.02763	3637	6.775	0.02566	3628	6.737	0.02394	3620	6.701	0.02242	3611	6.665
640	0.02842	3688	6.832	0.02641	3680	6.794	0.02465	3672	6.758	0.02310	3664	6.725
650	0.02881	3713	6.859	0.02677	3706	6.822	0.02500	3698	6.786	0.02343	3691	6.752
660	0.02919	3739	6.886	0.02714	3732	6.849	0.02535	3724	6.814	0.02376	3717	6.780
680	0.02995	3790	6.939	0.02786	3784	6.903	0.02603	3777	6.869	0.02440	3770	6.836
700	0.03071	3841	6.992	0.02857	3835	6.956	0.02671	3829	6.922	0.02505	3822	6.890
720	0.03146	3891	7.043	0.02927	3885	7.008	0.02739	3879	6.974	0.02569	3873	6.942
740	0.03221	3941	7.093	0.02998	3936	7.058	0.02806	3930	7.024	0.02633	3924	6.992
750	0.03258	3966	7.118	0.03033	3961	7.083	0.02839	3955	7.049	0.02664	3949	7.017
760	0.03295	3991	7.143	0.03069	3986	7.108	0.02872	3980	7.074	0.02696	3973	7.042
780	0.03370	4042	7.191	0.03138	4036	7.156	0.02936	4031	7.123	0.02758	4026	7.092
800	0.03442	4092	7.238	0.03206	4087	7.204	0.03001	4082	7.171	0.02819	4077	7.140
820	0.03514	4142	7.284	0.03275	4138	7.250	0.03066	4133	7.218	0.02881	4128	7.187
840	0.03588	4192	7.330	0.03344	4188	7.296	0.03131	4183	7.264	0.02941	4179	7.233
850	0.03624	4217	7.352	0.03378	4213	7.319	0.03162	4209	7.287	0.02971	4204	7.256
860	0.03660	4243	7.374	0.03412	4238	7.341	0.03194	4234	7.309	0.03001	4230	7.279
880	0.03732	4293	7.418	0.03479	4289	7.385	0.03257	4284	7.353	0.03061	4280	7.323
900	0.03803	4343	7.462	0.03545	4339	7.429	0.03320	4335	7.397	0.03121	4331	7.367
920	0.03873	4393	7.504	0.03612	4389	7.471	0.03382	4385	7.439	0.03181	4381	7.409
940	0.03943	4443	7.546	0.03678	4439	7.513	0.03445	4436	7.481	0.03240	4432	7.451
950	0.03978	4468	7.567	0.03710	4464	7.534	0.03475	4461	7.502	0.03269	4457	7.472
960	0.04013	4493	7.587	0.03743	4490	7.554	0.03506	4486	7.523	0.03298	4482	7.493
980	0.04083	4543	7.627	0.03809	4540	7.594	0.03567	4536	7.563	0.03356	4533	7.533
1000	0.04152	4593	7.667	0.03873	4590	7.634	0.03628	4587	7.603	0.03412	4584	7.573

Table 3-4 **Properties of Superheated Steam (H₂O)**   (*continued*)

Pressure p=	180 bar			190 bar			200 bar			220 bar		
Tempera-ture	t_s = 356.96 °C h'' = 2 510 kJ/kg v'' = 0.007504 m3/kg s'' = 5.107 kJ/(kg K)			t_s = 361.44 °C h'' = 2 466 kJ/kg v'' = 0.00668 m3/kg s'' = 5.027 kJ/(kg K)			t_s = 365.71 °C h'' = 2 410 kJ/kg v'' = 0.00585 m3/kg s'' = 4.928 kJ/(kg K)			t_s = 373.7 °C h'' = 2 168 kJ/kg v'' = 0.00367 m3/kg s'' = 4.591 kJ/(kg K)		
t	v	h	s	v	h	s	v	h	s	v	h	s
°C	m³/kg	kJ/kg	kJ/(kg K)	m³/kg	kJ/kg	kJ/(kg K)	m³/kg	kJ/kg	kJ/(kg K)	m³/kg	kJ/kg	kJ/(kg K)
0	0.0009913	18.2	0.0011	0.009908	19.2	0.0012	0.0009904	20.2	0.0013	0.0009893	22.2	0.0013
20	0.0009939	100.7	0.2921	0.0009934	101.7	0.2919	0.0009930	102.6	0.2918	0.0009920	104.5	0.2915
40	0.0009999	183.5	0.5647	0.0009994	184.4	0.5643	0.0009990	185.3	0.5640	0.0009981	187.1	0.5634
50	0.0010041	225.0	0.6942	0.0010037	225.8	0.6937	0.0010033	226.7	0.6933	0.0010024	228.4	0.6927
60	0.0010091	266.5	0.8200	0.0010087	267.3	0.8194	0.0010083	268.1	0.8188	0.0010073	269.8	0.8181
80	0.0010209	349.5	1.0620	0.0010204	350.3	1.0613	0.0010200	351.1	1.0605	0.0010190	352.7	1.0596
100	0.0010349	432.7	1.2923	0.0010344	433.4	1.2916	0.0010339	434.2	1.2909	0.0010329	435.7	1.2899
120	0.0010512	516.4	1.5115	0.0010506	517.1	1.5106	0.0010501	517.8	1.5098	0.0010490	519.3	1.5084
140	0.0010695	600.8	1.721	0.0010690	601.5	1.720	0.0010684	602.1	1.719	0.0010671	603.5	1.717
150	0.0010796	643.4	1.822	0.0010790	644.0	1.821	0.0010784	644.6	1.820	0.0010771	646.0	1.818
160	0.0010905	686.2	1.921	0.0010898	686.8	1.920	0.0010891	687.4	1.919	0.0010877	688.7	1.917
180	0.0011142	772.4	2.114	0.0011134	773.0	2.113	0.0011126	773.5	2.112	0.0011110	774.7	2.110
200	0.0011411	859.7	2.302	0.0011402	860.2	2.301	0.0011393	860.6	2.299	0.0011375	861.6	2.297
220	0.0011721	948.7	2.486	0.0011711	949.1	2.485	0.0011700	949.4	2.483	0.0011679	950.2	2.480
240	0.0012082	1039.9	2.668	0.0012069	1040.1	2.666	0.0012056	1040.3	2.664	0.0012030	1040.9	2.661
250	0.0012286	1086.4	2.758	0.0012271	1086.5	2.756	0.0012256	1086.6	2.754	0.0012226	1087.0	2.750
260	0.0012504	1133.7	2.848	0.0012487	1133.7	2.845	0.0012470	1133.6	2.843	0.0012437	1133.8	2.839
280	0.0013013	1231.6	3.028	0.0012990	1231.3	3.025	0.0012968	1230.9	3.023	0.0012926	1230.6	3.017
300	0.0013665	1334.6	3.211	0.0013631	1333.9	3.207	0.0013598	1333.2	3.204	0.0013535	1332.2	3.197
320	0.001455	1446.3	3.403	0.001450	1444.6	3.399	0.001444	1442.9	3.394	0.001434	1440.5	3.384
340	0.001592	1576.6	3.620	0.001580	1572.7	3.611	0.001569	1569.1	3.603	0.001551	1562.6	3.589
350	0.001704	1657	3.751	0.001684	1650	3.736	0.001665	1644	3.724	0.001636	1633	3.704
360	0.00810	2563	5.194	0.001874	1755	3.905	0.001824	1739	3.876	0.001757	1717	3.837
380	0.01042	2759	5.498	0.00932	2711	5.408	0.00828	2655	5.309	0.00610	2503	5.052
400	0.01194	2884	5.688	0.01092	2851	5.622	0.00998	2816	5.553	0.00828	2736	5.406
420	0.01314	2981	5.830	0.01212	2955	5.774	0.01119	2928	5.719	0.00959	2871	5.606
440	0.01419	3062	5.943	0.01317	3041	5.895	0.01224	3019	5.847	0.01064	2974	5.752
450	0.01467	3100	5.995	0.01365	3080	5.949	0.01272	3060	5.903	0.01112	3017	5.813
460	0.01512	3136	6.044	0.01410	3118	6.000	0.01317	3098	5.956	0.01157	3058	5.870
480	0.01597	3203	6.137	0.01494	3188	6.095	0.01401	3170	6.055	0.01239	3135	5.975
500	0.01678	3267	6.221	0.01573	3253	6.182	0.01478	3238	6.144	0.01312	3207	6.070
520	0.01755	3327	6.300	0.01648	3315	6.263	0.01550	3301	6.227	0.01381	3274	6.159
540	0.01830	3384	6.373	0.01720	3373	6.338	0.01619	3361	6.304	0.01448	3337	6.239
550	0.01867	3412	6.407	0.01755	3401	6.373	0.01653	3390	6.339	0.01481	3367	6.276
560	0.01903	3440	6.441	0.01790	3429	6.407	0.01687	3418	6.374	0.01511	3396	6.312
580	0.01975	3194	6.507	0.01858	3484	6.474	0.01752	3474	6.442	0.01571	3454	6.382
600	0.02043	3549	6.572	0.01924	3540	6.540	0.01816	3530	6.508	0.01631	3512	6.449
620	0.02108	3603	6.633	0.01987	3594	6.601	0.01877	3586	6.571	0.01688	3568	6.513
640	0.02172	3656	6.691	0.02049	3648	6.660	0.01937	3640	6.631	0.01745	3624	6.576
650	0.02204	3683	6.720	0.02079	3675	6.689	0.01967	3667	6.660	0.01773	3653	6.606
660	0.02235	3709	6.748	0.02109	3702	6.718	0.01996	3695	6.689	0.01801	3681	6.635
680	0.02296	3763	6.804	0.02168	3756	6.774	0.02053	3749	6.745	0.01855	3735	6.692
700	0.02357	3815	6.858	0.02227	3809	6.828	0.02109	3803	6.800	0.01907	3789	6.747
720	0.02418	3867	6.911	0.02286	3861	6.881	0.02165	3855	6.853	0.01958	3843	6.801
740	0.02480	3919	6.962	0.02345	3913	6.933	0.02221	3907	6.905	0.02008	3896	6.854
750	0.02511	3944	6.987	0.02374	3938	6.959	0.02249	3933	6.931	0.02034	3922	6.880
760	0.02541	3969	7.012	0.02402	3964	6.984	0.02276	3959	6.957	0.02059	3948	6.906
780	0.02599	4021	7.062	0.02458	4016	7.034	0.02330	4011	7.007	0.02109	4000	6.957
800	0.02658	4072	7.110	0.02514	4068	7.082	0.02383	4063	7.056	0.02160	4053	7.007
820	0.02716	4123	7.158	0.02569	4119	7.130	0.02436	4114	7.104	0.02209	4105	7.005
840	0.02774	4174	7.204	0.02624	4170	7.176	0.02489	4165	7.150	0.02257	4157	7.101
850	0.02803	4200	7.227	0.02652	4195	7.199	0.02515	4191	7.173	0.02281	4182	7.124
860	0.02832	4225	7.250	0.02679	4221	7.222	0.02541	4217	7.196	0.02305	4208	7.147
880	0.02889	4276	7.294	0.02733	4272	7.266	0.02594	4268	7.240	0.02352	4260	7.192
900	0.02945	4327	7.338	0.02787	4323	7.310	0.02645	4319	7.284	0.02399	4312	7.236
920	0.03001	4378	7.381	0.02841	4374	7.353	0.02696	4371	7.328	0.02446	4364	7.280
940	0.03056	4429	7.423	0.02893	4425	7.395	0.02746	4422	7.370	0.02492	4415	7.323
950	0.03084	4454	7.444	0.02919	4451	7.416	0.02771	4447	7.391	0.02515	4441	7.344
960	0.03112	4479	7.465	0.02945	4476	7.437	0.02796	4473	7.412	0.02538	4466	7.365
980	0.03167	4530	7.505	0.02997	4527	7.479	0.02846	4524	7.454	0.02584	4518	7.407
1000	0.03221	45381	7.545	0.03049	4578	7.519	0.02894	4575	7.494	0.02629	4569	7.447

Table 3-4 Properties of Superheated Steam (H₂O) (continued)

Pressure $p=$		230 bar			240 bar			250 bar			260 bar	
t	v	h	s	v	h	s	v	h	s	v	h	s
°C	m³/kg	kJ/kg	kJ/(kg K)	m³/kg	kJ/kg	kJ/(kg K)	m³/kg	kJ/kg	kJ/(kg K)	m³/kg	kJ/kg	kJ/(kg K)
0	0.0009889	23.2	0.0013	0.0009884	24.2	0.0013	0.0009880	25.2	0.0013	0.0009875	26.2	0.0013
20	0.0009916	105.5	0.2912	0.0009912	106.4	0.2911	0.0009908	107.3	0.2909	0.0009903	108.3	0.2908
40	0.0009977	188.0	0.5628	0.0009973	188.8	0.5625	0.0009969	189.7	0.5621	0.0009965	190.6	0.5618
50	0.0010020	229.3	0.6920	0.0010016	230.1	0.6916	0.0010012	231.0	0.6911	0.0010008	231.9	0.6907
60	0.0010069	270.7	0.8174	0.0010065	271.5	0.8169	0.0010061	272.3	0.8164	0.0010057	273.2	0.8159
80	0.0010186	353.5	1.0588	0.0010182	354.3	1.0582	0.0010178	355.1	1.0576	0.0010172	355.9	1.0570
100	0.0010325	436.5	1.2888	0.0010320	437.2	1.2881	0.0010316	438.0	1.2873	0.0010311	438.8	1.2865
120	0.0010485	520.1	1.5071	0.0010479	520.8	1.5062	0.0010475	521.5	1.5053	0.0010470	522.3	1.5045
140	0.0010666	604.2	1.716	0.0010660	604.9	1.715	0.0010654	605.6	1.714	0.0010649	606.3	1.713
150	0.0010765	646.6	1.817	0.0010759	647.3	1.816	0.0010753	647.9	1.815	0.0010747	648.6	1.814
160	0.0010871	689.3	1.916	0.0010864	689.9	1.915	0.0010858	690.5	1.914	0.0010851	691.1	1.913
180	0.0011102	775.2	2.109	0.0011095	775.7	2.108	0.0011087	776.3	2.107	0.0011080	776.9	2.105
200	0.0011366	862.1	2.296	0.0011357	862.6	2.295	0.0011349	863.0	2.293	0.0011340	863.5	2.292
220	0.0011668	950.6	2.478	0.0011658	950.9	2.477	0.0011648	951.3	2.475	0.0011638	951.7	2.474
240	0.0012017	1041.1	2.659	0.0012004	1041.3	2.657	0.0011992	1041.6	2.655	0.0011980	1041.8	2.653
250	0.0012211	1087.1	2.748	0.0012197	1087.3	2.746	0.0012183	1087.5	2.744	0.0012170	1087.7	2.742
260	0.0012421	1133.9	2.837	0.0012404	1134.0	2.835	0.0012388	1134.1	2.833	0.0012373	1134.2	2.831
280	0.0012904	1230.5	3.015	0.0012883	1230.3	3.011	0.0012863	1230.2	3.009	0.0012843	1230.1	3.006
300	0.0013505	1331.7	3.194	0.0013475	1331.2	3.190	0.0013446	1330.7	3.187	0.0013418	1330.3	3.183
320	0.001430	1439.4	3.380	0.001425	1438.3	3.375	0.001421	1437.3	3.371	0.001418	1436.4	3.367
340	0.001542	1559.8	3.581	0.001534	1557.3	3.573	0.001527	1555.3	3.567	0.001522	1553.4	3.561
350	0.001623	1629	3.694	0.001612	1625	3.684	0.001602	1621	3.675	0.001591	1618	3.667
360	0.001734	1709	3.821	0.001713	1702	3.807	0.001695	1696	3.794	0.001679	1691	3.782
380	0.00480	2327	4.802	0.00265	2050	4.348	0.00224	1926	4.149	0.00210	1894	4.096
400	0.00750	2690	5.324	0.00676	2638	5.236	0.00602	2579	5.137	0.00529	2511	5.028
420	0.00888	2839	5.546	0.00821	2807	5.484	0.00758	2772	5.420	0.00699	2733	5.355
440	0.00993	2949	5.704	0.00929	2924	5.655	0.00868	2896	5.604	0.00812	2867	5.553
450	0.01041	2994	5.769	0.00977	2971	5.723	0.00917	2947	5.677	0.00861	2922	5.631
460	0.01086	3037	5.828	0.01021	3016	5.785	0.00962	2994	5.743	0.00907	2972	5.701
480	0.01167	3117	5.936	0.01102	3098	5.898	0.01043	3080	5.860	0.00987	3061	5.823
500	0.01239	3191	6.034	0.01174	3174	5.999	0.01113	3157	5.965	0.01056	3141	5.932
520	0.01306	3260	6.125	0.01240	3245	6.092	0.01179	3230	6.059	0.01121	3215	6.028
540	0.01372	3324	6.207	0.01303	3312	6.176	0.01242	3299	6.145	0.01183	3286	6.116
550	0.01404	3355	6.246	0.01334	3343	6.216	0.01272	3331	6.186	0.01213	3319	6.157
560	0.01434	3385	6.283	0.01364	3374	6.254	0.01302	3362	6.225	0.01242	3350	6.196
580	0.01492	3444	6.353	0.01422	3434	6.325	0.01358	3423	6.298	0.01297	3412	6.270
600	0.01550	3502	6.421	0.01478	3493	6.394	0.01413	3483	6.367	0.01350	3473	6.340
620	0.01606	3559	6.485	0.01532	3551	6.459	0.01465	3542	6.433	0.01402	3533	6.408
640	0.01662	3616	6.549	0.01586	3608	6.523	0.01517	3600	6.498	0.01452	3592	6.473
650	0.01689	3645	6.580	0.01612	3637	6.554	0.01542	3629	6.529	0.01477	3622	6.505
660	0.01716	3673	6.609	0.01638	3666	6.584	0.01566	3658	6.560	0.01501	3651	6.536
680	0.01767	3728	6.666	0.01687	3721	6.641	0.01615	3714	6.618	0.01547	3707	6.595
700	0.01817	3783	6.721	0.01735	3776	6.697	0.01662	3770	6.674	0.01593	3763	6.651
720	0.01867	3837	6.776	0.01784	3830	6.752	0.01709	3824	6.729	0.01638	3818	6.707
740	0.01917	3890	6.830	0.01832	3884	6.806	0.01756	3878	6.783	0.01684	3872	6.761
750	0.01941	3911	6.856	0.01856	3910	6.832	0.01779	3905	6.810	0.01706	3899	6.788
760	0.01966	3942	6.882	0.01880	3937	6.858	0.01802	3932	6.836	0.01728	3926	6.814
780	0.02014	3995	6.933	0.01927	3990	6.910	0.01847	3985	6.888	0.01772	3979	6.866
800	0.02062	4048	6.983	0.01973	4043	6.960	0.01891	4038	6.938	0.01814	4033	6.916
820	0.02109	4100	7.031	0.02018	4095	7.008	0.01935	4090	6.986	0.01857	4086	6.964
840	0.02155	4152	7.078	0.02063	4148	7.056	0.01979	4143	7.034	0.01899	4139	7.012
850	0.02178	4178	7.102	0.02085	4174	7.080	0.02000	4169	7.058	0.01920	4165	7.036
860	0.02201	4204	7.125	0.02107	4200	7.103	0.02022	4196	7.081	0.01940	4192	7.069
860	0.02248	4256	7.170	0.02151	4252	7.148	0.02064	4248	7.126	0.01981	4244	7.105
900	0.02293	4308	7.214	0.02195	4304	7.192	0.02106	4300	7.170	0.02022	4297	7.150
920	0.02338	4360	7.258	0.02239	4356	7.236	0.02147	4353	7.214	0.02062	4349	7.194
940	0.02382	4412	7.301	0.02282	4408	7.279	0.02188	4405	7.258	0.02102	4401	7.238
950	0.02404	4447	7.322	0.02303	4443	7.300	0.02208	4431	7.279	0.02122	4428	7.259
960	0.02426	4463	7.343	0.02324	4460	7.321	0.02229	4457	7.300	0.02142	4454	7.280
980	0.02470	4515	7.385	0.02366	4512	7.363	0.02270	4509	7.342	0.02181	4506	7.322
1000	0.02513	4566	7.424	0.02408	4563	7.403	0.02310	4560	7.383	0.02220	4557	7.363

Table 3-4   Properties of Superheated Steam (H₂O)   (continued)

Pressure p=	280 bar			300 bar			350 bar			400 bar		
t	v	h	s	v	h	s	v	h	s	v	h	s
°C	m³/kg	kJ/kg	kJ/(kg K)	m³/kg	kJ/kg	kJ/(kg K)	m³/kg	kJ/kg	kJ/(kg K)	m³/kg	kJ/kg	kJ/(kg K)
0	0.0009866	28.1	0.0013	0.0009857	30.1	0.0013	0.0009833	34.9	0.0008	0.0009810	39.7	0.0004
20	0.0009894	110.1	0.2905	0.0009886	112.0	0.2902	0.0009864	116.6	0.2885	0.0009843	121.2	0.2873
40	0.0009957	192.4	0.5610	0.0009949	194.1	0.5603	0.0009928	198.5	0.5577	0.0009908	202.9	0.5557
50	0.0010000	233.6	0.6898	0.0009992	235.3	0.6889	0.0009971	239.6	0.6863	0.0009951	243.8	0.6840
60	0.0010049	274.9	0.8150	0.0010041	276.5	0.8140	0.0010020	280.7	0.8114	0.0010000	284.8	0.8090
80	0.0010164	357.5	1.0558	0.0010156	359.1	1.0545	0.0010133	353.1	1.0518	0.0010113	367.0	1.0489
100	0.0010302	440.4	1.2850	0.0010293	441.9	1.2834	0.0010269	445.7	1.2796	0.0010248	449.5	1.2757
120	0.0010459	523.9	1.5030	0.0010450	525.1	1.5014	0.0010425	528.8	1.4965	0.0010401	532.4	1.4919
140	0.0010638	607.7	1.711	0.0010626	609.0	1.709	0.0010598	612.4	1.704	0.0010572	615.8	1.6994
150	0.0010735	649.9	1.812	0.0010722	651.2	1.810	0.0010693	654.5	1.805	0.0010665	657.7	1.800
160	0.0010838	692.4	1.911	0.0010825	693.6	1.908	0.0010794	696.7	1.903	0.0010764	699.8	1.898
180	0.0011065	778.0	2.103	0.0011050	779.1	2.100	0.0011015	781.8	2.095	0.0010981	784.6	2.089
200	0.0011323	864.5	2.289	0.0011305	865.4	2.287	0.0011264	867.9	2.280	0.0011225	870.5	2.274
220	0.0011617	952.5	2.471	0.0011597	953.3	2.468	0.0011548	995.3	2.461	0.0011500	957.5	2.454
240	0.0011955	1042.4	2.650	0.0011931	1042.9	2.647	0.0011872	1044.4	2.638	0.0011814	1045.9	2.630
250	0.0012141	1088.1	2.738	0.0012115	1088.5	2.735	0.0012051	1089.7	2.726	0.0011988	1090.9	2.717
260	0.0012342	1134.5	2.826	0.0012313	1134.7	2.822	0.0012241	1135.6	2.813	0.0012174	1136.6	2.803
280	0.0012840	1230.0	3.001	0.0012764	1229.9	2.996	0.0012674	1230.1	2.985	0.0012589	1230.2	2.975
300	0.0013364	1329.6	3.178	0.0013311	1329.0	3.171	0.0013190	1327.8	3.157	0.0013079	1326.7	3.145
320	0.001410	1434.8	3.359	0.001403	1433.2	3.351	0.001383	1429.6	3.332	0.001367	1426.7	3.315
340	0.001509	1549.9	3.549	0.001496	1546.8	3.539	0.001466	1539.4	3.513	0.001442	1533.1	3.493
350	0.001573	1613	3.653	0.001556	1608	3.640	0.001520	1598.1	3.609	0.001489	1589.5	3.585
360	0.001654	1682	3.763	0.001634	1676	3.747	0.001585	1659.4	3.707	0.001545	1648.1	3.69
380	0.00196	1860	4.038	0.001887	1836	3.995	0.001776	1797	3.921	0.001691	1773	3.873
400	0.00387	2348	4.769	0.00283	2155	4.476	0.00213	1991	4.212	0.001922	1934	4.115
420	0.00589	2650	5.220	0.00493	2559	5.070	0.00310	2309	4.680	0.002371	2154	4.433
440	0.00710	2806	5.448	0.00621	2743	5.340	0.00440	2573	5.060	0.003211	2401	4.790
450	0.00760	2870	5.539	0.00672	2816	5.446	0.00494	2670	5.200	0.003691	2518	4.958
460	0.00807	2926	5.619	0.00719	2880	5.536	0.00542	2753	5.318	0.004145	2613	5.093
480	0.00887	3024	5.753	0.00800	2986	5.682	0.00625	2884	5.502	0.004961	2770	5.312
500	0.00956	3107	5.865	0.00869	3073	5.799	0.00694	2986	5.638	0.005627	2898	5.482
520	0.01019	3186	5.966	0.00932	3155	5.906	0.00754	3081	5.759	0.006209	3006	5.620
540	0.01080	3258	6.058	0.00989	3232	6.001	0.00808	3166	5.886	0.006737	3101	5.739
550	0.01108	3293	6.101	0.01016	3268	6.045	0.00834	3206	5.916	0.006983	3144	5.793
560	0.01135	3327	6.141	0.01043	3303	6.088	0.00858	3244	5.963	0.007221	3185	5.844
580	0.01187	3391	6.218	0.01094	3370	6.167	0.00906	3317	6.049	0.007673	3264	5.939
600	0.01239	3453	6.289	0.01144	3434	6.242	0.00951	3386	6.129	0.008094	3338	6.025
620	0.01289	3515	6.359	0.01191	3497	6.312	0.00993	3453	6.204	0.008493	3409	6.104
640	0.01337	3576	6.425	0.01237	3559	6.379	0.01035	3518	6.275	0.008873	3477	6.180
650	0.01360	3606	6.457	0.01259	3590	6.412	0.01056	3549	6.310	0.009057	3510	6.217
660	0.01383	3635	6.489	0.01281	3620	6.444	0.01076	3580	6.344	0.009238	3542	6.253
680	0.01427	3693	6.549	0.01323	3678	6.507	0.01116	3641	6.409	0.009489	3606	6.321
700	0.01471	3749	6.607	0.01365	3736	6.566	0.01153	3701	6.470	0.009937	3668	6.384
720	0.01514	3805	6.663	0.01405	3792	6.623	0.01189	3760	6.528	0.01026	3728	6.446
740	0.01556	3860	6.719	0.01445	3848	6.679	0.01225	3818	6.585	0.01058	3788	6.505
750	0.01577	3888	6.746	0.01465	3876	6.706	0.01243	3847	6.613	0.01074	3818	6.534
760	0.01598	3915	6.773	0.01485	3904	6.733	0.01260	3875	6.641	0.01090	3848	6.562
780	0.01639	3969	6.825	0.01523	3958	6.785	0.01294	3932	6.696	0.01121	3905	6.618
800	0.01679	4023	6.875	0.01562	4013	6.837	0.01328	3988	6.750	0.01152	3962	6.673
820	0.01720	4076	6.924	0.01600	4067	6.887	0.01360	4043	6.802	0.01182	4019	6.725
840	0.01759	4129	6.972	0.01637	4121	6.935	0.01394	4098	6.852	0.01212	4075	6.775
850	0.01779	4156	6.996	0.01655	4147	6.959	0.01410	4125	6.876	0.01227	4103	6.800
860	0.01798	4183	7.019	0.01674	4174	6.983	0.01426	4153	6.900	0.01241	4131	6.824
880	0.01837	4236	7.065	0.01710	4228	7.029	0.01458	4207	6.947	0.01268	4186	6.872
900	0.01874	4289	7.111	0.01746	4281	7.075	0.01489	4261	6.993	0.01296	4242	6.918
920	0.01911	4342	7.155	0.01782	4334	7.119	0.01520	4315	7.038	0.01325	4296	6.964
940	0.01948	4394	7.199	0.01817	4387	7.163	0.01551	4369	7.082	0.01353	4351	7.009
950	0.01967	4421	7.221	0.01834	4414	7.185	0.01567	4396	7.104	0.01366	4378	7.031
960	0.01986	4447	7.242	0.01851	4440	7.206	0.01581	4422	7.125	0.01380	4405	7.053
980	0.02023	4499	7.284	0.01885	4492	7.248	0.01611	4475	7.168	0.01408	4459	7.096
1000	0.02059	4551	7.325	0.01919	4544	7.290	0.01641	4529	7.210	0.01434	4513	7.138

Table 3-4   Properties of Superheated Steam (H₂O) *(continued)*

Pressure p=	450 bar			500 bar			550 bar			600 bar		
t	v	h	s	v	h	s	v	h	s	v	h	s
°C	m³/kg	kJ/kg	kJ/(kg K)	m³/kg	kJ/kg	kJ/(kg K)	m³/kg	kJ/kg	kJ/(kg K)	m³/kg	kJ/kg	kJ/(kg K)
0	0.0009789	44.5	0.0000	0.0009766	49.3	−0.0004	0.0009745	54.0	−0.0008	0.0009722	58.8	−0.0008
20	0.0009823	125.7	0.2856	0.0009802	130.2	0.2843	0.0009782	134.7	0.2830	0.0009761	139.2	0.2820
40	0.0009888	207.2	0.5535	0.0009868	211.5	0.5515	0.0009849	215.8	0.5498	0.0009829	220.0	0.5477
50	0.0009931	248.0	0.6817	0.0009911	252.2	0.6794	0.0009892	256.4	0.6773	0.0009872	260.5	0.7849
60	0.0009980	288.9	0.8064	0.0009960	293.0	0.8040	0.0009940	297.1	0.8014	0.0009920	301.1	0.7988
80	0.0010092	371.0	1.0455	0.0010071	374.9	1.0429	0.0010051	378.8	1.0397	0.0010031	382.5	1.0367
100	0.0010226	453.3	1.2720	0.0010204	457.1	1.2687	0.0010182	460.8	1.2653	0.0010161	464.4	1.2623
120	0.0010377	536.0	1.4879	0.0010354	539.6	1.4839	0.0010330	543.1	1.4805	0.0010307	546.7	1.4767
140	0.0010546	619.2	1.6944	0.0010520	622.6	1.6901	0.0010495	626.0	1.6860	0.0010469	629.4	1.6814
150	0.0010538	661.0	1.795	0.0010610	664.3	1.790	0.0010594	667.6	1.786	0.0010557	670.9	1.781
160	0.0010735	703.0	1.893	0.0010705	706.2	1.888	0.0010678	709.4	1.883	0.0010650	712.5	1.878
180	0.0010948	787.5	2.083	0.0010915	790.5	2.078	0.0010882	793.4	2.073	0.0010850	796.3	2.067
200	0.0011187	873.0	2.268	0.0011149	875.6	2.261	0.0011110	878.2	2.255	0.0011074	880.7	2.249
220	0.0011455	959.7	2.447	0.0011411	961.8	2.440	0.0011368	963.9	2.433	0.0011326	966.0	2.426
240	0.0011761	1047.6	2.622	0.0011709	1049.2	2.614	0.0011659	1051.0	2.606	0.0011610	1052.6	2.598
250	0.0011930	1092.2	2.708	0.0011873	1093.6	2.700	0.0011818	1095.2	2.692	0.0011765	1096.6	2.683
260	0.0012109	1137.6	2.794	0.0012047	1138.6	2.784	0.0011987	1139.2	2.776	0.0011930	1141.2	2.767
280	0.0012508	1230.3	2.964	0.0012431	1230.7	2.952	0.0012361	1231.5	2.942	0.0012294	1232.2	2.933
300	0.0012976	1326.2	3.132	0.0012877	1326.0	3.120	0.0012787	1326.0	3.108	0.0012703	1326.0	3.097
320	0.001353	1425.1	3.300	0.001340	1424.0	3.286	0.001329	1423.1	3.273	0.001319	1422.3	3.261
340	0.001422	1528.3	3.472	0.001405	1525.7	3.455	0.001389	1523.5	3.439	0.001376	1521.5	3.425
350	0.001463	1582.6	3.560	0.001443	1578.4	3.541	0.001425	1575.2	3.523	0.001409	1572.2	3.507
360	0.001511	1639.1	3.651	0.001497	1632.5	3.628	0.001465	1627.7	3.608	0.001445	1623.8	3.589
380	0.001635	1758	3.837	0.001595	1747	3.807	0.001560	1739	3.781	0.001530	1732	3.758
400	0.001816	1902	4.052	0.001741	1878	4.004	0.001682	1860	3.965	0.001638	1847	3.933
420	0.002087	2078	4.308	0.001939	2030	4.226	0.001848	1996	4.165	0.001778	1973	4.117
440	0.002595	2277	4.592	0.002272	2199	4.467	0.002090	2148	4.378	0.001966	2111	4.312
450	0.002920	2383	4.745	0.002492	2290	4.594	0.002247	2228	4.491	0.002085	2183	4.415
460	0.003274	2485	4.886	0.002742	2381	4.722	0.002430	2310	4.607	0.002226	2258	4.521
480	0.004004	2660	5.133	0.003319	2558	4.967	0.002870	2480	4.843	0.002564	2418	4.742
500	0.004637	2809	5.332	0.003892	2722	5.189	0.003350	2646	5.054	0.002955	2579	4.957
520	0.005191	2931	5.488	0.004413	2857	5.364	0.003816	2785	5.249	0.003362	2720	5.142
540	0.005693	3035	5.619	0.004891	2969	5.507	0.004257	2906	5.401	0.003759	2844	5.301
550	0.005929	3082	5.678	0.005114	3020	5.571	0.004464	2961	5.469	0.003951	2902	5.372
560	0.006157	3127	5.735	0.005327	3069	5.631	0.004664	3013	5.533	0.004137	2957	5.439
580	0.006585	3210	5.837	0.005731	3160	5.740	0.005047	3110	5.649	0.004493	3060	5.562
600	0.006982	3289	5.929	0.006109	3243	5.839	0.005405	3198	5.753	0.004828	3152	5.672
620	0.007355	3364	6.014	0.006462	3322	5.929	0.005741	3280	5.849	0.005148	3238	5.772
640	0.007712	3436	6.093	0.006797	3397	6.013	0.006058	3358	5.937	0.005449	3319	5.864
650	0.007886	3471	6.132	0.006969	3433	6.053	0.006211	3396	5.978	0.005593	3359	5.907
660	0.008057	3505	6.169	0.007118	3468	6.091	0.006360	3432	6.018	0.005733	3397	5.949
680	0.008389	3571	6.240	0.007426	3537	6.165	0.006647	3503	6.095	0.006007	3470	6.028
700	0.008707	3636	6.306	0.007721	3603	6.235	0.006926	3571	6.167	0.006271	3540	6.103
720	0.009012	3699	6.369	0.008010	3669	6.301	0.007197	3639	6.235	0.006525	3608	6.173
740	0.009311	3761	6.431	0.008290	3732	6.364	0.007459	3704	6.299	0.006772	3675	6.240
750	0.009458	3791	6.461	0.008426	3763	6.395	0.007587	3736	6.330	0.006892	3708	6.272
760	0.009602	3821	6.490	0.008560	3794	6.425	0.007712	3768	6.361	0.007009	3741	6.303
780	0.009885	3880	6.547	0.008823	3855	6.483	0.007959	3830	6.421	0.007239	3806	6.364
800	0.01017	3939	6.602	0.009081	3915	6.539	0.008198	3891	6.479	0.007464	3868	6.423
820	0.01045	3997	6.655	0.009333	3975	6.593	0.008432	3952	6.535	0.007684	3930	6.480
840	0.01071	4054	6.706	0.009581	4033	6.645	0.008663	4012	6.589	0.007901	3991	6.535
850	0.01084	4083	6.731	0.009705	4062	6.671	0.008777	4042	6.615	0.008008	4021	6.562
860	0.01097	4111	6.756	0.009827	4091	6.696	0.008891	4071	6.641	0.008113	4051	6.589
880	0.01123	4167	6.805	0.010070	4148	6.476	0.009114	4129	6.692	0.008324	4110	6.640
900	0.01149	4224	6.853	0.01030	4206	6.794	0.009333	4187	6.740	0.008531	4169	6.690
920	0.01174	4279	6.899	0.01053	4262	6.841	0.009551	4244	6.788	0.008735	4227	6.738
940	0.01199	4335	6.945	0.01077	4318	6.887	0.009765	4301	6.834	0.008935	4285	6.784
950	0.01211	4362	6.967	0.01088	4346	6.910	0.009870	4329	6.857	0.009034	4313	6.807
960	0.01223	4390	6.989	0.01099	4374	6.932	0.009975	4357	6.879	0.009133	4342	6.830
980	0.01247	4444	7.033	0.01121	4429	6.975	0.01018	4413	6.923	0.009329	4399	6.874
1000	0.01271	4498	7.075	0.01143	4483	7.018	0.01038	4468	6.966	0.009522	4455	6.918

Table 3-4 Properties of Superheated Steam (H₂O) *(continued)*

Pressure p=	650 bar			700 bar			750 bar			800 bar		
t	v	h	s	v	h	s	v	h	s	v	h	s
°C	m³/kg	kJ/kg	kJ/(kg K)	m³/kg	kJ/kg	kJ/(kg K)	m³/kg	kJ/kg	kJ/(kg K)	m³/kg	kJ/kg	kJ/(kg K)
0	0.0009702	63.5	–0.0008	0.0009681	68.2	–0.0013	0.0009661	72.8	–0.0013	0.0009641	77.5	–0.0013
20	0.0009741	143.7	0.2807	0.0009722	148.1	0.2794	0.0009703	152.5	0.2780	0.0009684	156.9	0.2766
40	0.0009810	224.2	0.5459	0.0009791	228.3	0.5438	0.0009773	232.5	0.5415	0.0009755	236.6	0.5397
50	0.0009853	264.6	0.6729	0.0009834	268.6	0.6706	0.0009816	272.6	0.6682	0.0009798	276.7	0.6660
60	0.0009901	305.1	0.7963	0.0009882	309.0	0.7939	0.0009864	312.9	0.7914	0.0009846	316.9	0.7888
80	0.0010012	386.3	1.0334	0.0009991	390.2	1.0300	0.0009972	394.0	1.0271	0.0009954	397.8	1.0245
100	0.0010140	468.1	1.2588	0.0010119	471.8	1.2554	0.0010099	475.6	1.2519	0.0010080	479.3	1.2486
120	0.0010284	550.3	1.4725	0.0010262	553.9	1.4690	0.0010242	557.5	1.4651	0.0010221	561.0	1.4616
140	0.0010445	632.8	1.6772	0.0010421	636.2	1.6727	0.0010398	639.6	1.6685	0.0010375	643.0	1.6646
150	0.0010532	674.1	1.776	0.0010507	667.4	1.771	0.0010482	680.8	1.767	0.0010458	648.1	1.763
160	0.0010624	715.6	1.873	0.0010597	718.8	1.868	0.0010571	722.0	1.863	0.0010545	725.2	1.859
180	0.0010820	779.1	2.061	0.0010791	801.9	2.056	0.0010762	804.8	2.050	0.0010732	807.8	2.045
200	0.0011039	883.0	2.243	0.0011006	885.5	2.237	0.0010972	888.1	2.230	0.0010941	891.0	2.225
220	0.0011286	967.8	2.419	0.0011246	970.0	2.412	0.0011209	972.3	2.405	0.0011173	975.0	2.399
240	0.0011562	1054.1	2.591	0.0011517	1055.9	2.583	0.0011474	1058.0	2.575	0.0011432	1060.1	2.568
250	0.0011715	1098.1	2.675	0.0011666	1099.7	2.667	0.0011619	1101.5	2.659	0.0011573	1103.2	2.651
260	0.0011876	1142.6	2.758	0.0011824	1144.0	2.749	0.0011773	1145.4	2.741	0.0011722	1146.7	2.733
280	0.0012229	1233.0	2.923	0.0012166	1233.9	2.913	0.0012105	1234.6	2.904	0.0012046	1235.2	2.895
300	0.0012627	1326.0	3.087	0.0012550	1326.0	3.076	0.0012474	1326.0	3.065	0.0012405	1326.0	3.055
320	0.001308	1421.2	3.249	0.001299	1420.4	3.236	0.001291	1419.7	3.224	0.001283	1419.2	3.213
340	0.001363	1519.2	3.410	0.001352	1517.5	3.396	0.001341	1515.8	3.382	0.001331	1514.4	3.369
350	0.001395	1569.5	3.491	0.001382	1567.0	3.476	0.001369	1564.7	3.461	0.001358	1562.7	3.447
360	0.001429	1620.6	3.572	0.001415	1617.2	3.555	0.001399	1614.2	3.540	0.001386	1611.5	3.524
380	0.001507	1727	3.737	0.001487	1721	3.716	0.001467	1717	3.697	0.001449	1712	4.679
400	0.001603	1839	3.906	0.001572	1831	3.880	0.001545	1824	3.857	0.001522	1817	3.835
420	0.001722	1958	4.080	0.001678	1945	4.048	0.001641	1935	4.019	0.001610	1926	3.992
440	0.001879	2085	4.262	0.001813	2065	4.219	0.001759	2050	4.183	0.001714	2037	4.153
450	0.001976	2151	4.356	0.001894	2128	4.308	0.001828	2110	4.267	0.001774	2095	4.234
460	0.002088	2220	4.453	0.001986	2193	4.400	0.001906	2172	4.355	0.001842	2155	4.317
480	0.002358	2369	4.661	0.002205	2331	4.594	0.002090	2302	4.538	0.002001	2277	4.489
500	0.002672	2521	4.865	0.002465	2474	4.785	0.002310	2436	4.718	0.002189	2404	4.660
520	0.003012	2659	5.044	0.002755	2608	4.960	0.002561	2565	4.888	0.002404	2528	4.824
540	0.003368	2785	5.205	0.003066	2733	5.120	0.002830	2689	5.046	0.002637	2649	4.978
550	0.003545	2844	5.279	0.003224	2793	5.195	0.002968	2748	5.121	0.002759	2708	5.052
560	0.003718	2901	5.349	0.003380	2851	5.267	0.003108	2806	5.193	0.002883	2765	5.124
580	0.004048	3009	5.479	0.003683	2961	5.401	0.003382	2917	5.329	0.003133	2877	5.262
600	0.004361	3107	5.594	0.003973	3063	5.522	0.003651	3022	5.453	0.003382	2983	5.388
620	0.004659	3196	5.700	0.004252	3157	5.631	0.003910	3118	5.566	0.003623	3083	5.504
640	0.004942	3281	5.796	0.004519	3243	5.730	0.004161	3208	5.668	0.003860	3175	5.609
650	0.005079	3321	5.841	0.004648	3285	5.777	0.004284	3251	5.716	0.003975	3219	5.658
660	0.005212	3361	5.884	0.004774	3326	5.821	0.004404	3292	5.762	0.004089	3261	5.705
680	0.005471	3437	5.965	0.005021	3404	5.905	0.004636	3372	5.848	0.004308	3342	5.793
700	0.005721	3510	6.042	0.005257	3479	5.984	0.004861	3449	5.928	0.004520	3421	5.876
720	0.005962	3580	6.114	0.005486	3551	6.058	0.005078	3523	6.004	0.004726	3498	5.953
740	0.006195	3648	6.183	0.005706	3622	6.128	0.005286	3596	6.076	0.004924	3572	6.027
750	0.006308	3682	6.216	0.005813	3657	6.162	0.005387	3632	6.111	0.005020	3609	6.062
760	0.006419	3716	6.248	0.005917	3691	6.195	0.005486	3667	6.145	0.005113	3645	6.097
780	0.006637	3781	6.311	0.006122	3758	6.259	0.005682	3737	6.211	0.005299	3715	6.164
800	0.006849	3845	6.371	0.006324	3824	6.320	0.005873	3803	6.273	0.005481	3783	6.228
820	0.007057	3909	6.429	0.006521	3888	6.380	0.006061	3869	6.334	0.005660	3850	6.290
840	0.007261	3971	6.485	0.006715	3952	6.437	0.006244	3934	6.392	0.005835	3915	6.349
850	0.007362	4002	6.513	0.006811	3983	6.465	0.006335	3966	6.421	0.005922	3948	6.378
860	0.007461	4032	6.540	0.006905	4014	6.492	0.006425	3997	6.449	0.006008	3980	6.407
880	0.007660	4092	6.592	0.007091	4076	6.546	0.006603	4060	6.503	0.006177	4044	6.462
900	0.007855	4152	6.642	0.007276	4136	6.597	0.006777	4122	6.554	0.006344	4106	6.514
920	0.008047	4211	6.691	0.007458	4196	6.647	0.006951	4182	6.605	0.006508	4168	6.566
940	0.008235	4270	6.738	0.007637	4256	6.694	0.007120	4243	6.654	0.006669	4230	6.615
950	0.008328	4299	6.761	0.007726	4285	6.718	0.007204	4272	6.677	0.006750	4250	6.639
960	0.008422	4328	6.784	0.007815	4314	6.741	0.007288	4302	6.700	0.006830	4289	6.662
980	0.008607	4385	6.829	0.007990	4372	6.786	0.007454	4361	6.746	0.006987	4349	6.708
1000	0.008789	4443	6.873	0.008162	4431	6.831	0.007618	4419	6.791	0.007143	4409	6.753

Table 3-4 Properties of Superheated Steam (H₂O) *(continued)*

Pressure p=		850 bar			900 bar			950 bar			970 bar	
t	v	h	s	v	h	s	v	h	s	v	h	s
°C	m³/kg	kJ/kg	kJ/(kg K)	m³/kg	kJ/kg	kJ/(kg K)	m³/kg	kJ/kg	kJ/(kg K)	m³/kg	kJ/kg	kJ/(kg K)
0	0.0009620	82.1	−0.0017	0.0009601	86.7	−0.0021	0.0009582	91.3	−0.0025	0.0009574	92.9	−0.0027
20	0.0009665	161.2	0.2758	0.0009647	165.5	0.2753	0.0009629	169.9	0.2746	0.0009621	171.5	0.2744
40	0.0009737	240.7	0.5381	0.0009719	244.9	0.5371	0.0009702	249.1	0.5355	0.0009694	250.4	0.5351
50	0.0009780	280.7	0.6644	0.0009763	284.8	0.6628	0.0009746	289.0	0.6609	0.0009738	290.2	0.6604
60	0.0009828	320.9	0.7870	0.0009811	324.9	0.7849	0.0009794	329.1	0.7826	0.0009786	330.2	0.7820
80	0.0009936	401.7	1.0217	0.0009918	405.7	1.0191	0.0009900	409.6	1.0166	0.0009892	410.7	1.0158
100	0.0010060	483.1	1.2451	0.0010041	486.9	1.2421	0.0010022	490.7	1.2389	0.0010014	491.8	1.2379
120	0.0010200	564.5	1.4580	0.0010180	568.2	1.4541	0.0010159	571.9	1.4507	0.0010150	573.0	1.4496
140	0.0010353	646.4	1.6605	0.0010331	649.8	1.6560	0.0010309	653.1	1.6526	0.0010299	654.2	1.6513
150	0.0010435	687.4	1.758	0.0010411	690.7	1.754	0.0010389	693.8	1.750	0.0010379	694.9	1.748
160	0.0010520	728.5	1.854	0.0010495	731.7	1.850	0.0010472	734.7	1.845	0.0010462	735.8	1.843
180	0.0010705	810.9	2.040	0.0010678	814.0	2.035	0.0010651	816.9	2.030	0.0010640	818.0	2.028
200	0.0010910	894.0	2.220	0.0010879	896.9	2.214	0.0010849	899.5	2.208	0.0010837	900.5	2.206
220	0.0011137	977.8	2.393	0.0011102	980.4	2.386	0.0011067	982.6	2.380	0.0011054	983.4	2.378
240	0.0011392	1062.4	2.562	0.0011351	1064.6	2.554	0.0011312	1066.4	2.546	0.0011297	1067.0	2.544
250	0.0011529	1105.1	2.644	0.0011483	1107.1	2.636	0.0011444	1108.7	2.628	0.0011428	1109.3	2.625
260	0.0011673	1148.2	2.725	0.0011627	1149.9	2.717	0.0011583	1151.3	2.708	0.0011565	1151.8	2.705
280	0.0011990	1235.9	2.885	0.0011935	1237.1	2.876	0.0011884	1238.0	2.866	0.0011864	1238.4	2.862
300	0.0012340	1326.0	3.044	0.0012279	1326.4	3.033	0.001222	1326.8	3.022	0.0012201	1326.9	4.018
320	0.001275	1418.5	3.200	0.001267	1417.9	3.187	0.001261	1417.4	3.175	0.001258	1417.3	3.171
340	0.001322	1512.7	3.354	0.001312	1511.3	3.340	0.001305	1509.8	3.326	0.001301	1509.4	3.321
350	0.001348	1560.5	3.431	0.001337	1558.7	3.416	0.001328	1556.8	3.401	0.001324	1556.2	3.396
360	0.001374	1608.9	3.508	0.001363	1606.5	3.491	0.001353	1604.2	3.476	0.001349	1603.5	3.470
380	0.001432	1708	3.660	0.001419	1704	3.641	0.001407	1701	3.624	0.001401	1699	3.618
400	0.001500	1811	3.813	0.001482	1805	3.791	0.001465	1800	3.772	0.001459	1798	3.764
420	0.001581	1917	3.967	0.001555	1909	3.943	0.001533	1901	3.919	0.001524	1898	3.910
440	0.001676	2027	4.124	0.001642	2016	4.096	0.001612	2005	4.067	0.001601	2001	4.056
450	0.001730	3083	4.203	0.001691	2071	4.172	0.001657	2058	4.141	0.001645	2053	4.129
460	0.001790	2140	4.283	0.001744	2126	4.249	0.001706	2111	4.215	0.001693	2106	4.202
480	0.001928	2256	4.444	0.001868	2238	4.403	0.001819	2219	4.363	0.001800	2212	4.348
500	0.002094	2375	4.606	0.002015	2351	4.557	0.001950	2328	4.513	0.001926	2320	4.496
520	0.002281	2495	4.765	0.002181	2466	4.712	0.002098	2441	4.665	0.002068	2430	4.647
540	0.002486	2614	4.918	0.002361	2483	4.864	0.002260	2556	4.815	0.002223	2545	4.796
550	0.002592	2673	4.992	0.002456	2641	4.938	0.002344	2612	4.888	0.002304	2601	4.869
560	0.002702	2730	5.064	0.002555	2698	5.009	0.002432	2668	4.959	0.002389	2657	4.940
580	0.002928	2841	5.201	0.002760	2808	5.145	0.002617	2777	5.093	0.002567	2766	5.073
600	0.003159	2947	5.327	0.002969	2914	5.271	0.002808	2883	5.219	0.002752	2871	5.198
620	0.003386	3047	5.444	0.003178	3015	5.389	0.003000	2984	5.337	0.002938	2972	5.316
640	0.003605	3141	5.552	0.003383	3110	5.497	0.003193	3081	5.447	0.003124	3069	5.426
650	0.003711	3186	5.602	0.003484	3155	5.549	0.003288	3127	5.499	0.003216	3116	5.478
660	0.003817	3230	5.650	0.003583	3200	5.598	0.003381	3172	5.549	0.003307	3162	5.529
680	0.004024	3314	5.741	0.003780	3286	5.691	0.003565	3260	5.644	0.003488	3250	5.625
700	0.004226	3395	5.826	0.003970	3369	5.777	0.003746	3344	5.731	0.003665	3334	5.714
720	0.004421	3473	5.904	0.004155	3449	5.857	0.003921	3425	5.813	0.003837	3416	5.797
740	0.004608	3549	5.979	0.004333	3525	5.935	0.004091	3503	5.893	0.004003	3495	5.876
750	0.004699	3586	6.016	0.004419	3563	5.972	0.004173	3542	5.931	0.004084	3534	5.914
760	0.004789	3622	6.051	0.004505	3601	6.009	0.004255	3579	5.968	0.004164	3571	5.952
780	0.004967	3694	6.119	0.004674	3673	6.078	0.004415	3653	6.039	0.004321	3646	6.023
800	0.005140	3763	6.185	0.004840	3744	6.145	0.004573	3725	6.106	0.004476	3718	6.092
820	0.005310	3831	6.249	0.005002	3814	6.209	0.004728	3795	6.171	0.004627	3788	6.157
840	0.005478	3898	6.309	0.005161	3881	6.270	0.004880	3864	6.234	0.004776	3857	6.219
850	0.005561	3931	6.338	0.005240	3914	6.300	0.004955	3897	6.264	0.004850	3891	6.249
860	0.005642	3964	6.367	0.005318	3948	6.329	0.005030	3931	6.293	0.004924	3925	6.279
880	0.005802	4028	6.422	0.005473	4013	6.385	0.005177	3998	6.350	0.005069	3992	6.336
900	0.005961	4092	6.475	0.005624	4078	6.439	0.005323	4064	6.405	0.005213	4058	6.391
920	0.006117	4155	6.527	0.005774	4142	6.491	0.005467	4128	6.458	0.005354	4123	6.444
940	0.006273	4217	6.577	0.005923	4204	6.542	0.005608	4192	6.509	0.005493	4187	6.495
950	0.006349	4247	6.601	0.005996	4235	6.566	0.005678	4223	6.533	0.005562	4219	6.520
960	0.006435	4277	6.625	0.006070	4266	6.590	0.005748	4254	6.557	0.005630	4250	6.545
980	0.006576	4337	6.671	0.006213	4326	6.637	0.005887	4316	6.604	0.005766	4312	6.591
1000	0.006726	4398	6.717	0.006356	4387	6.682	0.006022	4377	6.650	0.005900	4372	6.638

Table 3-5 Specific Heat Capacities c_p and c_V of Superheated Steam (H_2O) at a Constant Pressure p and a Constant Volume V

Pressure $p=$	0.980 665 bar (=1 at)		4.903 325 bar (=5 at)		9.806 65 bar (=10 at)		19.613 30 bar (=20 at)		29.419 95 bar (=30 at)	
Temperature	Specific heat capacity [1]									
t	c_p	c_V	c_p	c_V	c_p	c_V	c_p	c_V	c_p	c_V
°C	kJ/(kg K)	kJ/(kg K)	kJ/(kg K)	kJ/(kg K)	kJ/(kg K)	kJ/(kg K)	kJ/(kg K)	kJ/(kg K)	kJ/(kg K)	kJ/(kg K)
100	2.047	—	—	—	—	—	—	—	—	—
120	2.018	—	—	—	—	—	—	—	—	—
140	1.997	1.482	—	—	—	—	—	—	—	—
160	1.985	1.486	2.236	1.612	—	—	—	—	—	—
180	1.976	1.491	2.181	1.591	2.500	1.738	—	—	—	—
200	1.980	1.499	2.139	1.578	2.361	1.691	—	—	—	—
220	1.985	1.507	2.106	1.570	2.278	1.658	2.943	—	—	—
240	1.989	1.516	2.085	1.566	2.223	1.637	2.667	—	3.421	—
260	1.997	1.524	2.077	1.556	2.190	1.624	2.495	1.763	2.948	—
280	2.005	1.537	2.072	1.570	2.169	1.620	2.382	1.725	2.692	1.855
300	2.014	1.549	2.072	1.578	2.152	1.616	2.328	1.704	2.554	1.805
320	2.026	1.557	2.077	1.587	2.144	1.620	2.290	1.691	2.458	1.771
340	2.039	1.570	2.081	1.595	2.139	1.620	2.261	1.683	2.395	1.746
360	2.047	1.583	2.085	1.604	2.135	1.624	2.240	1.675	2.353	1.729
380	2.060	1.595	2.093	1.612	2.135	1.633	2.227	1.679	2.324	1.721
400	2.072	1.608	2.102	1.620	2.139	1.641	2.215	1.679	2.299	1.717
420	2.085	1.620	2.110	1.633	2.144	1.650	2.211	1.683	2.282	1.717
440	2.098	1.637	2.199	1.645	2.148	1.662	2.206	1.691	2.273	1.721
460	2.110	1.650	2.131	1.658	2.156	1.671	2.211	1.696	2.265	1.721
480	2.123	1.662	2.144	1.671	2.165	1.683	2.211	1.704	2.257	1.725
500	2.135	1.675	2.152	1.683	2.173	1.691	2.215	1.712	2.257	1.733
520	2.148	1.687	2.165	1.696	2.186	1.704	2.219	1.721	2.257	1.738
540	2.165	1.704	2.177	1.708	2.194	1.717	2.227	1.733	2.261	1.746
560	2.177	1.717	2.190	1.721	2.206	1.729	2.236	1.742	2.265	1.754
580	2.190	1.729	2.202	1.733	2.215	1.742	2.244	1.754	2.269	1.767
600	2.202	1.742	2.215	1.746	2.227	1.754	2.252	1.763	2.278	1.775
620	2.215	1.754	2.227	1.763	2.240	1.767	2.261	1.775	2.286	1.788
640	2.227	1.771	2.240	1.775	2.252	1.779	2.273	1.788	2.299	1.796
660	2.244	1.784	2.257	1.788	2.265	1.792	2.286	1.800	2.307	1.809
680	2.257	1.796	2.269	1.800	2.278	1.805	2.299	1.813	2.319	1.821
700	2.269	1.809	2.282	1.813	2.290	1.817	2.311	1.825	2.332	1.834

[1] Older name: Specific heat

Table 3-5 Specific Heat Capacities c_p and c_V of Superheated Steam (H_2O) *(continued)*
at a Constant Pressure p and a Constant Volume V

Pressure $p=$	39.226 60 bar (=40 at)		49.033 25 bar (=50 at)		58.839 90 bar (=60 at)		68.646 55 bar (=70 at)		78.453 20 bar (=80 at)	
Temperature	Specific heat capacity [1]									
t	c_p	c_V	c_p	c_V	c_p	c_V	c_p	c_V	c_p	c_V
°C	kJ/(kg K)	kJ/(kg K)	kJ/(kg K)	kJ/(kg K)	kJ/(kg K)	kJ/(kg K)	kJ/(kg K)	kJ/(kg K)	kJ/(kg K)	kJ/(kg K)
260	3.634	—	—	—	—	—	—	—	—	—
280	3.128	—	3.756	—	4.622	—	—	—	—	—
300	2.847	1.918	3.224	2.039	3.718	—	4.409	—	5.485	—
320	2.671	1.859	2.935	1.955	3.249	2.064	3.626	2.186	4.124	—
340	2.550	1.813	2.734	1.888	2.956	1.976	3.220	2.072	3.542	2.177
360	2.479	1.788	2.621	1.846	2.780	1.913	2.968	1.989	3.186	2.072
380	1.428	1.771	2.541	1.817	2.667	1.871	2.809	1.926	2.958	1.989
400	2.386	1.758	2.483	1.800	2.587	1.846	2.700	1.892	2.826	1.938
420	2.357	1.750	2.437	1.788	2.525	1.825	2.617	1.863	2.713	1.901
440	2.336	1.750	2.403	1.779	2.474	1.809	2.550	1.842	2.633	1.876
460	2.319	1.746	2.378	1.775	2.441	1.800	2.508	1.830	2.575	1.855
480	2.307	1.746	2.361	1.771	2.416	1.792	2.470	1.817	2.529	1.842
500	2.303	1.750	2.349	1.771	2.395	1.792	2.441	1.813	2.491	1.834
520	2.299	1.754	2.340	1.779	2.382	1.796	2.424	1.813	2.466	1.830
540	2.294	1.763	2.332	1.779	2.370	1.796	2.407	1.813	2.445	1.830
560	2.299	1.771	2.328	1.784	2.361	1.800	2.395	1.813	2.428	1.825
580	2.299	1.779	2.328	1.792	2.357	1.805	2.386	1.817	2.416	1.830
600	2.303	1.788	2.328	1.800	2.353	1.809	2.378	1.821	2.407	1.834
620	2.311	1.796	2.336	1.809	2.361	1.817	2.386	1.830	2.412	1.838
640	2.319	1.805	2.340	1.817	2.366	1.825	2.391	1.834	2.412	1.842
660	2.328	1.817	2.349	1.825	2.374	1.834	2.395	1.842	2.416	1.851
680	2.340	1.830	2.361	1.834	2.382	1.842	2.399	1.851	2.420	1.859
700	2.353	1.842	2.370	1.846	2.391	1.855	2.407	1.859	2.428	1.867

[1] Older name: Specific heat

Table 3-5 Specific Heat Capacities c_p and c_V of Superheated Steam (H_2O) *(continued)*
at a Constant Pressure p and a Constant Volume V

Pressure $p=$	88.259 85 bar (=90 at)		98.066 50 bar (=100 at)		107.873 15 bar (=110 at)		117.679 80 bar (=120 at)		127.486 45 bar (=130 at)	
Temperature	Specific heat capacity [1]									
t	c_p	c_V	c_p	c_V	c_p	c_V	c_p	c_V	c_p	c_V
°C	kJ/(kg K)	kJ/(kg K)	kJ/(kg K)	kJ/(kg K)	kJ/(kg K)	kJ/(kg K)	kJ/(kg K)	kJ/(kg K)	kJ/(kg K)	kJ/(kg K)
320	4.811	—	5.761	—	7.097	—	—	—	—	—
340	3.940	2.294	4.434	—	5.053	—	5.862	—	6.996	—
360	3.442	2.160	3.743	2.252	4.099	2.353	4.522	2.466	5.028	—
380	3.153	2.056	3.362	2.131	3.596	2.215	3.856	2.294	4.145	2.382
400	2.964	1.989	3.115	2.043	3.278	2.102	3.458	2.165	3.655	2.236
420	2.818	1.943	2.935	1.985	3.056	2.026	3.190	2.072	3.341	2.123
440	2.721	1.090	2.814	1.943	2.914	1.980	3.019	2.018	3.128	2.056
460	2.646	1.884	2.721	1.913	2.805	1.943	2.889	1.976	2.977	2.005
480	2.587	1.867	2.654	1.892	2.721	1.918	2.788	1.943	2.864	1.972
500	2.541	1.855	2.600	1.880	2.654	1.901	2.713	1.922	2.776	1.947
520	2.512	1.851	2.558	1.867	2.604	1.888	2.654	1.905	2.709	1.926
540	2.483	1.846	2.525	1.859	2.567	1.876	2.608	1.892	2.654	1.909
560	2.462	1.838	2.495	1.855	2.533	1.871	2.571	1.888	2.608	1.901
580	2.445	1.842	2.474	1.855	2.508	1.867	2.541	1.880	2.575	1.897
600	2.433	1.842	2.462	1.855	2.491	1.867	2.520	1.880	2.554	1.892
620	2.437	1.846	2.462	1.859	2.491	1.871	2.516	1.880	2.546	1.892
640	2.437	1.851	2.462	1.863	2.487	1.871	2.512	1.880	2.541	1.892
660	2.441	1.859	2.462	1.867	2.487	1.876	2.512	1.884	2.537	1.892
680	2.445	1.867	2.466	1.876	2.491	1.880	2.516	1.888	2.541	1.897
700	2.449	1.876	2.470	1.880	2.491	1.888	2.516	1.897	2.537	1.905

[1] Older name: Specific heat

Table 3-5   Specific Heat Capacities c_p and c_V of Superheated Steam (H_2O) *(continued)*
at a Constant Pressure p and a Constant Volume V

Pressure $p=$	137.293 10 bar (=140 at)		147.099 75 bar (=150 at)		156.906 40 bar (=160 at)		166.713 05 bar (=170 at)		176.519 70 bar (=180 at)	
Temperature	Specific heat capacity [1]									
t	c_p	c_V	c_p	c_V	c_p	c_V	c_p	c_V	c_p	c_V
°C	kJ/(kg K)	kJ/(kg K)	kJ/(kg K)	kJ/(kg K)	kJ/(kg K)	kJ/(kg K)	kJ/(kg K)	kJ/(kg K)	kJ/(kg K)	kJ/(kg K)
340	8.755	—	—	—	—	—	—	—	—	—
360	5.652	—	6.494	—	7.746	—	9.776	—	—	—
380	4.476	2.479	4.873	2.587	5.367	2.709	5.991	2.847	6.795	3.010
400	3.873	2.311	4.116	2.391	4.392	2.474	4.714	2.562	5.095	2.659
420	3.500	2.173	3.668	2.223	3.848	2.282	4.040	2.340	4.271	2.403
440	3.241	2.093	3.358	2.135	3.483	2.181	3.626	2.223	3.785	2.269
460	3.069	2.039	3.169	2.072	3.278	2.106	3.395	2.144	3.517	2.177
480	2.939	1.997	3.019	2.026	3.102	2.056	3.190	2.085	3.282	2.114
500	2.839	1.968	2.906	1.993	2.973	2.014	3.044	2.039	3.119	2.064
520	2.759	1.947	2.818	1.968	2.872	1.985	2.931	2.005	2.998	2.026
540	2.700	1.930	2.747	1.947	2.797	1.964	2.847	1.980	2.897	1.997
560	2.650	1.918	2.692	1.930	2.734	1.947	2.776	1.964	2.822	1.976
580	2.613	1.909	2.646	1.922	2.684	1.934	2.717	1.947	2.755	1.964
600	2.583	1.905	2.613	1.913	2.646	1.926	2.680	1.938	2.713	1.951
620	2.575	1.905	2.604	1.913	2.633	1.926	2.663	1.934	2.696	1.947
640	2.571	1.901	2.596	1.909	2.621	1.922	2.650	1.930	2.680	1.943
660	2.562	1.901	2.587	1.909	2.613	1.918	2.642	1.926	2.671	1.938
680	2.561	1.905	2.587	1.913	2.613	1.922	2.638	1.930	2.663	1.934
700	2.558	1.909	2.583	1.918	2.608	1.926	2.633	1.930	2.654	1.934

[1] Older name: Specific heat

Table 3-5   Specific Heat Capacities c_p and c_V of Superheated Steam (H_2O) *(continued)*
at a Constant Pressure p and a Constant Volume V

Pressure $p=$	186.326 35 bar (=190 at)		196.133 00 bar (=200 at)		205.939 65 bar (=210 at)		215.746 30 bar (=220 at)		225.552 95 bar (=230 at)	
Temperature	Specific heat capacity [1]									
t	c_p	c_V	c_p	c_V	c_p	c_V	c_p	c_V	c_p	c_V
°C	kJ/(kg K)	kJ/(kg K)	kJ/(kg K)	kJ/(kg K)	kJ/(kg K)	kJ/(kg K)	kJ/(kg K)	kJ/(kg K)	kJ/(kg K)	kJ/(kg K)
380	7.854	3.199	9.441	3.425	11.849	—	—	—	—	—
400	5.568	2.763	6.150	2.881	6.850	3.010	7.670	3.165	8.612	—
420	4.534	2.470	4.832	2.541	5.171	2.617	5.556	2.700	5.991	2.793
440	3.961	2.319	4.157	2.370	4.375	2.424	4.614	2.479	4.873	2.537
460	3.647	2.215	3.785	2.252	3.931	2.294	4.091	2.336	4.258	2.378
480	3.383	2.144	3.488	2.173	3.596	2.202	3.714	2.236	3.835	2.269
500	3.199	2.098	3.278	2.144	3.366	2.139	3.454	2.165	3.546	2.190
520	3.061	2.047	3.123	2.068	3.195	2.089	3.266	2.110	3.337	2.131
540	2.952	2.018	3.006	2.035	3.061	2.052	3.119	2.072	3.178	2.089
560	2.868	1.993	2.914	2.010	2.960	2.026	3.006	2.039	3.056	2.056
580	2.793	1.976	2.830	1.989	2.872	2.005	2.910	2.018	2.952	2.031
600	2.747	1.964	2.780	1.976	2.818	1.989	2.851	2.001	2.885	2.010
620	2.730	1.955	2.759	1.964	2.793	1.976	2.826	1.989	2.860	1.997
640	2.713	1.951	2.742	1.959	2.776	1.972	2.805	1.980	2.839	1.989
660	2.700	1.947	2.730	1.955	2.759	1.964	2.788	1.972	2.818	1.980
680	2.688	1.943	2.717	1.951	2.747	1.959	2.776	1.968	2.805	1.976
700	2.680	1.943	2.709	1.951	2.734	1.955	2.763	1.964	2.788	1.972

[1] Older name: Specific heat

Table 3-5   Specific Heat Capacities c_p and c_V of Superheated Steam (H_2O)   *(continued)*
at a Constant Pressure p and a Constant Volume V

Pressure $p=$	235.359 60 bar (=240 at)		245.166 25 bar (=250 at)		254.972 90 bar (=260 at)		264.779 55 bar (=270 at)		274.586 20 bar (=280 at)	
Temperature					Specific heat capacity [1]					
t	c_p	c_V	c_p	c_V	c_p	c_V	c_p	c_V	c_p	c_V
°C	kJ/(kg K)	kJ/(kg K)	kJ/(kg K)	kJ/(kg K)	kJ/(kg K)	kJ/(kg K)	kJ/(kg K)	kJ/(kg K)	kJ/(kg K)	kJ/(kg K)
400	9.713	—	11.137	—	—	—	—	—	—	—
420	6.481	2.893	7.030	2.998	7.641	3.132	8.332	—	9.119	—
440	5.154	2.600	5.455	2.667	5.778	2.742	6.121	2.818	6.485	2.897
460	4.438	2.420	4.626	2.466	4.827	2.512	5.041	2.562	5.259	2.613
480	3.961	2.299	4.091	2.332	4.229	2.370	4.375	2.403	4.526	2.441
500	3.643	2.215	3.739	2.240	3.835	2.269	3.940	2.294	4.044	2.324
520	3.412	2.152	3.492	2.177	3.571	2.198	3.655	2.219	3.739	2.240
540	3.241	2.106	3.303	2.127	3.366	2.144	3.429	2.165	3.496	2.181
560	3.107	2.072	3.161	2.089	3.211	2.102	3.266	2.199	3.324	2.135
580	2.994	2.043	3.040	2.060	3.086	2.072	3.132	2.085	3.178	2.098
600	2.922	2.022	2.960	2.035	2.998	2.047	3.035	2.060	3.073	2.068
620	2.893	2.005	2.931	2.018	2.964	2.026	3.002	2.039	3.035	2.047
640	2.872	1.997	2.906	2.005	2.939	2.014	2.977	2.022	3.010	2.031
660	2.851	1.989	2.881	1.997	2.914	2.005	2.948	2.014	2.981	2.022
680	2.834	1.985	2.864	1.989	2.893	1.997	2.927	2.005	2.960	2.014
700	2.818	1.980	2.847	1.985	2.876	1.993	2.906	2.001	2.939	2.005

[1] Older name: Specific heat

Table 3-5   Specific Heat Capacities c_p and c_V of Superheated Steam (H_2O)   *(continued)*
at a Constant Pressure p and a Constant Volume V

Pressure $p=$	284.392 85 bar (=290 at)		294.199 50 bar (=300 at)		Pressure $p=$	284.392 85 bar (=290 at)		294.199 50 bar (=300 at)	
Temperature	Specific heat capacity [1]				Temperature	Specific heat capacity [1]			
t	c_p	c_V	c_p	c_V	t	c_p	c_V	c_p	c_V
°C	kJ/(kg K)	kJ/(kg K)	kJ/(kg K)	kJ/(kg K)	°C	kJ/(kg K)	kJ/(kg K)	kJ/(kg K)	kJ/(kg K)
420	10.048	—	11.179	—	580	3.224	2.110	3.270	2.127
440	6.891	2.977	7.386	3.061					
460	5.476	2.663	5.690	2.713	600	3.111	2.081	3.153	2.093
480	4.677	2.474	4.827	2.512	620	3.073	2.056	3.111	2.068
					640	3.044	2.039	3.081	2.052
500	4.153	2.349	4.262	2.378	660	3.014	2.031	3.052	2.039
520	3.823	2.265	3.910	2.286	680	2.989	2.022	3.023	2.026
540	3.563	2.198	3.638	2.215					
560	3.379	2.148	3.437	2.165	700	2.968	2.014	2.998	2.018

[1] Older name: Specific heat

Table 3-6   Mean Specific Heat Capacity $\bar{c}_p$ of Superheated Steam (H$_2$O) at a Constant Pressure p (in the Range Between Temperature of Saturation t_s and a Given Temperature t)

Pressure $p=$	0.980 665 bar (=1 at)	4.903 325 bar (=5 at)	9.806 65 bar (=10 at)	19.613 30 bar (=20 at)	29.419 950 bar (=30 at)	39.226 60 bar (=40 at)
Temperature	Mean specific heat capacity [1]					
t	$\bar{c}_p$	$\bar{c}_p$	$\bar{c}_p$	$\bar{c}_p$	$\bar{c}_p$	$\bar{c}_p$
°C	kJ/(kg K)	kJ/(kg K)	kJ/(kg K)	kJ/(kg K)	kJ/(kg K)	kJ/(kg K)
120	2.043	—	—	—	—	—
140	2.005	—	—	—	—	—
160	1.993	2.353	—	—	—	—
180	1.989	2.232	—	—	—	—
200	1.985	2.177	2.416	—	—	—
220	1.980	2.152	2.370	2.815	—	—
240	1.980	2.139	2.328	2.734	3.123	—
260	1.985	2.131	2.294	2.621	2.986	3.483
280	1.989	2.127	2.278	2.567	2.876	3.262
300	1.989	2.123	2.261	2.525	2.801	3.136
320	1.993	2.119	2.244	2.487	2.734	3.027
340	1.993	2.110	2.232	2.453	2.680	2.931
360	1.997	2.110	2.219	2.424	2.633	2.851
380	2.001	2.110	2.211	2.399	2.596	2.793
400	2.005	2.106	2.206	2.378	2.562	2.742
420	2.014	2.106	2.198	2.361	2.533	2.700
440	2.018	2.110	2.194	2.349	2.508	2.663
460	2.022	2.110	2.194	2.340	2.487	2.633
480	2.026	2.110	2.190	2.332	2.466	2.604
500	2.031	2.114	2.190	2.324	2.453	2.579
520	2.039	2.114	2.190	2.315	2.441	2.558
540	2.043	2.119	2.190	2.311	2.428	2.541
560	2.047	2.123	2.190	2.307	2.416	2.525
580	2.056	2.127	2.190	2.303	2.407	2.512
600	2.060	2.127	2.194	2.299	2.399	2.500
620	2.064	2.135	2.194	2.299	2.395	2.487
640	2.072	2.139	2.198	2.294	2.391	2.479
660	2.077	2.144	2.198	2.294	2.386	2.470
680	2.085	2.148	2.202	2.294	2.382	2.466
700	2.089	2.152	2.206	2.294	2.378	2.458

[1] Older name: Mean specific heat

Table 3-6   Mean Specific Heat Capacity $\bar{c}_p$ of Superheated Steam (H$_2$O) at a Constant Pressure p (in the Range Between Temparature of Saturation t_s and a Given Temperature t)   *(continued)*

Pressure $p=$	49.033 25 bar (=50 at)	58.839 90 bar (=60 at)	68.646 55 bar (=70 at)	78.453 20 bar (=80 at)	88.259 85 bar (=90 at)	98.066 50 bar (=100 at)
Temperature	Mean specific heat capacity [1]					
t	$\bar{c}_p$	$\bar{c}_p$	$\bar{c}_p$	$\bar{c}_p$	$\bar{c}_p$	$\bar{c}_p$
°C	kJ/(kg K)	kJ/(kg K)	kJ/(kg K)	kJ/(kg K)	kJ/(kg K)	kJ/(kg K)
280	3.680	4.107	—	—	—	—
300	3.467	3.848	4.350	5.053	—	—
320	3.299	3.655	4.070	4.564	5.095	5.719
340	3.186	3.509	3.381	4.220	4.668	5.175
360	3.090	3.345	3.626	3.948	4.300	4.719
380	3.002	3.228	3.471	3.739	4.036	4.371
400	2.931	3.128	3.341	3.580	3.831	4.111
420	2.872	3.048	3.236	3.450	3.668	3.910
440	2.818	2.981	3.157	3.341	3.538	3.751
460	2.776	2.927	3.086	3.253	3.433	3.622
480	2.738	2.876	3.023	3.182	3.341	3.513
500	2.705	2.834	2.973	3.115	3.262	3.421
520	2.680	2.801	2.927	3.061	3.195	3.341
540	2.654	2.767	2.889	3.010	3.136	3.270
560	2.633	2.738	2.851	2.964	3.086	3.207
580	2.613	2.713	2.818	2.927	3.040	3.157
600	2.596	2.692	2.793	2.893	2.998	3.111
620	2.579	2.671	2.767	2.864	2.964	3.069
640	2.567	2.654	2.747	2.839	2.931	3.031
660	2.554	2.638	2.726	3.814	2.901	2.998
680	2.546	2.625	2.709	2.793	2.876	2.964
700	2.537	2.613	2.692	2.772	2.855	2.939

[1] Older name: Specific heat

Table 3-6 Mean Specific Heat Capacity $\bar{c}_p$ of Superheated Steam (H₂O) at a Constant *(continued)*
Pressure p (in the Range Between Temparature of Saturation t_s and a Given Temperature t)

Pressure p=	107.873 15 bar (=110 at)	117.679 80 bar (=120 at)	127.486 45 bar (=130 at)	137.293 10 bar (=140 at)	147.099 75 bar (=150 at)	156.906 40 bar (=160 at)
Temperature	Mean specific heat capacity [1]					
t	$\bar{c}_p$	$\bar{c}_p$	$\bar{c}_p$	$\bar{c}_p$	$\bar{c}_p$	$\bar{c}_p$
°C	kJ/(kg K)	kJ/(kg K)	kJ/(kg K)	kJ/(kg K)	kJ/(kg K)	kJ/(kg K)
320	6.490	—	—	—	—	—
340	5.795	6.626	7.825	9.466	—	—
360	5.171	5.694	6.368	7.193	8.269	9.659
380	4.756	5.171	5.673	6.247	6.925	7.746
400	4.434	4.773	5.175	5.594	6.121	6.716
420	4.183	4.472	4.802	5.158	5.568	6.029
440	3.986	4.237	4.518	4.819	5.158	5.535
460	3.831	4.049	4.291	4.547	4.836	5.158
480	3.701	3.894	4.107	4.333	4.585	4.865
500	3.588	3.764	3.961	4.162	4.384	4.631
520	3.496	3.655	3.831	4.015	4.216	4.434
540	3.416	3.563	3.772	3.890	4.070	4.226
560	3.345	3.479	3.626	3.781	3.948	4.128
580	3.282	3.408	3.546	3.689	3.843	4.007
600	3.228	3.345	3.471	3.605	3.747	3.902
620	3.178	3.287	3.408	3.529	3.663	3.810
640	3.132	3.326	3.349	3.467	3.592	3.726
660	3.094	3.195	3.299	3.412	3.525	3.655
680	3.061	3.153	3.253	3.358	3.467	3.588
700	3.027	3.119	3.211	3.312	3.416	3.529

[1] Older name: Mean specific heat

Table 3-6 Mean Specific Heat Capacity $\bar{c}_p$ of Superheated Steam (H₂O) at a Constant *(continued)*
Pressure p (in the Range Between Temparature of Saturation t_s and a Given Temperature t)

Pressure p=	166.713 05 bar (=170 at)	176.519 70 bar (=180 at)	186.326 35 bar (=190 at)	196.133 00 bar (=200 at)	205.939 65 bar (=210 at)	215.746 30 bar (=220 at)
Temperature	Mean specific heat capacity [1]					
t	$\bar{c}_p$	$\bar{c}_p$	$\bar{c}_p$	$\bar{c}_p$	$\bar{c}_p$	$\bar{c}_p$
°C	kJ/(kg K)	kJ/(kg K)	kJ/(kg K)	kJ/(kg K)	kJ/(kg K)	kJ/(kg K)
360	11.790	—	—	—	—	—
380	8.847	10.308	12.414	15.508	—	—
400	7.440	8.336	9.479	11.007	13.297	17.212
420	6.577	7.239	7.976	9.048	10.475	12.803
440	5.975	6.494	7.113	7.871	8.914	10.555
460	5.522	5.949	6.452	7.063	7.880	9.140
480	5.179	5.539	5.962	6.473	7.147	8.168
500	4.903	5.221	5.581	6.016	6.586	7.453
520	4.681	4.957	5.275	5.652	6.155	6.900
540	4.488	4.739	5.024	5.359	5.799	6.456
560	4.329	4.555	4.811	5.112	5.506	6.092
580	4.191	4.396	4.631	4.907	5.263	5.790
600	4.070	4.262	4.476	4.727	5.053	5.535
620	3.965	4.145	4.342	4.576	4.873	5.317
640	3.873	4.040	4.224	4.446	4.719	5.129
660	3.789	3.948	4.120	4.329	4.580	4.961
680	3.718	3.864	4.028	4.220	3.459	4.815
700	3.651	3.789	3.944	4.120	4.346	4.681

[1] Older name: Specific heat

Table 3-7 Physical Properties of Freons

Name	Chemical formula	Molar mass M (kg/kmol)	Boiling point[1] t_v (°C)	Freezing point t_t (°C)	Critical temperature t_k (°C)	Critical pressure (abs.) p_k (bar)	Critical density ρ_k (kg/m³)	Heat of vaporization[2] r (kJ/kg)	Surface tension at 25 °C σ (mN/m)	Specific heat capacity[2] of Liquid c (kJ/(kg K))	Density of liquid at 20 °C ρ (kg/m³)	Density of liquid at 40 °C ρ_k (kg/m³)	Specific heat ratio at 30 °C 1.013 bar $\gamma = c_p/c_v$	Solubility of water in liquid Frigen at 30 °C (g/hg)	at 0 °C (g/hg)	Refractive index of the liquid	Relative dielectric strength of vapor[3]	Dielectric constant Liquid (25 °C) ε_r	Vapor (0.5 bar) ε_r
Freon 11 Trichlorofluoromethane	CCl₃F	137.38	23.8	−111	198.0	44.0	548	182.2	19	0.883[4]	1488	1440	1.095	0.0125	0.0035	1.385[4]	3.1	2.5	1.0019[5]
Freon 12 Dichlorodifluoromethane	CCl₂F₂	120.92	−29.8	−158	112.0	41.6	558	166.0	9	0.894	1328	1252	1.116	0.0124	0.0024	1.328[6]	2.4	2.1	1.0016[7]
Freon 12 B1 Bromochlorodifluoromethane	CBrClF₂	165.4	−3.7	−161	154.6	41.2	713	133.2	—	0.737	1817	1743	1.106	—	—	1.373[8]	—	2.7[9]	—
Freon 13 Trifluoromonochloromethane	CClF₃	104.47	−81.4	−181	28.8	38.6	581	149.6	5[10]	0.900	924	581[11]	1.152[8]	0.0065[11]	0.0019	1.264[12]	1.4	2.3[8]	1.0013[7]
Freon 13 B1 Trifluorobromomethane	CBrF₃	148.93	−57.8	−168	67.0	39.8	745	118.2	7	0.669	1574	1412	1.127	0.012	0.0046	1.308[13]	1.8	2.7	—
Freon 14 Tetrafluoromethane	CF₄	88.005	−127.9	−184	−45.7	37.5	626	134.2	5[14]	1.052[15]	1465[15]	939[16]	1.218[15]	—	—	1.151	0.89	—	1.0006[17]
Freon 22 Difluoromonochloromethane	CHClF₂	86.48	−40.8	−160	96.2	49.9	513	234.7	9	1.094	1214	1131	1.167	0.15	0.060	1.252[18]	1.3	6.6	1.0035[19]
Freon 23 Trifluoromethane	CHF₃	70.01	−82.0	−155	26.3	48.7	527	240.8	6[10]	1.234	824	—	1.230[8]	—	—	—	0.82	—	—
Freon 113 Trichlorotrifluoroethane	C₂Cl₃F₃	187.39	47.6	−35	214.1	34.1	576	145.7	19	0.981	1576	1529	1.036[20]	0.013	0.0036	1.354[21]	2.6[22]	2.6	1.0024[23]
Freon 114 Dichlorotetrafluoroethane	C₂Cl₂F₄	170.93	3.6	−94	145.7	32.6	578	136.8	13	0.960	1476	1411	1.044	0.011	0.0026	1.309[9]	2.8	2.2	1.0021[24]
Freon 115 Chloropentafluoroethane	C₂ClF₅	154.48	−38.0	−106	80.0	31.3	591	126.3	4	0.947	1307	1200	1.074	—	—	1.263[25]	2.8	—	1.0018[23]
Freon 500 Azeotropic mixture Freons 12 and R 152a	CCl₂F₂/ CH₃—CHF₂	99.29	−33.5	−159	105.5	44.3	497	201.3	9	0.986	1173	1101	1.115	—	—	—	—	1.8	1.024[26]
Freon 502 Azeotropic mixture Freon 22 and Freon 115	CHClF₂/ C₂ClF₅	111.6	−45.6	−160	82.2	40.8	561	172.6	9	1.070	1239	1141	0.985	0.062	0.023	1.281[27]	2.7	—	—
Freon 503 Azeotropic mixture Freon 13 and Freon 23	CHF₃/ CClF₃	87.5	−88.7	−155	19.5	43.4	564	179.9	11.2[28]	0.711	1022[9]	—	1.173[8]	—	—	—	—	—	—

1) At a pressure of 1.013 bar
2) Boiling point
3) At a pressure of 1.013 bar and 23 °C (nitrogen = 1)
4) At a temperature of 20 °C
5) At a temperature of 26 °C
6) At a temperature of −29.8 °C
7) At a temperature of 29 °C
8) At a temperature of −30 °C
9) At a temperature of 0 °C
10) At a temperature of −20 °C
11) At a temperature of 28.8 °C
12) At a temperature of −29.8 °C
13) At a temperature of −57.8 °C
14) At a temperature of −70 °C
15) At a temperature of −100 °C
16) At a temperature of −50 °C
17) At a temperature of 24.5 °C
18) At a temperature of −81.4 °C
19) At a temperature of −57.8 °C
20) At a temperature of 50 °C
21) At a temperature of 25 °C
22) At a pressure of 1 bar
23) At a temperature of 28.8 °C
24) At a temperature of 26.8 °C
25) At a temperature of −38 °C
26) At a pressure of 1 bar
27) At a temperature of −45.6 °C
28) At a temperature of −60 °C

125

Table 3-8 Properties of Saturated "Freon-11" — Trichlorfluoromethane (CFCl₃)

Tempera-ture	Pressure	Specific volume		Density		Specific enthalpy		Heat of vaporization	Specific entropy	
		Liquid	Vapor	Liquid	Vapor	Liquid	Vapor		Liquid	Vapor
t	p	v'	v''	ρ'	ρ''	h'	h''	r	s'	s''
°C	bar	L/kg	L/kg	kg/L	kg/m³	kJ/kg	kJ/kg	kJ/kg	kJ/(kg K)	kJ/(kg K)
−50	0.027	0.609	5061.25	1.642	0.198	160.54	365.23	204.69	0.8409	1.7582
−49	0.028	0.610	4750.29	1.640	0.211	161.29	365.73	204.44	0.8442	1.7563
−48	0.030	0.611	4461.32	1.638	0.224	162.03	366.22	204.19	0.8475	1.7545
−47	0.033	0.611	4192.61	1.636	0.239	162.77	366.72	203.95	0.8508	1.7527
−46	0.035	0.612	3942.57	1.633	0.254	163.52	367.22	203.70	0.8541	1.7509
−45	0.037	0.613	3709.73	1.631	0.270	164.26	367.71	203.45	0.8574	1.7491
−44	0.040	0.614	3492.78	1.629	0.286	165.02	368.21	203.19	0.8607	1.7474
−43	0.042	0.615	3290.51	1.627	0.304	165.77	368.71	202.94	0.8640	1.7458
−42	0.045	0.615	3101.79	1.625	0.322	166.52	369.21	202.69	0.8672	1.7441
−41	0.048	0.616	2925.61	1.623	0.342	167.28	369.71	202.43	0.8705	1.7425
−40	0.051	0.617	2761.03	1.621	0.362	168.03	370.21	202.18	0.8737	1.7409
−39	0.054	0.618	2607.19	1.619	0.384	168.79	370.71	201.92	0.8770	1.7394
−38	0.058	0.618	2463.31	1.617	0.406	169.56	371.22	201.66	0.8802	1.7378
−37	0.061	0.619	2328.65	1.615	0.429	170.32	371.72	201.40	0.8835	1.7363
−36	0.065	0.620	2202.56	1.613	0.454	171.08	372.22	201.14	0.8867	1.7349
−35	0.069	0.621	2084.43	1.611	0.480	171.85	372.73	200.88	0.8899	1.7334
−34	0.073	0.622	1973.67	1.608	0.507	172.62	373.23	200.61	0.8932	1.7320
−33	0.077	0.623	1869.78	1.606	0.535	173.39	373.74	200.35	0.8963	1.7306
−32	0.082	0.623	1772.27	1.604	0.564	174.17	374.25	200.08	0.8996	1.7293
−31	0.087	0.624	1680.71	1.602	0.595	174.94	374.75	199.81	0.9028	1.7280
−30	0.092	0.625	1594.67	1.600	0.627	175.72	375.26	199.54	0.9060	1.7267
−29	0.097	0.626	1513.80	1.598	0.661	176.50	375.77	199.27	0.9092	1.7254
−28	0.102	0.627	1437.72	1.596	0.696	177.28	376.28	199.00	0.9124	1.7241
−27	0.108	0.628	1366.13	1.594	0.732	178.06	376.78	198.72	0.9156	1.7229
−26	0.114	0.628	1298.72	1.591	0.770	178.84	377.29	198.45	0.9187	1.7217
−25	0.121	0.629	1235.22	1.589	0.810	179.63	377.80	198.17	0.9219	1.7205
−24	0.127	0.630	1175.36	1.587	0.851	180.42	378.31	197.89	0.9251	1.7194
−23	0.134	0.631	1118.92	1.585	0.894	181.21	378.82	197.61	0.9282	1.7182
−22	0.141	0.632	1065.67	1.583	0.938	182.00	379.33	197.33	0.9314	1.7171
−21	0.149	0.633	1015.40	1.581	0.985	182.80	379.84	197.04	0.9346	1.7160
−20	0.157	0.634	967.93	1.579	1.033	183.60	380.36	196.76	0.9377	1.7150
−19	0.165	0.634	923.08	1.576	1.083	184.40	380.87	196.47	0.9409	1.7139
−18	0.174	0.635	880.68	1.574	1.135	185.20	381.38	196.18	0.9440	1.7129
−17	0.182	0.636	840.58	1.572	1.190	186.00	381.89	195.89	0.9472	1.7119
−16	0.192	0.637	802.65	1.570	1.246	186.80	382.40	195.60	0.9503	1.7109
−15	0.201	0.638	766.74	1.568	1.304	187.62	382.92	195.30	0.9534	1.7100
−14	0.212	0.639	732.73	1.565	1.365	188.43	383.43	195.00	0.9566	1.7091
−13	0.222	0.640	700.51	1.563	1.428	189.24	383.94	194.70	0.9597	1.7081
−12	0.233	0.641	669.98	1.561	1.493	190.06	384.46	194.40	0.9628	1.7072
−11	0.244	0.641	641.02	1.559	1.560	190.87	384.97	194.10	0.9659	1.7064
−10	0.256	0.642	613.55	1.557	1.630	191.70	385.49	193.79	0.9691	1.7055
−9	0.268	0.643	587.48	1.554	1.702	192.51	386.00	193.49	0.9721	1.7047
−8	0.281	0.644	562.73	1.552	1.777	193.33	386.51	193.18	0.9753	1.7038
−7	0.294	0.645	539.22	1.550	1.855	194.16	387.03	192.87	0.9784	1.7030
−6	0.308	0.646	516.88	1.548	1.935	194.99	387.54	192.55	0.9815	1.7023
−5	0.322	0.647	495.65	1.546	2.018	195.82	388.06	192.24	0.9846	1.7015
−4	0.337	0.648	475.45	1.543	2.103	196.65	388.57	191.92	0.9877	1.7007
−3	0.352	0.649	456.24	1.541	2.192	197.49	389.09	191.60	0.9908	1.7000
−2	0.368	0.650	437.96	1.539	2.283	198.32	398.60	191.28	0.9938	1.6993
−1	0.384	0.651	420.55	1.537	2.378	199.15	390.11	190.96	0.9969	1.6986

Tempera-ture	Pressure	Specific volume		Density		Specific enthalpy		Heat of vaporization	Specific entropy	
		Liquid	Vapor	Liquid	Vapor	Liquid	Vapor		Liquid	Vapor
t	p	v'	v''	ρ'	ρ''	h'	h''	r	s'	s''
°C	bar	L/kg	L/kg	kg/L	kg/m³	kJ/kg	kJ/kg	kJ/kg	kJ/(kg K)	kJ/(kg K)
0	0.401	0.652	403.97	1.534	2.475	200.00	390.63	190.63	1.0000	1.6979
1	0.419	0.653	388.18	1.532	2.576	200.84	391.14	190.30	1.0031	1.6972
2	0.437	0.654	373.12	1.530	2.680	201.69	391.66	189.97	1.0061	1.6966
3	0.456	0.655	358.76	1.528	2.787	202.53	392.17	189.64	1.0092	1.6960
4	0.476	0.656	345.07	1.525	2.898	203.39	392.69	189.30	1.0123	1.6953
5	0.496	0.657	332.01	1.523	3.012	204.23	393.20	188.97	1.0153	1.6947
6	0.517	0.658	319.54	1.521	3.130	205.08	393.71	188.63	1.0184	1.6941
7	0.538	0.659	307.63	1.518	3.251	205.95	394.23	188.28	1.0215	1.6936
8	0.560	0.660	296.25	1.516	3.375	206.80	394.74	187.94	1.0245	1.6930
9	0.583	0.661	285.39	1.514	3.504	207.67	395.26	187.59	1.0276	1.6924
10	0.607	0.662	275.00	1.512	3.636	208.53	395.77	187.24	1.0306	1.6919
11	0.632	0.663	265.07	1.509	3.773	209.39	396.28	186.89	1.0336	1.6914
12	0.657	0.664	255.57	1.507	3.913	210.25	396.79	186.54	1.0367	1.6909
13	0.683	0.665	246.48	1.505	4.057	211.13	397.31	186.18	1.0397	1.6904
14	0.710	0.666	237.78	1.502	4.205	211.99	397.82	185.83	1.0427	1.6899
15	0.738	0.667	229.46	1.500	4.358	212.87	398.33	185.46	1.0458	1.6894
16	0.766	0.668	221.48	1.498	4.515	213.74	398.84	185.10	1.0488	1.6890
17	0.796	0.669	213.84	1.495	4.676	214.61	399.35	184.74	1.0518	1.6885
18	0.826	0.670	206.52	1.493	4.842	215.49	399.86	184.37	1.0548	1.6881
19	0.857	0.671	199.51	1.491	5.012	216.37	400.37	184.00	1.0578	1.6877
20	0.889	0.672	192.78	1.488	5.187	217.26	400.88	183.62	1.0609	1.6872
21	0.922	0.673	186.32	1.486	5.367	218.14	401.39	183.25	1.0639	1.6868
22	0.956	0.674	180.13	1.484	5.551	219.03	401.90	182.87	1.0669	1.6865
23	0.991	0.675	174.19	1.481	5.741	219.92	402.41	182.49	1.0699	1.6861
24	1.027	0.676	168.49	1.479	5.935	220.81	402.92	182.11	1.0728	1.6857
25	1.064	0.677	163.01	1.476	6.135	221.71	403.43	181.72	1.0759	1.6854
26	1.103	0.678	157.75	1.474	6.339	222.59	403.93	181.34	1.0788	1.6850
27	1.142	0.679	152.69	1.472	6.549	223.49	404.44	180.95	1.0818	1.6847
28	1.182	0.681	147.84	1.469	6.764	224.40	404.95	180.55	1.0848	1.6844
29	1.223	0.682	143.17	1.467	6.985	225.29	405.45	180.16	1.0878	1.6840
30	1.266	0.683	138.68	1.465	7.211	226.20	405.96	179.76	1.0907	1.6837
31	1.309	0.684	134.36	1.462	7.443	227.10	406.46	179.36	1.0837	1.6834
32	1.354	0.685	130.20	1.460	7.680	228.00	406.96	178.96	1.0967	1.6831
33	1.400	0.686	126.20	1.457	7.924	228.92	407.47	178.55	1.0996	1.6829
34	1.447	0.687	122.36	1.455	8.173	229.82	407.97	178.15	1.1026	1.6826
35	1.495	0.689	118.65	1.452	8.428	230.73	408.47	177.74	1.1055	1.6823
36	1.545	0.690	115.08	1.450	8.690	231.65	408.97	177.32	1.1085	1.6821
37	1.595	0.691	111.64	1.447	8.957	232.56	409.47	176.91	1.1114	1.6818
38	1.647	0.692	108.33	1.445	9.231	233.48	409.97	176.49	1.1144	1.6816
39	1.701	0.693	105.14	1.443	9.511	234.40	410.47	176.07	1.1173	1.6814
40	1.755	0.694	102.06	1.440	9.798	235.32	410.97	175.65	1.1202	1.6812
41	1.811	0.696	99.09	1.438	10.092	236.25	411.47	175.22	1.1232	1.6810
42	1.869	0.697	96.23	1.435	10.392	237.16	411.96	174.80	1.1261	1.6808
43	1.928	0.698	93.47	1.433	10.699	238.09	412.46	174.37	1.1290	1.6806
44	1.988	0.699	90.80	1.430	11.013	239.02	412.95	173.93	1.1319	1.6804
45	2.049	0.700	88.23	1.428	11.334	239.95	413.45	173.50	1.1348	1.6802
46	2.112	0.702	85.75	1.425	11.662	240.88	413.94	173.06	1.1378	1.6800
47	2.177	0.703	83.35	1.423	11.998	241.81	414.43	172.62	1.1407	1.6799
48	2.243	0.704	81.03	1.420	12.341	242.75	414.93	172.18	1.1435	1.6797
49	2.310	0.705	78.79	1.417	12.691	243.69	415.42	171.73	1.1465	1.6795

Table 3-8   Properties of Saturated "Freon 11" — Trichlorfluoromethane (CFCl₃)   *(continued)*

Temperature	Pressure	Specific volume		Density		Specific enthalpy		Heat of vaporization	Specific entropy	
		Liquid	Vapor	Liquid	Vapor	Liquid	Vapor		Liquid	Vapor
t	p	v'	v''	ρ'	ρ''	h'	h''	r	s'	s''
°C	bar	L/kg	L/kg	kg/L	kg/m³	kJ/kg	kJ/kg	kJ/kg	kJ/(kg K)	kJ/(kg K)
50	2.379	0.707	76.63	1.415	13.049	244.62	415.91	171.29	1.1493	1.6794
51	2.450	0.708	74.54	1.412	13.415	245.55	416.39	170.84	1.1522	1.6793
52	2.522	0.709	72.52	1.410	13.789	246.50	416.88	170.38	1.1551	1.6791
53	2.596	0.711	70.57	1.407	14.170	247.44	417.37	169.93	1.1580	1.6790
54	2.671	0.712	68.68	1.405	14.560	248.38	417.85	169.47	1.1608	1.6789
55	2.748	0.713	66.86	1.402	14.958	249.33	418.34	169.01	1.1637	1.6788
56	2.827	0.715	65.09	1.399	15.364	250.27	418.82	168.55	1.1666	1.6787
57	2.907	0.716	63.38	1.397	15.778	251.22	419.30	168.08	1.1694	1.6786
58	2.990	0.717	61.72	1.394	16.202	252.17	419.79	167.62	1.1723	1.6785
59	3.073	0.719	60.12	1.392	16.634	253.12	420.27	167.15	1.1751	1.6784
60	3.159	0.720	58.57	1.389	17.074	254.08	420.75	166.67	1.1780	1.6783
61	3.246	0.721	57.06	1.386	17.524	255.02	421.22	166.20	1.1808	1.6782
62	3.336	0.723	55.61	1.384	17.983	255.98	421.70	165.72	1.1836	1.6781
63	3.427	0.724	54.20	1.381	18.451	256.94	422.18	165.24	1.1865	1.6781
64	3.519	0.725	52.83	1.378	18.928	257.89	422.65	164.76	1.1893	1.6780
65	3.614	0.727	51.51	1.376	19.415	258.85	423.12	164.27	1.1921	1.6779
66	3.711	0.728	50.22	1.373	19.912	259.81	423.60	163.79	1.1949	1.6779
67	3.809	0.730	48.98	1.370	20.418	260.77	424.07	163.30	1.1977	1.6778
68	3.910	0.731	47.77	1.368	20.934	261.74	424.54	162.80	1.2005	1.6778
69	4.012	0.733	46.60	1.365	21.460	262.69	425.00	162.31	1.2033	1.6777
70	4.117	0.734	45.46	1.362	21.997	263.66	425.47	161.81	1.2061	1.6777
71	4.223	0.736	44.36	1.359	22.544	264.63	425.94	161.31	1.2098	1.6776
72	4.332	0.737	43.29	1.357	23.101	265.59	426.40	160.81	1.2117	1.6776
73	4.442	0.739	42.25	1.354	23.669	266.56	426.86	160.30	1.2145	1.6776
74	4.555	0.740	41.24	1.351	24.248	267.54	427.33	159.79	1.2173	1.6776
75	4.669	0.742	40.26	1.348	24.838	268.51	427.79	159.28	1.2200	1.6775
76	4.786	0.743	39.31	1.346	25.439	269.48	428.25	158.77	1.2228	1.6775
77	4.905	0.745	38.39	1.343	26.051	270.45	428.70	158.25	1.2255	1.6775
78	5.026	0.746	37.49	1.340	26.675	271.42	429.16	157.74	1.2283	1.6775
79	5.150	0.748	36.62	1.337	27.310	272.39	429.61	157.22	1.2310	1.6775
80	5.275	0.749	35.77	1.334	27.957	273.38	430.07	156.69	1.2338	1.6775
81	5.403	0.751	34.94	1.332	28.617	274.35	430.52	156.17	1.2365	1.6775
82	5.533	0.753	34.14	1.329	29.288	275.33	430.97	155.64	1.2392	1.6775
83	5.666	0.754	33.36	1.326	29.972	276.31	431.42	155.11	1.2420	1.6775
84	5.800	0.756	32.61	1.323	30.668	277.29	431.86	154.57	1.2447	1.6775
85	5.937	0.757	31.87	1.320	31.377	278.27	432.31	154.04	1.2474	1.6775
86	6.077	0.759	31.15	1.317	32.099	279.25	432.75	153.50	1.2501	1.6775
87	6.219	0.761	30.46	1.314	32.834	280.24	433.19	152.95	1.2528	1.6775
88	6.363	0.763	29.78	1.311	33.582	281.22	433.63	152.41	1.2555	1.6775
89	6.510	0.764	29.12	1.309	34.344	282.21	434.07	151.86	1.2582	1.6776
90	6.659	0.766	28.47	1.306	35.120	283.20	434.51	151.31	1.2609	1.6776
91	6.810	0.768	27.85	1.303	35.909	284.18	434.94	150.76	1.2636	1.6776
92	6.965	0.769	27.24	1.300	36.713	285.17	435.37	150.20	1.2663	1.6776
93	7.121	0.771	26.64	1.297	37.531	286.17	435.81	149.64	1.2690	1.6777
94	7.280	0.773	26.07	1.294	38.363	287.16	436.24	149.08	1.2716	1.6777
95	7.442	0.775	25.50	1.291	39.211	288.14	436.66	148.52	1.2743	1.6777
96	7.607	0.777	24.95	1.288	40.073	289.14	437.09	147.95	1.2769	1.6777
97	7.774	0.778	24.42	1.285	40.951	290.13	437.51	147.38	1.2796	1.6778
98	7.944	0.780	23.90	1.282	41.845	291.12	437.93	146.81	1.2822	1.6778
99	8.116	0.782	23.39	1.278	42.754	292.12	438.35	146.23	1.2849	1.6778

Table 3-8 Properties of Saturated "Freon 11" — Trichlorfluoromethane (CFCl₃) (continued)

Temperature	Pressure	Specific volume		Density		Specific enthalpy		Heat of vaporization	Specific entropy	
		Liquid	Vapor	Liquid	Vapor	Liquid	Vapor		Liquid	Vapor
t	p	v'	v''	ρ'	ρ''	h'	h''	r	s'	s''
°C	bar	L/kg	L/kg	kg/L	kg/m³	kJ/kg	kJ/kg	kJ/kg	kJ/(kg K)	kJ/(kg K)
100	8.291	0.784	22.89	1.275	43.679	293.12	438.77	145.65	1.2875	1.6779
101	8.469	0.786	22.41	1.272	44.621	294.12	439.19	145.07	1.2901	1.6779
102	8.650	0.788	21.94	1.269	45.579	295.12	439.60	144.48	1.2928	1.6779
103	8.833	0.790	21.48	1.266	46.554	296.12	440.01	143.89	1.2954	1.6780
104	9.020	0.792	21.03	1.263	47.546	297.12	440.42	143.30	1.2980	1.6780
105	9.209	0.794	20.59	1.260	48.556	298.12	440.83	142.71	1.3006	1.6780
106	9.401	0.796	20.17	1.257	49.583	299.12	441.23	142.11	1.3032	1.6781
107	9.596	0.798	19.75	1.253	50.629	300.12	441.63	141.51	1.3058	1.6781
108	9.794	0.800	19.34	1.250	51.693	301.13	442.03	140.90	1.3085	1.6781
109	9.995	0.802	18.95	1.247	52.776	302.14	442.43	140.29	1.3111	1.6782
110	10.198	0.804	18.56	1.244	53.877	303.15	442.83	139.68	1.3136	1.6782
111	10.405	0.806	18.18	1.240	54.999	304.16	443.22	139.06	1.3162	1.6782
112	10.615	0.808	17.81	1.237	56.139	305.17	443.61	138.44	1.3188	1.6783
113	10.828	0.810	17.45	1.234	57.300	306.18	444.00	137.82	1.3214	1.6783
114	11.044	0.813	17.10	1.231	58.482	307.19	444.38	137.19	1.3240	1.6783
115	11.263	0.815	16.75	1.227	59.684	308.20	444.76	136.56	1.3265	1.6784
116	11.485	0.817	16.42	1.224	60.908	309.21	445.14	135.93	1.3291	1.6784
117	11.711	0.819	16.09	1.220	62.153	310.23	445.52	135.29	1.3316	1.6784
118	11.940	0.822	15.77	1.217	63.420	311.26	445.90	134.64	1.3342	1.6784
119	12.172	0.824	15.45	1.214	64.710	312.27	446.27	134.00	1.3367	1.6785
120	12.407	0.826	15.15	1.210	66.023	313.30	446.64	133.34	1.3393	1.6785
121	12.645	0.829	14.85	1.207	67.360	314.31	447.00	132.69	1.3418	1.6785
122	12.887	0.831	14.55	1.203	68.720	315.33	447.36	132.03	1.3444	1.6785
123	13.132	0.833	14.26	1.200	70.104	316.36	447.72	131.36	1.3469	1.6785
124	13.381	0.836	13.98	1.196	71.514	317.39	448.08	130.69	1.3495	1.6786
125	13.633	0.838	13.71	1.193	72.949	318.41	448.43	130.02	1.3520	1.6786
126	13.888	0.841	13.44	1.189	74.410	319.44	448.78	129.34	1.3545	1.6786
127	14.147	0.844	13.18	1.186	75.898	320.48	449.13	128.65	1.3571	1.6786
128	14.410	0.846	12.92	1.182	77.412	321.51	449.47	127.96	1.3596	1.6786
129	14.676	0.849	12.67	1.178	78.955	322.54	449.81	127.27	1.3621	1.6786
130	14.946	0.851	12.42	1.175	80.526	323.59	450.15	126.56	1.3646	1.6786
131	15.219	0.854	12.18	1.171	82.126	324.62	450.48	125.86	1.3671	1.6786
132	15.496	0.857	11.94	1.167	83.756	325.66	450.81	125.15	1.3696	1.6786
133	15.776	0.860	11.71	1.163	85.416	326.70	451.13	124.43	1.3722	1.6785
134	16.061	0.862	11.48	1.160	87.107	327.75	451.45	123.70	1.3747	1.6785
135	16.349	0.865	11.26	1.156	88.830	328.80	451.77	122.97	1.3772	1.6785
136	16.640	0.868	11.04	1.152	90.586	329.85	452.08	122.23	1.3797	1.6785
137	16.936	0.871	10.83	1.148	92.375	330.90	452.39	121.49	1.3822	1.6784
138	17.236	0.874	10.62	1.144	94.199	331.96	452.70	120.74	1.3847	1.6784
139	17.539	0.877	10.41	1.140	96.058	333.02	453.00	119.98	1.3872	1.6783
140	17.846	0.880	10.21	1.136	97.953	334.08	453.29	119.21	1.3897	1.6783
141	18.158	0.883	10.01	1.132	99.886	335.14	453.58	118.44	1.3922	1.6782
142	18.473	0.887	9.82	1.128	101.856	336.21	342.87	117.66	1.3947	1.6782
143	18.792	0.890	9.63	1.124	103.866	337.28	454.15	116.87	1.3972	1.6781
144	19.116	0.893	9.44	1.120	105.917	338.35	454.42	116.07	1.3998	1.6780
145	19.443	0.896	9.26	1.116	108.008	339.43	454.69	115.26	1.4023	1.6779
146	19.775	0.900	9.08	1.111	110.143	340.51	454.96	114.45	1.4048	1.6778
147	20.111	0.903	8.90	1.107	112.321	341.60	455.22	113.62	1.4073	1.6777
148	20.451	0.907	8.73	1.103	114.545	342.68	455.47	112.79	1.4098	1.6776
149	20.796	0.910	8.56	1.098	116.816	343.78	455.72	111.94	1.4123	1.6775

Table 3-8 Properties of Saturated "Freon 11" — Trichlorfluoromethane (CFCl₃) *(continued)*

Tempera-ture	Pressure	Specific volume		Density		Specific enthalpy		Heat of vaporization	Specific entropy	
		Liquid	Vapor	Liquid	Vapor	Liquid	Vapor		Liquid	Vapor
t	p	v'	v''	ρ'	ρ''	h'	h''	r	s'	s''
°C	bar	L/kg	L/kg	kg/L	kg/m³	kJ/kg	kJ/kg	kJ/kg	kJ/(kg K)	kJ/(kg K)
150	21.145	0.914	8.39	1.094	119.135	344.87	455.96	111.09	1.4148	1.6774
151	21.498	0.918	8.23	1.089	121.504	345.98	456.20	110.22	1.4174	1.6772
152	21.855	0.922	8.07	1.085	123.924	347.09	456.43	109.34	1.4199	1.6771
153	22.217	0.926	7.91	1.080	126.398	348.19	456.65	108.46	1.4224	1.6769
154	22.584	0.930	7.76	1.076	128.926	349.31	456.87	107.56	1.4249	1.6768
155	22.955	0.934	7.60	1.071	131.512	350.43	457.07	106.64	1.4275	1.6766
156	23.331	0.938	7.45	1.066	134.156	351.55	457.27	105.72	1.4300	1.6764
157	23.711	0.942	7.31	1.062	136.862	352.69	457.47	104.78	1.4326	1.6762
158	24.096	0.946	7.16	1.057	139.631	353.83	457.65	103.82	1.4352	1.6750
159	24.486	0.951	7.02	1.052	142.466	354.98	457.83	102.85	1.4377	1.6757
160	24.881	0.955	6.88	1.047	145.370	356.13	458.00	101.87	1.4403	1.6755
161	25.280	0.960	6.74	1.042	148.345	357.29	458.16	100.87	1.4429	1.6752
162	25.685	0.965	6.61	1.037	151.395	358.46	458.31	99.85	1.4455	1.6750
163	26.094	0.970	6.47	1.031	154.522	359.64	458.45	98.81	1.4481	1.6747
164	26.508	0.975	6.34	1.026	157.730	360.82	458.58	97.76	1.4507	1.6744
165	26.928	0.980	6.21	1.021	161.023	362.01	458.70	96.69	1.4534	1.6740
166	27.352	0.985	6.08	1.015	164.404	363.22	458.81	95.59	1.4560	1.6737
167	27.782	0.990	5.96	1.010	167.879	364.43	458.91	94.48	1.4587	1.6733
168	28.217	0.996	5.83	1.004	171.451	365.65	458.99	93.34	1.4614	1.6729
169	28.657	1.002	5.71	0.998	175.125	366.89	459.07	92.18	1.4640	1.6725
170	29.102	1.008	5.59	0.992	178.908	368.14	459.13	90.99	1.4668	1.6721
171	29.553	1.014	5.47	0.986	182.804	369.40	459.17	89.77	1.4695	1.6716
172	30.009	1.020	5.35	0.980	186.821	370.67	459.20	88.53	1.4723	1.6712
173	30.471	1.027	5.24	0.974	190.966	371.96	459.22	87.26	1.4750	1.6706
174	30.939	1.034	5.12	0.967	195.246	373.26	459.22	85.96	1.4778	1.6701
175	31.412	1.041	5.01	0.961	199.671	374.58	459.20	84.62	1.4807	1.6695
176	31.891	1.048	4.90	0.954	204.250	375.92	459.16	83.24	1.4836	1.6689
177	32.375	1.056	4.78	0.947	208.995	377.27	459.10	81.83	1.4865	1.6682
178	32.866	1.064	4.67	0.940	213.916	378.65	459.02	80.37	1.4894	1.6676
179	33.362	1.072	4.57	0.933	219.029	380.05	458.92	78.87	1.4924	1.6668
180	33.864	1.081	4.46	0.925	224.349	381.47	458.79	77.32	1.4954	1.6660
181	34.373	1.090	4.35	0.917	229.894	382.92	458.63	75.71	1.4985	1.6652
182	34.887	1.100	4.24	0.909	235.686	384.40	458.45	74.05	1.5016	1.6643
183	35.408	1.110	4.14	0.901	241.747	385.91	458.23	72.32	1.5048	1.6633
184	35.935	1.121	4.03	0.892	248.108	387.45	457.97	70.52	1.5080	1.6623
185	36.468	1.132	3.92	0.883	254.802	389.04	457.68	68.64	1.5114	1.6612
186	37.008	1.145	3.82	0.874	261.871	390.67	457.34	66.67	1.5148	1.6600
187	37.554	1.158	3.71	0.864	269.365	392.35	456.95	64.60	1.5183	1.6587
188	38.107	1.172	3.61	0.853	277.347	394.09	456.50	62.41	1.5220	1.6573
189	38.667	1.188	3.50	0.842	285.897	395.89	455.98	60.09	1.5257	1.6557
190	39.233	1.205	3.39	0.830	295.122	397.77	455.38	57.61	1.5296	1.6540
191	39.807	1.224	3.28	0.817	305.161	399.75	454.69	54.94	1.5337	1.6521
192	40.387	1.246	3.16	0.803	316.215	401.86	453.88	52.02	1.5381	1.6500
193	40.974	1.271	3.04	0.787	328.576	404.10	452.91	48.81	1.5428	1.6475
194	41.568	1.300	2.92	0.769	342.710	406.56	451.73	45.17	1.5479	1.6446
195	42.170	1.337	2.78	0.748	359.432	409.31	450.25	40.94	1.5536	1.6411
196	42.779	1.385	2.63	0.722	380.426	412.54	448.28	35.74	1.5603	1.6365
197	43.395	1.459	2.44	0.686	410.394	416.79	445.29	28.50	1.5692	1.6298
198	44.019	1.732	2.00	0.577	499.972	427.81	435.72	7.91	1.5924	1.6092
198.01	44.025	1.824	1.82	0.548	548.150	430.65	430.65	0.00	1.5984	1.5984

Table 3-9 Properties of Saturated "Freon 12" — Dichlorodifluoromethane (CF_2Cl_2)

Temperature	Pressure	Specific volume		Density		Specific enthalpy		Heat of vaporization	Specific entropy	
		Liquid	Vapor	Liquid	Vapor	Liquid	Vapor		Liquid	Vapor
t	p	v'	v''	ρ'	ρ''	h'	h''	r	s'	s''
°C	bar	L/kg	L/kg	kg/L	kg/m³	kJ/kg	kJ/kg	kJ/kg	kJ/(kg K)	kJ/(kg K)
−60	0.226	0.636	639.14	1.574	1.565	146.36	324.53	178.17	0.7794	1.6153
−59	0.240	0.637	605.89	1.571	1.650	147.23	325.01	177.78	0.7834	1.6136
−58	0.254	0.638	574.70	1.568	1.740	148.09	325.48	177.39	0.7874	1.6120
−57	0.268	0.639	545.43	1.565	1.833	148.96	325.96	177.00	0.7915	1.6104
−56	0.284	0.640	517.95	1.563	1.931	149.84	326.44	176.60	0.7955	1.6088
−55	0.300	0.641	492.12	1.560	2.032	150.71	326.92	176.21	0.7995	1.6073
−54	0.317	0.642	467.83	1.557	2.138	151.57	327.39	175.82	0.8034	1.6057
−53	0.334	0.643	444.98	1.554	2.247	152.45	327.87	175.42	0.8074	1.6043
−52	0.353	0.644	423.47	1.552	2.361	153.32	328.35	175.03	0.8114	1.6028
−51	0.372	0.646	403.21	1.549	2.480	154.19	328.82	174.63	0.8153	1.6014
−50	0.392	0.647	384.12	1.546	2.603	155.06	329.30	174.24	0.8192	1.6000
−49	0.412	0.648	366.11	1.543	2.731	155.94	329.78	173.84	0.8231	1.5987
−48	0.434	0.649	349.11	1.541	2.864	156.82	330.26	173.44	0.8270	1.5974
−47	0.457	0.650	333.07	1.538	3.002	157.69	330.73	173.04	0.8309	1.5961
−46	0.480	0.651	317.91	1.535	3.145	158.57	331.21	172.64	0.8348	1.5948
−45	0.505	0.653	303.59	1.532	3.294	159.45	331.69	172.24	0.8386	1.5936
−44	0.530	0.654	290.05	1.529	3.448	160.32	332.16	171.84	0.8424	1.5924
−43	0.556	0.655	277.23	1.526	3.607	161.20	332.64	171.44	0.8462	1.5912
−42	0.584	0.656	265.10	1.524	3.772	162.09	333.12	171.03	0.8501	1.5900
−41	0.612	0.658	253.61	1.521	3.943	162.96	333.59	170.63	1.8538	1.5889
−40	0.642	0.659	242.72	1.518	4.120	163.85	334.07	170.22	0.8576	1.5878
−39	0.673	0.660	232.40	1.515	4.303	164.73	334.54	169.81	0.8614	1.5867
−38	0.705	0.661	222.61	1.512	4.492	165.62	335.02	169.40	0.8652	1.5856
−37	0.738	0.663	213.32	1.509	4.688	166.50	335.49	168.99	0.8689	1.5846
−36	0.772	0.664	204.50	1.506	4.890	167.39	335.97	168.58	0.8727	1.5835
−35	0.807	0.665	196.12	1.504	5.099	168.27	336.44	168.17	0.8764	1.5825
−34	0.884	0.666	188.16	1.501	5.315	169.16	336.91	167.75	0.8801	1.5816
−33	0.882	0.668	180.59	1.498	5.537	170.05	337.39	167.34	0.8838	1.5806
−32	0.922	0.669	173.39	1.495	5.767	170.94	337.86	166.92	0.8875	1.5797
−31	0.962	0.670	166.54	1.492	6.005	171.83	338.33	166.50	0.8912	1.5788
−30	1.005	0.672	160.01	1.498	6.249	172.72	338.80	166.08	0.8948	1.5779
−29	1.048	0.673	153.80	1.496	6.502	173.61	339.27	165.66	0.8985	1.5770
−28	1.093	0.674	147.88	1.483	6.762	174.51	339.74	165.23	0.9021	1.6761
−27	1.140	0.676	142.24	1.480	7.030	175.40	340.21	164.81	0.9057	1.5753
−26	1.188	0.677	136.86	1.477	7.307	176.30	340.68	164.38	0.9094	1.5745
−25	1.237	0.678	131.73	1.474	7.591	177.20	341.15	163.95	0.9130	1.5737
−24	1.289	0.680	126.83	1.471	7.884	178.10	341.62	163.52	0.9166	1.5729
−23	1.342	0.681	122.16	1.468	8.186	178.99	342.08	163.09	0.9201	1.5721
−22	1.396	0.683	117.69	1.465	8.497	179.90	342.55	162.65	0.9237	1.5714
−21	1.452	0.684	113.42	1.462	8.817	180.79	343.01	162.22	0.9273	1.5707
−20	1.510	0.685	109.34	1.459	9.146	181.70	343.48	161.78	0.9308	1.5699
−19	1.570	0.687	105.44	1.456	9.484	182.60	343.94	131.34	0.9344	1.5692
−18	1.631	0.688	101.71	1.453	9.832	183.51	344.40	160.89	0.9380	1.5685
−17	1.695	0.690	98.14	1.450	10.189	184.41	314.86	160.45	0.9415	1.5679
−16	1.760	0.691	94.73	1.447	10.557	185.32	345.32	160.00	0.9450	1.5672
−15	1.827	0.693	91.45	1.444	10.935	186.23	345.78	159.55	0.9485	1.5666
−14	1.896	0.694	88.32	1.441	11.323	187.14	346.24	159.10	0.9520	1.5659
−13	1.967	0.696	85.32	1.438	11.721	188.05	346.70	158.65	0.9555	1.5653
−12	2.040	0.697	82.44	1.434	12.131	188.97	347.16	158.19	0.9590	1.5647
−11	2.115	0.699	79.68	1.431	12.551	189.87	347.61	157.74	0.9624	1.5641

Table 3-9 Properties of Saturated "Freon 12" — Dichlorodifluoromethane (CF$_2$Cl$_2$) *(continued)*

Temperature	Pressure	Specific volume		Density		Specific enthalpy		Heat of vaporization	Specific entropy	
		Liquid	Vapor	Liquid	Vapor	Liquid	Vapor		Liquid	Vapor
t	p	v'	v''	ρ'	ρ''	h'	h''	r	s'	s''
°C	bar	L/kg	L/kg	kg/L	kg/m^3	kJ/kg	kJ/kg	kJ/kg	kJ/(kg K)	kJ/(kg K)
−10	2.193	0.700	77.03	1.428	12.982	190.78	348.06	157.28	0.9659	1.5636
−9	2.272	0.702	74.49	1.425	13.425	191.71	348.52	156.81	0.9693	1.5630
−8	2.354	0.703	72.05	1.422	13.880	192.62	348.97	156.35	0.9728	1.5625
−7	2.437	0.705	69.71	1.419	14.346	193.54	349.42	155.88	0.9762	1.5619
−6	2.523	0.706	67.46	1.415	14.824	194.46	349.87	155.41	0.9796	1.5614
−5	2.612	0.708	65.30	1.412	15.315	195.38	350.32	154.94	0.9830	1.5609
−4	2.702	0.710	63.22	1.409	15.818	196.30	350.76	154.46	0.9865	1.5604
−3	2.795	0.711	61.22	1.406	16.334	197.22	351.21	153.99	0.9898	1.5599
−2	2.891	0.713	59.30	1.403	16.863	198.14	351.65	153.51	0.9932	1.5594
−1	2.989	0.715	57.46	1.399	17.405	199.08	352.10	153.02	0.9966	1.5589
0	3.089	0.716	55.68	1.396	17.960	200.00	352.54	152.54	1.0000	1.5585
1	3.192	0.718	53.97	1.393	18.529	200.93	352.98	152.05	1.0034	1.5580
2	3.297	0.720	52.32	1.389	19.113	201.85	353.41	151.56	1.0067	1.5576
3	3.405	0.721	50.74	1.386	19.710	202.79	353.85	151.06	1.0101	1.5571
4	3.516	0.723	49.21	1.383	20.322	203.73	354.29	150.56	1.0134	1.5567
5	3.629	0.725	47.74	1.379	20.948	204.66	354.72	150.06	1.0168	1.5563
6	3.746	0.727	46.32	1.376	21.590	205.59	355.15	149.56	1.0201	1.5559
7	3.865	0.728	44.95	1.373	22.247	206.53	355.58	149.05	1.0234	1.5555
8	3.986	0.730	43.63	1.369	22.919	207.47	356.01	148.54	1.0267	1.5551
9	4.111	0.732	42.36	1.366	23.608	208.42	356.44	148.02	1.0301	1.5547
10	4.238	0.734	41.13	1.363	24.312	209.35	356.86	147.51	1.0333	1.5543
11	4.369	0.736	39.95	1.359	25.033	210.30	357.29	146.99	1.0366	1.5539
12	4.502	0.738	38.80	1.356	25.771	211.25	357.71	146.46	1.0399	1.5536
13	4.639	0.739	37.70	1.352	26.526	212.20	358.13	145.93	1.0432	1.5532
14	4.778	0.741	36.63	1.349	27.299	213.14	358.54	145.40	1.0465	1.5529
15	4.921	0.743	35.60	1.345	28.089	214.09	358.96	144.87	1.0497	1.5525
16	5.067	0.745	34.61	1.342	28.897	215.04	359.37	144.33	1.0530	1.5522
17	5.216	0.747	33.64	1.338	29.724	216.01	359.79	143.78	1.0563	1.5518
18	5.368	0.749	32.71	1.335	30.569	216.97	360.20	143.23	1.0596	1.5515
19	5.524	0.751	31.81	1.331	31.434	217.92	360.60	142.68	1.0628	1.5512
20	5.682	0.753	30.94	1.328	32.318	218.88	361.01	142.13	1.0660	1.5509
21	5.845	0.755	30.10	1.324	33.222	219.84	361.41	141.57	1.0693	1.5506
22	6.011	0.757	29.29	1.320	34.146	220.81	361.81	141.00	1.0725	1.5503
23	6.180	0.759	28.50	1.317	35.091	221.78	362.21	140.43	1.0757	1.5499
24	6.352	0.762	27.73	1.313	36.057	222.75	362.61	139.86	1.0790	1.5496
25	6.529	0.764	26.99	1.309	37.045	223.72	363.00	139.28	1.0822	1.5494
26	6.709	0.766	26.28	1.306	38.054	224.70	363.40	138.70	1.0854	1.5491
27	6.892	0.768	25.58	1.302	39.086	225.68	363.79	138.11	1.0886	1.5488
28	7.080	0.770	24.91	1.298	40.141	226.65	364.17	137.52	1.0918	1.5485
29	7.271	0.772	24.26	1.295	41.219	227.64	364.56	136.92	1.0950	1.5482
30	7.465	0.775	23.63	1.291	42.320	228.62	364.94	136.32	1.0982	1.5479
31	7.664	0.777	23.02	1.287	43.446	229.61	365.32	135.71	1.1014	1.5476
32	7.867	0.779	22.42	1.283	44.597	230.59	365.69	135.10	1.1046	1.5474
33	8.073	0.782	21.85	1.279	45.773	231.59	366.07	134.48	1.1078	1.5471
34	8.284	0.784	21.29	1.275	46.975	232.59	366.44	133.85	1.1110	1.5468
35	8.498	0.786	20.75	1.271	48.204	233.59	366.81	133.22	1.1142	1.5466
36	8.717	0.789	20.22	1.268	49.459	234.58	367.17	132.59	1.1174	1.5463
37	8.940	0.791	19.71	1.264	50.742	235.59	367.53	131.94	1.1206	1.5460
38	9.167	0.794	19.21	1.260	52.052	236.60	367.89	131.29	1.1238	1.5457
39	9.398	0.796	18.73	1.256	53.392	237.61	368.25	130.64	1.1269	1.5455

Tempera-ture	Pressure	Specific volume		Density		Specific enthalpy		Heat of vaporization	Specific entropy	
		Liquid	Vapor	Liquid	Vapor	Liquid	Vapor		Liquid	Vapor
t	p	v'	v''	ρ'	ρ''	h'	h''	r	s'	s''
°C	bar	L/kg	L/kg	kg/L	kg/m³	kJ/kg	kJ/kg	kJ/kg	kJ/(kg K)	kJ/(kg K)
40	9.634	0.799	18.26	1.252	54.761	238.62	368.60	129.98	1.1301	1.5452
41	9.874	0.802	17.81	1.248	56.160	239.64	368.95	129.31	1.1333	1.5449
42	10.118	0.804	17.36	1.244	57.590	240.66	369.29	128.63	1.1365	1.5447
43	10.367	0.807	16.93	1.239	59.052	241.69	369.64	127.95	1.1397	1.5444
44	10.620	0.810	16.52	1.235	60.545	242.71	369.97	127.26	1.1429	1.5441
45	10.878	0.812	16.11	1.231	62.072	243.75	370.31	126.56	1.1461	1.5439
46	11.140	0.815	15.72	1.227	63.632	244.78	370.64	125.86	1.1492	1.5436
47	11.407	0.818	15.33	1.223	65.227	245.82	370.97	125.15	1.1524	1.5433
48	11.679	0.821	14.96	1.218	66.857	246.86	371.29	124.43	1.1556	1.5431
49	11.955	0.824	14.59	1.214	68.524	247.91	371.61	123.70	1.1588	1.5428
50	12.236	0.827	14.24	1.210	70.228	248.96	371.92	122.96	1.1620	1.5425
51	12.522	0.830	13.98	1.205	71.970	250.02	372.24	122.22	1.1652	1.5422
52	12.814	0.833	13.56	1.201	73.751	251.08	372.54	121.46	1.1684	1.5419
53	13.110	0.836	13.23	1.197	75.573	252.14	372.84	120.70	1.1716	1.5416
54	13.411	0.839	12.91	1.192	77.436	253.22	373.14	119.92	1.1748	1.5413
55	13.717	0.842	12.60	1.188	79.341	254.30	373.44	119.14	1.1780	1.5411
56	14.028	0.845	12.30	1.183	81.290	255.37	373.72	118.35	1.1812	1.5407
57	14.345	0.849	12.01	1.178	83.284	256.46	374.01	117.55	1.1844	1.5404
58	14.666	0.852	11.72	1.174	85.323	257.55	374.28	116.73	1.1876	1.5401
59	14.993	0.855	11.44	1.169	87.411	258.65	374.56	115.91	1.1908	1.5398
60	15.326	0.859	11.17	1.164	89.547	259.75	374.82	115.07	1.1941	1.5395
61	15.663	0.862	10.90	1.160	91.733	260.86	375.09	114.23	1.1973	1.5392
62	16.007	0.866	10.64	1.155	93.971	261.97	375.34	113.37	1.2005	1.5388
63	16.356	0.870	10.39	1.150	96.263	263.09	375.59	112.50	1.2038	1.5385
64	16.710	0.873	10.14	1.145	98.609	264.22	375.84	111.62	1.2070	1.5381
65	17.070	0.877	9.90	1.140	101.013	265.35	376.07	110.72	1.2103	1.5377
66	17.436	0.881	9.66	1.135	103.475	266.50	376.31	109.81	1.2136	1.5374
67	17.807	0.885	9.43	1.130	105.998	267.64	376.53	108.89	1.2168	1.5370
68	18.185	0.889	9.21	1.125	108.584	268.80	376.75	107.95	1.2201	1.5366
69	18.568	0.893	8.99	1.120	111.235	269.96	376.96	107.00	1.2234	1.5362
70	18.957	0.897	8.78	1.114	113.953	271.13	377.16	106.03	1.2268	1.5358
71	19.353	0.902	8.57	1.109	116.741	272.31	377.36	105.05	1.2301	1.5353
72	19.754	0.906	8.36	1.104	119.601	273.49	377.54	104.05	1.2334	1.5349
73	20.161	0.911	8.16	1.098	122.537	274.69	377.72	103.03	1.2368	1.5344
74	20.575	0.915	7.96	1.092	125.550	275.89	377.89	102.00	1.2401	1.5340
75	20.995	0.920	7.77	1.087	128.645	277.11	378.06	100.95	1.2435	1.5335
76	21.421	0.925	7.59	1.081	131.824	278.33	378.21	99.88	1.2469	1.5330
77	21.854	0.930	7.40	1.075	135.092	279.56	378.35	98.79	1.2503	1.5325
78	22.293	0.935	7.22	1.069	138.451	280.80	378.48	97.68	1.2537	1.5319
79	22.739	0.940	7.05	1.063	141.907	282.06	378.60	96.54	1.2572	1.5314
80	23.191	0.946	6.87	1.057	145.463	283.33	378.72	95.39	1.2607	1.5308
81	23.650	0.951	6.71	1.051	149.124	284.60	378.81	94.21	1.2642	1.5302
82	24.116	0.957	6.54	1.045	152.896	285.89	378.90	93.01	1.2677	1.5296
83	24.588	0.963	6.38	1.038	156.784	287.20	378.98	91.78	1.2712	1.5289
84	25.068	0.969	6.22	1.032	160.794	288.52	379.04	90.52	1.2748	1.5282
85	25.554	0.975	6.06	1.025	164.933	289.84	379.08	89.24	1.2784	1.5275
86	26.047	0.982	5.91	1.019	169.207	291.19	379.12	87.93	1.2820	1.5268
87	26.548	0.989	5.76	1.012	173.626	292.55	379.13	86.58	1.2856	1.5260
88	27.055	0.996	5.61	1.004	178.197	293.93	379.13	85.20	1.2893	1.5252
89	27.570	1.003	5.47	0.997	182.931	295.33	379.12	83.79	1.2930	1.5244

133

Table 3-9   Properties of Saturated "Freon 12" — Dichlorodifluoromethane (CF_2Cl_2)   (continued)

Tempera-ture	Pressure	Specific volume		Density		Specific enthalpy		Heat of vaporization	Specific entropy	
		Liquid	Vapor	Liquid	Vapor	Liquid	Vapor		Liquid	Vapor
t	p	v'	v''	ρ'	ρ''	h'	h''	r	s'	s''
°C	bar	L/kg	L/kg	kg/L	kg/m³	kJ/kg	kJ/kg	kJ/kg	kJ/(kg K)	kJ/(kg K)
90	28.092	1.010	5.32	0.990	187.837	296.74	379.08	82.34	1.2968	1.5235
91	28.621	1.018	5.18	0.982	192.929	298.17	379.02	80.85	1.3006	1.5226
92	29.158	1.026	5.04	0.974	198.219	299.63	378.95	79.32	1.3044	1.5216
93	29.702	1.035	4.91	0.966	203.723	301.10	378.84	77.74	1.3083	1.5206
94	30.254	1.044	4.77	0.958	209.458	302.61	378.72	76.11	1.3122	1.5196
95	30.814	1.053	4.64	0.949	215.444	304.14	378.57	74.43	1.3162	1.5184
96	31.381	1.063	4.51	0.941	221.703	305.69	378.38	72.69	1.3203	1.5172
97	31.956	1.074	4.38	0.931	228.263	307.29	378.17	70.88	1.3245	1.5160
98	32.539	1.085	4.25	0.922	235.153	308.91	377.92	69.01	1.3287	1.5146
99	33.130	1.097	4.13	0.912	242.413	310.57	377.63	67.06	1.3330	1.5132
100	33.729	1.109	4.00	0.901	250.085	312.28	377.30	65.02	1.3374	1.5116
101	34.337	1.123	3.87	0.891	258.226	314.04	376.92	62.88	1.3419	1.5100
102	34.952	1.138	3.75	0.879	266.902	315.85	376.48	60.63	1.3465	1.5082
103	35.576	1.154	3.62	0.867	276.202	317.71	375.97	58.26	1.3513	1.5062
104	36.208	1.171	3.49	0.854	286.238	319.67	375.39	55.72	1.3563	1.5040
105	36.848	1.191	3.37	0.840	297.163	321.70	374.71	53.01	1.3615	1.5017
106	37.497	1.213	3.23	0.824	309.191	323.85	373.92	50.07	1.3669	1.4990
107	38.155	1.238	3.10	0.807	322.641	326.14	372.97	46.83	1.3728	1.4960
108	38.821	1.269	2.96	0.788	338.011	328.63	371.83	43.20	1.3791	1.4924
109	39.496	1.306	2.81	0.766	356.180	331.40	370.40	39.00	1.3861	1.4882
110	40.180	1.355	2.64	0.738	378.959	334.62	368.49	33.87	1.3943	1.4827
111	40.874	1.430	2.43	0.700	411.464	338.78	365.59	26.81	1.4049	1.4747
112.00	41.576	1.792	1.79	0.558	558.000	351.71	351.71	0.00	1.4382	1.4382

Table 3-10 Properties of Saturated "Freon 12 B1" — Bromochlorodifluoromethane (CBrClF₂)

Temperature	Pressure	Specific volume		Density		Specific enthalpy		Heat of vaporization	Specific entropy	
		Liquid	Vapor	Liquid	Vapor	Liquid	Vapor		Liquid	Vapor
t	p	v'	v''	ρ'	ρ''	h'	h''	r	s'	s''
°C	bar	L/kg	L/kg	kg/L	kg/m³	kJ/kg	kJ/kg	kJ/kg	kJ/(kg K)	kJ/(kg K)
−40	0.197	0.496	586.96	2.016	1.704	174.53	316.81	142.28	0.8995	1.5098
−39	0.208	0.497	559.07	2.012	1.789	175.12	317.19	142.07	0.9021	1.5088
−38	0.219	0.498	532.76	2.009	1.877	175.73	317.58	141.85	0.9046	1.5079
−37	0.231	0.498	507.92	2.006	1.969	176.32	317.96	141.64	0.9072	1.5070
−36	0.243	0.499	484.45	2.003	2.064	176.92	318.34	141.42	0.9097	1.5061
−35	0.255	0.500	462.27	2.000	2.163	177.53	318.73	141.20	0.9122	1.5052
−34	0.269	0.501	441.30	1.997	2.266	178.13	319.11	140.98	0.9148	1.5043
−33	0.282	0.502	421.46	1.994	2.373	178.74	319.49	140.75	0.9173	1.5034
−32	0.296	0.502	402.68	1.991	2.483	179.36	319.88	140.52	0.9199	1.5026
−31	0.311	0.503	384.90	1.988	2.598	179.96	320.26	140.30	0.9224	1.5018
−30	0.327	0.504	368.06	1.984	2.717	180.58	320.64	140.06	0.9249	1.5010
−29	0.343	0.505	352.09	1.981	2.840	181.20	321.03	139.83	0.9275	1.5002
−28	0.359	0.506	336.96	1.978	2.968	181.81	321.41	139.60	0.9300	1.4994
−27	0.376	0.506	322.60	1.975	3.100	182.43	321.79	139.36	0.9325	1.4987
−26	0.394	0.507	308.97	1.972	3.237	183.06	322.18	139.12	0.9350	1.4979
−25	0.413	0.508	296.03	1.969	3.378	183.68	322.56	138.88	0.9375	1.4972
−24	0.432	0.509	283.74	1.965	3.524	184.31	322.94	138.63	0.9401	1.4965
−23	0.452	0.510	272.06	1.962	3.676	184.95	323.33	138.38	0.9426	1.4958
−22	0.473	0.510	260.96	1.959	3.832	185.58	323.71	138.13	0.9451	1.4951
−21	0.494	0.511	250.40	1.956	3.994	186.21	324.09	137.88	0.9476	1.4945
−20	0.517	0.512	240.35	1.953	4.161	186.84	324.47	137.63	0.9501	1.4938
−19	0.540	0.513	230.79	1.949	4.333	187.48	324.85	137.37	0.9526	1.4932
−18	0.564	0.514	221.68	1.946	4.511	188.13	325.24	137.11	0.9552	1.4925
−17	0.588	0.515	213.01	1.943	4.695	188.77	325.62	136.85	0.9577	1.4919
−16	0.614	0.516	204.74	1.940	4.884	189.41	326.00	136.59	0.9602	1.4913
−15	0.640	0.516	196.87	1.937	5.080	190.06	326.38	136.32	0.9627	1.4908
−14	0.668	0.517	189.35	1.933	5.281	190.71	326.76	136.05	0.9652	1.4902
−13	0.696	0.518	182.18	1.930	5.489	191.36	327.14	135.78	0.9677	1.4896
−12	0.725	0.519	175.34	1.927	5.703	192.01	327.52	135.51	0.9702	1.4891
−11	0.755	0.520	168.81	1.923	5.924	192.67	327.90	135.23	0.9727	1.4885
−10	0.787	0.521	162.58	1.920	6.151	193.32	328.27	134.95	0.9752	1.4880
−9	0.819	0.522	156.62	1.917	6.385	193.98	328.65	134.67	0.9777	1.4875
−8	0.852	0.523	150.92	1.914	6.626	194.64	329.03	134.39	0.9801	1.4870
−7	0.886	0.523	145.48	1.910	6.874	195.31	329.41	134.10	0.9826	1.4865
−6	0.921	0.524	140.27	1.907	7.129	195.96	329.78	133.82	0.9851	1.4860
−5	0.958	0.525	135.29	1.904	7.392	196.64	330.16	133.52	0.9876	1.4856
−4	0.995	0.526	130.52	1.900	7.662	197.31	330.54	133.23	0.9901	1.4851
−3	1.034	0.527	125.96	1.897	7.939	197.97	330.91	132.94	0.9926	1.4847
−2	1.074	0.528	121.59	1.894	8.225	198.65	331.29	132.64	0.9950	1.4842
−1	1.115	0.529	117.40	1.890	8.518	199.32	331.66	132.34	0.9975	1.4838
0	1.157	0.530	113.39	1.887	8.819	200.00	332.03	132.03	1.0000	1.4834
1	1.200	0.531	109.54	1.883	9.129	200.67	332.40	131.73	1.0025	1.4830
2	1.245	0.532	105.85	1.880	9.447	201.36	332.78	131.42	1.0049	1.4826
3	1.291	0.533	102.31	1.877	9.774	202.04	333.15	131.11	1.0074	1.4822
4	1.338	0.534	98.92	1.873	10.109	202.73	333.52	130.79	1.0099	1.4818
5	1.387	0.535	95.66	1.870	10.453	203.41	333.89	130.48	1.0123	1.4814
6	1.437	0.536	92.54	1.866	10.807	204.10	334.26	130.16	1.0148	1.4811
7	1.488	0.537	89.53	1.863	11.169	204.79	334.63	129.84	1.0172	1.4807
8	1.541	0.538	86.65	1.859	11.541	205.48	334.99	129.51	1.0197	1.4804
9	1.595	0.539	83.88	1.856	11.922	206.17	335.36	129.19	1.0221	1.4800

Table 3-10 Properties of Saturated "Freon 12 B1" — Bromochlorodifluoromethane (CBrClF₂) *(continued)*

Tempera-ture	Pressure	Specific volume		Density		Specific enthalpy		Heat of vaporization	Specific entropy	
		Liquid	Vapor	Liquid	Vapor	Liquid	Vapor		Liquid	Vapor
t	p	v'	v''	ρ'	ρ''	h'	h''	r	s'	s''
°C	bar	L/kg	L/kg	kg/L	kg/m³	kJ/kg	kJ/kg	kJ/kg	kJ/(kg K)	kJ/(kg K)
10	1.651	0.540	81.21	1.853	12.313	206.87	335.73	128.86	1.0246	1.4797
11	1.708	0.541	78.65	1.849	12.714	207.56	336.09	128.53	1.0270	1.4794
12	1.767	0.542	76.19	1.846	13.125	208.26	336.46	128.20	1.0295	1.4791
13	1.827	0.543	73.82	1.842	13.547	208.96	336.82	127.86	1.0319	1.4788
14	1.889	0.544	71.54	1.839	13.978	209.66	337.18	127.52	1.0344	1.4785
15	1.952	0.545	69.35	1.835	14.420	210.37	337.55	127.18	1.0368	1.4782
16	2.017	0.546	67.23	1.831	14.874	211.07	337.91	126.84	1.0392	1.4779
17	2.084	0.547	65.20	1.828	15.338	211.78	338.27	126.49	1.0416	1.4776
18	2.152	0.548	63.24	1.824	15.813	212.49	338.63	126.14	1.0441	1.4773
19	2.222	0.549	61.35	1.821	16.299	213.20	338.99	125.79	1.0465	1.4771
20	2.294	0.550	59.53	1.817	16.797	213.91	339.34	125.43	1.0489	1.4768
21	2.367	0.551	57.78	1.814	17.307	214.62	339.70	125.08	1.0513	1.4766
22	2.442	0.552	56.09	1.810	17.829	215.34	340.06	124.72	1.0537	1.4763
23	2.519	0.554	54.46	1.806	18.363	216.05	340.41	124.36	1.0561	1.4761
24	2.598	0.555	52.88	1.803	18.909	216.78	340.77	123.99	1.0586	1.4759
25	2.679	0.556	51.37	1.799	19.468	217.49	341.12	123.63	1.0610	1.4756
26	2.761	0.557	49.90	1.795	20.040	218.21	341.47	123.26	1.0634	1.4754
27	2.846	0.558	48.49	1.792	20.624	218.93	341.82	122.89	1.0657	1.4752
28	2.932	0.559	47.12	1.788	21.222	219.66	342.17	122.51	1.0682	1.4750
29	3.021	0.560	45.80	1.784	21.833	220.38	342.52	122.14	1.0705	1.4748
30	3.111	0.562	44.53	1.781	22.458	221.11	342.87	121.76	1.0729	1.4746
31	3.203	0.563	43.30	1.777	23.097	221.84	343.22	121.38	1.0753	1.4744
32	3.298	0.564	42.11	1.773	23.750	222.57	343.56	120.99	1.0777	1.4742
33	3.394	0.565	40.95	1.770	24.417	223.31	343.91	120.60	1.0801	1.4740
34	3.493	0.566	39.84	1.766	25.099	224.03	344.25	120.22	1.0824	1.4738
35	3.594	0.568	38.77	1.762	25.796	224.77	344.59	119.82	1.0848	1.4737
36	3.697	0.569	37.73	1.758	26.507	225.51	344.94	119.43	1.0872	1.4735
37	3.802	0.570	36.72	1.754	27.234	226.25	345.28	119.03	1.0895	1.4733
38	3.909	0.571	35.74	1.751	27.977	226.99	345.62	118.63	1.0919	1.4732
39	4.018	0.572	34.80	1.747	28.735	227.72	345.95	118.23	1.0942	1.4730
40	4.130	0.574	33.89	1.743	29.510	228.46	346.29	117.83	1.0966	1.4729
41	4.244	0.575	33.00	1.739	30.301	229.21	346.63	117.42	1.0989	1.4727
42	4.361	0.576	32.15	1.735	31.109	229.95	346.96	117.01	1.1013	1.4726
43	4.480	0.578	31.32	1.731	31.933	230.69	347.29	116.60	1.1036	1.4724
44	4.601	0.579	30.51	1.727	32.775	231.45	347.63	116.18	1.1060	1.4723
45	4.724	0.580	29.73	1.724	33.635	232.20	347.96	115.76	1.1083	1.4722
46	4.850	0.582	28.98	1.720	34.512	232.95	348.29	115.34	1.1106	1.4721
47	4.979	0.583	28.24	1.716	35.407	233.70	348.62	114.92	1.1130	1.4719
48	5.110	0.584	27.53	1.712	36.321	234.45	348.94	114.49	1.1153	1.4718
49	5.244	0.586	26.84	1.708	37.254	235.21	349.27	114.06	1.1176	1.4717
50	5.380	0.587	26.17	1.704	38.205	235.96	349.59	113.63	1.1199	1.4716
51	5.518	0.588	25.53	1.700	39.176	236.72	349.92	113.20	1.1222	1.4715
52	5.660	0.590	24.90	1.696	40.167	237.48	350.24	112.76	1.1246	1.4714
53	5.804	0.591	24.28	1.692	41.178	238.24	350.56	112.32	1.1269	1.4713
54	5.951	0.593	23.69	1.687	42.210	239.00	350.88	111.88	1.1292	1.4712
55	6.100	0.594	23.11	1.683	43.262	239.76	351.19	111.43	1.1315	1.4711
56	6.252	0.595	22.56	1.679	44.336	240.53	351.51	110.98	1.1338	1.4710
57	6.407	0.597	22.01	1.675	45.431	241.29	351.82	110.53	1.1361	1.4709
58	6.565	0.598	21.48	1.671	46.549	242.06	352.14	110.08	1.1383	1.4708
59	6.725	0.600	20.97	1.667	47.688	242.83	352.45	109.62	1.1406	1.4707

Table 3-10 Properties of Saturated "Freon 12 B1" — Bromochlorodifluoromethane (CBrClF$_2$) (continued)

Tempera-ture	Pressure	Specific volume		Density		Specific enthalpy		Heat of vaporization	Specific entropy	
		Liquid	Vapor	Liquid	Vapor	Liquid	Vapor		Liquid	Vapor
t	p	v'	v''	ρ'	ρ''	h'	h''	r	s'	s''
°C	bar	L/kg	L/kg	kg/L	kg/m^3	kJ/kg	kJ/kg	kJ/kg	kJ/(kg K)	kJ/(kg K)
60	6.889	0.601	20.47	1.663	48.851	243.60	352.76	109.16	1.1429	1.4706
61	7.055	0.603	19.99	1.658	50.037	244.38	353.07	108.69	1.1452	1.4705
62	7.225	0.605	19.51	1.654	51.247	245.14	353.37	108.23	1.1475	1.4704
63	7.397	0.606	19.05	1.540	52.481	245.92	353.68	107.76	1.1498	1.4704
64	7.572	0.608	18.61	1.646	53.739	246.70	353.98	107.28	1.1521	1.4703
65	7.750	0.609	18.17	1.641	55.023	247.48	354.29	106.81	1.1543	1.4702
66	7.932	0.611	17.75	1.637	56.332	248.26	354.59	106.33	1.1566	1.4701
67	8.116	0.612	17.34	1.633	57.668	249.04	354.88	105.84	1.1589	1.4701
68	8.304	0.614	16.94	1.628	59.030	249.82	355.18	105.36	1.1611	1.4700
69	8.495	0.616	16.55	1.624	60.420	250.62	355.48	104.86	1.1634	1.4699
70	8.689	0.617	16.17	1.619	61.837	251.40	355.77	104.37	1.1657	1.4698
71	8.886	0.619	15.80	1.615	63.283	252.19	356.06	103.87	1.1679	1.4698
72	9.086	0.621	15.44	1.611	64.757	252.98	356.35	103.37	1.1702	1.4697
73	9.290	0.623	15.09	1.606	66.262	253.77	356.64	102.87	1.1724	1.4696
74	9.497	0.624	14.75	1.602	67.797	254.56	356.92	102.36	1.1747	1.4696
75	9.707	0.626	14.42	1.597	69.362	255.37	357.21	101.84	1.1770	1.4695
76	9.921	0.628	14.09	1.592	70.959	256.17	357.49	101.32	1.1792	1.4694
77	10.138	0.630	13.78	1.588	72.589	256.97	357.77	100.80	1.1815	1.4694
78	10.359	0.632	13.47	1.583	74.252	257.77	358.05	100.28	1.1837	1.4693
79	10.583	0.634	13.17	1.579	75.948	258.57	358.32	99.75	1.1860	1.4692
80	10.811	0.635	12.87	1.574	77.680	259.39	358.60	99.21	1.1882	1.4692
81	11.043	0.637	12.59	1.569	79.446	260.20	358.87	98.67	1.1905	1.4691
82	11.278	0.639	12.31	1.564	81.249	261.01	359.14	98.13	1.1927	1.4690
83	11.516	0.641	12.04	1.560	83.090	261.82	359.40	97.58	1.1950	1.4690
84	11.759	0.643	11.77	1.555	84.969	262.65	359.67	97.02	1.1972	1.4689
85	12.005	0.645	11.51	1.550	86.886	263.47	359.93	96.46	1.1995	1.4688
86	12.254	0.647	11.26	1.545	88.844	264.29	360.19	95.90	1.2017	1.4688
87	12.508	0.649	11.01	1.540	90.844	265.11	360.44	95.33	1.2040	1.4687
88	12.766	0.651	10.77	1.535	92.886	265.95	360.70	94.75	1.2063	1.4686
89	13.027	0.654	10.53	1.530	94.971	266.78	360.95	94.17	1.2085	1.4686
90	13.292	0.656	10.30	1.525	97.101	267.62	361.20	93.58	1.2108	1.4685
91	13.561	0.658	10.07	1.520	99.277	268.45	361.44	92.99	1.2130	1.4684
92	13.835	0.660	9.85	1.515	101.500	269.30	361.69	92.39	1.2153	1.4683
93	14.112	0.662	9.64	1.510	103.772	270.14	361.92	91.78	1.2176	1.4682
94	14.393	0.665	9.43	1.505	106.095	270.99	362.16	91.17	1.2198	1.4681
95	14.679	0.667	9.22	1.499	108.469	271.84	362.39	90.55	1.2221	1.4681
96	14.969	0.669	9.02	1.494	110.896	272.70	362.62	89.92	1.2244	1.4680
97	15.263	0.672	8.82	1.489	113.379	273.56	362.85	89.29	1.2266	1.4679
98	15.561	0.674	8.63	1.483	115.918	274.42	363.07	88.65	1.2289	1.4678
99	15.863	0.677	8.44	1.478	118.516	275.29	363.29	88.00	1.2312	1.4677
100	16.170	0.679	8.25	1.472	121.174	276.17	363.51	87.34	1.2335	1.4675
101	16.481	0.682	8.07	1.467	123.895	277.05	363.72	86.67	1.2358	1.4674
102	16.797	0.684	7.89	1.461	126.681	277.94	363.93	85.99	1.2381	1.4673
103	17.117	0.687	7.72	1.456	129.535	278.82	364.13	85.31	1.2404	1.4672
104	17.442	0.690	7.55	1.450	132.458	279.72	364.33	84.61	1.2427	1.4671
105	17.771	0.692	7.38	1.444	135.453	280.61	364.52	83.91	1.2450	1.4669
106	18.106	0.695	7.22	1.438	138.523	281.52	364.71	83.19	1.2474	1.4668
107	18.444	0.698	7.06	1.433	141.672	282.43	364.90	82.47	1.2497	1.4666
108	18.788	0.701	6.90	1.427	144.901	283.35	365.08	81.73	1.2520	1.4665
109	19.136	0.704	6.75	1.421	148.215	284.28	365.26	80.98	1.2544	1.4663

Table 3-10 Properties of Saturated "Freon 12 B1" — Bromochlorodifluoromethane (CBrClF$_2$) *(continued)*

Tempera-ture	Pressure	Specific volume		Density		Specific enthalpy		Heat of vaporization	Specific entropy	
		Liquid	Vapor	Liquid	Vapor	Liquid	Vapor		Liquid	Vapor
t	p	v'	v''	ρ'	ρ''	h'	h''	r	s'	s''
°C	bar	L/kg	L/kg	kg/L	kg/m^3	kJ/kg	kJ/kg	kJ/kg	kJ/(kg K)	kJ/(kg K)
110	19.489	0.707	6.60	1.415	151.617	285.20	365.42	80.22	1.2568	1.4661
111	19.847	0.710	6.45	1.408	155.111	286.15	365.59	79.44	1.2592	1.4660
112	20.210	0.713	6.30	1.402	158.700	287.09	365.75	78.66	1.2615	1.4658
113	20.578	0.716	6.16	1.396	162.390	288.04	365.90	77.86	1.2639	1.4656
114	20.951	0.720	6.02	1.389	166.184	289.00	366.04	77.04	1.2664	1.4654
115	21.329	0.723	5.88	1.383	170.088	289.97	366.18	76.21	1.2688	1.4651
116	21.713	0.727	5.74	1.376	174.108	290.95	366.32	75.37	1.2712	1.4649
117	22.102	0.730	5.61	1.370	178.248	291.94	366.44	74.50	1.2737	1.4647
118	22.496	0.734	5.48	1.363	182.516	292.94	366.56	73.62	1.2762	1.4644
119	22.895	0.737	5.35	1.356	186.917	293.94	366.67	72.73	1.2787	1.4641
120	23.300	0.741	5.22	1.349	191.460	294.96	366.77	71.81	1.2812	1.4638
121	23.710	0.745	5.10	1.342	196.151	295.99	366.86	70.87	1.2837	1.4635
122	24.126	0.749	4.98	1.335	201.001	297.02	366.94	69.92	1.2863	1.4632
123	24.548	0.753	4.85	1.328	206.018	298.07	367.01	68.94	1.2888	1.4629
124	24.975	0.757	4.73	1.320	211.212	299.14	367.08	67.94	1.2914	1.4625
125	25.408	0.762	4.62	1.313	216.596	300.22	367.13	66.91	1.2941	1.4621
126	25.847	0.766	4.50	1.305	222.180	301.31	367.17	65.86	1.2967	1.4617
127	26.291	0.771	4.39	1.297	227.979	302.41	367.19	64.78	1.2994	1.4613
128	26.742	0.776	4.27	1.289	234.008	303.54	367.21	63.67	1.3021	1.4608
129	27.199	0.781	4.16	1.281	240.284	304.68	367.21	62.53	1.3049	1.4604
130	27.662	0.786	4.05	1.273	246.824	305.83	367.19	61.36	1.3076	1.4599
131	28.131	0.791	3.94	1.264	253.650	307.00	367.16	60.16	1.3104	1.4593
132	28.607	0.797	3.83	1.255	260.783	308.19	367.11	58.92	1.3133	1.4587
133	29.089	0.802	3.73	1.246	268.250	309.41	367.05	57.64	1.3162	1.4581
134	29.577	0.808	3.62	1.237	276.080	310.64	366.96	56.32	1.3191	1.4575
135	30.072	0.815	3.52	1.228	284.303	311.89	366.85	54.96	1.3221	1.4568
136	30.574	0.821	3.41	1.218	292.957	313.16	366.72	53.56	1.3251	1.4560
137	31.082	0.828	3.31	1.208	302.082	314.47	366.57	52.10	1.3282	1.4552
138	31.598	0.835	3.21	1.197	311.724	315.80	366.39	50.59	1.3313	1.4544
139	32.120	0.843	3.11	1.187	321.936	317.16	366.18	40.02	1.3345	1.4535
140	32.649	0.851	3.01	1.175	332.777	318.53	365.93	47.40	1.3378	1.4525
141	33.185	0.859	2.90	1.164	344.314	319.95	365.66	45.71	1.3411	1.4514
142	33.728	0.868	2.80	1.151	356.624	321.40	365.35	43.95	1.3444	1.4503
143	34.279	0.878	2.70	1.139	369.795	322.87	364.99	42.12	1.3479	1.4491
144	34.837	0.889	2.60	1.125	383.927	324.38	364.59	40.21	1.3514	1.4478
145	35.403	0.900	2.51	1.111	399.134	325.93	364.15	38.22	1.3550	1.4464
146	35.976	0.913	2.41	1.096	415.551	327.52	363.65	36.13	1.3586	1.4449
147	36.557	0.926	2.31	1.079	433.337	329.15	363.09	33.94	1.3624	1.4432
148	37.146	0.942	2.21	1.062	452.686	330.84	362.47	31.63	1.3663	1.4414
149	37.743	0.959	2.11	1.042	473.855	332.58	361.76	29.18	1.3703	1.4394
150	38.347	0.980	2.01	1.021	497.205	334.39	360.96	26.57	1.3744	1.4372
151	38.960	1.004	1.91	0.996	523.304	336.32	360.04	23.72	1.3788	1.4348
152	39.582	1.036	1.81	0.966	553.178	338.42	358.95	20.53	1.3836	1.4319
153	40.211	1.079	1.70	0.927	589.072	340.83	357.55	16.72	1.3891	1.4284
154	40.850	1.154	1.57	0.867	638.340	344.14	355.46	11.32	1.3967	1.4233
154.60	41.237	1.403	1.40	0.713	713.012	351.77	351.77	0.00	1.4145	1.4145

Table 3-11 Properties of Saturated "Freon 13" — Trifluoromonochloromethane (CCIF₃)

Tempera-ture	Pressure	Specific volume		Density		Specific enthalpy		Heat of vaporization	Specific entropy	
		Liquid	Vapor	Liquid	Vapor	Liquid	Vapor		Liquid	Vapor
t	p	v'	v''	ρ'	ρ''	h'	h''	r	s'	s''
°C	bar	L/kg	L/kg	kg/L	kg/m³	kJ/kg	kJ/kg	kJ/kg	kJ/(kg K)	kJ/(kg K)
−120	0.070	0.601	1737.84	1.664	0.575	83.83	249.73	165.90	0.4561	1.5394
−119	0.076	0.602	1599.83	1.661	0.625	84.63	250.18	165.55	0.4613	1.5353
−118	0.083	0.603	1474.58	1.657	0.678	85.42	250.62	165.20	0.4664	1.5312
−117	0.091	0.605	1360.75	1.654	0.735	86.21	251.06	164.85	0.4715	1.5272
−116	0.099	0.606	1257.18	1.650	0.795	87.00	251.50	164.50	0.4765	1.5233
−115	0.107	0.607	1162.83	1.647	0.860	87.80	251.94	164.14	0.4816	1.5195
−114	0.117	0.609	1076.76	1.643	0.929	88.59	252.37	163.78	0.4866	1.5157
−113	0.126	0.610	998.16	1.640	1.002	89.40	252.81	163.41	0.4916	1.5120
−112	0.137	0.611	926.29	1.636	1.080	90.20	253.24	163.04	0.4966	1.5084
−111	0.148	0.612	860.50	1.633	1.162	91.00	253.67	162.67	0.5016	1.5048
−110	0.160	0.614	800.20	1.629	1.250	91.81	254.10	162.29	0.5065	1.5013
−109	0.173	0.615	744.88	1.626	1.342	92.62	254.53	161.91	0.5115	1.4979
−108	0.187	0.616	694.07	1.622	1.441	93.44	254.96	161.52	0.5164	1.4945
−107	0.201	0.618	647.35	1.619	1.545	94.26	255.39	161.13	0.5214	1.4912
−106	0.217	0.619	604.35	1.615	1.655	95.07	255.81	160.74	0.5263	1.4879
−105	0.233	0.621	564.73	1.611	1.771	95.90	256.24	160.34	0.5312	1.4848
−104	0.251	0.622	528.19	1.608	1.893	96.72	256.66	159.94	0.5361	1.4816
−103	0.269	0.623	494.45	1.604	2.022	97.55	257.08	159.53	0.5410	1.4786
−102	0.289	0.625	463.27	1.601	2.159	98.39	257.51	159.12	0.5458	1.4756
−101	0.309	0.626	434.43	1.597	2.302	99.23	257.93	158.70	0.5507	1.4726
−100	0.331	0.628	407.72	1.593	2.453	100.07	258.35	158.28	0.5556	1.4697
−99	0.354	0.629	382.97	1.590	2.611	100.92	258.77	157.85	0.5605	1.4669
−98	0.379	0.631	360.02	1.586	2.778	101.77	259.19	157.42	0.5653	1.4641
−97	0.404	0.632	338.70	1.582	2.952	102.61	259.60	156.99	0.5701	1.4614
−96	0.431	0.633	318.90	1.579	3.136	103.47	260.02	156.55	0.5750	1.4587
−95	0.460	0.635	300.48	1.575	3.328	104.34	260.44	156.10	0.5798	1.4561
−94	0.490	0.636	283.33	1.571	3.529	105.20	260.85	155.65	0.5847	1.4535
−93	0.521	0.638	267.36	1.568	3.740	106.06	261.26	155.20	0.5895	1.4510
−92	0.554	0.639	252.47	1.564	3.961	106.94	261.68	154.74	0.5943	1.4485
−91	0.589	0.641	238.57	1.560	4.192	107.82	262.09	154.27	0.5991	1.4461
−90	0.626	0.643	225.59	1.556	4.433	108.69	262.50	153.81	0.6039	1.4437
−89	0.664	0.644	213.46	1.553	4.685	109.58	262.91	153.33	0.6087	1.4414
−88	0.704	0.646	202.12	1.549	4.947	110.47	263.32	152.85	0.6135	1.4391
−87	0.746	0.647	191.51	1.545	5.222	111.35	263.72	152.37	0.6183	1.4368
−86	0.790	0.649	181.56	1.541	5.508	112.25	264.13	151.88	0.6230	1.4346
−85	0.836	0.650	172.24	1.537	5.806	113.15	264.53	151.38	0.6278	1.4324
−84	0.884	0.652	163.50	1.533	6.116	114.06	264.94	150.88	0.6326	1.4303
−83	0.934	0.654	155.29	1.530	6.439	114.96	265.34	150.38	0.6374	1.4282
−82	0.986	0.655	147.59	1.526	6.776	115.87	265.74	149.87	0.6421	1.4262
−81	1.040	0.657	140.34	1.522	7.125	116.78	266.13	149.35	0.6469	1.4242
−80	1.097	0.659	133.53	1.518	7.489	117.70	266.53	148.83	0.6516	1.4222
−79	1.156	0.660	127.12	1.514	7.867	118.62	266.93	148.31	0.6563	1.4202
−78	1.218	0.662	121.08	1.510	8.259	119.54	267.32	147.78	0.6611	1.4183
−77	1.282	0.664	115.39	1.506	8.667	120.47	267.71	147.24	0.6658	1.4165
−76	1.349	0.666	110.02	1.502	9.089	121.40	268.10	146.70	0.6705	1.4146
−75	1.418	0.667	104.96	1.498	9.528	122.34	268.49	146.15	0.6752	1.4128
−74	1.490	0.669	100.18	1.494	9.982	123.28	268.88	145.60	0.6799	1.4111
−73	1.565	0.671	95.66	1.490	10.454	124.22	269.27	145.05	0.6846	1.4093
−72	1.643	0.673	91.39	1.486	10.942	125.16	269.65	144.49	0.6893	1.4076
−71	1.724	0.675	87.36	1.482	11.447	126.11	270.03	143.92	0.6940	1.4059

Table 3-11　Properties of Saturated "Freon 13" — Trifluoromonochloromethane ($CCIF_3$)　　(continued)

Temperature	Pressure	Specific volume		Density		Specific enthalpy		Heat of vaporization	Specific entropy	
		Liquid	Vapor	Liquid	Vapor	Liquid	Vapor		Liquid	Vapor
t	p	v'	v''	ρ'	ρ''	h'	h''	r	s'	s''
°C	bar	L/kg	L/kg	kg/L	kg/m³	kJ/kg	kJ/kg	kJ/kg	kJ/(kg K)	kJ/(kg K)
−70	1.807	0.677	83.54	1.478	11.971	127.06	270.41	143.35	0.6986	1.4043
−69	1.894	0.678	79.92	1.474	12.512	128.02	270.79	142.77	0.7033	1.4026
−68	1.984	0.680	76.50	1.470	13.073	128.97	271.16	142.19	0.7079	1.4011
−67	2.077	0.682	73.25	1.466	13.652	129.94	271.54	141.60	0.7126	1.3995
−66	2.173	0.684	70.17	1.462	14.251	130.90	271.91	141.01	0.7172	1.3979
−65	2.273	0.686	67.25	1.458	14.870	131.86	272.28	140.42	0.7218	1.3964
−64	2.376	0.688	64.48	1.453	15.510	132.83	272.65	139.82	0.7264	1.3949
−63	2.482	0.690	61.84	1.449	16.170	133.80	273.01	139.21	0.7310	1.3935
−62	2.594	0.692	59.34	1.445	16.853	134.77	273.37	138.60	0.7356	1.3920
−61	2.706	0.694	56.96	1.441	17.557	135.75	273.73	137.98	0.7402	1.3906
−60	2.824	0.696	54.69	1.437	18.283	136.73	274.09	137.36	0.7447	1.3892
−59	2.945	0.698	52.54	1.432	19.033	137.72	274.45	136.73	0.7493	1.3878
−58	3.070	0.700	50.49	1.428	19.806	138.70	274.80	136.10	0.7539	1.3865
−57	3.119	0.702	48.54	1.424	20.603	139.68	275.15	135.47	0.7584	1.3851
−56	3.332	0.704	46.67	1.419	21.425	140.67	275.50	134.83	0.7629	1.3838
−55	3.469	0.707	44.90	1.415	22.272	141.66	275.84	134.18	0.7674	1.3825
−54	3.611	0.709	43.21	1.411	23.145	142.66	276.19	133.53	0.7719	1.3812
−53	3.756	0.711	41.59	1.406	24.044	143.66	276.53	132.87	0.7764	1.3800
−52	3.906	0.713	40.05	1.402	24.970	144.65	276.86	132.21	0.7809	1.3787
−51	4.060	0.716	38.58	1.398	25.923	145.65	277.20	131.55	0.7853	1.3775
−50	4.219	0.718	37.17	1.393	26.905	146.66	277.53	130.87	0.7898	1.3763
−49	4.382	0.720	35.82	1.389	27.915	147.66	277.86	130.20	0.7942	1.3751
−48	4.550	0.723	34.54	1.384	28.955	148.67	278.19	129.52	0.7987	1.3739
−47	4.722	0.725	33.31	1.379	30.025	149.68	278.51	128.83	0.8031	1.3728
−46	4.900	0.727	32.13	1.375	31.126	150.69	278.83	128.14	0.8075	1.3716
−45	5.082	0.730	31.00	1.370	32.259	151.70	279.15	127.45	0.8118	1.3705
−44	5.269	0.732	29.92	1.366	33.424	152.72	279.46	126.74	0.8163	1.3694
−43	5.461	0.735	28.88	1.361	34.621	153.73	279.77	126.04	0.8206	1.3683
−42	5.658	0.737	27.89	1.356	35.853	154.75	280.08	125.33	0.8249	1.3672
−41	5.860	0.740	26.94	1.352	37.119	155.77	280.38	124.61	0.8293	1.3661
−40	6.068	0.742	26.03	1.347	38.421	156.79	280.68	123.89	0.8336	1.3650
−39	6.280	0.745	25.15	1.342	39.759	157.82	280.98	123.16	0.8379	1.3640
−38	6.499	0.748	24.31	1.337	41.135	158.84	281.27	122.43	0.8422	1.3629
−37	6.722	0.750	23.50	1.332	42.548	159.87	281.56	121.69	0.8465	1.3619
−36	6.952	0.753	22.73	1.328	44.000	160.90	281.84	120.94	0.8508	1.3608
−35	7.187	0.756	21.98	1.323	45.493	161.94	282.13	120.19	0.8551	1.3598
−34	7.427	0.759	21.26	1.318	47.026	162.96	282.40	119.44	0.8593	1.3588
−33	7.674	0.762	20.58	1.313	48.602	164.00	282.68	118.68	0.8636	1.3578
−32	7.926	0.765	19.91	1.308	50.221	165.04	282.95	117.91	0.8678	1.3568
−31	8.185	0.768	19.27	1.303	51.884	166.08	283.21	117.13	0.8721	1.3558
−30	8.449	0.771	18.66	1.298	53.593	167.12	283.47	116.35	0.8763	1.3548
−29	8.720	0.774	18.07	1.292	55.348	168.16	283.73	115.57	0.8804	1.3538
−28	8.996	0.777	17.50	1.287	57.151	169.21	283.98	114.77	0.8846	1.3528
−27	9.280	0.780	16.95	1.282	59.004	170.26	284.23	114.97	0.8888	1.3518
−26	9.569	0.783	16.42	1.277	60.908	171.31	284.47	113.16	0.8930	1.3509
−25	9.865	0.787	15.91	1.271	62.864	172.36	284.71	112.35	0.8971	1.3499
−24	10.168	0.790	15.41	1.266	64.873	173.42	284.94	111.52	0.9013	1.3489
−23	10.478	0.793	14.94	1.261	66.938	174.48	285.17	110.69	0.9054	1.3480
−22	10.794	0.797	14.48	1.255	69.061	175.54	285.39	109.85	0.9096	1.3470
−21	11.117	0.800	14.04	1.250	71.241	176.60	285.61	109.01	0.9137	1.3460

Table 3-11 Properties of Saturated "Freon 13" — Trifluoromonochloromethane (CClF$_3$) *(continued)*

Tempera-ture	Pressure	Specific volume		Density		Specific enthalpy		Heat of vaporization	Specific entropy	
		Liquid	Vapor	Liquid	Vapor	Liquid	Vapor		Liquid	Vapor
t	p	v'	v''	ρ'	ρ''	h'	h''	r	s'	s''
°C	bar	L/kg	L/kg	kg/L	kg/m^3	kJ/kg	kJ/kg	kJ/kg	kJ/(kg K)	kJ/(kg K)
−20	11.447	0.804	13.61	1.244	73.483	177.67	285.82	108.15	0.9178	1.3450
−19	11.784	0.807	13.19	1.238	75.787	178.74	286.03	107.29	0.9219	1.3441
−18	12.129	0.811	12.79	1.233	78.156	179.81	286.22	106.41	0.9260	1.3431
−17	12.480	0.815	12.41	1.227	80.591	180.89	286.42	105.53	0.9301	1.3421
−16	12.839	0.819	12.03	1.221	83.096	181.97	286.60	104.63	0.9342	1.3411
−15	13.206	0.823	11.67	1.215	85.672	183.05	286.78	103.73	0.9383	1.3401
−14	13.580	0.827	11.32	1.209	88.323	184.15	286.96	102.81	0.9424	1.3392
−13	13.962	0.831	10.98	1.203	91.050	185.23	287.12	101.89	0.9465	1.3382
−12	14.352	0.835	10.65	1.197	93.856	186.33	287.28	100.95	0.9506	1.3371
−11	14.750	0.839	10.34	1.191	96.746	187.44	287.43	99.99	0.9547	1.3361
−10	15.155	0.844	10.03	1.185	99.721	188.54	287.57	99.03	0.9587	1.3351
−9	15.569	0.848	9.73	1.179	102.786	189.66	287.71	98.05	0.9628	1.3341
−8	15.991	0.853	9.44	1.172	105.944	190.77	287.83	97.06	0.9669	1.3330
−7	16.422	0.858	9.16	1.166	109.198	191.90	287.95	96.05	0.9710	1.3319
−6	16.861	0.863	8.88	1.159	112.555	193.04	288.06	95.02	0.9751	1.3308
−5	17.309	0.868	8.62	1.153	116.016	194.17	288.15	93.98	0.9792	1.3297
−4	17.765	0.873	8.36	1.146	119.589	195.32	288.24	92.92	0.9834	1.3286
−3	18.231	0.878	8.11	1.139	123.277	196.48	288.32	91.84	0.9875	1.3275
−2	18.705	0.883	7.87	1.132	127.088	197.64	288.38	90.74	0.9917	1.3263
−1	19.189	0.889	7.63	1.125	131.025	198.81	288.43	89.62	0.9958	1.3251
0	19.682	0.895	7.40	1.118	135.098	200.00	288.47	88.47	1.0000	1.3239
1	20.185	0.901	7.18	1.110	139.312	201.19	288.50	87.31	1.0042	1.3227
2	20.697	0.907	6.96	1.103	143.676	202.40	288.51	86.11	1.0084	1.3214
3	21.219	0.913	6.75	1.095	148.198	203.62	288.51	84.89	1.0127	1.3201
4	21.751	0.920	6.54	1.087	152.889	204.85	288.49	83.64	1.0170	1.3188
5	22.293	0.927	6.34	1.079	157.757	206.10	288.46	82.36	1.0213	1.3174
6	22.845	0.934	6.14	1.071	162.817	207.37	288.41	81.04	1.0256	1.3159
7	23.408	0.941	5.95	1.063	168.079	208.64	288.33	79.69	1.0300	1.3145
8	23.981	0.949	5.76	1.054	173.559	209.94	288.24	78.30	1.0344	1.3130
9	24.565	0.957	5.58	1.045	179.273	211.26	277.13	76.87	1.0389	1.3114
10	25.160	0.965	5.40	1.036	185.240	212.60	287.99	75.39	1.0435	1.3097
11	25.766	0.974	5.22	1.027	191.481	213.97	287.83	73.86	1.0481	1.3080
12	26.384	0.983	5.05	1.017	198.019	215.36	287.64	72.28	1.0527	1.3062
13	27.013	0.993	4.88	1.007	204.883	216.78	287.42	70.64	1.0575	1.3044
14	27.654	1.003	4.71	0.997	212.104	218.23	287.16	68.93	1.0623	1.3024
15	28.307	1.014	4.55	0.986	219.721	219.72	286.87	67.15	1.0673	1.3003
16	28.972	1.026	4.39	0.975	227.780	221.25	286.54	65.29	1.0724	1.2982
17	29.649	1.038	4.23	0.963	236.334	222.82	286.16	63.34	1.0775	1.2959
18	30.340	1.052	4.07	0.951	245.451	224.44	285.73	61.29	1.0829	1.2934
19	31.043	1.066	3.92	0.938	255.215	226.14	285.25	59.11	1.0884	1.2908
20	31.759	1.082	3.76	0.924	265.731	227.89	284.69	56.80	1.0941	1.2879
21	32.488	1.099	3.61	0.910	277.141	229.73	284.05	54.32	1.1001	1.2848
22	33.231	1.119	3.45	0.894	289.633	231.66	283.31	51.65	1.1064	1.2814
23	33.988	1.141	3.30	0.876	303.474	233.72	282.45	48.73	1.1131	1.2777
24	34.759	1.167	3.13	0.857	319.064	235.94	281.43	45.49	1.1203	1.2734
25	35.545	1.198	2.97	0.835	337.043	238.38	280.20	41.82	1.1282	1.2684
26	36.345	1.236	2.79	0.809	358.567	241.13	278.65	37.52	1.1370	1.2625
27	37.160	1.288	2.59	0.776	386.133	244.42	276.57	32.15	1.1477	1.2548
28	37.991	1.373	2.34	0.728	427.652	248.92	273.28	24.36	1.1622	1.2432
28.78	38.649	1.721	1.72	0.581	581.060	260.93	260.93	0.00	1.2018	1.2018

Table 3-12 Properties of Saturated "Freon 13 B1" — Trifluorobromomethane (CBrF₃)

Tempera-ture	Pressure	Specific volume		Density		Specific enthalpy		Heat of vaporization	Specific entropy	
		Liquid	Vapor	Liquid	Vapor	Liquid	Vapor		Liquid	Vapor
t	p	v'	v''	ρ'	ρ''	h'	h''	r	s'	s''
°C	bar	L/kg	L/kg	kg/L	kg/m³	kJ/kg	kJ/kg	kJ/kg	kJ/(kg K)	kJ/(kg K)
−80	0.305	0.479	347.88	2.086	2.875	144.78	269.34	124.56	0.7657	1.4106
−79	0.324	0.480	328.89	2.082	3.041	145.37	269.68	124.31	0.7687	1.4090
−78	0.344	0.481	311.13	2.077	3.214	145.97	270.02	124.05	0.7718	1.4075
−77	0.365	0.482	294.51	2.073	3.395	146.58	270.37	123.79	0.7748	1.4059
−76	0.387	0.483	278.96	2.069	3.585	147.18	270.71	123.53	0.7779	1.4045
−75	0.410	0.484	264.38	2.065	3.782	147.79	271.05	123.26	0.7809	1.4030
−74	0.434	0.485	250.72	2.061	3.989	148.39	271.39	123.00	0.7839	1.4016
−73	0.459	0.486	237.90	2.057	4.203	149.00	271.73	122.73	0.7869	1.4001
−72	0.486	0.487	225.87	2.053	4.427	149.62	272.07	122.45	0.7900	1.3988
−71	0.513	0.488	214.56	2.049	4.661	150.23	272.41	122.18	0.7930	1.3974
−70	0.542	0.489	203.94	2.044	4.903	150.85	272.75	121.90	0.7960	1.3961
−69	0.572	0.490	193.94	2.040	5.156	151.48	273.09	121.61	0.7991	1.3948
−68	0.604	0.491	184.54	2.036	5.419	152.10	273.43	121.33	0.8021	1.3935
−67	0.637	0.492	175.68	2.032	5.692	152.72	273.76	121.04	0.8051	1.3923
−66	0.671	0.493	167.34	2.028	5.976	153.35	274.10	120.75	0.8081	1.3910
−65	0.707	0.494	159.47	2.023	6.271	153.99	274.44	120.45	0.8111	1.3898
−64	0.744	0.495	152.05	2.019	6.577	154.62	274.78	120.16	0.8141	1.3886
−63	0.782	0.496	145.04	2.015	6.895	155.25	275.11	119.86	0.8171	1.3875
−62	0.823	0.497	138.42	2.010	7.224	155.90	275.45	119.55	0.8202	1.3864
−61	0.864	0.498	132.17	2.006	7.566	156.54	275.78	119.24	0.8232	1.3852
−60	0.908	0.500	126.26	2.002	7.920	157.19	276.12	118.93	0.8262	1.3842
−59	0.953	0.501	120.67	1.997	8.287	157.83	276.45	118.62	0.8292	1.3831
−58	1.000	0.502	115.38	1.993	8.667	158.49	276.79	118.30	0.8322	1.3820
−57	1.049	0.503	110.37	1.989	9.061	159.14	277.12	117.98	0.8352	1.3810
−56	1.100	0.504	105.62	1.084	9.468	159.79	277.45	117.66	0.8381	1.3800
−55	1.152	0.505	101.12	1.980	9.889	160.45	277.78	117.33	0.8412	1.3790
−54	1.207	0.506	96.85	1.975	10.325	161.11	278.11	117.00	0.8441	1.3780
−53	1.263	0.507	92.81	1.971	10.775	161.77	278.44	116.67	0.8471	1.3771
−52	1.321	0.508	88.96	1.967	11.241	162.44	278.77	116.33	0.8501	1.3762
−51	1.382	0.510	85.31	1.962	11.722	163.10	279.10	116.00	0.8531	1.3752
−50	1.445	0.511	81.84	1.958	12.219	163.78	279.43	115.65	0.8561	1.3743
−49	1.509	0.512	78.54	1.953	12.732	164.44	279.75	115.31	0.8590	1.3735
−48	1.576	0.513	75.41	1.949	13.261	165.12	280.08	114.96	0.8620	1.3726
−47	1.646	0.514	72.42	1.944	13.807	165.80	280.40	114.60	0.8650	1.3717
−46	1.717	0.516	69.58	1.939	14.371	166.48	280.73	114.25	0.8679	1.3709
−45	1.791	0.517	66.88	1.935	14.952	167.16	281.05	113.89	0.8709	1.3701
−44	1.868	0.518	64.30	1.930	15.552	167.85	281.37	113.52	0.8739	1.3693
−43	1.947	0.519	61.85	1.926	16.169	168.53	281.69	113.16	0.8768	1.3685
−42	2.028	0.521	59.50	1.921	16.806	169.22	282.01	112.79	0.8798	1.3677
−41	2.112	0.522	57.27	1.916	17.462	169.92	282.33	112.41	0.8827	1.3670
−40	2.199	0.523	55.14	1.912	18.137	170.60	282.64	112.04	0.8857	1.3662
−39	2.288	0.524	53.10	1.907	18.832	171.30	282.96	111.66	0.8886	1.3655
−38	2.380	0.526	51.16	1.902	19.548	172.00	283.27	111.27	0.8916	1.3648
−37	2.475	0.527	49.30	1.897	20.285	172.70	283.59	110.89	0.8945	1.3641
−36	2.573	0.528	47.52	1.893	21.043	173.40	283.90	110.50	0.8974	1.3634
−35	2.674	0.530	45.82	1.888	21.823	174.11	284.21	110.10	0.9004	1.3627
−34	2.777	0.531	44.20	1.883	22.625	174.81	284.52	109.71	0.9032	1.3620
−33	2.884	0.532	42.64	1.878	23.449	175.52	284.83	109.31	0.9062	1.3614
−32	2.993	0.534	41.16	1.873	24.297	176.23	285.13	108.90	0.9091	1.3607
−31	3.106	0.535	39.73	1.869	25.169	176.95	285.44	108.49	0.9120	1.3601

Table 3-12 Properties of Saturated "Freon 13 B1" — Trifluorobromomethane (CBrF₃) *(continued)*

Tempera-ture	Pressure	Specific volume		Density		Specific enthalpy		Heat of vaporization	Specific entropy	
		Liquid	Vapor	Liquid	Vapor	Liquid	Vapor		Liquid	Vapor
t	p	v'	v''	ρ'	ρ''	h'	h''	r	s'	s''
°C	bar	L/kg	L/kg	kg/L	kg/m³	kJ/kg	kJ/kg	kJ/kg	kJ/(kg K)	kJ/(kg K)
−30	3.222	0.537	38.37	1.864	26.064	177.66	285.74	108.08	0.9149	1.3594
−29	3.341	0.538	37.06	1.859	26.984	178.38	286.05	107.67	0.9178	1.3588
−28	3.463	0.539	35.80	1.854	27.930	179.10	286.35	107.25	0.9207	1.3582
−27	3.589	0.541	34.60	1.849	28.900	179.82	286.65	106.83	0.9236	1.3576
−26	3.718	0.542	33.45	1.844	29.897	180.54	286.94	106.40	0.9265	1.3570
−25	3.851	0.544	32.34	1.839	30.921	181.26	287.24	105.98	0.9294	1.3565
−24	3.987	0.545	31.28	1.834	31.972	181.99	287.53	105.54	0.9323	1.3559
−23	4.127	0.547	30.26	1.829	33.050	182.72	287.83	105.11	0.9351	1.3553
−22	4.270	0.548	29.28	1.824	34.157	183.45	288.12	104.67	0.9380	1.3548
−21	4.417	0.550	28.33	1.818	35.293	184.19	288.41	104.22	0.9409	1.3542
−20	4.567	0.552	27.43	1.813	36.458	184.92	288.70	103.78	0.9437	1.3537
−19	4.722	0.553	26.56	1.808	37.653	185.65	288.98	103.33	0.9466	1.3532
−18	4.880	0.555	25.72	1.803	38.879	186.40	289.27	102.87	0.9495	1.3526
−17	5.042	0.556	24.91	1.798	40.137	187.13	289.55	102.42	0.9523	1.3521
−16	5.208	0.558	24.14	1.792	41.426	187.88	289.83	101.95	0.9551	1.3516
−15	5.379	0.560	23.39	1.787	42.749	188.62	290.11	101.49	0.9580	1.3511
−14	5.553	0.561	22.67	1.782	44.104	189.36	290.38	101.02	0.9608	1.3506
−13	5.731	0.563	21.98	1.776	45.494	190.11	290.66	100.55	0.9636	1.3501
−12	5.914	0.565	21.31	1.771	46.918	190.86	290.93	100.07	0.9665	1.3497
−11	6.101	0.566	20.67	1.765	48.379	191.61	291.20	99.59	0.9693	1.3492
−10	6.292	0.568	20.05	1.760	49.875	192.37	291.47	99.10	0.9721	1.3487
−9	6.487	0.570	19.45	1.754	51.409	193.12	291.73	98.61	0.9749	1.3482
−8	6.687	0.572	18.87	1.749	52.980	193.88	292.00	98.12	0.9777	1.3478
−7	6.892	0.574	18.32	1.743	54.591	194.64	292.26	97.62	0.9805	1.3473
−6	7.101	0.576	17.78	1.738	56.241	195.39	292.51	97.12	0.9833	1.3469
−5	7.314	0.577	17.26	1.732	57.931	196.16	292.77	96.61	0.9861	1.3464
−4	7.533	0.579	16.76	1.726	59.663	196.92	293.02	96.10	0.9889	1.3460
−3	7.756	0.581	16.28	1.720	61.438	197.69	293.28	95.59	0.9917	1.3455
−2	7.984	0.583	15.81	1.715	63.256	198.45	293.52	95.07	0.9944	1.3451
−1	8.216	0.585	15.36	1.709	65.118	199.23	293.77	94.54	0.9972	1.3446
0	8.454	0.587	14.92	1.703	67.026	200.00	294.01	94.01	1.0000	1.3442
1	8.697	0.589	14.50	1.697	68.980	200.77	294.25	93.48	1.0028	1.3438
2	8.944	0.591	14.09	1.691	70.983	201.55	294.49	92.94	1.0055	1.3433
3	9.197	0.593	13.69	1.685	73.034	202.33	294.73	92.40	1.0083	1.3429
4	9.455	0.596	13.31	1.679	75.135	203.11	294.96	91.85	1.0110	1.3425
5	9.719	0.598	12.94	1.673	77.288	203.89	295.19	91.30	1.0138	1.3420
6	9.987	0.600	12.58	1.667	79.493	204.67	295.41	90.74	1.0165	1.3416
7	10.261	0.602	12.23	1.660	81.753	205.47	295.64	90.17	1.0193	1.3412
8	10.541	0.605	11.90	1.654	84.068	206.26	295.86	89.60	1.0220	1.3408
9	10.826	0.607	11.57	1.648	86.440	207.05	296.07	89.02	1.0248	1.3403
10	11.117	0.609	11.25	1.642	88.870	207.84	296.28	88.44	1.0275	1.3399
11	11.413	0.612	10.95	1.635	91.361	208.64	296.49	87.85	1.0303	1.3395
12	11.715	0.614	10.65	1.629	93.914	209.44	296.70	87.26	1.0330	1.3390
13	12.023	0.617	10.36	1.622	96.530	210.24	296.90	86.66	1.0357	1.3386
14	12.337	0.619	10.08	1.615	99.212	211.05	297.10	86.05	1.0385	1.3382
15	12.656	0.622	9.81	1.609	101.961	211.86	297.29	85.43	1.0412	1.3377
16	12.982	0.624	9.54	1.602	104.780	212.67	297.48	84.81	1.0439	1.3373
17	13.314	0.627	9.29	1.595	107.670	213.48	297.66	84.18	1.0467	1.3368
18	13.652	0.630	9.04	1.588	110.634	214.29	297.84	83.55	1.0494	1.3364
19	13.997	0.632	8.80	1.581	113.675	215.12	298.02	82.90	1.0521	1.3359

Table 3-12 Properties of Saturated "Freon 13 B1" — Trifluorobromomethane (CBrF₃) *(continued)*

Tempera-ture	Pressure	Specific volume		Density		Specific enthalpy		Heat of vaporization	Specific entropy	
		Liquid	Vapor	Liquid	Vapor	Liquid	Vapor		Liquid	Vapor
t	p	v'	v''	ρ'	ρ''	h'	h''	r	s'	s''
°C	bar	L/kg	L/kg	kg/L	kg/m³	kJ/kg	kJ/kg	kJ/kg	kJ/(kg K)	kJ/(kg K)
20	14.347	0.635	8.56	1.574	116.794	215.94	298.19	82.25	1.0549	1.3354
21	14.705	0.638	8.33	1.567	119.994	216.77	298.19	81.59	1.0576	1.3350
22	15.068	0.641	8.11	1.560	123.279	217.60	298.52	80.92	1.0603	1.3345
23	15.439	0.644	7.90	1.553	126.650	218.44	298.68	80.24	1.0631	1.3340
24	15.816	0.647	7.69	1.545	130.112	219.28	298.83	79.55	1.0658	1.3335
25	16.199	0.650	7.48	1.538	133.667	220.12	298.97	78.85	1.0686	1.3330
26	16.590	0.653	7.28	1.530	137.318	220.97	299.11	78.14	1.0713	1.3325
27	16.988	0.657	7.09	1.523	141.070	221.82	299.24	77.42	1.0741	1.3320
28	17.392	0.660	6.90	1.515	144.927	222.68	299.37	76.69	1.0768	1.3315
29	17.804	0.664	6.72	1.507	148.892	223.54	299.49	75.95	1.0796	1.3310
30	18.223	0.667	6.54	1.499	152.970	224.42	299.61	75.19	1.0824	1.3304
31	18.649	0.671	6.36	1.491	157.165	225.28	299.71	74.43	1.0851	1.3298
32	19.083	0.674	6.19	1.483	161.483	226.16	299.81	73.65	1.0879	1.3293
33	19.524	0.678	6.03	1.474	165.930	227.06	299.91	72.85	1.0907	1.3287
34	19.973	0.682	5.86	1.466	170.510	227.95	299.99	72.04	1.0935	1.3281
35	20.429	0.686	5.71	1.457	175.231	228.85	300.07	71.22	1.0963	1.3275
36	20.894	0.690	5.55	1.448	180.099	229.75	300.13	70.38	1.0992	1.3268
37	21.366	0.695	5.40	1.439	185.121	230.67	300.19	69.52	1.1020	1.3262
38	21.846	0.699	5.25	1.430	190.306	231.60	300.24	68.64	1.1049	1.3255
39	22.334	0.704	5.11	1.421	195.661	232.53	300.28	67.75	1.1077	1.3248
40	22.831	0.708	4.97	1.412	201.197	233.47	300.30	66.83	1.1107	1.3241
41	23.226	0.713	4.83	1.402	206.924	234.43	300.32	65.89	1.1136	1.3233
42	23.849	0.718	4.70	1.392	212.853	235.39	300.32	64.93	1.1165	1.3226
43	23.372	0.724	4.57	1.382	218.996	236.36	300.31	63.95	1.1195	1.3218
44	24.902	0.729	4.44	1.372	225.368	237.35	300.29	62.94	1.1225	1.3209
45	25.442	0.735	4.31	1.361	231.983	238.35	300.25	61.90	1.1255	1.3201
46	25.991	0.741	4.19	1.350	238.859	239.37	300.20	60.83	1.1285	1.3192
47	26.548	0.747	4.06	1.339	246.015	240.40	300.13	59.73	1.1316	1.3182
48	27.115	0.753	3.95	1.327	253.473	241.45	300.04	58.59	1.1348	1.3172
49	27.692	0.760	3.83	1.316	261.258	242.52	299.94	57.42	1.1379	1.3162
50	28.277	0.767	3.71	1.303	269.396	243.61	299.81	56.20	1.1412	1.3151
51	28.873	0.775	3.60	1.291	277.922	244.72	299.66	54.94	1.1445	1.3140
52	29.478	0.783	3.49	1.278	286.872	245.86	299.49	53.63	1.1478	1.3128
53	30.094	0.791	3.38	1.264	296.292	247.01	299.28	52.27	1.1512	1.3115
54	30.719	0.800	3.27	1.250	306.233	248.20	299.05	50.85	1.1547	1.3101
55	31.355	0.810	3.16	1.235	316.760	249.43	298.78	49.35	1.1583	1.3087
56	32.001	0.820	3.05	1.219	327.949	250.69	298.47	47.78	1.1620	1.3071
57	32.657	0.831	2.94	1.203	339.898	251.99	298.12	46.13	1.1657	1.3055
58	33.325	0.844	2.84	1.185	352.729	253.35	297.72	44.37	1.1697	1.3037
59	34.003	0.857	2.73	1.167	366.601	254.77	297.26	42.49	1.1738	1.3017
60	34.693	0.872	2.62	1.146	381.731	256.26	296.72	40.46	1.1781	1.2995
61	35.393	0.889	2.51	1.124	398.419	257.85	296.10	38.25	1.1826	1.2971
62	36.106	0.909	2.40	1.100	417.108	259.54	295.36	35.82	1.1875	1.2944
63	36.830	0.932	2.28	1.073	438.503	261.39	294.46	33.07	1.1928	1.2912
64	37.565	0.961	2.16	1.040	463.832	263.47	293.34	29.87	1.1988	1.2874
65	38.313	0.999	2.02	1.001	495.628	265.90	291.85	25.95	1.2057	1.2825
66	39.073	1.058	1.85	0.945	541.023	269.08	289.61	20.54	1.2149	1.2754
67.0	39.846	1.343	1.34	0.745	744.790	279.02	279.02	0.00	1.2439	1.2439

Table 3-13 Properties of Saturated "Freon 14" — Tetrafluoromethane (CF$_4$)

Tempera-ture	Pressure	Specific volume		Density		Specific enthalpy		Heat of vaporization	Specific entropy	
		Liquid	Vapor	Liquid	Vapor	Liquid	Vapor		Liquid	Vapor
t	p	v'	v''	ρ'	ρ''	h'	h''	r	s'	s''
°C	bar	L/kg	L/kg	kg/L	kg/m³	kJ/kg	kJ/kg	kJ/kg	kJ/(kg K)	kJ/(kg K)
−140	0.395	0.589	311.14	1.698	3.214	160.71	301.56	140.85	0.7450	1.8029
−139	0.430	0.591	287.33	1.693	3.480	161.60	301.94	140.34	0.7516	1.7978
−138	0.468	0.593	265.70	1.687	3.764	162.50	302.32	139.82	0.7583	1.7928
−137	0.508	0.594	246.00	1.682	4.065	163.39	302.69	139.30	0.7648	1.7880
−136	0.551	0.596	228.05	1.677	4.385	164.29	303.06	138.77	0.7714	1.7832
−135	0.597	0.598	211.66	1.672	4.724	165.20	303.43	138.23	0.7780	1.7786
−134	0.646	0.600	196.69	1.666	5.084	166.12	303.80	137.68	0.7846	1.7740
−133	0.698	0.602	182.98	1.661	5.465	167.04	304.16	137.12	0.7912	1.7696
−132	0.753	0.604	170.42	1.655	5.868	167.96	304.52	136.56	0.7977	1.7652
−131	0.812	0.606	158.89	1.650	6.294	168.89	304.88	135.99	0.8042	1.7609
−130	0.874	0.608	148.30	1.645	6.743	169.82	305.23	135.41	0.8107	1.7567
−129	0.940	0.610	138.55	1.639	7.217	170.76	305.58	134.82	0.8172	1.7526
−128	1.010	0.612	129.58	1.634	7.717	171.70	305.93	134.23	0.8237	1.7485
−127	1.084	0.614	121.31	1.628	8.243	172.66	306.28	133.62	0.8302	1.7445
−126	1.162	0.616	113.67	1.623	8.797	173.61	306.62	133.01	0.8367	1.7406
−125	1.244	0.618	106.62	1.617	9.379	174.57	306.96	132.39	0.8431	1.7368
−124	1.330	0.621	100.09	1.611	9.991	175.53	307.29	131.76	0.8496	1.7330
−123	1.421	0.623	94.04	1.606	10.633	176.50	307.62	131.12	0.8560	1.7293
−122	1.517	0.625	88.44	1.600	11.307	177.47	307.95	130.48	0.8624	1.7257
−121	1.618	0.627	83.24	1.594	12.013	178.45	308.27	129.82	0.8689	1.7221
−120	1.724	0.630	78.41	1.588	12.753	179.43	308.59	129.16	0.8752	1.7186
−119	1.835	0.632	73.92	1.583	13.528	180.42	308.91	128.49	0.8816	1.7152
−118	1.951	0.634	69.74	1.577	14.339	181.41	309.22	127.81	0.8880	1.7118
−117	2.073	0.637	65.84	1.571	15.187	182.41	309.53	127.12	0.8943	1.7085
−116	2.201	0.639	62.21	1.565	16.074	183.41	309.83	126.42	0.9007	1.7052
−115	2.335	0.641	58.83	1.559	16.999	184.42	310.13	125.71	0.9070	1.7019
−114	2.475	0.644	55.66	1.553	17.966	185.43	310.42	124.99	0.9134	1.6988
−113	2.620	0.646	52.70	1.547	18.975	186.44	310.71	124.27	0.9196	1.6956
−112	2.773	0.649	49.93	1.541	20.027	187.45	310.99	123.54	0.9259	1.6925
−111	2.932	0.651	47.34	1.535	21.123	188.48	311.27	122.79	0.9322	1.6895
−110	3.097	0.654	44.91	1.529	22.266	189.51	311.55	122.04	0.9384	1.6865
−109	3.270	0.657	42.63	1.523	23.457	190.54	311.82	121.28	0.9446	1.6835
−108	3.449	0.659	40.49	1.516	24.696	191.57	312.08	120.51	0.9509	1.6806
−107	3.636	0.662	38.48	1.510	25.986	192.61	312.34	119.73	0.9571	1.6777
−106	3.830	0.665	36.59	1.504	27.328	193.66	312.60	118.94	0.9633	1.6749
−105	4.032	0.668	34.82	1.497	28.723	194.71	312.85	118.14	0.9694	1.6721
−104	4.242	0.671	33.14	1.491	30.173	195.75	313.09	117.34	0.9755	1.6693
−103	4.460	0.674	31.56	1.484	31.681	196.61	313.33	116.52	0.9817	1.6665
−102	4.685	0.677	30.08	1.478	33.247	197.87	313.56	115.69	0.9878	1.6638
−101	4.920	0.680	28.67	1.471	34.874	198.93	313.79	114.86	0.9939	1.6611
−100	5.162	0.683	27.35	1.465	36.563	200.00	314.01	114.01	1.0000	1.6585
−99	5.413	0.686	26.10	1.458	38.316	201.07	314.23	113.16	1.0060	1.6559
−98	5.674	0.689	24.92	1.451	40.136	202.14	314.43	112.29	1.0121	1.6532
−97	5.943	0.692	23.80	1.444	42.024	203.23	314.64	111.41	1.0182	1.6507
−96	6.221	0.696	22.74	1.438	43.983	204.30	314.83	110.53	1.0341	1.6481
−95	6.509	0.699	21.73	1.431	46.015	205.39	315.02	109.63	1.0302	1.6456
−94	6.806	0.702	20.78	1.424	48.122	206.47	315.20	108.73	1.0361	1.6431
−93	7.114	0.706	19.88	1.417	50.307	207.57	315.38	107.81	1.0421	1.6406
−92	7.431	0.710	19.02	1.409	52.572	208.67	315.55	106.88	1.0480	1.6381
−91	7.758	0.713	18.21	1.402	54.920	209.77	315.71	105.94	1.0540	1.6356

145

Table 3-13 Properties of Saturated "Freon 14" — Tetrafluoromethane (CF$_4$) *(continued)*

Tempera-ture	Pressure	Specific volume		Density		Specific enthalpy		Heat of vaporization	Specific entropy	
		Liquid	Vapor	Liquid	Vapor	Liquid	Vapor		Liquid	Vapor
t	p	v'	v''	ρ'	ρ''	h'	h''	r	s'	s''
°C	bar	L/kg	L/kg	kg/L	kg/m^3	kJ/kg	kJ/kg	kJ/kg	kJ/(kg K)	kJ/(kg K)
−90	8.096	0.717	17.44	1.395	57.355	210.87	315.86	104.99	1.0599	1.6331
−89	8.444	0.721	16.70	1.388	59.879	211.97	316.00	104.03	1.0657	1.6307
−88	8.803	0.725	16.00	1.380	62.495	213.09	316.14	103.05	1.0717	1.6283
−87	9.173	0.729	15.34	1.373	65.207	214.20	316.27	102.07	1.0775	1.6258
−86	9.554	0.733	14.70	1.365	68.018	215.32	316.39	101.07	1.0833	1.6234
−85	9.946	0.737	14.10	1.357	70.933	216.45	316.50	100.05	1.0892	1.6210
−84	10.350	0.741	13.52	1.349	73.954	217.57	316.60	99.03	1.0950	1.6186
−83	10.765	0.745	12.97	1.341	77.088	218.71	316.70	97.99	1.1008	1.6162
−82	11.193	0.750	12.45	1.333	80.337	219.85	316.78	96.93	1.1066	1.6138
−81	11.633	0.755	11.95	1.325	83.707	220.99	316.85	95.86	1.1124	1.6113
−80	12.085	0.759	11.47	1.317	87.204	222.13	316.91	94.78	1.1182	1.6089
−79	12.549	0.764	11.01	1.309	90.833	223.30	316.97	93.67	1.1240	1.6065
−78	13.027	0.769	10.57	1.300	94.600	224.45	317.00	92.55	1.1298	1.6040
−77	13.517	0.774	10.15	1.292	98.512	225.61	317.03	91.42	1.1355	1.6016
−76	14.021	0.780	9.75	1.283	102.576	226.79	317.05	90.26	1.1413	1.5991
−75	14.538	0.785	9.36	1.274	106.800	227.97	317.05	89.08	1.1470	1.5966
−74	15.069	0.791	8.99	1.265	111.193	229.15	317.03	87.88	1.1528	1.5941
−73	15.614	0.796	8.64	1.256	115.762	230.35	317.01	86.66	1.1586	1.5916
−72	16.174	0.802	8.30	1.246	120.520	231.54	316.96	85.42	1.1643	1.5890
−71	16.747	0.809	7.97	1.237	125.477	232.75	316.90	84.15	1.1701	1.5864
−70	17.336	0.815	7.65	1.227	130.645	233.98	316.83	82.85	1.1759	1.5837
−69	17.940	0.822	7.35	1.217	136.039	235.21	316.73	81.52	1.1817	1.5810
−68	18.560	0.829	7.06	1.207	141.674	236.45	316.61	80.16	1.1875	1.5783
−67	19.195	0.836	6.78	1.196	147.567	237.71	316.48	78.77	1.1933	1.5755
−66	19.846	0.844	6.50	1.185	153.737	238.97	316.31	77.34	1.1992	1.5726
−65	20.514	0.851	6.24	1.174	160.208	240.26	316.13	75.87	1.2051	1.5696
−64	21.199	0.860	5.99	1.163	167.004	241.55	315.91	74.36	1.2111	1.5666
−63	21.901	0.868	5.74	1.151	174.155	242.87	315.67	72.80	1.2170	1.5635
−62	22.621	0.878	5.50	1.139	181.693	244.22	315.40	71.18	1.2231	1.5603
−61	23.359	0.887	5.27	1.127	189.660	245.58	315.08	69.50	1.2293	1.5569
−60	24.115	0.897	5.05	1.114	198.101	246.97	314.73	67.76	1.2455	1.5534
−59	24.891	0.908	4.83	1.101	207.072	248.39	314.34	65.95	1.2418	1.5498
−58	25.686	0.920	4.62	1.087	216.640	249.84	313.89	64.05	1.2482	1.5460
−57	26.502	0.932	4.41	1.072	226.889	251.34	313.39	62.05	1.2548	1.5419
−56	27.339	0.946	4.20	1.057	237.922	252.89	312.82	59.93	1.2616	1.5376
−55	28.197	0.961	4.00	1.041	249.869	254.49	312.18	57.69	1.2686	1.5331
−54	29.078	0.977	3.80	1.024	262.903	256.15	311.44	55.29	1.2758	1.5281
−53	29.982	0.995	3.61	1.005	277.253	257.91	310.60	52.69	1.2834	1.5228
−52	30.911	1.015	3.41	0.986	293.242	259.77	309.62	49.85	1.2914	1.5168
−51	31.865	1.038	3.21	0.964	311.339	261.76	308.47	46.71	1.2999	1.5102
−50	32.846	1.065	3.01	0.939	332.273	263.92	307.08	43.16	1.3092	1.5026
−49	33.855	1.097	2.80	0.911	357.290	266.35	305.37	39.02	1.3196	1.4937
−48	34.893	1.140	2.57	0.878	388.818	269.17	303.15	33.98	1.3316	1.4825
−47	35.963	1.200	2.31	0.833	432.909	272.69	299.95	27.26	1.4567	1.4672
−46	37.067	1.322	1.93	0.756	517.906	278.21	293.71	15.50	1.3704	1.4386
−45.65	37.460	1.598	1.60	0.626	625.682	286.08	286.08	0.00	1.4048	1.4048

146

Table 3-14 Properties of Saturated "Freon 22" — Difluoromonochloromethane (CHClF$_2$)

Tempera-ture	Pressure	Specific volume		Density		Specific enthalpy		Heat of vaporization	Specific entropy	
		Liquid	Vapor	Liquid	Vapor	Liquid	Vapor		Liquid	Vapor
t	p	v'	v''	ρ'	ρ''	h'	h''	r	s'	s''
°C	bar	L/kg	L/kg	kg/L	kg/m³	kJ/kg	kJ/kg	kJ/kg	kJ/(kg K)	kJ/(kg K)
−100	0.021	0.639	7906.83	1.565	0.126	95.96	357.78	261.82	0.5340	2.0461
−99	0.023	0.640	7265.23	1.563	0.138	96.80	358.27	261.47	0.5388	2.0403
−98	0.025	0.641	6683.08	1.560	0.150	97.66	358.77	261.11	0.5437	2.0345
−97	0.027	0.642	6154.25	1.558	0.162	98.52	359.26	260.74	0.5487	2.0289
−96	0.030	0.643	5673.31	1.555	0.176	99.38	359.76	260.38	0.5535	2.0234
−95	0.033	0.644	5235.42	1.553	0.191	100.25	360.26	260.01	0.5584	2.0179
−94	0.036	0.645	4836.30	1.551	0.207	101.11	360.76	259.65	0.5632	2.0126
−93	0.039	0.646	4472.11	1.548	0.224	101.98	361.26	259.28	0.5681	2.0073
−92	0.042	0.647	4139.44	1.546	0.242	102.85	361.76	258.91	0.5729	2.0022
−91	0.046	0.648	3835.25	1.543	0.261	103.74	362.27	258.53	0.5777	1.9971
−90	0.049	0.649	3556.81	1.541	0.281	104.62	362.77	258.15	0.5826	1.9921
−89	0.054	0.650	3301.67	1.539	0.303	105.51	363.28	257.77	0.5874	1.9872
−88	0.058	0.651	3067.67	1.536	0.326	106.39	363.78	257.39	0.5922	1.9824
−87	0.063	0.652	2852.83	1.534	0.351	107.28	364.29	257.01	0.5969	1.9776
−86	0.068	0.653	2655.40	1.531	0.377	108.18	364.80	256.62	0.6018	1.9730
−85	0.073	0.654	2473.79	1.529	0.404	109.07	365.30	256.23	0.6065	1.9684
−84	0.079	0.655	2306.58	1.526	0.434	109.97	365.81	255.84	0.6113	1.9639
−83	0.085	0.656	2152.48	1.524	0.465	110.88	366.32	255.44	0.6161	1.9595
−82	0.091	0.657	2010.35	1.521	0.497	111.79	366.83	255.04	0.6208	1.9551
−81	0.098	0.658	1879.13	1.519	0.532	112.71	367.34	254.63	0.6256	1.9508
−80	0.105	0.659	1757.88	1.516	0.569	113.62	367.85	254.23	0.6304	1.9466
−79	0.113	0.661	1645.75	1.514	0.608	114.54	368.36	253.82	0.6351	1.9425
−78	0.121	0.662	1541.97	1.511	0.649	115.47	368.87	253.40	0.6399	1.9384
−77	0.130	0.663	1445.82	1.509	0.692	116.39	369.38	252.99	0.6446	1.9344
−76	0.139	0.664	1356.69	1.506	0.737	117.34	369.90	252.56	0.6494	1.9305
−75	0.149	0.665	1273.99	1.504	0.785	118.27	370.41	252.14	0.6541	1.9266
−74	0.159	0.666	1197.19	1.501	0.835	119.21	370.92	251.71	0.6588	1.9228
−73	0.170	0.667	1125.81	1.499	0.888	120.15	371.43	251.28	0.6625	1.9190
−72	0.181	0.668	1059.43	1.496	0.944	121.10	371.94	250.84	0.6683	1.9153
−71	0.193	0.669	997.65	1.494	1.002	122.06	372.46	250.40	0.6730	1.9117
−70	0.206	0.671	940.11	1.491	1.064	123.02	372.97	249.95	0.6777	1.9081
−69	0.220	0.672	886.47	1.489	1.128	123.98	373.48	249.50	0.6825	1.9046
−68	0.234	0.673	836.43	1.486	1.196	124.95	373.99	249.04	0.6872	1.9012
−67	0.249	0.674	789.73	1.483	1.266	125.92	374.50	248.58	0.6919	1.8978
−66	0.264	0.675	746.10	1.481	1.340	126.89	375.01	248.12	0.7966	1.8944
−65	0.281	0.677	705.32	1.478	1.418	127.87	375.52	247.65	0.7013	1.8911
−64	0.298	0.678	667.17	1.476	1.499	128.86	376.03	237.17	0.7061	1.8879
−63	0.316	0.679	631.47	1.473	1.584	129.85	376.54	246.69	0.7108	1.8847
−62	0.335	0.680	598.03	1.470	1.672	130.84	377.05	246.21	0.7155	1.8815
−61	0.355	0.681	566.68	1.468	1.756	131.84	377.56	245.72	0.7202	1.8784
−60	0.376	0.683	537.29	1.465	1.861	132.84	378.07	245.23	0.7248	1.8754
−59	0.398	0.684	509.71	1.462	1.962	133.85	378.58	244.73	0.7295	1.8724
−58	0.421	0.685	483.81	1.460	2.067	134.86	379.08	244.22	0.7343	1.8694
−57	0.445	0.686	459.47	1.457	2.176	135.88	379.59	243.71	0.7290	1.8665
−56	0.470	0.688	436.59	1.454	2.290	136.90	380.09	243.19	0.7437	1.8636
−55	0.497	0.689	415.07	1.452	2.409	137.92	380.59	242.67	0.7484	1.8608
−54	0.524	0.690	394.81	1.449	2.533	138.95	381.09	242.14	0.7531	1.8580
−53	0.553	0.691	375.73	1.446	2.661	139.98	381.59	241.61	0.7578	1.8553
−52	0.583	0.693	357.76	1.443	2.795	141.02	382.09	241.07	0.7625	1.8526
−51	0.614	0.694	340.81	1.441	2.934	142.06	382.59	240.53	0.7671	1.8499

Tempera-ture	Pressure	Specific volume		Density		Specific enthalpy		Heat of vaporization	Specific entropy	
		Liquid	Vapor	Liquid	Vapor	Liquid	Vapor		Liquid	Vapor
t	p	v'	v''	ρ'	ρ''	h'	h''	r	s'	s''
°C	bar	L/kg	L/kg	kg/L	kg/m³	kJ/kg	kJ/kg	kJ/kg	kJ/(kg K)	kJ/(kg K)
−50	0.646	0.695	324.82	1.438	3.079	143.11	383.09	239.98	0.7718	1.8473
−49	0.680	0.697	309.72	1.435	3.229	144.15	383.58	239.43	0.7765	1.8447
−48	0.715	0.698	295.47	1.432	3.384	145.22	384.08	238.86	0.7812	1.8421
−47	0.752	0.699	282.00	1.430	3.546	146.27	384.57	238.30	0.7859	1.8396
−46	0.790	0.701	269.27	1.427	3.714	147.34	385.06	237.72	0.7906	1.8371
−45	0.830	0.702	257.23	1.424	3.888	148.40	385.55	237.15	0.7952	1.8347
−44	0.871	0.704	245.83	1.421	4.068	149.48	386.04	236.56	0.7999	1.8323
−43	0.914	0.705	235.04	1.419	4.255	150.55	386.52	235.97	0.8046	1.8299
−42	0.959	0.706	224.82	1.416	4.448	151.63	387.01	235.38	0.8092	1.8275
−41	1.005	0.708	215.13	1.413	4.648	152.72	387.49	234.77	0.8139	1.8252
−40	1.053	0.709	205.95	1.410	4.856	153.81	387.97	234.16	0.8186	1.8229
−39	1.103	0.711	197.24	1.407	5.070	154.90	388.45	233.55	0.8232	1.8207
−38	1.155	0.712	188.97	1.404	5.292	155.99	388.92	232.93	0.8279	1.8185
−37	1.208	0.714	181.11	1.401	5.521	157.10	389.40	232.30	0.8325	1.8163
−36	1.264	0.715	173.66	1.399	5.759	158.20	389.87	231.67	0.8372	1.8141
−35	1.321	0.717	166.57	1.396	6.004	159.31	390.34	231.03	0.8418	1.8119
−34	1.381	0.718	159.83	1.393	6.257	160.41	390.80	230.39	0.8464	1.8098
−33	1.442	0.720	153.42	1.390	6.518	161.53	391.27	229.74	0.8511	1.8077
−32	1.506	0.721	147.32	1.387	6.788	162.65	391.73	229.08	0.8557	1.8057
−31	1.572	0.723	141.51	1.384	7.067	163.77	392.19	228.42	0.8603	1.8036
−30	1.640	0.724	135.98	1.381	7.354	164.90	392.65	227.75	0.8649	1.8016
−29	1.711	0.726	130.71	1.378	7.651	166.02	393.10	227.08	0.8695	1.7996
−28	1.783	0.727	125.69	1.375	7.956	167.16	393.55	226.39	0.8742	1.7977
−27	1.858	0.729	120.90	1.372	8.271	168.29	394.00	225.71	0.8788	1.7957
−26	1.936	0.730	116.33	1.369	8.596	169.44	394.45	225.01	0.8834	1.7938
−25	2.016	0.732	111.97	1.366	8.931	170.57	394.89	224.32	0.8879	1.7919
−24	2.099	0.734	107.81	1.363	9.276	171.72	395.33	223.61	0.8925	1.7901
−23	2.184	0.735	103.83	1.360	9.631	172.87	395.77	222.90	0.8971	1.7882
−22	2.271	0.737	100.03	1.357	9.997	174.03	396.21	222.18	0.9017	1.7864
−21	2.362	0.739	96.40	1.354	10.373	175.18	396.64	221.46	0.9062	1.7845
−20	2.445	0.740	92.93	1.351	10.761	176.34	397.07	220.73	0.9108	1.7828
−19	2.551	0.742	89.61	1.348	11.159	177.49	397.49	220.00	0.9153	1.7810
−18	2.650	0.744	86.44	1.344	11.569	178.66	397.92	219.26	0.9199	1.7792
−17	2.752	0.746	83.40	1.341	11.991	179.82	298.33	218.51	0.9244	1.7775
−16	2.856	0.747	80.49	1.338	12.425	180.99	398.75	217.76	0.9289	1.7758
−15	2.964	0.749	77.70	1.335	12.870	182.16	399.16	217.00	0.9334	1.7741
−14	3.075	0.751	75.03	1.332	13.328	183.34	399.57	216.23	0.9380	1.7724
−13	3.189	0.753	72.47	1.329	13.799	184.52	399.98	215.46	0.9425	1.7707
−12	3.306	0.754	70.01	1.326	14.283	185.69	400.38	214.69	0.9469	1.7690
−11	3.426	0.756	67.66	1.322	14.780	186.87	400.78	213.91	0.9514	1.7674
−10	3.550	0.758	65.40	1.319	15.290	188.06	401.18	213.12	0.9559	1.7658
−9	3.677	0.760	63.23	1.316	15.814	189.24	401.57	212.33	0.9603	1.7642
−8	3.807	0.762	61.15	1.313	16.352	190.43	401.96	211.53	0.9648	1.7626
−7	3.941	0.764	59.16	1.309	16.905	191.62	402.34	210.72	0.9692	1.7610
−6	4.078	0.766	57.24	1.306	17.471	192.81	402.72	209.91	0.9737	1.7594
−5	4.219	0.768	55.39	1.303	18.053	194.00	403.10	209.10	0.9781	1.7579
−4	4.364	0.770	53.62	1.299	18.650	195.20	403.47	208.27	0.9825	1.7563
−3	4.512	0.772	51.92	1.296	19.262	196.39	403.84	207.45	0.9869	1.7548
−2	4.664	0.774	50.28	1.293	19.890	197.60	404.21	206.61	0.9913	1.7533
−1	4.820	0.776	48.70	1.289	20.534	198.80	404.57	205.77	0.9956	1.7518

Table 3-14 Properties of Saturated "Freon 22" — Difluoromonochloromethane (CHClF$_2$) *(continued)*

Tempera-ture	Pressure	Specific volume		Density		Specific enthalpy		Heat of vaporization	Specific entropy	
		Liquid	Vapor	Liquid	Vapor	Liquid	Vapor		Liquid	Vapor
t	p	v'	v''	ρ'	ρ''	h'	h''	r	s'	s''
°C	bar	L/kg	L/kg	kg/L	kg/m^3	kJ/kg	kJ/kg	kJ/kg	kJ/(kg K)	kJ/(kg K)
0	4.980	0.778	47.18	1.286	21.194	200.00	404.93	204.93	1.0000	1.7503
1	5.143	0.780	45.72	1.282	21.871	201.20	405.28	204.08	1.0043	1.7488
2	5.311	0.782	44.32	1.279	22.566	202.41	405.63	203.22	1.0087	1.7473
3	5.483	0.784	42.96	1.276	23.277	203.61	405.97	202.36	1.0130	1.7458
4	5.659	0.786	41.66	1.272	24.006	204.83	406.32	201.49	1.0173	1.7444
5	5.839	0.788	40.40	1.269	24.753	206.03	406.65	200.62	1.0216	1.7429
6	6.023	0.790	39.19	1.265	25.519	207.24	406.98	199.74	1.0259	1.7415
7	6.211	0.793	38.02	1.262	26.304	208.46	407.31	198.85	1.0302	1.7400
8	6.404	0.795	36.89	1.258	27.107	209.67	407.63	197.96	1.0345	1.7386
9	6.601	0.797	35.80	1.254	27.930	210.89	407.95	197.06	1.0388	1.7372
10	6.803	0.799	34.75	1.251	28.774	212.11	408.27	196.16	1.0430	1.7358
11	7.010	0.802	33.74	1.247	29.637	213.33	408.58	195.25	1.0472	1.7344
12	7.220	0.804	32.76	1.244	30.522	214.54	408.88	194.34	1.0515	1.7330
13	7.436	0.806	31.82	1.240	31.427	215.76	409.18	193.42	1.0557	1.7316
14	7.656	0.809	30.91	1.236	32.355	216.99	409.48	192.49	1.0599	1.7302
15	7.882	0.811	30.03	1.233	33.304	218.21	409.77	191.56	1.0641	1.7289
16	8.112	0.814	29.17	1.229	34.276	219.43	410.05	190.62	1.0682	1.7275
17	8.346	0.816	28.35	1.225	35.271	220.66	410.33	189.67	1.0724	1.7261
18	8.586	0.819	27.56	1.221	36.290	221.89	410.61	188.72	1.0766	1.7248
19	8.831	0.821	26.79	1.218	37.333	223.11	410.88	187.77	1.0807	1.7234
20	9.081	0.824	26.04	1.214	38.401	224.34	411.14	186.80	1.0848	1.7221
21	9.337	0.827	25.32	1.210	39.493	225.57	411.40	185.83	1.0889	1.7207
22	9.597	0.829	24.62	1.206	40.612	226.81	411.66	184.85	1.0930	1.7194
23	9.863	0.832	23.95	1.202	41.756	228.03	411.90	183.87	1.0971	1.7180
24	10.135	0.835	23.29	1.198	42.928	229.27	412.15	182.88	1.1012	1.7167
25	10.411	0.837	22.66	1.194	44.127	230.50	412.38	181.88	1.1053	1.7153
26	10.694	0.840	22.05	1.190	45.354	231.74	412.62	180.88	1.1093	1.7140
27	10.982	0.843	21.45	1.186	46.610	232.97	412.84	179.87	1.1134	1.7127
28	11.275	0.846	20.88	1.182	47.896	234.21	413.06	178.85	1.1174	1.7113
29	11.575	0.849	20.32	1.178	49.212	235.45	413.27	177.82	1.1215	1.7100
30	11.880	0.852	19.78	1.174	50.558	236.69	413.48	176.79	1.1255	1.7086
31	12.191	0.855	19.25	1.170	51.937	237.93	413.68	175.75	1.1295	1.7073
32	12.508	0.858	18.74	1.166	53.348	339.18	413.88	174.70	1.1334	1.7060
33	12.831	0.861	18.25	1.161	54.792	240.43	414.07	173.64	1.1374	1.7046
34	13.160	0.864	17.77	1.157	56.271	241.68	414.25	173.57	1.1414	1.7033
35	13.496	0.867	17.31	1.153	57.784	242.93	414.42	171.49	1.1454	1.7019
36	13.837	0.871	16.85	1.149	59.333	244.18	414.59	170.41	1.1494	1.7006
37	14.185	0.874	16.42	1.144	60.920	245.44	414.75	169.31	1.1533	1.6992
38	14.540	0.877	15.99	1.140	62.544	246.69	414.90	168.21	1.1573	1.6979
39	14.901	0.881	15.57	1.136	64.208	247.95	415.05	167.10	1.1612	1.6965
40	15.269	0.884	15.17	1.131	65.911	249.22	415.19	165.97	1.1651	1.6952
41	15.643	0.888	14.78	1.127	67.656	250.48	415.32	164.84	1.1691	1.6938
42	16.024	0.891	14.40	1.122	69.443	251.75	415.44	163.69	1.1730	1.6924
43	16.412	0.895	14.03	1.117	71.274	253.02	415.56	162.54	1.1769	1.6910
44	16.807	0.899	13.67	1.113	73.150	354.29	415.66	161.37	1.1808	1.6896
45	17.209	0.902	13.32	1.108	75.072	255.57	415.76	160.19	1.1847	1.6882
46	17.618	0.906	12.98	1.103	77.042	256.86	415.85	158.99	1.1886	1.6868
47	18.034	0.910	12.65	1.099	79.062	258.15	415.93	157.78	1.1926	1.6854
48	18.458	0.914	12.33	1.094	81.133	259.44	416.00	156.56	1.1965	1.6840
49	18.889	0.918	12.01	1.089	83.226	260.73	416.06	155.33	1.2003	1.6825

149

Table 3-14 Properties of Saturated "Freon 22" — Difluoromonochloromethane (CHClF$_2$) *(continued)*

Tempera-ture	Pressure	Specific volume		Density		Specific enthalpy		Heat of vaporization	Specific entropy	
		Liquid	Vapor	Liquid	Vapor	Liquid	Vapor		Liquid	Vapor
t	p	v'	v''	ρ'	ρ''	h'	h''	r	s'	s''
°C	bar	L/kg	L/kg	kg/L	kg/m^3	kJ/kg	kJ/kg	kJ/kg	kJ/(kg K)	kJ/(kg K)
50	19.327	0.923	11.70	1.084	85.434	262.03	416.11	154.08	1.2042	1.6811
51	19.773	0.927	11.41	1.079	87.668	263.34	416.15	152.81	1.2082	1.6796
52	20.227	0.931	11.12	1.074	89.961	264.65	416.18	151.53	1.2121	1.6781
53	20.688	0.936	10.83	1.069	92.315	265.97	416.20	150.23	1.2160	1.6766
54	21.158	0.940	10.56	1.063	94.731	267.29	416.20	148.91	1.2199	1.6751
55	21.635	0.945	10.29	1.058	97.212	268.62	416.20	147.58	1.2238	1.6736
56	22.121	0.950	10.02	1.053	99.762	269.96	416.18	146.22	1.2278	1.6720
57	22.614	0.955	9.77	1.048	102.381	271.30	416.15	144.85	1.2317	1.6705
58	23.116	0.960	9.52	1.042	105.075	272.66	416.11	143.45	1.2357	1.6689
59	23.627	0.965	9.27	1.037	107.845	274.03	416.06	142.03	1.2396	1.6672
60	24.146	0.970	9.03	1.031	110.694	275.41	415.99	140.58	1.2436	1.6656
61	24.673	0.975	8.80	1.025	113.628	276.79	415.90	139.11	1.2276	1.6639
62	25.210	0.981	8.57	1.019	116.648	278.18	415.80	137.62	1.2516	1.6623
63	25.755	0.987	8.35	1.014	119.760	279.59	415.68	136.09	1.2557	1.6605
64	26.310	0.992	8.13	1.008	122.969	381.01	415.55	134.54	1.2597	1.6588
65	26.873	0.999	7.92	1.001	126.278	282.44	415.40	132.96	1.2638	1.6570
66	27.446	1.005	7.71	0.995	129.693	283.89	415.23	131.34	1.2679	1.6552
67	28.028	1.011	7.51	0.989	133.220	285.35	415.04	129.69	1.2720	1.6533
68	28.620	1.018	7.31	0.983	136.866	286.83	414.83	128.00	1.2762	1.6514
69	29.222	1.025	7.11	0.976	140.636	288.33	414.60	126.27	1.2804	1.6495
70	29.833	1.032	6.92	0.969	144.540	289.86	414.35	124.49	1.2847	1.6475
71	30.454	1.039	6.73	0.963	148.584	291.39	414.07	122.68	1.2889	1.6454
72	31.086	1.046	6.55	0.956	152.779	292.95	413.76	120.81	1.2933	1.6433
73	31.727	1.054	6.36	0.948	157.134	294.54	413.43	118.89	1.2977	1.6412
74	32.379	1.062	6.19	0.941	161.662	396.15	413.07	116.92	1.3021	1.6389
75	33.042	1.071	6.01	0.934	166.374	397.79	412.67	114.88	1.3066	1.6366
76	33.716	1.080	5.84	0.926	171.287	299.45	412.24	112.79	1.3112	1.6343
77	34.400	1.089	5.67	0.918	176.415	301.16	411.78	110.62	1.3159	1.6318
78	35.096	1.099	5.50	0.910	181.778	302.90	411.27	108.37	1.3206	1.6292
79	35.802	1.109	5.34	0.902	187.298	304.67	410.72	106.05	1.3254	1.6266
80	36.520	1.120	5.17	0.893	193.300	306.49	410.12	103.63	1.3304	1.6238
81	37.250	1.131	5.01	0.884	199.513	308.36	409.47	101.11	1.3354	1.6209
82	37.992	1.143	4.85	0.875	206.072	310.28	408.76	98.48	1.3406	1.6179
83	38.746	1.156	4.69	0.865	213.018	312.26	407.99	95.73	1.3459	1.6147
84	39.511	1.170	4.54	0.855	220.402	314.30	407.14	92.84	1.3514	1.6114
85	40.290	1.185	4.38	0.844	228.286	316.43	406.22	89.79	1.3571	1.6078
86	41.080	1.200	4.22	0.833	336.745	318.63	405.19	86.56	1.3630	1.6040
87	41.884	1.218	4.07	0.821	245.880	320.93	404.05	83.12	1.3691	1.5999
88	42.701	1.237	3.91	0.809	255.816	323.35	402.79	79.44	1.3755	1.5955
89	43.531	1.258	3.75	0.795	266.728	325.89	401.36	75.47	1.3823	1.5907
90	44.374	1.282	3.59	0.780	278.856	328.61	399.75	71.14	1.3894	1.5853
91	45.231	1.309	3.42	0.764	292.554	331.53	397.88	66.35	1.3972	1.5794
92	46.102	1.341	3.24	0.745	308.374	334.73	395.68	60.96	1.4056	1.5726
93	46.987	1.381	3.06	0.724	327.266	338.28	393.00	54.72	1.4150	1.5645
94	47.887	1.432	2.85	0.698	351.110	342.44	389.58	47.14	1.4260	1.5544
95	48.802	1.509	2.60	0.663	384.732	347.71	384.72	37.01	1.4400	1.5405
96	49.731	1.688	2.30	0.592	454.726	357.09	374.75	17.66	1.4650	1.5129
96.18	49.900	1.949	1.95	0.513	513.084	366.83	366.83	0.00	1.4913	1.4913

Table 3-15 Properties of Saturated "Freon 23" — Trifluoromethane (CHF$_3$)

Tempera-ture	Pressure	Specific volume		Density		Specific enthalpy		Heat of vaporization	Specific entropy	
		Liquid	Vapor	Liquid	Vapor	Liquid	Vapor		Liquid	Vapor
t	p	v'	v''	ρ'	ρ''	h'	h''	r	s'	s''
°C	bar	L/kg	L/kg	kg/L	kg/m^3	kJ/kg	kJ/kg	kJ/kg	kJ/(kg K)	kJ/(kg K)
−120	0.059	0.623	3082.91	1.605	0.324	40.76	307.99	267.23	0.2533	1.9982
−119	0.065	0.624	2818.75	1.602	0.355	41.81	308.49	266.68	0.2601	1.9902
−118	0.071	0.626	2880.68	1.598	0.387	42.87	308.99	266.12	0.2670	1.9823
−117	0.078	0.627	2365.76	1.594	0.423	43.94	309.49	265.55	0.2739	1.9745
−116	0.085	0.629	2171.50	1.591	0.461	45.01	309.98	264.97	0.2808	1.9669
−115	0.093	0.630	1995.67	1.587	0.501	46.09	310.48	264.39	0.2876	1.9594
−114	0.102	0.632	1836.31	1.583	0.545	47.17	310.98	263.81	0.2944	1.9520
−113	0.112	0.633	1691.69	1.580	0.591	48.27	311.48	263.21	0.3012	1.9448
−112	0.122	0.635	1560.27	1.576	0.641	49.36	311.97	262.61	0.3081	1.9377
−111	0.132	0.636	1440.72	1.572	0.694	50.47	312.47	262.00	0.3149	1.9307
−110	0.144	0.638	1331.81	1.568	0.751	51.57	312.96	261.39	0.3217	1.9238
−109	0.157	0.639	1232.48	1.565	0.811	52.68	313.45	260.77	0.3285	1.9171
−108	0.170	0.641	1141.79	1.561	0.876	53.80	313.94	260.14	0.3353	1.9105
−107	0.184	0.642	1058.88	1.557	0.944	54.93	314.43	259.50	0.3421	1.9039
−106	0.199	0.644	983.00	1.553	1.017	56.06	314.92	258.86	0.3488	1.8975
−105	0.216	0.645	913.48	1.550	1.095	57.20	315.41	258.21	0.3556	1.8912
−104	0.233	0.647	849.71	1.546	1.177	58.34	315.89	257.55	0.3624	1.8850
−103	0.252	0.648	791.16	1.542	1.264	59.49	316.37	256.88	0.3692	1.8789
−102	0.271	0.650	737.35	1.538	1.356	60.65	316.85	256.20	0.3760	1.8729
−101	0.292	0.652	687.83	1.535	1.454	61.81	317.33	255.52	0.3827	1.8670
−100	0.315	0.653	642.22	1.531	1.557	62.99	317.81	254.82	0.3895	1.8612
−99	0.338	0.655	600.17	1.527	1.666	64.16	318.28	254.12	0.3962	1.8555
−98	0.363	0.657	561.36	1.523	1.781	65.34	318.75	253.41	0.4030	1.8498
−97	0.390	0.658	525.51	1.519	1.903	66.53	319.22	252.69	0.4097	1.8443
−96	0.418	0.660	492.36	1.515	2.031	67.72	319.68	251.96	0.4165	1.8388
−95	0.448	0.662	461.69	1.511	2.166	68.91	320.14	251.23	0.4232	1.8334
−94	0.479	0.663	433.27	1.508	2.308	70.12	320.60	250.48	0.4299	1.8281
−93	0.512	0.665	406.92	1.504	2.457	71.33	321.06	249.73	0.4366	1.8229
−92	0.547	0.667	382.47	1.500	2.615	72.55	321.51	248.96	0.4434	1.8178
−91	0.584	0.669	359.76	1.496	2.780	73.77	321.96	248.19	0.4501	1.8127
−90	0.623	0.670	338.66	1.492	2.953	75.00	322.41	247.41	0.4568	1.8077
−89	0.664	0.672	319.02	1.488	3.135	76.23	322.85	246.62	0.4635	1.8028
−88	0.707	0.674	300.74	1.484	3.325	77.48	323.29	245.81	0.4703	1.7979
−87	0.753	0.676	283.70	1.480	3.525	78.73	323.73	245.00	0.4769	1.7931
−86	0.800	0.677	267.81	1.476	3.734	79.97	324.16	244.19	0.4836	1.7884
−85	0.851	0.679	252.98	1.472	3.953	81.23	324.59	243.36	0.4903	1.7837
−84	0.903	0.681	239.13	1.468	4.182	82.49	325.01	242.52	0.4969	1.7791
−83	0.958	0.683	226.18	1.464	4.421	83.76	325.43	241.67	0.5036	1.7746
−82	1.016	0.685	214.08	1.460	4.671	85.02	325.84	240.82	0.5102	1.7701
−81	1.076	0.687	202.74	1.456	4.932	86.31	326.26	239.95	0.5169	1.7657
−80	1.139	0.689	192.12	1.452	5.205	87.58	326.66	239.08	0.5235	1.7613
−79	1.206	0.691	182.17	1.448	5.489	88.87	327.06	238.19	0.5302	1.7570
−78	1.275	0.693	172.84	1.444	6.786	90.16	327.46	237.30	0.5367	1.7528
−77	1.347	0.695	164.07	1.440	6.095	91.46	327.86	236.10	0.5433	1.7486
−76	1.422	0.697	155.84	1.435	6.417	92.76	328.24	235.48	0.5500	1.7444
−75	1.501	0.699	148.11	1.431	6.752	94.07	328.63	234.56	0.5565	1.7403
−74	1.583	0.701	140.83	1.427	7.101	95.38	329.01	233.63	0.5631	1.7362
−73	1.668	0.703	133.98	1.423	7.464	96.68	329.38	232.70	0.5696	1.7322
−72	1.757	0.705	127.53	1.419	7.841	98.00	329.75	231.75	0.5761	1.7283
−71	1.850	0.707	121.46	1.414	8.233	99.32	330.11	230.79	0.5827	1.7244

Table 3-15 Properties of Saturated "Freon 23" — Trifluoromethane (CHF₃) *(continued)*

Tempera-ture	Pressure	Specific volume		Density		Specific enthalpy		Heat of vaporization	Specific entropy	
		Liquid	Vapor	Liquid	Vapor	Liquid	Vapor		Liquid	Vapor
t	p	v'	v''	ρ'	ρ''	h'	h''	r	s'	s''
°C	bar	L/kg	L/kg	kg/L	kg/m³	kJ/kg	kJ/kg	kJ/kg	kJ/(kg K)	kJ/(kg K)
−70	1.947	0.709	115.73	1.410	8.641	100.64	330.47	229.83	0.5891	1.7205
−69	2.047	0.711	110.33	1.406	9.064	101.98	330.83	228.85	0.5956	1.7167
−68	2.151	0.713	105.23	1.402	9.503	103.30	331.17	227.87	0.6021	1.7129
−67	2.259	0.716	100.41	1.397	9.959	104.64	331.52	226.88	0.6085	1.7091
−66	2.372	0.718	95.86	1.393	10.432	105.98	331.86	225.88	0.6150	1.7054
−65	2.489	0.720	91.55	1.389	10.923	107.32	332.19	224.87	0.6214	1.7018
−64	2.610	0.722	87.48	1.384	11.431	108.67	332.52	223.85	0.6278	1.6981
−63	2.735	0.725	83.62	1.380	11.958	110.02	332.84	222.82	0.6342	1.6945
−62	2.866	0.727	79.97	1.376	12.504	111.36	333.15	221.79	0.6406	1.6910
−61	3.001	0.729	76.51	1.371	13.070	112.71	333.46	220.75	0.6469	1.6875
−60	3.140	0.732	73.23	1.367	13.655	114.07	333.77	219.70	0.6532	1.6840
−59	3.285	0.734	70.12	1.362	14.261	115.43	334.07	218.64	0.6595	1.6805
−58	3.435	0.736	67.17	1.358	14.888	116.79	334.36	217.57	0.6658	1.6771
−57	3.589	0.739	64.37	1.354	15.536	118.15	334.65	216.50	0.6721	1.6737
−56	3.750	0.741	61.70	1.349	16.207	119.52	334.93	215.41	0.6784	1.6704
−55	3.915	0.744	59.17	1.345	16.900	120.89	335.21	214.32	0.6846	1.6670
−54	4.086	0.746	56.77	1.340	17.616	122.26	335.48	213.22	0.6908	1.6638
−53	4.262	0.749	54.48	1.335	18.357	123.62	335.74	212.12	0.6969	1.6605
−52	4.445	0.751	52.30	1.331	19.122	125.00	336.00	211.00	0.7031	1.6573
−51	4.633	0.754	50.22	1.326	19.912	126.37	336.25	209.88	0.7093	1.6540
−50	4.827	0.757	48.25	1.322	20.727	127.75	336.50	208.75	0.7154	1.6509
−49	5.027	0.759	46.36	1.317	21.569	129.13	336.74	207.61	0.7215	1.6477
−48	5.233	0.762	44.57	1.312	22.438	130.51	336.97	206.46	0.7276	1.6446
−47	5.445	0.765	42.85	1.307	23.335	131.89	337.20	205.31	0.7336	1.6415
−46	5.664	0.768	41.22	1.303	24.261	133.28	337.43	204.15	0.7396	1.6384
−45	5.890	0.770	39.66	1.298	25.216	134.66	337.64	202.98	0.7456	1.6353
−44	6.122	0.773	38.17	1.293	26.200	136.05	337.85	201.80	0.7516	1.6323
−43	6.361	0.776	36.74	1.288	27.216	137.44	338.05	200.61	0.7576	1.6293
−42	6.607	0.779	35.38	1.283	28.263	138.83	338.25	199.42	0.7636	1.6263
−41	6.860	0.782	34.08	1.279	29.342	140.22	338.44	198.22	0.7695	1.6233
−40	7.120	0.785	32.84	1.274	30.455	141.62	338.63	197.01	0.7754	1.6204
−39	7.387	0.788	31.64	1.269	31.601	143.02	338.81	195.79	0.7813	1.6175
−38	7.662	0.791	30.50	1.264	32.783	144.41	338.98	194.57	0.7871	1.6146
−37	7.944	0.795	29.41	1.259	34.001	145.81	339.14	193.33	0.7930	1.6117
−36	8.234	0.798	28.36	1.254	35.255	147.21	339.30	192.09	0.7988	1.6088
−35	8.532	0.801	27.36	1.248	36.548	148.61	339.45	190.84	0.8046	1.6060
−34	8.837	0.804	26.40	1.243	37.880	150.02	339.60	189.58	0.8104	1.6031
−33	9.151	0.808	25.48	1.238	39.251	151.42	339.73	188.31	0.8162	1.6003
−32	9.473	0.811	24.59	1.233	40.664	152.84	339.87	187.03	0.8219	1.5975
−31	9.803	0.815	23.74	1.228	42.120	154.24	339.99	185.75	0.8276	1.5947
−30	10.142	0.818	22.93	1.222	43.618	155.66	340.11	184.45	0.8333	1.5919
−29	10.490	0.822	22.14	1.217	45.162	157.07	340.22	183.15	0.8390	1.5892
−28	10.846	0.825	21.39	1.212	46.752	158.49	340.32	181.83	0.8447	1.5864
−27	11.211	0.829	20.67	1.206	48.389	159.91	340.42	180.51	0.8503	1.5837
−26	11.585	0.833	19.97	1.201	50.075	161.33	340.50	179.17	0.8560	1.5810
−25	11.969	0.837	19.30	1.195	51.812	162.75	340.58	177.83	0.7616	1.5783
−24	12.362	0.841	18.66	1.190	53.601	164.19	340.66	176.47	0.8672	1.5755
−23	12.764	0.844	18.04	1.184	55.443	165.62	340.72	175.10	0.8728	1.5728
−22	13.176	0.849	17.44	1.178	57.340	167.05	340.78	173.73	0.8784	1.5702
−21	13.598	0.853	16.87	1.173	59.294	168.50	340.83	172.33	0.8840	1.5675

Table 3-15   Properties of Saturated "Freon 23" — Trifluoromethane (CHF₃)   (continued)

Tempera-ture	Pressure	Specific volume		Density		Specific enthalpy		Heat of vaporization	Specific entropy	
		Liquid	Vapor	Liquid	Vapor	Liquid	Vapor		Liquid	Vapor
t	p	v'	v''	ρ'	ρ''	h'	h''	r	s'	s''
°C	bar	L/kg	L/kg	kg/L	kg/m³	kJ/kg	kJ/kg	kJ/kg	kJ/(kg K)	kJ/(kg K)
−20	14.030	0.857	16.31	1.167	61.307	169.94	340.87	170.93	0.8896	1.5648
−19	14.472	0.861	15.78	1.161	63.381	171.38	340.90	169.52	0.8951	1.5621
−18	14.924	0.866	15.26	1.155	63.517	172.83	340.92	168.09	0.9007	1.5595
−17	15.387	0.870	14.77	1.149	67.718	174.29	340.94	166.65	0.9062	1.5568
−16	15.861	0.875	14.29	1.143	69.986	175.75	340.94	165.19	0.9117	1.5541
−15	16.345	0.879	13.83	1.137	72.323	177.22	340.94	163.72	0.9173	1.5515
−14	16.840	0.884	13.38	1.141	74.731	178.68	340.92	162.24	0.9228	1.5488
−13	17.347	0.889	12.95	1.125	77.214	180.16	340.90	160.74	0.9283	1.5462
−12	17.865	0.894	12.54	1.119	79.773	181.65	340.87	159.22	0.9338	1.5435
−11	18.395	0.899	12.13	1.112	82.412	183.13	340.82	157.69	0.9393	1.5408
−10	18.936	0.904	11.75	1.106	85.133	184.63	340.77	156.14	0.9448	1.5382
−9	19.489	0.910	11.37	1.099	87.939	186.13	340.70	154.57	0.9503	1.5355
−8	20.055	0.915	11.01	1.092	90.833	187.64	340.63	152.99	0.9558	1.5328
−7	20.633	0.921	10.66	1.086	93.820	189.15	340.54	151.39	0.9613	1.5301
−6	21.223	0.927	10.32	1.079	96.901	190.68	340.44	149.76	0.9668	1.5274
−5	21.826	0.933	9.99	1.072	100.081	192.21	340.33	148.12	0.9723	1.5247
−4	22.443	0.939	9.67	1.065	103.363	193.75	340.20	146.45	0.9779	1.5220
−3	23.072	0.945	9.37	1.058	106.752	195.29	340.06	144.77	0.9834	1.5193
−2	23.715	0.952	9.07	1.050	110.251	196.85	339.91	143.06	0.9889	1.5156
−1	24.372	0.959	8.78	1.043	113.866	198.43	339.75	141.32	0.9945	1.5138
0	25.043	0.966	8.50	1.035	117.600	200.00	339.57	139.57	1.0000	1.5110
1	25.728	0.973	8.23	1.028	121.458	201.59	339.37	127.78	1.0056	1.5082
2	26.428	0.981	7.97	1.020	125.446	203.19	339.16	135.97	1.0111	1.5053
3	27.142	0.988	7.72	1.012	129.569	204.80	338.93	134.13	1.0167	1.5025
4	27.871	0.997	7.47	1.003	133.832	206.42	338.68	132.26	1.0223	1.4996
5	28.616	1.005	7.23	0.995	138.243	208.07	338.42	130.35	1.0280	1.4967
6	29.376	1.014	7.00	0.986	142.807	209.73	338.14	128.41	1.0337	1.4937
7	30.152	1.023	6.78	0.978	147.532	211.40	337.84	126.44	1.0394	1.4907
8	30.945	1.033	6.56	0.968	152.426	213.09	337.51	124.42	1.0451	1.4877
9	31.754	1.043	6.35	0.959	157.498	214.81	337.17	122.36	1.0509	1.4846
10	32.579	1.053	6.14	0.949	162.758	216.54	336.79	120.25	1.0567	1.4814
11	33.422	1.065	5.94	0.939	168.216	218.31	336.40	118.09	1.0626	1.4782
12	34.283	1.076	5.75	0.929	173.886	220.10	335.97	115.87	1.0686	1.4750
13	35.161	1.089	5.56	0.918	179.782	221.93	335.51	113.58	1.0747	1.4716
14	36.058	1.103	5.38	0.907	185.921	223.80	335.02	111.22	1.0809	1.4682
15	36.973	1.117	5.20	0.895	192.324	225.71	334.48	108.77	1.0872	1.4647
16	37.907	1.133	5.02	0.883	199.017	227.70	333.91	106.21	1.0937	1.4610
17	38.861	1.150	4.85	0.870	206.028	229.75	333.28	103.53	1.1004	1.4572
18	39.834	1.169	4.69	0.856	213.397	231.87	332.59	100.72	1.1073	1.4533
19	40.828	1.189	4.52	0.841	221.171	234.12	331.84	97.72	1.1146	1.4491
20	41.842	1.213	4.36	0.824	229.413	236.48	331.00	94.52	1.1223	1.4447
21	42.878	1.240	4.20	0.807	238.206	239.03	330.07	91.04	1.1305	1.4400
22	43.935	1.271	4.04	0.787	247.662	241.80	329.01	87.21	1.1395	1.4349
23	45.014	1.310	3.88	0.764	257.943	244.90	327.80	82.90	1.1495	1.4294
24	46.116	1.359	3.71	0.736	269.293	248.52	326.39	77.87	1.1612	1.4232
25	47.241	1.432	3.54	0.698	282.104	253.10	324.70	71.60	1.1760	1.4162
26	48.390	1.584	3.37	0.631	297.090	260.75	322.60	61.85	1.2011	1.4078
26.30	48.739	1.898	1.90	0.527	527.009	286.03	286.03	0.00	1.2851	1.2851

Table 3-16 Properties of Saturated "Freon 113" — Trichlorotrifluoroethane ($C_2Cl_3F_3$)

Tempera-ture	Pressure	Specific volume		Density		Specific enthalpy		Heat of vaporization	Specific entropy	
		Liquid	Vapor	Liquid	Vapor	Liquid	Vapor		Liquid	Vapor
t	p	v'	v''	ρ'	ρ''	h'	h''	r	s'	s''
°C	bar	L/kg	L/kg	kg/L	kg/m³	kJ/kg	kJ/kg	kJ/kg	kJ/(kg K)	kJ/(kg K)
−35	0.020	0.590	5229.12	1.696	0.191	170.18	337.45	167.27	0.8833	1.5857
−34	0.022	0.590	4913.75	1.694	0.204	171.00	338.06	167.06	0.8868	1.5853
−33	0.023	0.591	4620.19	1.692	0.216	171.82	338.67	166.85	0.8902	1.5850
−32	0.025	0.592	4346.78	1.690	0.230	172.65	339.28	166.63	0.8936	1.5846
−31	0.026	0.592	4091.97	1.688	0.244	173.48	339.89	166.41	0.8970	1.5843
−30	0.028	0.593	3854.33	1.686	0.259	174.30	340.50	166.20	0.9004	1.5840
−29	0.030	0.594	3632.59	1.684	0.275	175.13	341.11	165.98	0.9038	1.5837
−28	0.032	0.595	3425.54	1.682	0.292	175.96	341.72	165.76	0.9072	1.5834
−27	0.034	0.595	3232.11	1.679	0.309	176.80	342.34	165.54	0.9106	1.5832
−26	0.036	0.596	3051.28	1.677	0.328	177.63	342.95	165.32	0.9140	1.5829
−25	0.038	0.597	2882.14	1.675	0.347	178.47	343.57	165.10	0.9174	1.5827
−24	0.040	0.598	2723.84	1.673	0.367	179.30	344.18	164.88	0.9208	1.5826
−23	0.043	0.598	2575.60	1.671	0.388	180.14	344.80	164.66	0.9241	1.5824
−22	0.046	0.599	2436.70	1.669	0.410	180.98	345.42	164.44	0.9275	1.5822
−21	0.048	0.600	2306.49	1.667	0.434	181.83	346.04	164.21	0.9308	1.5821
−20	0.051	0.601	2184.34	1.665	0.458	182.67	346.66	163.99	0.9342	1.5820
−19	0.054	0.602	2069.71	1.662	0.483	183.53	347.29	163.76	0.9375	1.5819
−18	0.057	0.602	1962.07	1.660	0.510	184.37	347.91	163.54	0.9409	1.5818
−17	0.061	0.603	1860.94	1.658	0.537	185.22	348.53	163.31	0.9442	1.5818
−16	0.064	0.604	1765.87	1.656	0.566	186.08	349.16	163.08	0.9475	1.5817
−15	0.068	0.605	1676.46	1.654	0.596	186.94	349.79	162.85	0.9508	1.5817
−14	0.072	0.605	1592.33	1.652	0.628	187.79	350.41	162.62	0.9542	1.5817
−13	0.076	0.606	1513.13	1.649	0.661	188.65	351.04	162.39	0.9575	1.5817
−12	0.080	0.607	1438.52	1.647	0.695	189.51	351.67	162.16	0.9608	1.5817
−11	0.085	0.608	1368.22	1.645	0.731	190.37	352.30	161.93	0.9640	1.5818
−10	0.089	0.609	1301.93	1.643	0.768	191.24	352.93	161.69	0.9674	1.5818
−9	0.094	0.609	1239.40	1.641	0.807	192.10	353.56	161.46	0.9706	1.5819
−8	0.099	0.610	1180.39	1.639	0.847	192.98	354.20	161.22	0.9739	1.5820
−7	0.104	0.611	1124.67	1.636	0.889	193.85	354.83	160.98	0.9772	1.5821
−6	0.110	0.612	1072.05	1.634	0.933	194.72	355.46	160.74	0.9805	1.5822
−5	0.115	0.613	1022.32	1.632	0.978	195.60	356.10	160.50	0.9838	1.5823
−4	0.121	0.614	975.29	1.630	1.025	196.48	356.74	160.26	0.9870	1.5825
−3	0.128	0.614	930.81	1.628	1.074	197.35	357.37	160.02	0.9903	1.5826
−2	0.134	0.615	888.71	1.625	1.125	198.23	358.01	159.78	0.9935	1.5828
−1	0.141	0.616	848.86	1.623	1.178	199.12	358.65	159.53	0.9968	1.5830
0	0.148	0.617	811.11	1.621	1.233	200.00	359.29	159.29	1.0000	1.5832
1	0.155	0.618	775.35	1.619	1.290	200.89	359.93	159.04	1.0032	1.5834
2	0.163	0.619	741.44	1.616	1.349	201.78	360.57	158.79	1.0065	1.5836
3	0.171	0.619	709.29	1.614	1.410	202.67	361.21	158.54	1.0097	1.5838
4	0.179	0.620	678.78	1.612	1.473	203.56	361.85	158.29	1.0129	1.5841
5	0.188	0.621	649.83	1.610	1.539	204.45	362.49	158.04	1.0162	1.5844
6	0.197	0.622	622.34	1.608	1.607	205.35	363.13	157.78	1.0194	1.5846
7	0.206	0.623	596.23	1.605	1.677	206.25	363.78	157.53	1.0226	1.5849
8	0.216	0.624	571.42	1.603	1.750	207.15	364.42	157.27	1.0258	1.5852
9	0.226	0.625	547.83	1.601	1.825	208.06	365.07	157.01	1.0290	1.5855
10	0.236	0.626	525.40	1.599	1.903	208.96	365.71	156.75	1.0322	1.5858
11	0.247	0.626	504.06	1.696	1.984	209.87	366.36	156.49	1.0354	1.5862
12	0.258	0.627	483.75	1.594	2.067	210.77	367.00	156.23	1.0386	1.5865
13	0.269	0.628	464.41	1.592	2.153	211.69	367.65	155.96	1.0418	1.5868
14	0.281	0.629	446.00	1.589	2.242	212.60	368.30	155.70	1.0450	1.5872

Table 3-16   Properties of Saturated "Freon 113" — Trichlorotrifluoroethane ($C_2Cl_3F_3$)   (continued)

Tempera-ture	Pressure	Specific volume		Density		Specific enthalpy		Heat of vaporization	Specific entropy	
		Liquid	Vapor	Liquid	Vapor	Liquid	Vapor		Liquid	Vapor
t	p	v'	v''	ρ'	ρ''	h'	h''	r	s'	s''
°C	bar	L/kg	L/kg	kg/L	kg/m³	kJ/kg	kJ/kg	kJ/kg	kJ/(kg K)	kJ/(kg K)
15	0.294	0.630	428.45	1.587	2.334	213.52	368.95	155.43	1.0481	1.5876
16	0.307	0.631	411.73	1.585	2.429	214.43	369.59	155.16	1.0513	1.5879
17	0.320	0.632	395.78	1.583	2.527	215.35	370.24	154.89	1.0545	1.5883
18	0.334	0.633	380.58	1.580	2.628	216.27	370.89	154.62	1.0577	1.5887
19	0.348	0.634	366.07	1.578	2.732	217.20	371.54	154.34	1.0608	1.5891
20	0.363	0.635	352.22	1.576	2.839	218.12	372.19	154.07	1.0640	1.5896
21	0.378	0.636	339.00	1.573	2.950	219.05	372.84	153.79	1.0671	1.5900
22	0.393	0.637	326.37	1.571	3.064	219.98	373.49	153.51	1.0703	1.5904
23	0.410	0.637	314.31	1.569	3.182	220.91	374.14	153.23	1.0734	1.5909
24	0.426	0.638	302.78	1.566	3.303	221.85	374.80	152.95	1.0766	1.5913
25	0.444	0.639	291.75	1.564	3.428	222.79	375.45	152.66	1.0797	1.5918
26	0.462	0.640	281.21	1.562	3.556	223.72	376.10	152.38	1.0829	1.5922
27	0.480	0.641	271.13	1.559	3.688	224.66	376.75	152.09	1.0860	1.5927
28	0.499	0.642	261.48	1.557	3.824	225.60	377.40	151.80	1.0891	1.5932
29	0.519	0.643	252.24	1.555	3.964	226.55	378.06	151.51	1.0922	1.5937
30	0.539	0.644	243.40	1.552	4.109	227.50	378.71	151.21	1.0954	1.5942
31	0.560	0.645	234.92	1.550	4.257	228.44	379.36	150.92	1.0985	1.5947
32	0.581	0.646	226.81	1.548	4.409	229.40	380.02	150.62	1.1016	1.5952
33	0.603	0.647	219.03	1.545	4.566	230.35	380.67	150.32	1.1047	1.5957
34	0.626	0.648	211.57	1.543	4.727	231.30	381.32	150.02	1.1078	1.5963
35	0.650	0.649	204.42	1.541	4.892	232.26	381.98	149.72	1.1109	1.5968
36	0.674	0.650	197.56	1.538	5.062	233.21	382.63	149.42	1.1140	1.5974
37	0.699	0.651	190.98	1.536	5.236	234.17	383.28	149.11	1.1171	1.5979
38	0.725	0.652	184.66	1.533	5.415	235.14	383.94	148.80	1.1202	1.5985
39	0.751	0.653	178.59	1.531	5.599	236.10	384.59	148.49	1.1233	1.5990
40	0.778	0.654	172.77	1.529	5.788	237.07	385.25	148.18	1.1264	1.5996
41	0.806	0.655	167.17	1.526	5.982	238.03	385.90	147.87	1.1295	1.6002
42	0.835	0.656	161.80	1.524	6.181	239.01	386.56	147.55	1.1325	1.6008
43	0.864	0.657	156.63	1.521	6.384	239.98	387.21	147.23	1.1356	1.6013
44	0.894	0.658	151.66	1.519	6.594	240.95	387.86	146.91	1.1387	1.6019
45	0.925	0.659	146.89	1.517	6.808	241.93	388.52	146.59	1.1418	1.6025
46	0.957	0.660	142.29	1.514	7.028	242.90	389.17	146.27	1.1448	1.6031
47	0.990	0.662	137.87	1.512	7.253	243.89	389.83	145.94	1.1479	1.6037
48	1.024	0.663	133.62	1.509	7.484	244.86	390.48	145.62	1.1509	1.6044
49	1.058	0.664	129.52	1.507	7.721	245.84	391.13	145.29	1.1540	1.6050
50	1.094	0.665	125.58	1.504	7.963	246.83	391.79	144.96	1.1570	1.6056
51	1.130	0.666	121.78	1.502	8.211	247.82	392.44	144.62	1.1601	1.6062
52	1.167	0.667	118.12	1.499	8.466	248.81	393.10	144.29	1.1631	1.6069
53	1.206	0.668	114.60	1.497	8.726	249.80	393.75	143.95	1.1661	1.6075
54	1.245	0.669	111.20	1.494	8.993	250.79	394.40	143.61	1.1692	1.6082
55	1.285	0.670	107.93	1.492	9.265	251.79	395.06	143.27	1.1722	1.6088
56	1.326	0.671	104.77	1.489	9.545	252.78	395.71	142.93	1.1752	1.6095
57	1.369	0.673	101.72	1.487	9.830	253.77	396.36	142.59	1.1782	1.6101
58	1.412	0.674	98.79	1.484	10.123	254.77	397.01	142.24	1.1812	1.6108
59	1.456	0.675	95.95	1.482	10.422	255.78	397.67	141.89	1.1842	1.6114
60	1.501	0.676	93.22	1.479	10.728	256.78	398.32	141.54	1.1872	1.6121
61	1.548	0.677	90.57	1.477	11.041	257.78	398.97	141.19	1.1902	1.6128
62	1.596	0.678	88.02	1.474	11.361	258.79	399.62	140.83	1.1932	1.6135
63	1.644	0.680	85.56	1.472	11.688	259.79	400.27	140.48	1.1962	1.6141
64	1.694	0.681	83.18	1.469	12.022	260.80	400.92	140.12	1.1992	1.6148

Table 3-16 Properties of Saturated "Freon 113" — Trichlorotrifluoroethane (C₂Cl₃F₃) *(continued)*

Tempera-ture	Pressure	Specific volume		Density		Specific enthalpy		Heat of vaporization	Specific entropy	
		Liquid	Vapor	Liquid	Vapor	Liquid	Vapor		Liquid	Vapor
t	p	v'	v''	ρ'	ρ''	h'	h''	r	s'	s''
°C	bar	L/kg	L/kg	kg/L	kg/m³	kJ/kg	kJ/kg	kJ/kg	kJ/(kg K)	kJ/(kg K)
65	1.745	0.682	80.88	1.467	12.363	261.81	401.57	139.76	1.2022	1.6155
66	1.797	0.683	78.66	1.464	12.713	262.82	402.22	139.40	1.2052	1.6162
67	1.850	0.684	76.51	1.461	13.069	263.84	402.87	139.03	1.2082	1.6169
68	1.905	0.686	74.44	1.459	13.434	264.86	403.52	138.66	1.2111	1.6176
69	1.961	0.687	72.43	1.456	13.806	265.87	404.17	138.30	1.2141	1.6183
70	2.018	0.688	70.49	1.454	14.187	266.89	404.82	137.93	1.2170	1.6190
71	2.076	0.689	68.61	1.451	14.575	267.92	405.47	137.55	1.2200	1.6197
72	2.135	0.690	66.79	1.448	14.972	268.93	406.11	137.18	1.2230	1.6204
73	2.196	0.692	65.03	1.446	15.377	269.96	406.76	136.80	1.2259	1.6211
74	2.258	0.693	63.33	1.443	15.790	270.98	407.41	136.43	1.2288	1.6219
75	2.322	0.694	61.68	1.440	16.212	272.00	408.05	136.05	1.2318	1.6226
76	2.386	0.696	60.09	1.438	16.643	273.04	408.70	135.66	1.2347	1.6233
77	2.452	0.697	58.54	1.435	17.082	274.07	409.35	135.28	1.2377	1.6240
78	2.520	0.698	57.04	1.432	17.531	275.10	409.99	134.89	1.2406	1.6248
79	2.589	0.699	55.59	1.430	17.989	276.13	410.64	134.51	1.2435	1.6255
80	2.659	0.701	54.18	1.427	18.456	277.16	411.28	134.12	1.2464	1.6262
81	2.731	0.702	52.82	1.424	18.932	278.20	411.92	133.72	1.2494	1.6269
82	2.804	0.703	51.50	1.422	19.418	279.24	412.57	133.33	1.2522	1.6277
83	2.879	0.705	50.22	1.419	19.914	280.28	413.21	132.93	1.2552	1.6284
84	2.955	0.706	48.97	1.416	20.419	281.31	413.85	132.54	1.2580	1.6292
85	3.032	0.707	47.77	1.413	20.935	282.35	414.49	132.14	1.2609	1.6299
86	3.112	0.709	46.60	1.411	21.460	283.40	415.13	131.73	1.2639	1.6306
87	3.192	0.710	45.46	1.408	21.996	284.44	415.77	131.33	1.2667	1.6314
88	3.275	0.712	44.36	1.405	22.542	285.48	416.41	130.93	1.2696	1.6321
89	3.358	0.713	43.29	1.402	23.099	286.53	417.05	130.52	1.2725	1.6329
90	3.444	0.714	42.25	1.400	23.667	287.58	417.69	130.11	1.2753	1.6336
91	3.531	0.716	41.25	1.397	24.245	288.62	418.32	129.70	1.2782	1.6344
92	3.620	0.717	40.27	1.394	24.835	289.68	418.96	129.28	1.2811	1.6351
93	3.710	0.719	39.31	1.391	25.436	290.70	419.60	128.87	1.2839	1.6359
94	3.802	0.720	38.39	1.388	26.048	291.78	420.23	128.45	1.2868	1.6367
95	3.896	0.722	37.49	1.386	26.672	292.84	420.87	128.03	1.2896	1.6374
96	3.991	0.723	36.62	1.383	27.307	293.89	421.50	127.61	1.2925	1.6382
97	4.088	0.725	35.77	1.380	27.955	294.95	422.13	127.18	1.2953	1.6389
98	4.187	0.726	34.95	1.377	28.614	296.00	422.76	126.76	1.2982	1.6397
99	4.288	0.728	34.15	1.374	29.286	297.07	423.40	126.33	1.3010	1.6405
100	4.390	0.729	33.37	1.371	29.971	298.13	424.03	125.90	1.3038	1.6412
101	4.495	0.731	32.61	1.368	30.668	299.19	424.66	125.47	1.3066	1.6420
102	4.601	0.732	31.87	1.365	31.378	300.26	425.29	125.03	1.3095	1.6428
103	4.709	0.734	31.15	1.362	32.101	301.32	425.91	124.59	1.3123	1.6435
104	4.819	0.736	30.45	1.359	32.837	302.38	426.54	124.16	1.3151	1.6443
105	4.930	0.737	29.77	1.356	33.587	303.46	427.17	123.71	1.3179	1.6451
106	5.044	0.739	29.11	1.353	34.351	304.52	427.79	123.27	1.3207	1.6458
107	5.160	0.740	28.47	1.351	35.128	305.59	428.42	122.83	1.3235	1.6466
108	5.277	0.742	27.84	1.348	35.920	306.66	429.04	122.38	1.3263	1.6474
109	5.397	0.744	27.23	1.344	36.726	307.74	429.67	121.93	1.3291	1.6481
110	5.518	0.745	26.63	1.341	37.546	308.82	430.29	121.47	1.3319	1.6489
111	5.641	0.747	26.05	1.338	38.382	309.89	430.91	121.02	1.3346	1.6497
112	5.767	0.749	25.49	1.335	39.232	310.97	431.53	120.56	1.3374	1.6505
113	5.895	0.751	24.94	1.332	40.098	312.05	432.15	120.10	1.3402	1.6512
114	6.024	0.752	24.40	1.329	40.980	313.13	432.77	119.64	1.3430	1.6520

Table 3-16 Properties of Saturated "Freon 113" — Trichlorotrifluoroethane (C₂Cl₃F₃) (continued)

Tempera-ture	Pressure	Specific volume		Density		Specific enthalpy		Heat of vaporization	Specific entropy	
		Liquid	Vapor	Liquid	Vapor	Liquid	Vapor		Liquid	Vapor
t	p	v'	v''	ρ'	ρ''	h'	h''	r	s'	s''
°C	bar	L/kg	L/kg	kg/L	kg/m³	kJ/kg	kJ/kg	kJ/kg	kJ/(kg K)	kJ/(kg K)
115	6.156	0.754	23.88	1.326	41.877	314.20	433.38	119.18	1.3457	1.6528
116	6.290	0.756	23.37	1.323	42.790	315.29	434.00	118.71	1.3485	1.6535
117	6.426	0.758	22.87	1.320	43.720	316.37	434.61	118.24	1.3512	1.6543
118	6.564	0.759	22.39	1.317	44.667	317.46	435.23	117.77	1.3540	1.6551
119	6.704	0.761	21.92	1.314	45.631	318.55	435.84	117.29	1.3567	1.6559
120	6.847	0.763	21.45	1.310	46.611	319.64	436.45	116.81	1.3595	1.6566
121	6.991	0.765	21.00	1.307	47.610	320.73	437.06	116.33	1.3622	1.6574
122	7.138	0.767	20.57	1.304	48.626	321.82	437.67	115.85	1.3650	1.6582
123	7.288	0.769	20.14	1.301	49.661	322.92	438.28	115.36	1.3677	1.6589
124	7.439	0.771	19.72	1.297	50.714	324.00	438.88	114.88	1.3704	1.6597
125	7.593	0.773	19.31	1.294	51.786	325.11	439.49	114.38	1.3732	1.6605
126	7.749	0.775	18.91	1.291	52.878	326.20	440.09	113.89	1.3759	1.6612
127	7.908	0.777	18.52	1.288	53.989	327.30	440.69	113.39	1.3786	1.6620
128	8.068	0.779	18.14	1.284	55.120	328.40	441.29	112.89	1.3813	1.6628
129	8.232	0.781	17.77	1.281	56.271	329.51	441.89	112.38	1.3841	1.6635
130	8.397	0.783	17.41	1.278	57.444	330.62	442.49	111.87	1.3868	1.6643
131	8.566	0.785	17.05	1.274	58.637	331.73	443.09	111.36	1.3895	1.6650
132	8.736	0.787	16.71	1.271	59.853	332.83	443.68	110.85	1.3922	1.6658
133	8.909	0.789	16.37	1.267	61.090	333.94	444.27	110.33	1.3949	1.6665
134	9.085	0.791	16.04	1.264	62.350	335.05	444.86	109.81	1.3976	1.6673
135	9.263	0.793	15.72	1.260	63.633	336.17	445.45	109.28	1.4003	1.6681
136	9.444	0.796	15.40	1.257	64.940	337.29	446.04	108.75	1.4030	1.6688
137	9.627	0.798	15.09	1.253	66.270	338.42	446.63	108.21	1.4057	1.6695
138	9.813	0.800	14.79	1.250	67.626	339.53	447.21	107.68	1.4084	1.6703
139	10.002	0.802	14.49	1.246	69.006	340.66	447.79	107.13	1.4111	1.6710
140	10.193	0.805	14.20	1.243	70.412	341.78	448.37	106.59	1.4138	1.6718
141	10.387	0.807	13.92	1.239	71.815	342.92	448.95	106.03	1.4165	1.6725
142	10.583	0.809	13.64	1.236	73.304	344.04	449.52	105.48	1.4191	1.6732
143	10.783	0.812	13.37	1.232	74.791	345.17	450.09	104.92	1.4218	1.6740
144	10.985	0.814	13.11	1.228	76.306	346.31	450.66	104.35	1.4215	1.6747
145	11.190	0.817	12.85	1.224	77.850	347.15	451.23	103.78	1.4272	1.6754
146	11.398	0.819	12.59	1.221	79.421	348.59	451.79	103.20	1.4299	1.6761
147	11.608	0.822	12.34	1.217	81.028	349.73	452.35	102.62	1.4326	1.6768
148	11.822	0.824	12.10	1.213	82.663	350.88	452.91	102.03	1.4353	1.6776
149	12.038	0.827	11.86	1.209	84.331	352.03	453.47	101.44	1.4379	1.6783
150	12.257	0.830	11.62	1.205	86.031	353.18	454.02	100.84	1.4406	1.6790
151	12.840	0.832	11.39	1.202	87.765	354.34	454.57	100.23	1.4433	1.6796
152	12.705	0.835	11.17	1.198	89.534	355.50	455.12	99.62	1.4460	1.6803
153	12.933	0.838	10.95	1.194	91.338	356.66	455.66	99.00	1.4487	1.6810
154	13.164	0.841	10.73	1.190	93.179	357.82	456.20	98.38	1.4514	1.6817
155	13.399	0.843	10.52	1.186	95.058	358.98	456.73	97.75	1.4540	1.6824
156	13.636	0.846	10.31	1.181	96.976	360.16	457.27	97.11	1.4567	1.6830
157	13.877	0.849	10.11	1.177	98.933	361.33	457.79	96.46	1.4594	1.6837
158	14.121	0.852	9.91	1.173	100.932	362.51	458.32	95.81	1.4621	1.6843
159	14.368	0.855	9.71	1.169	102.974	363.69	458.83	95.14	1.4648	1.6850
160	14.618	0.859	9.52	1.165	105.059	364.88	459.35	94.47	1.4675	1.6856
161	14.872	0.862	9.33	1.161	107.190	366.07	459.86	93.79	1.4702	1.6862
162	15.128	0.865	9.14	1.156	109.368	367.25	460.36	93.11	1.4728	1.6868
163	15.389	0.868	8.96	1.152	111.595	368.45	460.86	92.41	1.4755	1.6874
164	15.652	0.872	8.78	1.147	113.871	369.65	461.35	91.70	1.4782	1.6880

Table 3-16 Properties of Saturated "Freon 113" — Trichlorotrifluoroethane (C$_2$Cl$_3$F$_3$) *(continued)*

Tempera-ture	Pressure	Specific volume		Density		Specific enthalpy		Heat of vaporization	Specific entropy	
		Liquid	Vapor	Liquid	Vapor	Liquid	Vapor		Liquid	Vapor
t	p	v'	v''	ρ'	ρ''	h'	h''	r	s'	s''
°C	bar	L/kg	L/kg	kg/L	kg/m³	kJ/kg	kJ/kg	kJ/kg	kJ/(kg K)	kJ/(kg K)
165	15.919	0.875	8.61	1.143	116.200	370.85	461.83	90.98	1.4809	1.6886
166	16.189	0.878	8.43	1.138	118.582	372.06	462.31	90.25	1.4836	1.6892
167	16.463	0.882	8.26	1.134	121.020	373.27	462.79	89.52	1.4863	1.6897
168	16.740	0.886	8.10	1.129	123.516	374.48	463.25	88.77	1.4890	1.6903
169	17.021	0.889	7.93	1.125	126.073	375.71	463.71	88.00	1.4918	1.6908
170	17.306	0.893	7.77	1.120	128.692	376.93	464.16	87.23	1.4945	1.6913
171	17.594	0.897	7.61	1.115	131.376	378.17	464.61	86.44	1.4972	1.6918
172	17.885	0.901	7.46	1.110	134.128	379.39	465.04	85.65	1.4999	1.6923
173	18.181	0.905	7.30	1.105	136.950	380.64	465.47	84.83	1.5026	1.6928
174	18.480	0.909	7.15	1.100	139.846	381.88	465.89	84.01	1.5053	1.6932
175	18.783	0.913	7.00	1.095	142.820	383.13	466.29	83.16	1.5081	1.6936
176	19.090	0.917	6.86	1.090	145.873	384.38	466.69	82.31	1.5108	1.6941
177	19.400	0.922	6.71	1.085	149.011	385.64	467.07	81.43	1.5135	1.6944
178	19.715	0.926	6.57	1.080	152.238	386.91	467.45	80.54	1.5163	1.6948
179	20.033	0.931	6.43	1.074	155.556	388.18	467.81	79.63	1.5190	1.6951
180	20.355	0.936	6.29	1.069	158.973	389.45	468.15	78.70	1.5218	1.6955
181	20.682	0.941	6.15	1.063	162.491	390.73	468.49	77.76	1.5245	1.6957
182	21.012	0.946	6.02	1.058	166.118	392.01	468.80	76.79	1.5273	1.6960
183	21.347	0.951	5.89	1.052	169.858	393.31	469.11	75.80	1.5300	1.6962
184	21.685	0.956	5.76	1.046	173.719	394.60	469.39	74.79	1.5328	1.6964
185	22.028	0.962	5.63	1.040	177.706	395.90	469.66	73.76	1.5356	1.6966
186	22.376	0.967	5.50	1.034	181.829	397.21	469.91	72.70	1.5383	1.6967
187	22.727	0.973	5.37	1.028	186.095	398.52	470.13	71.61	1.5411	1.6968
188	23.083	0.979	5.25	1.021	190.513	399.84	470.34	70.50	1.5439	1.6968
189	23.443	0.985	5.13	1.015	195.094	401.16	470.52	69.36	1.5467	1.6968
190	23.808	0.992	5.00	1.008	199.849	402.49	470.67	68.18	1.5495	1.6967
191	24.177	0.999	4.88	1.001	204.791	403.81	470.79	66.98	1.5523	1.6966
192	24.551	1.006	4.76	0.994	209.932	405.15	470.89	65.74	1.5551	1.6964
193	24.929	1.013	4.64	0.987	215.289	406.49	470.95	64.46	1.5579	1.6962
194	25.313	1.021	4.53	0.980	220.880	407.84	470.98	63.14	1.5607	1.6958
195	25.700	1.028	4.41	0.972	226.722	409.19	470.97	61.78	1.5635	1.6955
196	26.093	1.037	4.29	0.964	232.840	410.54	470.91	60.37	1.5663	1.6950
197	26.490	1.046	4.18	0.956	239.257	411.89	470.81	58.92	1.5691	1.6944
198	26.893	1.055	4.06	0.948	246.004	413.25	470.66	57.41	1.5719	1.6937
199	27.300	1.065	3.95	0.939	253.112	414.61	470.45	55.84	1.5746	1.6929
200	27.712	1.075	3.84	0.930	260.621	415.96	470.17	54.21	1.5774	1.6920
201	28.130	1.086	3.72	0.921	268.577	417.32	469.83	52.51	1.5802	1.6909
202	28.552	1.098	3.61	0.911	277.031	418.67	469.41	50.74	1.5829	1.6897
203	28.980	1.111	3.50	0.900	286.047	420.01	468.89	48.88	1.5857	1.6883
204	29.413	1.124	3.38	0.889	295.699	421.35	468.28	46.93	1.5884	1.6867
205	29.852	1.139	3.27	0.878	306.075	422.68	467.56	44.88	1.5910	1.6849
206	30.296	1.156	3.15	0.865	317.277	423.99	466.70	42.71	1.5937	1.6828
207	30.745	1.174	3.04	0.852	329.417	425.29	465.70	40.41	1.5963	1.6805
208	31.200	1.195	2.92	0.837	342.597	426.57	464.54	37.97	1.5988	1.6778
209	31.661	1.218	2.80	0.821	356.815	427.83	463.22	35.39	1.6013	1.6747
210	32.127	1.246	2.69	0.802	371.635	429.07	461.81	32.74	1.6038	1.6716
211	32.599	1.280	2.60	0.781	385.220	430.32	460.57	30.25	1.6063	1.6687
212	33.077	1.325	2.54	0.755	394.382	431.73	459.96	28.23	1.6090	1.6672
213	33.561	1.392	2.51	0.718	399.100	433.63	459.98	26.35	1.6128	1.6670
214	34.051	1.567	2.49	0.638	401.602	438.13	460.30	22.17	1.6219	1.6674
214.10	34.100	1.735	1.74	0.576	576.369	440.04	440.04	0.00	1.6258	1.6258

Table 3-17 Properties of Saturated "Freon 114" — Dichlorotetrafluoroethane ($C_2Cl_2F_4$)

Temperature	Pressure	Specific volume		Density		Specific enthalpy		Heat of vaporization	Specific entropy	
		Liquid	Vapor	Liquid	Vapor	Liquid	Vapor		Liquid	Vapor
t	p	v'	v''	ρ'	ρ''	h'	h''	r	s'	s''
°C	bar	L/kg	L/kg	kg/L	kg/m³	kJ/kg	kJ/kg	kJ/kg	kJ/(kg K)	kJ/(kg K)
−50	0.071	0.596	1516.17	1.678	0.660	153.53	306.38	152.85	0.8128	1.4977
−49	0.076	0.597	1429.40	1.675	0.700	154.39	306.99	152.60	0.8166	1.4974
−48	0.081	0.598	1348.44	1.672	0.742	155.26	307.60	152.34	0.8205	1.4971
−47	0.086	0.599	1272.83	1.670	0.786	156.13	308.22	152.09	0.8243	1.4968
−46	0.091	0.600	1202.17	1.667	0.832	157.00	308.83	151.83	0.8282	1.4966
−45	0.097	0.601	1136.11	1.664	0.880	157.87	309.45	151.58	0.8320	1.4964
−44	0.103	0.602	1074.31	1.662	0.931	158.74	310.06	151.32	0.8358	1.4962
−43	0.109	0.603	1016.44	1.659	0.984	159.62	310.68	151.06	0.8396	1.4960
−42	0.116	0.604	962.23	1.656	1.039	160.51	311.30	150.79	0.8435	1.4959
−41	0.123	0.605	911.42	1.654	1.097	161.39	311.92	150.53	0.8473	1.4957
−40	0.130	0.606	863.76	1.651	1.158	162.28	312.55	150.27	0.8511	1.4956
−39	0.138	0.607	819.04	1.648	1.221	163.17	313.17	150.00	0.8549	1.4955
−38	0.146	0.608	777.04	1.646	1.287	164.06	313.79	149.73	0.8587	1.4955
−37	0.154	0.609	737.58	1.643	1.356	164.96	314.42	149.46	0.8625	1.4954
−36	0.163	0.610	700.49	1.640	1.428	165.85	315.04	149.19	0.8663	1.4954
−35	0.172	0.611	665.60	1.637	1.502	166.75	315.67	148.92	0.8701	1.4954
−34	0.182	0.612	632.76	1.635	1.580	167.66	316.30	148.64	0.8739	1.4954
−33	0.192	0.613	601.84	1.632	1.662	168.57	316.93	148.36	0.8777	1.4955
−32	0.202	0.614	572.71	1.629	1.746	169.48	317.56	148.08	0.8814	1.4955
−31	0.213	0.615	545.25	1.626	1.834	170.39	318.19	147.80	0.8852	1.4956
−30	0.225	0.616	519.35	1.624	1.925	171.30	318.83	147.52	0.8890	1.4957
−29	0.237	0.617	494.92	1.621	2.021	172.21	319.45	147.24	0.8927	1.4958
−28	0.249	0.618	471.84	1.618	2.119	173.14	320.09	146.95	0.8965	1.4959
−27	0.262	0.619	450.05	1.615	2.222	174.06	320.72	146.66	0.9002	1.4961
−26	0.276	0.620	429.46	1.612	2.329	174.99	321.36	146.37	0.9040	1.4962
−25	0.290	0.621	409.98	1.610	2.439	175.91	321.99	146.08	0.9077	1.4964
−24	0.305	0.622	391.56	1.607	2.554	176.84	322.63	145.79	0.9114	1.4966
−23	0.320	0.623	374.13	1.604	2.673	177.78	323.27	145.49	0.9152	1.4968
−22	0.336	0.625	357.62	1.601	2.796	178.72	323.91	145.19	0.9189	1.4971
−21	0.352	0.626	341.99	1.598	2.924	179.66	324.55	144.89	0.9227	1.4973
−20	0.369	0.627	327.17	1.596	3.057	180.59	325.18	144.59	0.9264	1.4976
−19	0.387	0.628	313.11	1.593	3.194	181.54	322.83	144.29	0.9301	1.4978
−18	0.406	0.629	299.79	1.590	3.336	182.49	326.47	143.98	0.9338	1.4981
−17	0.425	0.630	287.14	1.587	3.483	183.44	327.11	143.67	0.9375	1.4984
−16	0.445	0.631	275.13	1.584	3.635	184.39	327.75	143.36	0.9412	1.4987
−15	0.466	0.632	263.72	1.581	3.792	185.34	328.39	143.05	0.9449	1.4991
−14	0.487	0.634	252.88	1.579	3.954	186.31	339.04	142.73	0.9486	1.4994
−13	0.509	0.635	242.58	1.576	4.122	187.26	329.68	142.42	0.9523	1.4998
−12	0.532	0.636	232.78	1.573	4.296	188.32	330.32	142.10	0.9560	1.5002
−11	0.556	0.637	223.45	1.570	4.475	189.19	330.97	141.78	0.9597	1.5005
−10	0.581	0.638	214.58	1.567	4.660	190.16	331.61	141.45	0.9634	1.5009
−9	0.606	0.639	206.13	1.564	4.851	191.13	332.26	141.13	0.9670	1.5013
−8	0.633	0.641	198.08	1.561	5.048	192.11	332.91	140.80	0.9707	1.5018
−7	0.660	0.642	190.41	1.558	5.252	193.08	333.55	140.47	0.9744	1.5022
−6	0.688	0.643	183.10	1.555	5.461	194.07	334.20	140.13	0.9781	1.5026
−5	0.718	0.644	176.13	1.552	5.678	195.05	334.85	139.80	0.9817	1.5031
−4	0.748	0.645	169.48	1.549	5.901	196.03	335.49	139.46	0.9854	1.5036
−3	0.779	0.647	163.13	1.546	6.130	197.02	336.14	139.12	0.9891	1.5040
−2	0.811	0.648	157.07	1.544	6.367	198.01	336.79	138.78	0.9927	1.5045
−1	0.845	0.649	151.28	1.541	6.610	199.01	337.44	138.43	0.9964	1.5050

Table 3-17 Properties of Saturated "Freon 114" — Dichlorotetrafluoroethane ($C_2Cl_2F_4$) (continued)

Temperature	Pressure	Specific volume		Density		Specific enthalpy		Heat of vaporization	Specific entropy	
		Liquid	Vapor	Liquid	Vapor	Liquid	Vapor		Liquid	Vapor
t	p	v'	v''	ρ'	ρ''	h'	h''	r	s'	s''
°C	bar	L/kg	L/kg	kg/L	kg/m³	kJ/kg	kJ/kg	kJ/kg	kJ/(kg K)	kJ/(kg K)
0	0.879	0.650	145.75	1.538	6.861	200.00	338.08	138.08	1.0000	1.5055
1	0.914	0.652	140.46	1.535	7.119	201.00	338.73	137.73	1.0037	1.5061
2	0.951	0.653	135.41	1.532	7.382	202.00	339.38	137.38	1.0073	1.5066
3	0.988	0.654	130.57	1.529	7.659	203.00	340.03	137.03	1.0109	1.5071
4	1.027	0.655	125.95	1.526	7.940	204.01	340.68	136.67	1.0145	1.5077
5	1.067	0.657	121.52	1.523	8.229	205.02	341.33	136.31	1.0182	1.5082
6	1.108	0.658	117.29	1.520	8.526	206.03	341.98	135.95	1.0218	1.5088
7	1.151	0.659	113.23	1.517	8.832	207.05	342.63	135.58	1.0254	1.5094
8	1.194	0.661	109.34	1.514	9.146	208.06	343.28	135.22	1.0290	1.5100
9	1.239	0.662	105.61	1.510	9.469	209.07	343.92	134.85	1.0326	1.5106
10	1.285	0.663	102.04	1.507	9.800	210.09	344.57	134.48	1.0362	1.5112
11	1.333	0.665	98.62	1.504	10.140	211.12	345.22	134.10	1.0398	1.5118
12	1.382	0.666	95.33	1.501	10.490	212.15	345.87	133.72	1.0434	1.5124
13	1.432	0.667	92.18	1.498	10.849	213.18	346.52	133.34	1.0470	1.5130
14	1.484	0.669	89.15	1.495	11.217	214.21	347.17	132.96	1.0506	1.5136
15	1.537	0.670	86.25	1.492	11.595	215.24	347.83	132.58	1.0541	1.5143
16	1.591	0.672	83.46	1.489	11.982	216.28	348.47	132.19	1.0577	1.5149
17	1.647	0.673	80.78	1.486	12.380	217.31	349.11	131.80	1.0613	1.5156
18	1.704	0.675	78.20	1.483	12.788	318.35	349.76	131.41	1.0649	1.5162
19	1.763	0.676	75.72	1.479	13.206	219.40	350.41	131.01	1.0684	1.5169
20	1.824	0.677	73.34	1.476	13.635	220.45	351.06	130.61	1.0720	1.5176
21	1.886	0.679	71.05	1.473	14.074	221.49	351.70	130.21	1.0755	1.5182
22	1.950	0.680	68.85	1.470	14.525	222.54	352.35	129.81	1.0791	1.5189
23	2.015	0.682	66.73	1.467	14.986	233.59	353.00	129.41	1.0826	1.2196
24	2.082	0.683	64.69	1.464	15.459	224.64	353.64	129.00	1.0862	1.5203
25	2.151	0.685	62.72	1.460	15.943	225.70	354.29	128.59	1.0897	1.5210
26	2.221	0.686	60.83	1.457	16.439	226.75	354.93	128.18	1.0932	1.5217
27	2.293	0.688	59.01	1.454	16.947	227.82	355.58	127.76	1.0967	1.5224
28	2.367	0.689	57.25	1.451	17.468	228.88	356.22	127.34	1.1003	1.5231
29	2.443	0.691	55.56	1.447	18.000	229.94	356.86	126.92	1.1038	1.5238
30	2.520	0.692	53.92	1.444	18.545	331.01	357.51	126.50	1.1073	1.5246
31	2.600	0.694	52.35	1.441	19.103	232.08	358.15	126.07	1.1108	1.5253
32	2.681	0.696	50.83	1.437	19.674	233.15	358.79	125.64	1.1143	1.5260
33	2.764	0.697	49.36	1.434	20.258	234.22	359.43	122.21	1.1178	1.5268
34	2.849	0.699	47.95	1.431	20.856	235.29	360.07	124.78	1.1212	1.5275
35	2.936	0.701	46.58	1.428	21.467	236.37	360.71	124.34	1.1247	1.5282
36	3.025	0.702	45.26	1.424	22.092	237.45	361.35	123.90	1.1282	1.5290
37	3.116	0.704	43.99	1.421	22.732	238.53	361.99	123.46	1.1316	1.5297
38	3.209	0.705	42.76	1.417	23.386	239.61	362.62	123.01	1.1351	1.5305
39	3.304	0.707	41.57	1.414	24.055	240.70	363.36	122.56	1.1386	1.5312
40	3.401	0.709	40.42	1.411	24.738	241.79	363.90	122.11	1.1420	1.5320
41	3.500	0.711	39.31	1.407	25.437	242.87	364.53	121.66	1.1455	1.5328
42	3.602	0.712	38.24	1.404	26.151	243.96	365.16	121.20	1.1489	1.5335
43	3.705	0.714	37.20	1.400	26.882	245.06	365.80	120.74	1.1524	1.5343
44	3.811	0.716	36.20	1.397	27.628	246.15	366.43	120.28	1.1558	1.5351
45	3.919	0.718	35.22	1.393	28.391	247.24	367.06	119.82	1.1592	1.5358
46	4.029	0.719	34.28	1.390	29.170	248.34	367.69	119.35	1.1626	1.5366
47	4.142	0.721	33.37	1.386	29.966	249.44	368.32	118.88	1.1660	1.5374
48	4.257	0.723	32.49	1.383	30.779	250.54	368.95	118.41	1.1694	1.5382
49	4.374	0.725	31.64	1.379	31.610	251.64	369.57	117.93	1.1728	1.5389

Table 3-17 Properties of Saturated "Freon 114" — Dichlorotetrafluoroethane (C$_2$Cl$_2$F$_4$) *(continued)*

Tempera-ture	Pressure	Specific volume		Density		Specific enthalpy		Heat of vaporization	Specific entropy	
		Liquid	Vapor	Liquid	Vapor	Liquid	Vapor		Liquid	Vapor
t	p	v'	v''	ρ'	ρ''	h'	h''	r	s'	s''
°C	bar	L/kg	L/kg	kg/L	kg/m^3	kJ/kg	kJ/kg	kJ/kg	kJ/(kg K)	kJ/(kg K)
50	4.494	0.727	30.81	1.376	32.459	252.75	370.20	117.45	1.1762	1.5397
51	4.616	0.729	30.01	1.372	33.327	253.85	370.82	116.97	1.1796	1.5405
52	4.740	0.731	29.23	1.369	34.212	254.96	371.44	116.48	1.1830	1.5413
53	4.867	0.733	28.48	1.365	35.117	256.07	372.06	115.99	1.1864	1.5421
54	4.997	0.735	27.75	1.361	36.041	257.18	373.68	115.50	1.1898	1.5428
55	5.129	0.736	27.04	1.358	36.984	258.29	373.30	115.01	1.1931	1.5436
56	5.263	0.738	26.35	1.354	37.948	259.41	373.92	114.51	1.1965	1.5444
57	5.400	0.740	25.69	1.350	38.932	260.53	374.54	114.01	1.1999	1.5452
58	5.540	0.743	25.04	1.347	39.937	261.64	375.15	113.51	1.2032	1.5460
59	5.682	0.745	24.41	1.343	40.962	262.76	375.76	113.00	1.2065	1.5468
60	5.828	0.747	23.80	1.339	42.010	263.88	376.37	112.49	1.2099	1.5476
61	5.975	0.749	23.21	1.336	43.079	265.01	376.98	111.97	1.2132	1.5483
62	6.126	0.751	22.64	1.332	44.171	266.13	377.59	111.46	1.2165	1.5491
63	6.279	0.753	22.08	1.328	45.286	267.26	378.19	110.93	1.2199	1.5499
64	6.435	0.755	21.54	1.324	46.425	268.39	378.80	110.41	1.2232	1.5507
65	6.594	0.757	21.01	1.320	47.587	269.52	379.40	109.88	1.2265	1.5515
66	6.756	0.760	20.50	1.317	48.773	270.65	380.00	109.35	1.2298	1.5522
67	6.921	0.762	20.01	1.313	49.985	271.79	380.60	108.81	1.2331	1.5530
68	7.089	0.764	19.52	1.309	51.222	272.92	381.19	108.27	1.2364	1.5538
69	7.259	0.766	19.05	1.305	52.485	274.06	381.79	107.73	1.2397	1.5546
70	7.433	0.769	18.60	1.301	53.774	275.20	382.38	107.18	1.2430	1.5553
71	7.610	0.771	18.15	1.297	55.090	276.34	382.97	106.63	1.2463	1.5561
72	7.790	0.773	17.72	1.293	56.435	277.48	383.56	106.08	1.2495	1.5569
73	7.973	0.776	17.30	1.289	57.807	278.62	384.14	105.52	1.2528	1.5577
74	8.159	0.778	16.89	1.285	59.209	279.77	384.72	104.95	1.2561	1.5584
75	8.348	0.781	16.49	1.281	60.640	280.92	385.30	104.38	1.2593	1.5592
76	8.540	0.783	16.10	1.277	62.101	282.07	385.88	103.81	1.2626	1.5599
77	8.736	0.786	15.72	1.272	63.594	283.23	386.46	103.23	1.2659	1.5607
78	8.935	0.788	15.36	1.268	65.119	284.38	387.03	102.65	1.2691	1.5614
79	9.137	0.791	15.00	1.264	66.676	285.54	387.60	102.06	1.2723	1.5622
80	9.343	0.794	14.65	1.260	68.266	286.69	388.16	101.47	1.2756	1.5629
81	9.552	0.796	14.31	1.256	69.891	287.86	388.73	100.87	1.2788	1.5637
82	9.765	0.799	13.98	1.251	71.551	289.02	389.29	100.27	1.2820	1.5644
83	9.981	0.802	13.65	1.247	73.247	290.18	389.84	99.66	1.2853	1.5651
84	10.200	0.805	13.34	1.243	74.980	291.35	390.40	99.05	1.2885	1.5658
85	10.423	0.808	13.03	1.238	76.750	292.52	390.95	98.43	1.2917	1.5666
86	10.650	0.810	12.73	1.234	78.560	293.70	391.50	97.80	1.2949	1.5673
87	10.880	0.813	13.44	1.229	80.410	294.87	392.04	97.17	1.2982	1.5680
88	11.114	0.816	12.15	1.225	82.302	296.05	392.58	96.53	1.3014	1.5687
89	11.352	0.819	11.87	1.220	84.235	297.23	393.11	95.88	1.3046	1.5694
90	11.594	0.823	11.60	1.216	86.213	298.42	393.65	95.23	1.3078	1.5701
91	11.839	0.836	11.33	1.211	88.235	299.60	394.17	94.57	1.3110	1.5707
92	12.088	0.829	11.07	1.206	90.304	300.79	394.70	93.91	1.3142	1.5714
93	12.341	0.832	10.82	1.202	92.420	301.99	395.22	93.23	1.3174	1.5721
94	12.598	0.835	10.57	1.197	94.586	303.18	395.73	92.55	1.3206	1.5727
95	12.859	0.839	10.33	1.192	96.802	304.38	396.24	91.86	1.3238	1.5734
96	13.124	0.842	10.09	1.187	99.071	305.59	396.75	91.16	1.3270	1.5740
97	13.393	0.846	9.86	1.182	101.395	306.79	397.25	90.46	1.3302	1.5746
98	13.666	0.849	9.64	1.178	103.774	308.00	397.74	89.74	1.3334	1.5752
99	13.943	0.853	9.42	1.173	106.211	309.22	398.23	89.01	1.3367	1.5759

Table 3-17 Properties of Saturated "Freon 114" — Dichlorotetrafluoroethane ($C_2Cl_2F_4$) (continued)

Tempera-ture	Pressure	Specific volume		Density		Specific enthalpy		Heat of vaporization	Specific entropy	
		Liquid	Vapor	Liquid	Vapor	Liquid	Vapor		Liquid	Vapor
t	p	v'	v''	ρ'	ρ''	h'	h''	r	s'	s''
°C	bar	L/kg	L/kg	kg/L	kg/m³	kJ/kg	kJ/kg	kJ/kg	kJ/(kg K)	kJ/(kg K)
100	14.225	0.857	9.20	1.167	108.709	310.44	398.72	88.28	1.3399	1.5765
101	14.510	0.860	8.99	1.162	111.269	311.67	399.20	87.53	1.3431	1.5770
102	14.800	0.864	8.78	1.157	113.893	312.89	399.67	86.78	1.3463	1.5776
103	15.095	0.868	8.58	1.152	116.585	314.13	400.14	86.01	1.3495	1.5782
104	15.394	0.872	8.38	1.147	119.347	315.36	400.59	85.23	1.3527	1.5787
105	15.697	0.876	8.18	1.141	122.180	316.61	401.05	84.44	1.3559	1.5793
106	16.005	0.880	7.99	1.136	125.090	317.86	401.49	83.63	1.3592	1.5798
107	16.317	0.885	7.81	1.130	128.078	319.11	401.93	82.82	1.3624	1.5803
108	16.634	0.889	7.62	1.125	131.148	320.37	402.36	81.99	1.3656	1.5808
109	16.956	0.894	7.45	1.119	134.304	321.64	402.78	81.14	1.3689	1.5812
110	17.282	0.898	7.27	1.113	137.550	322.92	403.20	80.28	1.3722	1.5817
111	17.614	0.903	7.10	1.108	140.889	324.20	403.60	79.40	1.3754	1.5821
112	17.950	0.908	6.93	1.102	144.327	325.49	404.00	78.51	1.3787	1.5825
113	18.291	0.913	6.76	1.096	147.868	326.79	404.39	77.60	1.3820	1.5829
114	18.637	0.918	6.60	1.090	151.518	328.09	404.76	76.67	1.3853	1.5833
115	18.988	0.923	6.44	1.083	155.282	329.41	405.13	75.72	1.3886	1.5837
116	19.344	0.928	6.28	1.077	159.167	330.73	405.48	74.75	1.3919	1.5840
117	19.705	0.934	6.13	1.071	163.179	332.06	405.82	73.76	1.3952	1.5843
118	20.072	0.940	5.98	1.064	167.326	333.40	406.15	72.75	1.3986	1.5846
119	20.444	0.946	5.83	1.057	171.616	334.75	406.46	71.71	1.4019	1.5848
120	20.821	0.952	5.68	1.050	176.058	336.12	406.76	70.64	1.4053	1.5850
121	21.204	0.958	5.54	1.043	180.663	337.50	407.05	69.55	1.4087	1.5852
122	21.593	0.965	5.39	1.036	185.441	338.89	407.32	68.43	1.4122	1.5853
123	21.986	0.972	5.25	1.029	190.404	340.30	407.57	67.27	1.4156	1.5854
124	22.386	0.979	5.11	1.022	195.567	341.72	407.80	66.08	1.4191	1.5855
125	22.791	0.986	4.98	1.014	200.945	343.16	408.02	64.86	1.4226	1.5855
126	23.203	0.994	4.84	1.006	206.556	344.62	408.21	63.59	1.4262	1.5855
127	23.620	1.002	4.71	0.998	212.420	346.08	408.37	62.29	1.4297	1.5854
128	24.043	1.011	4.58	0.989	218.560	347.57	408.51	60.94	1.4334	1.5853
129	24.472	1.020	4.44	0.981	225.002	349.10	408.63	59.53	1.4370	1.5851
130	24.908	1.029	4.31	0.972	231.778	350.63	408.71	58.08	1.4407	1.5848
131	25.349	1.039	4.19	0.962	238.925	352.20	408.76	56.56	1.4445	1.5845
132	25.797	1.050	4.06	0.953	246.484	353.80	408.77	54.97	1.4483	1.5840
133	26.252	1.061	3.93	0.943	254.510	355.42	408.74	53.32	1.4522	1.5835
134	26.713	1.073	3.80	0.932	263.064	357.08	408.65	51.57	1.4562	1.5829
135	27.180	1.086	3.67	0.921	272.227	358.79	408.52	49.73	1.4603	1.5821
136	27.655	1.100	3.54	0.909	282.097	360.53	408.32	47.79	1.4644	1.5812
137	28.136	1.115	3.42	0.896	292.803	362.33	408.04	45.71	1.4687	1.5801
138	28.624	1.132	3.28	0.883	304.516	364.20	407.68	43.48	1.4731	1.5788
139	29.119	1.151	3.15	0.868	317.471	366.14	407.21	41.07	1.4776	1.5773
140	29.622	1.173	3.01	0.852	332.005	368.16	406.59	38.43	1.4824	1.5754
141	30.131	1.198	2.87	0.835	348.633	370.30	405.80	35.50	1.4874	1.5732
142	30.648	1.228	2.72	0.814	368.205	372.61	404.76	32.15	1.4929	1.5703
143	31.172	1.266	2.55	0.790	392.321	375.13	403.33	28.20	1.4988	1.5665
144	31.704	1.318	2.35	0.759	424.731	378.05	401.22	23.17	1.5056	1.5612
145	32.244	1.405	2.07	0.712	481.999	381.87	397.10	15.23	1.5146	1.5510
145.7	32.627	1.730	1.73	0.578	578.030	390.14	390.14	0.00	1.5342	1.5342

Table 3-18   Properties of Saturated "Freon 115" — Chloropentafluoroethane (C_2ClF_5)

Temperature	Pressure	Specific volume		Density		Specific enthalpy		Heat of vaporization	Specific entropy	
		Liquid	Vapor	Liquid	Vapor	Liquid	Vapor		Liquid	Vapor
t	p	v'	v''	ρ'	ρ''	h'	h''	r	s'	s''
°C	bar	L/kg	L/kg	kg/L	kg/m³	kJ/kg	kJ/kg	kJ/kg	kJ/(kg K)	kJ/(kg K)
−60	0.346	0.617	323.97	1.620	3.087	145.05	279.68	134.63	0.7747	1.4063
−59	0.366	0.619	307.44	1.617	3.253	145.89	280.17	134.28	0.7786	1.4057
−58	0.387	0.620	291.91	1.613	3.426	146.73	280.66	133.93	0.7825	1.4050
−57	0.409	0.621	277.33	1.610	3.606	147.57	281.15	133.58	0.7864	1.4044
−56	0.432	0.622	263.61	1.607	3.793	148.42	281.64	133.22	0.7903	1.4038
−55	0.456	0.624	250.71	1.603	3.989	149.27	282.13	132.86	0.7942	1.4033
−54	0.480	0.625	238.56	1.600	4.192	150.13	282.62	132.49	0.7981	1.4027
−53	0.506	0.626	227.12	1.596	4.403	150.98	283.11	132.13	0.8020	1.4022
−52	0.533	0.628	216.34	1.593	4.622	151.84	283.60	131.76	0.8059	1.4017
−51	0.562	0.629	206.17	1.590	4.850	152.71	284.09	131.38	0.8098	1.4012
−50	0.591	0.630	196.58	1.586	5.087	153.57	284.58	131.01	0.8137	1.4008
−49	0.622	0.632	187.52	1.583	5.333	154.44	285.07	130.63	0.8176	1.4004
−48	0.653	0.633	178.97	1.579	5.588	155.31	285.56	130.25	0.8214	1.3999
−47	0.686	0.635	170.88	1.576	5.852	156.18	286.05	129.87	0.8253	1.3995
−46	0.721	0.636	163.24	1.572	6.126	157.06	286.54	129.48	0.8291	1.3992
−45	0.757	0.637	156.01	1.569	6.410	157.94	287.03	129.09	0.8330	1.3988
−44	0.794	0.639	149.16	1.565	6.704	158.82	287.52	128.70	0.8368	1.3985
−43	0.832	0.640	142.68	1.562	7.009	159.71	288.01	128.30	0.8407	1.3982
−42	0.872	0.642	136.53	1.558	7.324	160.59	288.50	127.91	0.8445	1.3979
−41	0.914	0.643	130.71	1.555	7.650	161.48	288.98	127.50	0.8483	1.3976
−40	0.957	0.645	125.19	1.551	7.988	162.37	289.47	127.10	0.8522	1.3973
−39	1.001	0.646	119.95	1.548	8.337	163.27	289.96	126.69	0.8560	1.3971
−38	1.047	0.648	114.97	1.544	8.698	164.17	290.45	126.28	0.8598	1.3968
−37	1.095	0.649	110.25	1.541	9.070	165.06	290.93	125.87	0.8636	1.3966
−36	1.145	0.651	105.76	1.537	9.455	165.96	291.42	125.46	0.8674	1.3964
−35	1.196	0.652	101.49	1.533	9.853	166.87	291.91	125.04	0.8712	1.3962
−34	1.249	0.654	97.43	1.530	10.264	167.78	292.39	124.61	0.8750	1.3961
−33	1.304	0.655	93.57	1.526	10.687	168.69	292.88	124.19	0.8788	1.3959
−32	1.360	0.657	89.89	1.522	11.124	169.60	293.36	123.76	0.8825	1.3958
−31	1.419	0.658	86.39	1.519	11.575	170.52	293.85	123.33	0.8863	1.3956
−30	1.479	0.660	83.05	1.515	12.040	171.43	294.33	122.90	0.8901	1.3955
−29	1.541	0.662	79.87	1.511	12.520	172.36	294.82	122.46	0.8938	1.3954
−28	1.606	0.663	76.84	1.508	13.014	173.28	295.30	122.02	0.8976	1.3953
−27	1.672	0.665	73.95	1.504	13.523	174.20	295.78	121.58	0.9013	1.3953
−26	1.741	0.667	71.19	1.500	14.047	175.13	296.26	121.13	0.9051	1.3952
−25	1.811	0.668	68.56	1.497	14.587	176.05	296.74	120.69	0.9088	1.3952
−24	1.884	0.670	66.04	1.493	15.142	176.99	297.22	120.23	0.9125	1.3951
−23	1.959	0.672	63.63	1.489	15.715	177.92	297.70	119.78	0.9162	1.3951
−22	2.036	0.673	61.34	1.485	16.303	178.86	298.18	119.32	0.9200	1.3951
−21	2.115	0.675	59.14	1.481	16.909	179.80	298.66	118.86	0.9237	1.3951
−20	2.197	0.677	57.04	1.478	17.532	180.74	299.14	118.40	0.9274	1.3951
−19	2.281	0.679	55.03	1.474	18.173	181.68	299.61	117.93	0.9311	1.3951
−18	2.368	0.680	53.10	1.470	18.832	182.63	300.09	117.46	0.9348	1.3951
−17	2.457	0.682	51.26	1.466	19.509	183.57	300.56	116.99	0.9384	1.3952
−16	2.549	0.684	49.49	1.462	20.205	184.53	301.04	116.51	0.9421	1.3952
−15	2.643	0.686	47.80	1.458	20.921	185.47	301.51	116.04	0.9458	1.3953
−14	2.739	0.688	46.18	1.454	21.656	186.43	301.98	115.55	0.9495	1.3954
−13	2.839	0.690	44.62	1.450	22.410	187.38	302.45	115.07	0.9531	1.3954
−12	2.941	0.691	43.13	1.446	23.186	188.34	302.92	114.58	0.9567	1.3955
−11	3.046	0.693	41.70	1.442	23.982	189.30	303.39	114.09	0.9604	1.3956

Table 3-18 Properties of Saturated "Freon 115" — Chloropentafluoroethane (C$_2$ClF$_5$) *(continued)*

Tempera-ture	Pressure	Specific volume		Density		Specific enthalpy		Heat of vaporization	Specific entropy	
		Liquid	Vapor	Liquid	Vapor	Liquid	Vapor		Liquid	Vapor
t	p	v'	v''	ρ'	ρ''	h'	h''	r	s'	s''
°C	bar	L/kg	L/kg	kg/L	kg/m^3	kJ/kg	kJ/kg	kJ/kg	kJ/(kg K)	kJ/(kg K)
−10	3.153	0.695	40.32	1.438	24.799	190.27	303.86	113.59	0.9640	1.3957
−9	3.263	0.697	39.00	1.434	25.639	191.23	304.33	113.10	0.9676	1.3958
−8	3.377	0.699	37.74	1.430	26.500	192.19	304.79	112.60	0.9713	1.3959
−7	3.493	0.701	36.52	1.426	27.384	193.17	305.26	112.09	0.9749	1.3961
−6	3.612	0.703	35.35	1.422	28.291	194.14	305.72	111.58	0.9785	1.3962
−5	3.734	0.705	34.22	1.418	29.221	195.11	306.18	111.07	0.9821	1.3963
−4	3.859	0.707	33.14	1.414	30.176	196.08	306.64	110.56	0.9857	1.3965
−3	3.987	0.709	32.10	1.410	31.155	197.06	307.10	110.04	0.9893	1.3966
−2	4.119	0.711	31.10	1.405	32.160	198.04	307.56	109.52	0.9929	1.3968
−1	5.253	0.714	30.13	1.401	33.189	199.01	308.01	109.00	0.9964	1.3970
0	4.391	0.716	29.20	1.397	34.246	200.00	308.47	108.47	1.0000	1.3971
1	4.532	0.718	28.31	1.393	35.328	200.98	308.92	107.94	1.0036	1.3973
2	4.676	0.720	27.44	1.389	36.439	201.98	309.38	107.40	1.0071	1.3975
3	4.824	0.722	26.61	1.384	37.577	202.97	309.83	106.86	1.0107	1.3977
4	4.975	0.725	25.81	1.380	38.743	203.95	310.27	106.32	1.0142	1.3979
5	5.130	0.727	25.04	1.376	39.939	204.94	310.72	105.78	1.0177	1.3981
6	5.288	0.729	24.29	1.371	41.165	205.94	311.17	105.23	1.0213	1.3982
7	5.450	0.732	23.57	1.367	42.421	206.94	311.61	104.67	1.0248	1.3984
8	5.616	0.734	22.88	1.362	43.708	207.93	312.05	104.12	1.0283	1.3987
9	5.785	0.736	22.21	1.358	45.027	208.94	312.49	103.55	1.0318	1.3989
10	5.957	0.739	21.56	1.353	46.379	209.94	312.93	102.99	1.0353	1.3991
11	6.134	0.741	20.94	1.349	47.765	210.95	313.37	102.42	1.0388	1.3993
12	6.314	0.744	20.33	1.344	49.184	211.96	313.80	101.84	1.0423	1.3995
13	6.499	0.746	19.75	1.340	50.639	212.97	314.23	101.26	1.0458	1.3997
14	6.687	0.749	19.18	1.335	52.130	213.98	314.66	100.68	1.0493	1.3999
15	6.879	0.752	18.64	1.330	53.657	215.00	315.09	100.09	1.0528	1.4002
16	7.075	0.754	18.11	1.326	55.222	216.01	315.51	99.50	1.0563	1.4004
17	7.276	0.757	17.60	1.321	56.826	217.03	315.93	98.90	1.0597	1.4006
18	7.480	0.760	17.10	1.316	58.470	218.05	316.35	98.30	1.0632	1.4008
19	7.689	0.763	16.62	1.311	60.155	219.08	316.77	97.69	1.0667	1.4011
20	7.902	0.765	16.16	1.307	61.881	220.11	317.18	97.07	1.0701	1.4013
21	8.119	0.768	15.71	1.302	63.650	221.14	317.60	96.46	1.0736	1.4015
22	8.341	0.771	15.28	1.297	65.464	222.17	318.00	95.83	1.0770	1.4017
23	8.567	0.774	14.85	1.292	67.323	223.21	318.41	95.20	1.0805	1.4019
24	8.797	0.777	14.44	1.287	69.229	224.25	318.81	94.56	1.0839	1.4022
25	9.033	0.780	14.05	1.382	71.183	225.29	319.21	93.92	1.0873	1.4024
26	9.272	0.783	13.66	1.277	73.186	226.34	319.61	93.27	1.0908	1.4026
27	9.517	0.786	13.29	1.272	75.240	227.39	320.00	92.61	1.0942	1.4028
28	9.766	0.790	12.93	1.266	77.347	228.44	320.39	91.95	1.0977	1.4030
29	10.020	0.793	12.58	1.261	79.509	229.49	320.77	91.28	1.1011	1.4032
30	10.279	0.796	12.24	1.256	81.726	230.55	321.15	90.60	1.1045	1.4034
31	10.542	0.800	11.90	1.251	84.001	231.62	321.53	89.91	1.1080	1.4036
32	10.811	0.803	11.58	1.245	86.335	232.68	321.90	89.22	1.1114	1.4038
33	11.085	0.807	11.27	1.240	88.732	233.76	322.27	88.51	1.1148	1.4040
34	11.364	0.810	10.97	1.234	91.192	234.83	322.63	87.80	1.1183	1.4041
35	11.648	0.814	10.67	1.229	93.719	235.91	322.99	87.08	1.1217	1.4043
36	11.937	0.818	10.38	1.223	96.314	236.99	323.34	86.35	1.1251	1.4045
37	12.232	0.821	10.10	1.217	98.980	238.09	323.69	85.60	1.1286	1.4046
38	12.532	0.825	9.83	1.212	101.720	239.19	324.04	84.85	1.1320	1.4047
39	12.838	0.829	9.57	1.206	104.537	240.28	324.37	84.09	1.1355	1.4049

Table 3-18 Properties of Saturated "Freon 115" — Chloropentafluoroethane (C₂ClF₅) (continued)

Tempera-ture	Pressure	Specific volume		Density		Specific enthalpy		Heat of vaporization	Specific entropy	
		Liquid	Vapor	Liquid	Vapor	Liquid	Vapor		Liquid	Vapor
t	p	v'	v''	ρ'	ρ''	h'	h''	r	s'	s''
°C	bar	L/kg	L/kg	kg/L	kg/m³	kJ/kg	kJ/kg	kJ/kg	kJ/(kg K)	kJ/(kg K)
40	13.149	0.833	9.31	1.200	107.434	241.39	324.70	83.31	1.1389	1.4050
41	13.466	0.838	9.06	1.194	110.414	242.51	325.03	82.52	1.1424	1.4051
42	13.788	0.842	8.81	1.188	113.480	243.63	325.35	81.72	1.1459	1.4052
43	14.116	0.846	8.57	1.182	116.637	244.75	325.66	80.91	1.1493	1.4053
44	14.451	0.851	8.34	1.175	119.888	245.88	325.96	80.08	1.1528	1.4053
45	14.791	0.855	8.11	1.169	123.238	247.02	326.26	79.24	1.1563	1.4054
46	15.137	0.860	7.89	1.163	126.692	248.17	326.55	78.38	1.1598	1.4054
47	15.489	0.865	7.68	1.156	130.253	249.33	326.83	77.50	1.1634	1.4055
48	15.848	0.870	7.47	1.149	133.929	250.49	327.10	76.61	1.1669	1.4054
49	16.212	0.875	7.26	1.143	137.724	251.66	327.36	75.70	1.1704	1.4054
50	16.584	0.880	7.06	1.136	141.646	252.84	327.61	74.77	1.1740	1.4054
51	16.961	0.886	6.86	1.129	145.700	254.03	327.85	73.82	1.1776	1.4053
52	17.346	0.892	6.67	1.122	149.896	255.24	328.08	72.84	1.1812	1.4052
53	17.737	0.897	6.48	1.114	154.241	256.45	328.30	71.85	1.1848	1.4051
54	18.134	0.903	6.30	1.107	158.744	257.68	328.50	70.82	1.1885	1.4050
55	18.539	0.910	6.12	1.099	163.415	258.92	328.69	69.77	1.1921	1.4048
56	18.951	0.916	5.94	1.092	168.266	260.17	328.87	68.70	1.1958	1.4046
57	19.370	0.923	5.77	1.084	173.310	261.44	329.03	67.59	1.1996	1.4043
58	19.796	0.930	5.60	1.076	178.560	262.73	329.18	66.45	1.2033	1.4040
59	20.229	0.937	5.43	1.067	184.031	264.04	329.31	65.27	1.2071	1.4037
60	20.670	0.945	5.27	1.059	189.743	265.35	329.41	64.06	1.2110	1.4033
61	21.118	0.952	5.11	1.050	195.714	266.69	329.50	62.81	1.2149	1.4028
62	21.574	0.961	4.95	1.041	201.968	268.05	329.56	61.51	1.2188	1.4024
63	22.038	0.969	4.80	1.031	208.531	269.44	329.60	60.16	1.2228	1.4018
64	22.510	0.979	4.64	1.022	215.434	270.86	329.62	58.76	1.2269	1.4012
65	22.990	0.988	4.49	1.012	222.713	272.30	329.60	57.30	1.2310	1.4005
66	23.478	0.999	4.34	1.001	230.410	273.76	329.54	55.78	1.2352	1.3997
67	23.974	1.010	4.19	0.990	238.576	275.27	329.45	54.18	1.2395	1.3988
68	24.479	1.021	4.04	0.979	247.272	276.81	329.32	52.51	1.2438	1.3978
69	24.993	1.034	3.90	0.967	256.574	278.40	329.14	50.74	1.2483	1.3967
70	25.515	1.048	3.75	0.955	266.576	280.03	328.90	48.87	1.2530	1.3954
71	26.046	1.063	3.60	0.941	277.398	281.73	328.60	46.87	1.2577	1.3939
72	26.587	1.079	3.46	0.927	289.198	283.48	328.32	44.74	1.2626	1.3923
73	27.136	1.097	3.31	0.911	302.190	285.32	327.75	42.43	1.2678	1.3904
74	27.695	1.118	3.16	0.894	316.673	287.24	327.16	39.92	1.2731	1.3882
75	28.264	1.142	3.00	0.876	333.089	289.28	326.42	37.14	1.2788	1.3855
76	28.842	1.170	2.84	0.854	352.141	291.48	325.48	34.00	1.2850	1.3824
77	29.431	1.205	2.67	0.830	375.058	293.91	324.26	30.35	1.2917	1.3784
78	30.029	1.252	2.47	0.799	404.376	296.68	322.55	25.87	1.2994	1.3731
79	30.638	1.324	2.24	0.755	447.259	300.18	319.88	19.70	1.3091	1.3651
80.0	31.257	1.691	1.69	0.591	591.366	310.48	310.48	0.00	1.3381	1.3381

Table 3-19 Properties of Saturated "Freon 500" — Azeotropic mixture: mass fraction of Freon 12 (CCl_2F_2) 73.8% and R 152a 26.2%

Temperature t °C	Pressure p bar	Specific volume		Density		Specific enthalpy		Heat of vaporization	Specific entropy	
		Liquid v' L/kg	Vapor v'' L/kg	Liquid ρ' kg/L	Vapor ρ'' kg/m³	Liquid h' kJ/kg	Vapor h'' kJ/kg	r kJ/kg	Liquid s' kJ/(kg K)	Vapor s'' kJ/(kg K)
−40	0.756	0.741	248.94	1.350	4.017	157.54	362.19	204.65	0.8329	1.7107
−39	0.792	0.742	238.35	1.347	4.195	158.58	362.72	204.14	0.8373	1.7092
−38	0.829	0.744	228.31	1.345	4.380	159.62	363.25	203.63	0.8417	1.7077
−37	0.868	0.745	218.78	1.342	4.571	160.65	363.77	203.12	0.8461	1.7063
−36	0.908	0.747	209.73	1.339	4.768	161.70	364.30	202.60	0.8505	1.7049
−35	0.950	0.748	201.13	1.337	4.972	162.74	364.82	202.08	0.8549	1.7035
−34	0.993	0.750	192.96	1.334	5.182	163.78	365.34	201.56	0.8593	1.7021
−33	1.038	0.751	185.19	1.331	5.400	164.82	365.86	201.04	0.8636	1.7008
−32	1.084	0.753	177.80	1.328	5.624	165.87	366.39	200.52	0.8679	1.6994
−31	1.132	0.754	170.76	1.326	5.856	166.92	366.91	199.99	0.8722	1.6982
−30	1.181	0.756	164.06	1.323	6.095	167.95	367.42	199.47	0.8765	1.6969
−29	1.232	0.757	157.68	1.320	6.342	169.00	367.94	198.94	0.8808	1.6956
−28	1.285	0.759	151.60	1.317	6.596	170.06	368.46	198.40	0.8851	1.6944
−27	1.339	0.761	145.81	1.315	6.858	171.11	368.98	197.87	0.8893	1.6932
−26	1.396	0.762	140.28	1.312	7.129	172.16	369.49	197.33	0.8936	1.6920
−25	1.454	0.764	135.01	1.309	7.407	173.21	370.00	196.79	0.8978	1.6909
−24	1.514	0.765	129.97	1.306	7.694	174.27	370.52	196.25	0.9021	1.6898
−23	1.576	0.767	125.17	1.304	7.989	175.32	371.03	195.71	0.9062	1.6886
−22	1.640	0.769	120.58	1.301	8.294	176.38	371.54	195.16	0.9105	1.6875
−21	1.706	0.770	116.19	1.298	8.607	177.43	372.05	194.62	0.9146	1.6865
−20	1.773	0.772	112.00	1.295	8.929	178.49	372.55	194.06	0.9188	1.6854
−19	1.843	0.774	107.99	1.292	9.261	179.55	373.06	193.51	0.9230	1.6844
−18	1.915	0.776	104.15	1.289	9.602	180.62	373.57	192.95	0.9271	1.6834
−17	1.990	0.777	100.48	1.287	9.952	181.68	374.07	192.39	0.9313	1.6824
−16	2.066	0.779	96.96	1.284	10.313	182.74	374.57	191.83	0.9354	1.6814
−15	2.145	0.781	93.60	1.281	10.684	183.80	375.07	191.27	0.9395	1.6804
−14	2.226	0.782	90.38	1.278	11.065	184.87	375.57	190.70	0.9436	1.6795
−13	2.309	0.784	87.29	1.275	11.456	185.94	376.07	190.13	0.9477	1.6785
−12	2.395	0.786	84.33	1.272	11.859	187.02	376.57	189.55	0.9518	1.6776
−11	2.483	0.788	81.49	1.269	12.272	188.08	377.06	188.98	0.9558	1.6767
−10	2.574	0.790	78.76	1.266	12.697	189.17	377.56	188.39	0.9599	1.6758
−9	2.667	0.791	76.15	1.263	13.132	190.24	378.05	187.81	0.9639	1.6750
−8	2.762	0.793	73.64	1.261	13.580	191.32	378.54	187.22	0.9680	1.6741
−7	2.860	0.795	71.23	1.258	14.039	192.40	379.03	186.63	0.9720	1.6733
−6	2.961	0.797	68.92	1.255	14.510	193.47	379.51	186.04	0.9760	1.6724
−5	3.065	0.799	66.69	1.252	14.994	194.56	380.00	185.44	0.9801	1.6716
−4	3.171	0.801	64.56	1.249	15.490	195.64	380.48	184.84	0.9841	1.6708
−3	3.280	0.803	62.50	1.246	15.999	196.73	380.97	184.24	0.9881	1.6701
−2	3.392	0.805	60.53	1.243	16.521	197.82	381.45	183.63	0.9920	1.6693
−1	3.507	0.807	58.63	1.240	17.057	198.91	381.93	183.02	0.9960	1.6685
0	3.625	0.809	56.80	1.237	17.605	200.00	382.40	182.40	1.0000	1.6678
1	3.746	0.811	55.04	1.234	18.168	201.10	382.88	181.78	1.0040	1.6671
2	3.870	0.813	53.35	1.230	18.745	202.19	383.35	181.16	1.0079	1.6663
3	3.996	0.815	51.72	1.227	19.336	203.29	383.82	180.53	1.0119	1.6656
4	4.126	0.817	50.14	1.224	19.942	204.39	384.29	179.90	1.0158	1.6649
5	4.260	0.819	48.63	1.221	20.563	205.50	384.76	179.26	1.0198	1.6642
6	4.396	0.821	47.17	1.218	21.199	206.60	385.22	178.62	1.0237	1.6636
7	4.536	0.823	45.76	1.215	21.851	207.70	385.68	177.98	1.0276	1.6629
8	4.679	0.825	44.41	1.212	22.518	208.82	386.14	177.32	1.0315	1.6622
9	4.825	0.827	43.10	1.209	23.202	209.93	386.60	176.67	1.0354	1.6616

Table 3-19 Properties of Saturated "Freon 500" — Azeotropic mixture: mass fraction of Freon 12 (CCl$_2$F$_2$) 73.8% and R 152a 26.2%

(continued)

Tempera-ture	Pressure	Specific volume		Density		Specific enthalpy		Heat of vaporization	Specific entropy	
		Liquid	Vapor	Liquid	Vapor	Liquid	Vapor		Liquid	Vapor
t	p	v'	v''	ρ'	ρ''	h'	h''	r	s'	s''
°C	bar	L/kg	L/kg	kg/L	kg/m^3	kJ/kg	kJ/kg	kJ/kg	kJ/(kg K)	kJ/(kg K)
10	4.975	0.830	41.84	1.205	23.902	211.05	387.06	176.01	1.0393	1.6610
11	5.128	0.832	40.62	1.202	24.619	212.16	387.51	175.35	1.0432	1.6603
12	5.285	0.834	39.44	1.199	25.354	213.28	387.96	174.68	1.0471	1.6597
13	5.446	0.836	38.31	1.196	26.105	214.41	388.41	174.00	1.0510	1.6591
14	5.610	0.838	37.21	1.193	26.875	215.54	388.86	173.32	1.0549	1.6585
15	5.778	0.841	36.15	1.189	27.663	216.66	389.30	172.64	1.0588	1.6579
16	5.949	0.843	35.13	1.186	28.469	217.80	389.75	171.95	1.0626	1.6573
17	6.125	0.845	34.14	1.183	29.295	218.93	390.18	171.25	1.0665	1.6567
18	6.304	0.848	33.18	1.180	30.139	220.07	390.62	170.55	1.0704	1.6562
19	6.487	0.850	32.25	1.176	31.004	221.22	391.06	169.84	1.0742	1.6556
20	6.674	0.853	31.36	1.173	31.889	222.36	391.49	169.13	1.0781	1.6550
21	6.865	0.855	30.49	1.169	32.794	223.50	391.91	168.41	1.0819	1.6545
22	7.061	0.858	29.66	1.166	33.720	224.66	392.34	167.68	1.0858	1.6539
23	7.260	0.860	28.84	1.163	34.668	225.81	392.76	166.95	1.0896	1.6534
24	7.463	0.863	28.06	1.159	35.638	226.97	393.18	166.21	1.0935	1.6528
25	7.671	0.865	27.30	1.156	36.630	228.14	393.60	165.46	1.0973	1.6523
26	7.883	0.868	26.56	1.152	37.646	229.30	394.01	164.71	1.1012	1.6518
27	8.100	0.870	25.85	1.149	38.684	230.47	394.42	163.95	1.1050	1.6513
28	8.321	0.873	25.16	1.145	39.747	231.65	394.83	163.18	1.1089	1.6507
29	8.546	0.876	24.49	1.142	40.834	232.83	395.23	162.40	1.1127	1.6502
30	8.776	0.878	23.84	1.138	41.946	234.01	395.63	161.62	1.1165	1.6497
31	9.010	0.881	23.21	1.135	43.083	235.20	396.03	160.83	1.1204	1.6492
32	9.250	0.884	22.60	1.131	44.247	236.39	396.42	160.03	1.1242	1.6487
33	9.494	0.887	22.01	1.128	45.438	237.59	396.81	159.22	1.1281	1.6482
34	9.742	0.890	21.43	1.124	46.656	238.78	397.19	158.41	1.1319	1.6477
35	9.996	0.893	20.88	1.120	47.902	239.99	397.57	157.58	1.1358	1.6472
36	10.254	0.896	20.33	1.117	49.177	241.20	397.95	156.75	1.1396	1.6467
37	10.517	0.899	19.81	1.113	50.481	242.41	398.32	155.91	1.1434	1.6462
38	10.786	0.902	19.30	1.109	51.815	243.64	398.69	155.05	1.1473	1.6456
39	11.059	0.905	18.80	1.105	53.181	244.86	399.05	154.19	1.1512	1.6451
40	11.338	0.908	18.32	1.101	54.578	246.09	399.41	153.32	1.1550	1.6446
41	11.621	0.911	17.85	1.098	56.007	247.33	399.77	152.44	1.1589	1.6441
42	11.910	0.914	17.40	1.094	57.470	248.57	400.12	151.55	1.1627	1.6436
43	12.205	0.918	16.96	1.090	58.967	249.81	400.46	150.65	1.1666	1.6431
44	12.505	0.921	16.53	1.086	60.499	251.07	400.80	149.73	1.1705	1.6426
45	12.810	0.924	16.11	1.082	62.067	252.33	401.14	148.81	1.1743	1.6421
46	13.121	0.928	15.71	1.078	63.672	253.60	401.47	147.87	1.1782	1.6416
47	13.437	0.931	15.31	1.074	65.315	254.87	401.79	146.92	1.1821	1.6411
48	13.759	0.935	14.93	1.070	66.997	256.15	402.11	145.96	1.1860	1.6405
49	14.087	0.938	14.55	1.066	68.720	257.44	402.42	144.98	1.1899	1.6400
50	14.420	0.942	14.19	1.061	70.484	258.73	402.73	144.00	1.1938	1.6395
51	14.760	0.946	13.83	1.057	72.290	260.03	403.03	143.00	1.1978	1.6389
52	15.105	0.950	13.49	1.053	74.141	261.34	403.32	141.98	1.2017	1.6384
53	15.456	0.954	13.15	1.049	76.037	262.66	403.61	140.95	1.2056	1.6378
54	15.813	0.957	12.82	1.044	77.979	263.98	403.89	139.91	1.2096	1.6373
55	16.177	0.962	12.50	1.040	79.969	265.31	404.16	138.85	1.2135	1.6367
56	16.547	0.966	12.19	1.036	82.010	266.66	404.43	137.77	1.2175	1.6361
57	16.923	0.970	11.89	1.031	84.101	268.01	404.69	136.68	1.2215	1.6355
58	17.305	0.974	11.59	1.027	86.245	269.37	404.94	135.57	1.2255	1.6349
59	17.694	0.978	11.31	1.022	88.445	270.73	405.18	134.45	1.2295	1.6343

Table 3-19   Properties of Saturated "Freon 500" — Azeotropic mixture: mass fraction   *(continued)*
of Freon 12 (CCl$_2$F$_2$) 73.8% and R 152a 26.2%

Tempera-ture	Pressure	Specific volume		Density		Specific enthalpy		Heat of vaporization	Specific entropy	
		Liquid	Vapor	Liquid	Vapor	Liquid	Vapor		Liquid	Vapor
t	p	v'	v''	ρ'	ρ''	h'	h''	r	s'	s''
°C	bar	L/kg	L/kg	kg/L	kg/m^3	kJ/kg	kJ/kg	kJ/kg	kJ/(kg K)	kJ/(kg K)
60	18.089	0.983	11.03	1.017	90.701	272.11	405.41	133.30	1.2335	1.6337
61	18.491	0.987	10.75	1.013	93.016	273.50	405.64	132.14	1.2376	1.6330
62	18.899	0.992	10.48	1.008	95.392	274.89	405.85	130.96	1.2416	1.6324
63	19.314	0.997	10.22	1.003	97.831	276.30	406.06	129.76	1.2457	1.6317
64	19.736	1.002	9.97	0.998	100.335	277.71	406.25	128.54	1.2498	1.6310
65	20.165	1.007	9.72	0.993	102.908	279.15	406.44	127.29	1.2539	1.6303
66	20.600	1.012	9.47	0.988	105.552	280.59	406.62	126.03	1.2580	1.6296
67	21.043	1.017	9.24	0.983	108.269	282.04	406.78	124.74	1.2622	1.6289
68	21.493	1.022	9.00	0.978	111.063	283.51	406.93	123.42	1.2663	1.6281
69	21.949	1.028	8.78	0.973	113.938	284.99	407.07	122.08	1.2705	1.6274
70	22.414	1.034	8.55	0.968	116.896	286.48	407.20	120.72	1.2747	1.6266
71	22.885	1.039	8.34	0.962	119.942	287.98	407.31	119.33	1.2790	1.6257
72	23.364	1.045	8.12	0.957	123.079	289.50	407.41	117.91	1.2832	1.6249
73	23.850	1.051	7.92	0.951	126.313	291.04	407.50	116.46	1.2875	1.6240
74	24.344	1.058	7.71	0.945	129.648	292.59	407.57	114.98	1.2919	1.6231
75	24.846	1.064	7.51	0.940	133.088	294.16	407.63	113.47	1.2962	1.6221
76	25.355	1.071	7.32	0.934	136.641	295.74	407.66	111.92	1.3006	1.6212
77	25.872	1.078	7.13	0.928	140.311	297.34	407.68	110.34	1.3050	1.6202
78	26.397	1.085	6.94	0.922	144.106	298.96	407.68	108.72	1.3095	1.6191
79	26.930	1.093	6.76	0.915	148.033	300.60	407.66	107.06	1.3140	1.6180
80	27.471	1.100	6.57	0.909	152.100	302.26	407.62	105.36	1.3185	1.6169
81	28.020	1.108	6.40	0.902	156.315	303.95	407.56	103.61	1.3231	1.6157
82	28.577	1.117	6.22	0.896	160.690	305.65	407.47	101.82	1.3277	1.6144
83	29.143	1.125	6.05	0.889	165.234	307.39	407.36	99.97	1.3324	1.6131
84	29.717	1.134	5.88	0.882	169.961	309.14	407.22	98.08	1.3372	1.6118
85	30.299	1.144	5.72	0.874	174.883	310.91	407.04	96.13	1.3419	1.6104
86	30.890	1.154	5.56	0.867	180.017	312.73	406.84	94.11	1.3468	1.6089
87	31.490	1.164	5.39	0.859	185.381	314.56	406.60	92.04	1.3517	1.6073
88	32.098	1.175	5.24	0.851	190.994	316.44	406.33	89.89	1.3567	1.6056
89	32.716	1.186	5.08	0.843	196.880	318.35	406.01	87.66	1.3618	1.6039
90	33.342	1.198	4.92	0.835	203.066	320.30	405.65	85.35	1.3670	1.6020
91	33.977	1.211	4.77	0.826	209.585	322.29	405.24	82.95	1.3723	1.6001
92	34.622	1.225	4.62	0.816	216.473	324.22	404.78	80.45	1.3776	1.5979
93	35.275	1.239	4.47	0.807	223.777	326.41	404.25	77.84	1.3831	1.5957
94	35.938	1.255	4.32	0.797	231.552	328.55	403.65	75.10	1.3887	1.5933
95	36.611	1.272	4.17	0.786	239.867	330.76	402.98	72.22	1.3945	1.5907
96	37.293	1.291	4.02	0.775	248.807	333.04	402.21	69.17	1.4004	1.5878
97	37.984	1.311	3.87	0.764	258.484	335.41	401.34	65.93	1.4066	1.5847
98	38.686	1.333	3.72	0.750	269.045	337.86	400.33	62.47	1.4130	1.5813
99	39.397	1.358	3.56	0.736	280.692	340.45	399.18	58.73	1.4197	1.5775
100	40.118	1.387	3.40	0.721	293.716	343.18	397.83	54.65	1.4267	1.5732
101	40.849	1.421	3.24	0.704	308.558	346.09	396.22	50.13	1.4342	1.5682
102	41.590	1.461	3.07	0.685	325.948	349.27	394.26	44.99	1.4424	1.5624
103	42.341	1.512	2.88	0.661	347.258	352.84	391.76	38.92	1.4517	1.5551
104	43.103	1.582	2.66	0.632	375.708	357.09	388.30	31.21	1.4626	1.5454
105	43.875	1.707	2.35	0.586	424.935	363.11	382.10	18.99	1.4782	1.5285
105.5	44.265	2.014	2.01	0.497	496.570	373.21	373.21	0.00	1.5047	1.5047

Table 3-20 Properties of Saturated "Freon 502" — Azeotropic mixture: mass fraction of Freon 22 (CHClF$_2$) 48.8% and Freon 115 (C$_2$ClF$_5$) 51.2%

Temperature	Pressure	Specific volume		Density		Specific enthalpy		Heat of vaporization	Specific entropy	
		Liquid	Vapor	Liquid	Vapor	Liquid	Vapor		Liquid	Vapor
t	p	v'	v''	ρ'	ρ''	h'	h''	r	s'	s''
°C	bar	L/kg	L/kg	kg/L	kg/m^3	kJ/kg	kJ/kg	kJ/kg	kJ/(kg K)	kJ/(kg K)
−65	0.369	0.648	411.90	1.542	2.428	135.70	315.56	179.86	0.7346	1.5987
−64	0.391	0.650	390.78	1.539	2.559	136.54	316.07	179.53	0.7386	1.5970
−63	0.413	0.651	370.95	1.536	2.696	137.38	316.58	179.20	0.7426	1.5953
−62	0.437	0.652	352.31	1.533	2.838	138.23	317.09	178.86	0.7466	1.5937
−61	0.461	0.653	334.78	1.530	2.987	139.07	317.59	178.52	0.7506	1.5921
−60	0.487	0.655	318.29	1.527	3.142	139.93	318.10	178.17	0.7546	1.5905
−59	0.514	0.656	302.76	1.524	3.303	140.80	318.61	177.81	0.7587	1.5890
−58	0.542	0.657	288.14	1.521	3.471	141.67	319.12	177.45	0.7627	1.5875
−57	0.571	0.659	274.36	1.518	3.645	142.53	319.62	177.09	0.7667	1.5860
−56	0.602	0.660	261.37	1.515	3.826	143.41	320.13	176.72	0.7707	1.5846
−55	0.634	0.661	249.10	1.512	4.014	144.29	320.63	176.34	0.7748	1.5832
−54	0.667	0.663	237.53	1.509	4.210	145.18	321.14	175.96	0.7788	1.5818
−53	0.702	0.664	226.60	1.505	4.413	146.06	321.64	175.58	0.7828	1.5804
−52	0.738	0.666	216.27	1.502	4.624	146.96	322.15	175.19	0.7869	1.5791
−51	0.775	0.667	206.50	1.499	4.843	147.86	322.65	174.79	0.7910	1.5778
−50	0.814	0.668	197.26	1.496	5.069	148.77	323.16	174.39	0.7950	1.5765
−49	0.855	0.670	188.52	1.493	5.304	149.68	323.66	173.98	0.7991	1.5753
−48	0.897	0.671	180.24	1.490	5.548	150.59	324.16	173.57	0.8031	1.5740
−47	0.941	0.673	172.40	1.487	5.801	151.51	324.66	173.15	0.8072	1.5728
−46	0.986	0.674	164.96	1.483	6.062	152.44	325.16	172.72	0.8113	1.5717
−45	1.033	0.676	157.91	1.480	6.333	153.37	325.66	172.29	0.8153	1.5705
−44	1.082	0.677	151.23	1.477	6.613	154.30	326.16	171.86	0.8194	1.5694
−43	1.133	0.679	144.88	1.474	6.902	155.23	326.65	171.42	0.8234	1.5683
−42	1.185	0.680	138.85	1.470	7.202	156.18	327.15	170.97	0.8275	1.5672
−41	1.240	0.682	133.13	1.467	7.512	157.13	327.65	170.52	0.8316	1.5661
−40	1.296	0.683	127.69	1.464	7.832	158.08	328.14	170.06	0.8357	1.5651
−39	1.355	0.685	122.51	1.461	8.162	159.04	328.63	169.59	0.8398	1.5641
−38	1.415	0.686	117.59	1.457	8.504	160.01	329.13	169.12	0.8439	1.5631
−37	1.478	0.688	112.91	1.454	8.857	160.98	329.62	168.64	0.8480	1.5621
−36	1.543	0.689	108.45	1.451	9.221	161.95	330.11	168.16	0.8521	1.5612
−35	1.610	0.691	104.20	1.448	9.597	162.93	330.60	167.67	0.8562	1.5602
−34	1.679	0.692	100.16	1.444	9.984	163.90	331.08	167.18	0.8602	1.5593
−33	1.750	0.694	96.30	1.441	10.384	164.89	331.57	166.68	0.8643	1.5584
−32	1.824	0.696	92.62	1.438	10.796	165.89	332.06	166.17	0.8684	1.5575
−31	1.900	0.697	89.12	1.434	11.221	166.88	332.54	165.66	0.8725	1.5567
−30	1.979	0.699	85.77	1.431	11.659	167.88	333.02	165.14	0.8766	1.5558
−29	2.060	0.701	82.57	1.427	12.110	168.89	333.50	164.61	0.8808	1.5550
−28	2.143	0.702	79.52	1.424	12.575	169.90	333.98	164.08	0.8849	1.5542
−27	2.230	0.704	76.61	1.421	13.054	170.92	334.46	163.54	0.8890	1.5534
−26	2.318	0.706	73.82	1.417	13.547	171.93	334.93	163.00	0.8931	1.5526
−25	2.410	0.707	71.15	1.414	14.054	172.96	335.41	162.45	0.8972	1.5519
−24	2.504	0.709	68.61	1.410	14.576	173.99	335.88	161.89	0.9013	1.5511
−23	2.601	0.711	66.17	1.407	15.113	175.02	336.35	161.33	0.9054	1.5504
−22	2.701	0.713	63.83	1.403	15.665	176.06	336.82	160.76	0.9095	1.5497
−21	2.804	0.714	61.60	1.400	16.234	177.10	337.29	160.19	0.9136	1.5489
−20	2.910	0.716	59.46	1.396	16.818	178.15	337.76	159.61	0.9177	1.5483
−19	3.019	0.718	57.41	1.393	17.418	179.20	338.22	159.02	0.9219	1.5476
−18	3.131	0.720	55.45	1.389	18.036	180.25	338.68	158.43	0.9260	1.5469
−17	3.246	0.722	53.56	1.386	18.670	181.32	339.14	157.82	0.9301	1.5463
−16	3.364	0.724	51.76	1.382	19.322	182.38	339.60	157.22	0.9342	1.5456

Table 3-20 **Properties of Saturated "Freon 502" — Azeotropic mixture: mass fraction** *(continued)*
of Freon 22 ($CHClF_2$) 48.8% and Freon 115 (C_2ClF_5) 51.2%

Temperature	Pressure	Specific volume		Density		Specific enthalpy		Heat of vaporization	Specific entropy	
		Liquid	Vapor	Liquid	Vapor	Liquid	Vapor		Liquid	Vapor
t	p	v'	v''	ρ'	ρ''	h'	h''	r	s'	s''
°C	bar	L/kg	L/kg	kg/L	kg/m³	kJ/kg	kJ/kg	kJ/kg	kJ/(kg K)	kJ/(kg K)
−15	3.486	0.725	50.02	1.379	19.991	183.45	340.06	156.61	0.9383	1.5450
−14	3.610	0.727	48.36	1.375	20.678	184.52	340.51	155.99	0.9424	1.5444
−13	3.738	0.729	46.76	1.371	21.384	185.60	340.96	155.36	0.9466	1.5438
−12	3.870	0.731	45.23	1.368	22.109	186.68	341.41	154.73	0.9507	1.5432
−11	4.005	0.733	43.76	1.364	22.853	187.77	341.86	154.09	0.9548	1.5426
−10	4.143	0.735	42.34	1.360	23.617	188.87	342.31	153.44	0.9589	1.5420
−9	4.285	0.737	40.98	1.357	24.401	189.96	342.75	152.79	0.9630	1.5415
−8	4.430	0.739	39.67	1.353	25.205	191.06	343.19	152.13	0.9671	1.5409
−7	4.580	0.741	38.42	1.349	26.030	192.16	343.63	151.47	0.9712	1.5404
−6	4.733	0.743	37.21	1.345	26.877	193.27	344.07	150.80	0.9753	1.5398
−5	4.889	0.745	36.04	1.342	27.745	194.38	344.50	150.12	0.9795	1.5393
−4	5.050	0.747	34.92	1.338	28.635	195.50	344.93	149.43	0.9836	1.5388
−3	5.214	0.750	33.84	1.334	29.548	196.62	345.36	148.74	0.9877	1.5383
−2	5.383	0.752	32.80	1.330	30.483	197.74	345.78	148.04	0.9918	1.5378
−1	5.555	0.754	31.80	1.326	31.443	198.87	346.21	147.34	0.9959	1.5373
0	5.731	0.756	30.84	1.323	32.426	200.00	346.63	146.63	1.0000	1.5368
1	5.912	0.758	29.91	1.319	33.434	201.14	347.05	145.91	1.0041	1.5363
2	6.097	0.761	29.01	1.315	34.467	202.27	347.46	145.19	1.0082	1.5359
3	6.285	0.763	28.15	1.311	35.526	203.42	347.87	144.45	1.0123	1.5354
4	6.479	0.765	27.31	1.307	36.611	204.56	348.28	143.72	1.0164	1.5350
5	6.676	0.768	26.51	1.303	37.722	205.72	348.69	142.97	1.0205	1.5345
6	6.878	0.770	25.73	1.299	38.861	206.87	349.09	142.22	1.0246	1.5341
7	7.084	0.772	24.98	1.295	40.027	208.03	349.49	141.46	1.0287	1.5336
8	7.295	0.775	24.26	1.291	41.222	209.20	349.89	140.69	1.0328	1.5332
9	7.511	0.777	23.56	1.287	42.446	210.36	350.28	139.92	1.0368	1.5327
10	7.731	0.780	22.88	1.282	43.700	211.53	350.67	139.14	1.0409	1.5323
11	7.955	0.782	22.23	1.278	44.984	212.71	351.06	138.35	1.0450	1.5319
12	8.185	0.785	21.60	1.274	46.299	213.88	351.44	137.56	1.0490	1.5315
13	8.419	0.787	20.99	1.270	47.646	215.06	351.82	136.76	1.0531	1.5311
14	8.658	0.790	20.40	1.266	49.025	216.24	352.95	135.95	1.0572	1.5306
15	8.902	0.793	19.83	1.261	50.438	217.44	352.57	135.13	1.0613	1.5302
16	9.151	0.796	19.27	1.257	51.884	218.62	352.93	134.31	1.0653	1.5298
17	9.405	0.798	18.74	1.253	53.365	219.82	353.30	133.48	1.0694	1.5294
18	9.664	0.801	18.22	1.248	54.882	221.02	353.66	132.64	1.0734	1.5290
19	9.928	0.804	17.72	1.244	56.436	222.22	354.01	131.79	1.0775	1.5286
20	10.197	0.807	17.23	1.239	58.027	223.42	354.36	130.94	1.0815	1.5282
21	10.471	0.810	16.76	1.235	59.656	224.63	354.71	130.08	1.0855	1.5278
22	10.751	0.813	16.31	1.230	61.324	225.84	355.05	129.21	1.0896	1.5274
23	11.037	0.816	15.86	1.226	63.033	227.06	355.39	128.33	1.0936	1.5270
24	11.327	0.819	15.44	1.221	64.783	228.29	355.73	127.44	1.0977	1.5266
25	11.623	0.822	15.02	1.217	66.576	229.51	356.06	126.55	1.1017	1.5261
26	11.925	0.825	14.62	1.212	68.412	230.74	356.38	125.64	1.1057	1.5257
27	12.233	0.828	14.23	1.207	70.293	231.97	356.70	124.73	1.1097	1.5253
28	12.546	0.832	13.85	1.202	72.220	233.20	357.01	123.81	1.1138	1.5249
29	12.864	0.835	13.48	1.198	74.194	234.44	357.32	122.88	1.1178	1.5245
30	13.189	0.838	13.12	1.193	76.217	235.67	357.62	121.95	1.1218	1.5240
31	13.519	0.842	12.77	1.188	78.290	236.92	357.92	121.00	1.1258	1.5236
32	13.856	0.846	12.44	1.183	80.415	238.17	358.21	120.04	1.1298	1.5232
33	14.198	0.849	12.11	1.178	82.593	239.43	358.50	119.07	1.1338	1.5227
34	14.547	0.853	11.79	1.173	84.826	240.67	358.77	118.10	1.1378	1.5223

Table 3-20   Properties of Saturated "Freon 502" — Azeotropic mixture: mass fraction *(continued)*
of Freon 22 (CHClF₂) 48.8% and Freon 115 (C₂ClF₅) 51.2%

Tempera-ture	Pressure	Specific volume		Density		Specific enthalpy		Heat of vaporization	Specific entropy	
		Liquid	Vapor	Liquid	Vapor	Liquid	Vapor		Liquid	Vapor
t	p	v'	v''	ρ'	ρ''	h'	h''	r	s'	s''
°C	bar	L/kg	L/kg	kg/L	kg/m³	kJ/kg	kJ/kg	kJ/kg	kJ/(kg K)	kJ/(kg K)
35	14.902	0.857	11.48	1.167	87.116	241.94	359.05	117.11	1.1418	1.5218
36	15.262	0.860	11.18	1.162	89.464	243.20	359.31	116.11	1.1458	1.5214
37	15.630	0.864	10.88	1.157	91.873	244.47	359.57	115.10	1.1498	1.5209
38	16.003	0.868	10.60	1.152	94.344	245.74	359.82	114.08	1.1538	1.5204
39	16.383	0.872	10.32	1.146	96.880	247.02	360.07	113.05	1.1577	1.5199
40	16.770	0.877	10.05	1.141	99.483	248.29	360.30	112.01	1.1617	1.5194
41	17.163	0.881	9.79	1.135	102.155	249.58	360.53	110.95	1.1657	1.5189
42	17.563	0.885	9.53	1.130	104.900	250.87	360.75	109.88	1.1697	1.5184
43	17.970	0.890	9.28	1.124	107.720	252.16	360.96	108.80	1.1737	1.5178
44	18.383	0.894	9.04	1.118	110.617	253.46	361.17	107.71	1.1777	1.5173
45	18.803	0.899	8.80	1.112	113.596	254.76	361.36	106.60	1.1816	1.5167
46	19.231	0.904	8.57	1.106	116.659	256.07	361.54	105.47	1.1856	1.5161
47	19.665	0.909	8.35	1.100	119.810	257.39	361.72	104.33	1.1896	1.5155
48	20.107	0.914	8.13	1.094	123.054	258.70	361.88	103.18	1.1936	1.5149
49	20.556	0.919	7.91	1.088	126.393	260.03	362.03	102.00	1.1976	1.5142
50	21.013	0.925	7.70	1.081	129.834	261.36	362.17	100.81	1.2016	1.5136
51	21.477	0.930	7.50	1.075	133.382	262.70	362.30	99.60	1.2056	1.5129
52	21.949	0.936	7.30	1.068	137.040	264.05	362.42	98.37	1.2096	1.5122
53	22.428	0.942	7.10	1.062	140.816	265.40	362.52	97.12	1.2136	1.5114
54	22.916	0.948	6.91	1.055	144.715	266.76	362.61	95.85	1.2176	1.5106
55	23.411	0.954	6.72	1.048	148.746	268.13	362.68	94.55	1.2217	1.5098
56	23.915	0.961	6.54	1.041	152.915	269.50	362.73	93.23	1.2257	1.5090
57	24.427	0.968	6.36	1.033	157.232	270.89	362.77	91.88	1.2298	1.5081
58	24.947	0.975	6.18	1.026	161.705	272.29	362.79	90.50	1.2339	1.5072
59	25.476	0.982	6.01	1.018	166.345	273.70	362.79	89.09	1.2380	1.5062
60	26.014	0.990	5.84	1.010	171.165	275.13	362.77	87.64	1.2421	1.5052
61	26.560	0.998	5.68	1.002	176.177	276.57	362.73	86.16	1.2462	1.5041
62	27.116	1.006	5.51	0.994	181.396	278.03	362.67	84.64	1.2504	1.5030
63	27.681	1.015	5.35	0.986	186.840	279.49	362.57	83.08	1.2546	1.5018
64	28.256	1.024	5.19	0.977	192.527	280.98	362.45	81.47	1.2589	1.5005
65	28.840	1.033	5.04	0.968	198.480	282.49	362.30	79.81	1.2632	1.4992
66	29.435	1.043	4.88	0.958	204.725	284.02	362.11	78.09	1.2675	1.4978
67	30.039	1.054	4.73	0.949	211.292	285.59	361.89	76.30	1.2719	1.4963
68	30.655	1.066	4.58	0.938	218.217	287.17	361.62	74.45	1.2764	1.4946
69	31.281	1.078	4.43	0.928	225.543	288.80	361.31	72.51	1.2810	1.4929
70	31.918	1.091	4.29	0.917	233.321	290.47	360.95	70.48	1.2856	1.4910
71	32.566	1.105	4.14	0.905	241.614	292.18	360.52	68.34	1.2904	1.4890
72	33.227	1.120	3.99	0.893	250.502	293.95	360.03	66.08	1.2953	1.4868
73	33.900	1.136	3.84	0.880	260.085	295.78	359.46	63.68	1.3004	1.4844
74	34.586	1.155	3.70	0.866	270.495	297.69	358.79	61.10	1.3057	1.4817
75	35.285	1.175	3.55	0.851	281.909	299.69	358.00	58.31	1.3112	1.4787
76	35.998	1.198	3.39	0.835	294.572	301.83	357.08	55.25	1.3171	1.4753
77	36.725	1.224	3.24	0.817	308.846	304.13	355.97	51.84	1.3234	1.4715
78	37.469	1.255	3.07	0.797	325.295	306.65	354.62	47.97	1.3303	1.4670
79	38.228	1.293	2.90	0.774	344.887	309.48	352.92	43.44	1.3381	1.4615
80	39.005	1.342	2.71	0.745	369.545	312.82	350.66	37.84	1.3473	1.4545
81	39.800	1.414	2.47	0.707	404.276	317.14	347.33	30.19	1.3592	1.4445
82	40.615	1.582	2.09	0.632	479.403	325.03	339.80	14.77	1.3811	1.4227
82.16	40.748	1.784	1.78	0.561	560.644	331.82	331.82	0.00	1.4002	1.4002

Table 3-21 Properties of Saturated "Freon 503" — Azeotropic mixture: mass fraction of Freon 13 ($CClF_3$) 59.9% and Freon 23 (CHF_3) 40.1%

Temperature	Pressure	Specific volume		Density		Specific enthalpy		Heat of vaporization	Specific entropy	
		Liquid	Vapor	Liquid	Vapor	Liquid	Vapor		Liquid	Vapor
t	p	v'	v''	ρ'	ρ''	h'	h''	r	s'	s''
°C	bar	L/kg	L/kg	kg/L	kg/m^3	kJ/kg	kJ/kg	kJ/kg	kJ/(kg K)	kJ/(kg K)
−120	0.100	0.641	1444.48	1.560	0.692	61.29	260.22	198.93	0.3515	1.6505
−119	0.110	0.642	1329.15	1.557	0.752	62.28	260.66	198.38	0.3579	1.6449
−118	0.120	0.643	1224.56	1.555	0.817	63.25	261.09	197.84	0.3643	1.6394
−117	0.130	0.644	1129.61	1.553	0.885	64.24	261.53	197.29	0.3706	1.6341
−116	0.142	0.645	1043.27	1.550	0.959	65.23	261.96	196.73	0.3769	1.6288
−115	0.154	0.646	964.68	1.548	1.037	66.23	262.40	196.17	0.3832	1.6236
−114	0.168	0.647	893.04	1.546	1.120	67.22	262.83	195.61	0.3895	1.6186
−113	0.182	0.648	827.66	1.543	1.208	68.22	263.26	195.04	0.3957	1.6136
−112	0.197	0.649	767.91	1.541	1.302	69.22	263.69	194.47	0.4020	1.6088
−111	0.213	0.650	713.25	1.539	1.402	70.22	264.12	193.90	0.4081	1.6040
−110	0.231	0.651	663.18	1.536	1.508	71.23	264.55	193.32	0.4143	1.5993
−109	0.249	0.652	617.27	1.534	1.620	72.25	264.98	192.73	0.4206	1.5947
−108	0.269	0.653	575.12	1.531	1.739	73.26	265.41	192.15	0.4267	1.5902
−107	0.290	0.654	536.38	1.529	1.864	74.28	265.84	191.56	0.4328	1.5858
−106	0.312	0.655	500.73	1.526	1.997	75.30	266.26	190.96	0.4390	1.5814
−105	0.335	0.656	467.90	1.523	2.137	76.33	266.69	190.36	0.4451	1.5772
−104	0.360	0.658	437.63	1.521	2.285	77.36	267.11	189.75	0.4512	1.5730
−103	0.387	0.659	409.69	1.518	2.441	78.39	267.53	189.14	0.4572	1.5689
−102	0.415	0.660	383.88	1.516	2.605	79.42	267.95	188.53	0.4633	1.5648
−101	0.444	0.661	360.01	1.513	2.778	80.46	268.37	187.91	0.4693	1.5609
−100	0.476	0.662	337.91	1.510	2.959	81.50	268.79	187.29	0.4753	1.5570
−99	0.508	0.663	317.44	1.507	3.150	82.54	269.20	186.66	0.4813	1.5532
−98	0.543	0.665	298.45	1.505	3.351	83.59	269.62	186.03	0.4873	1.5494
−97	0.580	0.666	280.82	1.502	3.561	84.63	270.03	185.40	0.4932	1.5457
−96	0.618	0.667	264.44	1.499	3.782	85.68	270.44	184.76	0.4991	1.5421
−95	0.659	0.668	249.21	1.496	4.013	86.74	270.85	184.11	0.5051	1.5386
−94	0.702	0.670	235.03	1.493	4.255	87.80	271.26	183.46	0.5110	1.5351
−93	0.746	0.671	221.82	1.490	4.508	88.85	271.66	183.81	0.5168	1.5316
−92	0.793	0.672	209.51	1.487	4.773	89.91	273.06	182.15	0.5227	1.5282
−91	0.843	0.674	198.02	1.484	5.050	90.98	272.47	181.49	0.5285	1.5249
−90	0.894	0.675	187.29	1.481	5.339	92.04	272.86	180.82	0.5344	1.5217
−89	0.949	0.676	177.26	1.478	5.641	93.11	273.26	180.15	0.5401	1.5185
−88	1.005	0.678	167.88	1.475	5.957	94.19	273.66	179.47	0.5459	1.5153
−87	1.065	0.679	159.10	1.472	6.285	95.26	274.05	178.79	0.5517	1.5122
−86	1.127	0.681	150.88	1.469	6.628	96.33	274.44	178.11	0.5574	1.5091
−85	1.191	0.682	143.17	1.466	6.985	97.41	274.83	177.42	0.5631	1.5061
−84	1.259	0.684	135.93	1.463	7.357	98.49	275.21	176.72	0.5689	1.5032
−83	1.329	0.685	129.14	1.459	7.743	99.58	275.60	176.02	0.5746	1.5003
−82	1.403	0.687	122.76	1.456	8.146	100.66	275.98	175.32	0.5802	1.4974
−81	1.480	0.688	116.77	1.453	8.564	101.75	276.36	174.61	0.5858	1.4946
−80	1.560	0.690	111.13	1.450	8.999	102.83	276.73	173.90	0.5915	1.4918
−79	1.643	0.691	105.82	1.446	9.450	103.93	277.11	173.18	0.5971	1.4891
−78	1.729	0.693	100.81	1.443	9.919	105.02	277.48	172.46	0.6026	1.4864
−77	1.819	0.695	96.10	1.439	10.406	106.11	277.84	171.73	0.6082	1.4838
−76	1.913	0.696	91.65	1.436	10.911	107.21	278.21	171.00	0.6138	1.4811
−75	2.010	0.698	87.45	1.432	11.434	108.31	278.57	170.26	0.6193	1.4786
−74	2.111	0.700	83.49	1.429	11.977	109.41	278.93	169.52	0.6248	1.4760
−73	2.216	0.702	79.75	1.425	12.540	110.51	279.29	168.78	0.6303	1.4736
−72	2.324	0.703	76.21	1.422	13.122	111.61	279.64	168.03	0.6357	1.4711
−71	2.437	0.705	72.86	1.418	13.726	112.72	279.99	167.27	0.6412	1.4687

Table 3-21   Properties of Saturated "Freon 503" — Azeotropic mixture: mass fraction   *(continued)*
of Freon 13 (CClF$_3$) 59.9% and Freon 23 (CHF$_3$) 40.1%

Tempera-ture	Pressure	Specific volume		Density		Specific enthalpy		Heat of vaporization	Specific entropy	
		Liquid	Vapor	Liquid	Vapor	Liquid	Vapor		Liquid	Vapor
t	p	v'	v''	ρ'	ρ''	h'	h''	r	s'	s''
°C	bar	L/kg	L/kg	kg/L	kg/m^3	kJ/kg	kJ/kg	kJ/kg	kJ/(kg K)	kJ/(kg K)
−70	2.554	0.707	69.68	1.414	14.350	113.82	280.34	166.52	0.6466	1.4663
−69	2.675	0.709	66.68	1.411	14.997	114.94	280.69	165.75	0.6520	1.4639
−68	2.800	0.711	63.84	1.407	15.665	116.05	281.03	164.98	0.6574	1.4616
−67	2.930	0.713	61.14	1.403	16.357	117.16	281.37	164.21	0.6627	1.4593
−66	3.064	0.715	58.58	1.399	17.072	118.27	281.70	163.43	0.6681	1.4571
−65	3.202	0.717	56.15	1.396	17.810	119.38	282.03	162.65	0.6734	1.4548
−64	3.346	0.719	53.84	1.392	18.574	120.50	282.36	161.86	0.6787	1.4526
−63	3.494	0.721	51.65	1.388	19.362	121.62	282.69	161.07	0.6840	1.4505
−62	3.647	0.723	49.56	1.384	20.177	122.74	283.01	160.27	0.6893	1.4483
−61	3.805	0.725	47.58	1.380	21.017	123.87	283.33	159.46	0.6945	1.4462
−60	3.968	0.727	45.69	1.376	21.885	124.99	283.64	158.65	0.6998	1.4441
−59	4.136	0.729	43.90	1.372	22.781	126.12	283.96	157.84	0.7050	1.4420
−58	4.309	0.731	42.19	1.368	23.704	127.24	284.26	157.02	0.7102	1.4400
−57	4.488	0.733	40.56	1.363	24.658	128.37	284.57	156.20	0.7153	1.4380
−56	4.672	0.736	39.00	1.359	25.640	129.51	284.87	155.36	0.7205	1.4360
−55	4.862	0.738	37.52	1.355	26.654	130.63	285.16	154.53	0.7256	1.4340
−54	5.057	0.740	36.10	1.351	27.698	131.77	285.46	153.69	0.7307	1.4321
−53	5.259	0.743	34.75	1.346	28.775	132.90	285.74	152.84	0.7358	1.4301
−52	5.466	0.745	33.46	1.342	29.885	134.05	286.03	151.98	0.7410	1.4282
−51	5.679	0.748	32.23	1.337	31.028	135.19	286.31	151.12	0.7460	1.4263
−50	5.898	0.750	31.05	1.333	32.206	136.33	386.58	150.26	0.7511	1.4244
−49	6.123	0.753	29.92	1.328	33.420	137.47	286.85	149.38	0.7561	1.4426
−48	6.355	0.755	28.84	1.324	34.670	138.62	287.12	148.50	0.7612	1.4207
−47	6.593	0.758	27.81	1.319	35.957	139.76	287.38	147.62	0.7661	1.4189
−46	6.838	0.761	26.82	1.315	37.283	140.92	287.64	146.72	0.7712	1.4171
−45	7.089	0.763	25.87	1.310	38.648	142.07	287.89	145.82	0.7761	1.4153
−44	7.347	0.766	24.97	1.305	40.053	143.23	288.14	144.91	0.7811	1.4135
−43	7.611	0.769	24.10	1.300	41.499	144.38	288.38	144.00	0.7860	1.4117
−42	7.883	0.772	23.26	1.295	42.989	145.55	288.62	143.07	0.7910	1.4100
−41	8.162	0.775	22.46	1.291	44.522	146.71	288.85	142.14	0.7959	1.4082
−40	8.448	0.778	21.69	1.286	46.100	147.88	289.08	141.20	0.8009	1.4065
−39	8.741	0.781	20.95	1.281	47.724	149.05	289.03	140.25	0.8058	1.4048
−38	9.012	0.784	20.24	1.275	49.396	150.22	289.51	139.29	0.8107	1.4030
−37	9.350	0.787	19.56	1.270	51.117	151.40	289.72	138.32	0.8156	1.4013
−36	9.666	0.790	18.91	1.265	52.889	152.57	289.92	137.35	0.8204	1.3996
−35	9.989	0.794	18.28	1.260	54.712	153.76	290.12	136.36	0.8353	1.3979
−34	10.321	0.797	17.67	1.255	56.589	154.95	290.31	135.36	0.8302	1.3962
−33	10.660	0.801	17.09	1.249	58.521	156.14	290.49	134.35	0.8350	1.3945
−32	11.008	0.804	16.53	1.244	60.510	157.34	290.67	133.33	0.8399	1.3928
−31	11.364	0.808	15.99	1.238	62.558	158.54	290.84	132.30	0.8447	1.3911
−30	11.728	0.811	15.46	1.233	64.666	159.74	291.00	131.26	0.8496	1.3894
−29	12.101	0.815	14.96	1.227	66.837	160.96	291.16	130.20	0.8544	1.3877
−28	12.482	0.819	14.48	1.221	69.073	162.17	291.30	129.13	0.8593	1.3860
−27	12.872	0.823	14.01	1.216	71.376	163.39	291.44	128.05	0.8641	1.3843
−26	13.271	0.827	13.56	1.210	73.748	164.62	291.57	126.95	0.8690	1.3826
−25	13.679	0.831	13.12	1.204	76.192	165.85	291.69	125.84	0.8738	1.3809
−24	14.096	0.835	12.70	1.198	78.711	167.09	291.80	124.71	0.8787	1.3792
−23	14.522	0.839	12.30	1.192	81.306	168.33	291.90	123.57	0.8835	1.3775
−22	14.958	0.843	11.91	1.186	83.983	169.59	292.00	122.41	0.8883	1.3758
−21	15.403	0.848	11.53	1.179	86.742	170.85	292.08	121.23	0.8932	1.3740

Table 3-21 Properties of Saturated "Freon 503" — Azeotropic mixture: mass fraction of Freon 13 (CCIF$_3$) 59.9% and Freon 23 (CHF$_3$) 40.1% *(continued)*

Tempera-ture	Pressure	Specific volume		Density		Specific enthalpy		Heat of vaporization	Specific entropy	
		Liquid	Vapor	Liquid	Vapor	Liquid	Vapor		Liquid	Vapor
t	p	v'	v''	ρ'	ρ''	h'	h''	r	s'	s''
°C	bar	L/kg	L/kg	kg/L	kg/m^3	kJ/kg	kJ/kg	kJ/kg	kJ/(kg K)	kJ/(kg K)
–20	15.858	0.852	11.16	1.173	89.589	172.12	292.15	120.03	0.8981	1.3722
–19	16.323	0.857	10.81	1.167	92.525	173.39	292.21	118.82	0.9029	1.3705
–18	16.798	0.862	10.47	1.160	95.556	174.68	292.26	117.58	0.9078	1.3687
–17	17.283	0.867	10.13	1.154	98.685	175.98	292.30	116.32	0.9127	1.3669
–16	17.778	0.872	9.81	1.147	101.917	177.28	292.32	115.04	0.9177	1.3650
–15	18.284	0.877	9.50	1.140	105.256	178.59	292.33	113.74	0.9226	1.3632
–14	18.800	0.883	9.20	1.133	108.708	179.92	292.33	112.41	0.9275	1.3613
–13	19.327	0.888	8.91	1.126	112.277	181.25	292.31	111.06	0.9325	1.3594
–12	19.865	0.894	8.62	1.119	115.970	182.60	292.28	109.68	0.9375	1.3575
–11	20.414	0.899	8.35	1.112	119.793	183.96	292.23	108.27	0.9425	1.3555
–10	20.974	0.905	8.08	1.104	123.754	185.33	292.16	106.83	0.9475	1.3535
–9	21.546	0.912	7.82	1.097	127.858	186.72	292.08	105.36	0.9526	1.3514
–8	22.129	0.918	7.57	1.089	132.116	188.12	391.97	103.85	0.9577	1.3494
–7	22.724	0.925	7.32	1.082	136.536	189.54	291.85	102.31	0.9628	1.3472
–6	23.330	0.931	7.09	1.074	141.127	190.98	291.71	100.73	0.9680	1.3451
–5	23.949	0.938	6.85	1.066	145.901	192.43	291.54	99.11	0.9732	1.3428
–4	24.580	0.946	6.63	1.057	150.869	193.90	291.35	97.45	0.9784	1.3405
–3	25.224	0.953	6.41	1.049	156.046	195.39	291.13	95.74	0.9837	1.3382
–2	25.880	0.961	6.19	1.040	161.446	196.91	290.89	93.98	0.9891	1.3357
–1	26.548	0.970	5.98	1.031	167.087	198.44	290.61	92.17	0.9945	1.3332
0	27.230	0.978	5.78	1.022	172.986	200.00	290.31	90.31	1.0000	1.3306
1	27.925	0.987	5.58	1.013	179.165	201.59	289.97	88.38	1.0055	1.3279
2	28.634	0.996	5.39	1.004	185.650	203.20	289.59	86.39	1.0112	1.3252
3	29.356	1.006	5.20	0.994	192.467	204.85	289.17	84.32	1.0169	1.3222
4	30.092	1.017	5.01	0.984	199.650	206.53	388.71	82.18	1.0227	1.3192
5	30.841	1.027	4.83	0.973	207.237	208.23	288.19	79.96	1.0286	1.3160
6	31.606	1.039	4.65	0.963	215.273	209.99	287.63	77.64	1.0346	1.3127
7	32.384	1.051	4.47	0.951	223.809	211.78	287.00	75.22	1.0407	1.3092
8	33.177	1.064	4.29	0.940	232.912	213.63	286.31	72.68	1.0470	1.3055
9	33.985	1.078	4.12	0.927	242.660	215.52	285.54	70.02	1.0534	1.3015
10	34.809	1.093	3.95	0.915	253.149	217.47	284.68	67.21	1.0600	1.2973
11	35.647	1.110	3.78	0.901	264.502	219.49	283.72	64.23	1.0668	1.2928
12	36.502	1.128	3.61	0.887	276.880	221.59	282.64	61.05	1.0738	1.2879
13	37.372	1.148	3.44	0.871	290.492	223.78	281.42	57.64	1.0811	1.2826
14	38.258	1.171	3.27	0.854	305.625	226.08	280.03	53.95	1.0888	1.2767
15	39.160	1.197	3.10	0.835	322.687	228.51	278.42	49.91	1.0969	1.2701
16	40.080	1.229	2.92	0.814	342.271	231.14	276.54	45.40	1.1056	1.2626
17	41.016	1.269	2.74	0.788	365.303	234.04	274.29	40.25	1.1152	1.2539
18	41.969	1.325	2.54	0.755	393.170	237.42	271.55	34.13	1.1264	1.2436
19	42.940	1.429	2.34	0.700	427.476	242.14	268.20	26.06	1.1421	1.2313
19.5	43.432	1.773	1.77	0.564	564.000	253.71	253.71	0.00	1.1814	1.1814

Table 3-22 Physical Properties of Refrigerants

Name	Chemical formula	Molar mass	Gas constant	Specific heat capacity at 0 °C and 1.013 bar		at 0 °C	Temperature at 1.013 bar		Critical constant		
				Liquid	Vapor		Boiling point	Melting point	Tempera-ture	Pressure	Density
		M	R	c	c_p	$\gamma = c_p / c_v$	t_b	t_m	t_{cr}	p_{cr}	ρ_{cr}
		kg/kmol	J/kg K	kJ/(kg K)	kJ/(kg K)		°C	°C	°C	bar	kg/m^3
Ammonia	NH_3	17.032	488.263	4.647	2.060	1.312	−33.35	−77.9	132.4	112.9726	235
Carbon dioxide	CO_2	44.01	188.955		0.825	1.30	−78.48	−56.6	31.0	73.7558	460
Ethane	C_2H_6	30.07	276.557		1.729	1.202	−88.63	−183.6	32.1	49.3274	210
Ethylene	C_2H_4	28.05	296.651		1.612	1.25	−103.6	−104	9.4	50.4062	216
Methane	CH_4	16.04	157.201		2.177	1.30	−161.6	−182.6	−82	46.3855	162
Methyl chloride	CH_3Cl	50.491	164.752	1.549	0.737	1.27	−24.0	−91.5	143.1	66.7833	370
Propane	C_3H_8	44.09	188.611		1.528	1.15	−42.5	−189.9	96.85	42.5609	226
Sulphur dioxide	SO_2	64.06	129.820	1.357	0.607	1.271	−10.02	−75.5	157.2	78.7474	524
Water (steam)	H_2O	18.02	461.501	4.220	1.859	1.40	+100	0	374.15	221.2871	322

Table 3-23 Properties of Saturated Ammonia (NH₃)

Tempera-ture	Pressure	Density		Specific volume		Specific enthalpy		Heat of vaporization	Specific entropy	
		Liquid	Vapor	Liquid	Vapor	Liquid	Vapor		Liquid	Vapor
t	p	ρ'	ρ''	v'	v''	h'	h''	r	s'	s''
°C	bar	kg/m³	kg/m³	m³/kg	m³/kg	kJ/kg	kJ/kg	kJ/kg	kJ/(kg K)	kJ/(kg K)
−75	0.07502	731.0	0.0775	0.001368	12.89	87.504	1563.770	1476.266	2.7771	10.2288
−70	0.10925	725.3	0.1110	0.0013788	9.009	108.438	1572.981	1464.543	2.8797	10.0906
−68	0.12621	723.0	0.1271	0.0013832	7.870	116.812	1576.749	1459.937	2.9203	10.0383
−66	0.14563	720.7	0.1453	0.0013876	6.882	125.185	1580.098	1454.913	2.9617	9.9868
−64	0.16730	718.4	0.1655	0.0013920	6.044	133.978	1583.866	1449.889	3.0032	9.9370
−62	0.19162	716.1	0.1878	0.0013965	5.324	142.351	1587.216	1444.865	3.0438	9.8884
−60	0.21898	713.8	0.2128	0.0014010	4.699	150.725	1590.984	1440.259	3.0840	9.8419
−58	0.24938	711.4	0.2403	0.0014056	4.161	159.517	1594.333	1434.816	3.1238	9.7942
−56	0.28331	709.1	0.2708	0.0014103	3.693	168.309	1598.102	1429.792	3.1631	9.7490
−54	0.32087	706.7	0.3041	0.0014150	3.288	176.683	1601.451	1424.768	3.2021	9.7050
−52	0.36255	704.4	0.3409	0.0014197	2.933	185.057	1604.800	1419.744	3.2410	9.6623
−50	0.40874	702.0	0.3812	0.0014245	2.623	193.849	1608.150	1414.301	3.3000	9.6204
−48	0.45954	699.6	0.425	0.0014293	2.351	202.641	1611.499	1409.277	3.3206	9.5493
−46	0.51544	697.2	0.473	0.0014242	2.112	211.015	1614.849	1403.834	3.3582	9.5396
−44	0.57683	694.8	0.526	0.0014392	1.901	219.807	1618.198	1398.391	3.3963	9.5007
−42	0.64410	692.4	0.583	0.0014442	1.715	228.599	1621.548	1392.948	3.4344	9.4622
−40	0.71765	690.0	0.645	0.0014493	1.550	237.810	1624.897	1387.087	3.4730	9.4245
−39	0.75698	688.8	0.678	0.0014519	1.4752	242.081	1626.530	1384.449	3.4918	9.4056
−38	0.79797	687.5	0.712	0.0014545	1.4045	246.519	1628.163	1381.602	3.5106	9.3872
−37	0.84072	686.3	0.748	0.0014571	1.3377	250.957	1629.796	1378.755	3.5295	9.3692
−36	0.88534	685.1	0.785	0.0014597	1.2746	255.437	1631.387	1375.908	3.5483	9.3516
−35	0.93193	683.9	0.823	0.0014623	1.2151	259.917	1632.978	1373.061	3.5672	9.3341
−34	0.98057	682.6	0.863	0.0014649	1.1589	264.396	1634.569	1370.172	3.5860	9.3165
−33	1.03117	681.4	0.905	0.0014676	1.1058	268.834	1636.160	1367.283	3.6048	9.2993
−32	1.08383	680.1	0.948	0.0014703	1.0555	273.314	1637.751	1364.394	3.6233	9.2821
−31	1.13855	678.9	0.992	0.0014730	1.0080	277.794	1639.300	1361.505	3.6417	9.2654
−30	1.19543	677.7	1.038	0.0014757	0.9630	282.274	1640.849	1358.575	3.6601	9.2486
−29	1.25427	676.4	1.086	0.0014784	0.9204	286.754	1642.398	1355.644	3.6785	9.2319
−28	1.31605	675.2	1.136	0.0014811	0.8801	291.234	1643.905	1352.671	3.7179	9.2156
−27	1.37980	673.9	1.188	0.0014839	0.8418	295.714	1645.412	1349.699	3.7154	9.1992
−26	1.44648	672.6	1.242	0.0014867	0.8056	300.235	1646.920	1346.726	3.7334	9.1813
−25	1.51611	671.4	1.297	0.0014895	0.7712	304.715	1648.427	1343.712	3.7514	9.1674
−24	1.58770	670.1	1.354	0.0014923	0.7386	309.237	1649.892	1340.697	3.7694	9.1515
−23	1.66223	668.8	1.413	0.0014951	0.7076	313.717	1651.358	1337.641	3.7874	9.1360
−22	1.73970	667.6	1.474	0.0014980	0.6782	318.239	1652.823	1334.584	3.8054	9.1205
−21	1.82011	666.3	1.538	0.0015008	0.6502	322.760	1654.288	1331.528	3.8234	9.1050
−20	1.90249	665.0	1.604	0.0015037	0.6236	327.282	1655.712	1328.430	3.8414	9.0895
−19	1.98781	663.7	1.672	0.0015066	0.5983	331.801	1657.135	1325.332	3.8590	9.0745
−18	2.07607	662.4	1.742	0.0015096	0.5742	336.326	1658.517	1322.191	3.8766	9.0594
−17	2.16825	661.1	1.814	0.0015125	0.5513	340.847	1659.899	1319.051	3.8941	9.0443
−16	2.26436	659.8	1.889	0.0015155	0.5295	345.411	1661.280	1315.869	3.9117	9.0297
−15	2.36340	658.5	1.966	0.0015185	0.5087	349.975	1662.662	1312.687	3.9293	9.0150
−14	2.46539	657.2	2.046	0.0015215	0.4889	354.538	1664.002	1309.464	3.9469	9.0008
−13	2.57032	655.9	2.128	0.0015245	0.4700	359.060	1665.300	1306.240	3.9645	8.9865
−12	2.67918	654.6	2.212	0.0015276	0.4520	363.624	1666.598	1302.974	3.9821	8.9723
−11	2.79195	653.3	2.300	0.0015307	0.4348	368.187	1667.896	1299.708	3.9992	8.9581
−10	2.90865	652.0	2.390	0.0015338	0.4184	372.751	1669.152	1296.401	4.0164	8.9438
−9	3.02927	650.7	2.483	0.0015369	0.4028	377.314	1670.408	1293.093	4.0336	8.9300
−8	3.15382	649.3	2.579	0.0015400	0.3878	381.878	1671.664	1289.786	4.0507	8.9162
−7	3.28229	648.0	2.678	0.0015432	0.3735	386.442	1672.878	1286.394	4.0679	8.9024

Table 3-23   Properties of Saturated Ammonia (NH₃) *(continued)*

Tempera-ture	Pressure	Density		Specific volume		Specific enthalpy		Heat of vaporization	Specific entropy	
		Liquid	Vapor	Liquid	Vapor	Liquid	Vapor		Liquid	Vapor
t	p	ρ'	ρ''	v'	v''	h'	h''	r	s'	s''
°C	bar	kg/m³	kg/m³	m³/kg	m³/kg	kJ/kg	kJ/kg	kJ/kg	kJ/(kg K)	kJ/(kg K)
−6	3.41369	646.7	2.779	0.0015164	0.3599	391.047	1674.092	1283.045	4.0851	8.8890
−5	3.54903	645.3	2.883	0.0015496	0.3169	395.653	1675.306	1279.654	4.1022	8.8756
−4	3.68828	644.0	2.991	0.0015528	0.3344	400.216	1676.478	1276.262	4.1194	8.8622
−3	3.83244	642.6	3.102	0.0015561	0.3225	404.822	1677.651	1272.829	4.1366	8.8488
−2	3.98150	641.3	3.216	0.0015594	0.3111	409.427	1678.823	1269.396	4.1533	8.8354
−1	1.13546	639.9	3.332	0.0015627	0.3002	414.033	1679.954	1265.921	4.1701	8.8224
0	4.29433	638.6	3.452	0.0015660	0.2897	418.680	1681.084	1262.404	4.1868	8.8094
1	4.45712	637.2	3.576	0.0015694	0.2797	423.285	1682.173	1258.887	4.2035	8.7965
2	4.62482	635.8	3.702	0.0015727	0.2700	427.933	1683.261	1255.370	4.2203	8.7835
3	1.79741	634.5	3.834	0.0015761	0.2608	432.580	1684.350	1251.811	4.2370	8.7709
4	4.97491	633.1	3.969	0.0015796	0.2520	437.228	1685.396	1248.211	4.2538	8.7584
5	5.15732	631.7	4.108	0.0015831	0.2435	441.875	1686.443	1244.568	4.2705	8.7458
6	5.34462	630.3	4.250	0.0015866	0.2353	446.522	1687.448	1240.926	4.2873	8.7332
7	5.53782	628.9	4.396	0.0015901	0.2275	451.170	1688.411	1237.241	4.3040	8.7207
8	5.73591	627.5	4.546	0.0015936	0.2200	455.817	1689.374	1233.557	4.3204	8.7081
9	5.93989	626.1	4.700	0.0015972	0.2128	460.506	1690.337	1229.831	4.3367	8.6960
10	6.14975	624.7	4.859	0.0016008	0.2058	465.195	1691.258	1226.063	4.3530	8.6838
11	6.36452	623.3	5.022	0.0016045	0.1992	469.885	1692.179	1222.294	4.3693	8.6717
12	6.58517	621.8	5.189	0.0016081	0.1927	474.574	1693.058	1218.484	4.3857	8.6596
13	6.81170	620.4	5.361	0.0016118	0.1866	479.263	1693.937	1214.674	4.4020	8.6474
14	7.04412	619.0	5.537	0.0016156	0.1806	483.952	1694.775	1210.823	4.4183	8.6357
15	7.28340	617.5	5.718	0.0016193	0.1749	488.683	1695.612	1206.929	4.4317	8.6240
16	7.52857	616.1	5.904	0.0016231	0.1694	493.414	1696.449	1203.035	4.4510	8.6122
17	7.77962	614.6	6.094	0.0016270	0.1642	498.145	1697.245	1199.100	4.4673	8.6005
18	8.03753	613.2	6.289	0.0016308	0.1591	502.877	1698.040	1195.164	4.4836	8.5888
19	8.30133	611.7	6.489	0.0016347	0.1512	507.608	1698.794	1191.186	4.4996	8.5771
20	8.57199	610.3	6.694	0.0016386	0.1494	512.381	1699.548	1187.167	4.5155	8.5658
21	8.84952	608.8	6.904	0.0016426	0.1449	517.154	1700.259	1183.106	4.5318	8.5545
22	9.13391	607.3	7.119	0.0016466	0.1405	521.926	1700.971	1179.045	4.5477	8.5432
23	9.42517	605.8	7.339	0.0016507	0.1363	526.699	1701.641	1171.942	4.5636	8.5319
24	9.72329	604.3	7.564	0.0016546	0.1322	531.472	1702.311	1170.839	4.5795	8.5206
25	10.02730	602.8	7.795	0.0016588	0.1283	536.287	1702.981	1166.694	4.5954	8.5093
26	10.34013	601.3	8.031	0.0016630	0.1245	541.102	1703.567	1162.507	4.6113	8.4979
27	10.65983	599.8	8.273	0.0016672	0.1209	545.917	1704.153	1158.278	4.6273	8.4866
28	10.98737	598.3	8.521	0.0016714	0.1174	550.732	1704.739	1154.050	4.6432	8.4753
29	11.32276	596.8	8.775	0.0016757	0.1140	555.546	1705.284	1149.779	4.6591	8.4645
30	11.66501	595.2	9.034	0.0016800	0.1107	560.361	1705.828	1145.467	4.6746	8.4536
31	12.01511	593.7	9.300	0.0016844	0.1075	565.218	1706.330	1141.112	4.6905	8.4427
32	12.37305	592.1	9.573	0.0016888	0.1045	570.075	1706.833	1136.716	4.7064	8.4318
33	12.73982	590.6	9.852	0.0016932	0.1015	574.931	1707.293	1132.320	4.7219	8.4209
34	13.11541	589.0	10.138	0.0016977	0.0986	579.788	1707.712	1127.882	4.7374	8.4100
35	13.49885	587.5	10.431	0.0017023	0.0959	584.687	1708.089	1123.402	4.7529	8.3991
36	13.89112	585.9	10.731	0.0017069	0.0932	589.585	1708.466	1118.880	4.7688	8.3883
37	14.29123	584.3	11.038	0.0017115	0.0906	594.484	1708.842	1114.317	4.7843	8.3774
38	11.70017	582.7	11.353	0.0017162	0.0881	599.382	1709.177	1109.753	4.7997	8.3669
39	15.11695	581.1	11.675	0.0017209	0.0857	604.323	1709.940	1105.148	4.8152	8.3560
40	15.54354	579.5	12.005	0.0017257	0.0833	609.263	1709.764	1100.500	4.8307	8.3455
41	15.97896	577.9	12.34	0.0017305	0.0810	614.204	1710.015	1095.811	4.8462	8.3351
42	16.42320	576.2	12.69	0.0017354	0.0788	619.144	1710.266	1091.080	4.8617	8.3242
43	16.87724	574.6	13.04	0.0017404	0.0767	624.084	1710.475	1086.349	4.8772	8.3137

Table 3-23 Properties of Saturated Ammonia (NH₃) *(continued)*

Tempera-ture	Pressure	Density		Specific volume		Specific enthalpy		Heat of vaporization	Specific entropy	
		Liquid	Vapor	Liquid	Vapor	Liquid	Vapor		Liquid	Vapor
t	p	ρ'	ρ''	v'	v''	h'	h''	r	s'	s''
°C	bar	kg/m³	kg/m³	m³/kg	m³/kg	kJ/kg	kJ/kg	kJ/kg	kJ/(kg K)	kJ/(kg K)
44	17.34012	572.9	13.40	0.0017454	0.0746	629.025	1710.643	1081.576	4.8927	8.3033
45	17.81378	571.3	13.77	0.0017504	0.0726	634.007	1710.768	1076.761	4.9078	8.2928
46	18.29725	569.6	14.15	0.0017555	0.0707	638.989	1710.894	1071.905	4.9233	8.2819
47	18.79052	568.0	14.54	0.0017607	0.0688	643.972	1710.978	1067.006	4.9387	8.2714
48	19.29262	566.3	14.94	0.0017659	0.0670	648.954	1711.061	1062.066	4.9538	8.2610
49	19.80453	564.6	15.34	0.0017712	0.0652	653.978	1711.145	1057.083	4.9689	8.2505
50	20.32624	562.8	15.75	0.0017775	0.0635	658.919	1711.229	1052.310	4.9844	8.2409
52	21.40792	559.1	16.59	0.001788	0.0602	669.051	1711.145	1042.095	5.0166	8.2220
54	22.52588	555.4	17.47	0.001800	0.0572	679.099	1711.564	1032.465	5.0476	8.2019
56	23.68306	551.6	18.39	0.001812	0.0543	689.147	1711.564	1022.417	5.0786	8.1818
58	24.87947	547.8	19.35	0.001825	0.0515	699.614	1711.145	1011.531	5.1100	8.1617
60	36.14453	544.0	20.35	0.001838	0.0489	710.081	1710.726	996.458	5.1414	8.1412
62	27.43901	540.2	21.41	0.001851	0.0464	720.967	1710.308	989.341	5.1724	8.1207
64	28.79232	536.4	22.53	0.001864	0.0441	731.853	1709.470	977.618	5.2034	8.1002
66	30.17506	632.6	23.73	0.001877	0.0420	742.738	1708.214	965.476	5.2343	8.0793
68	31.62645	528.8	35.01	0.001891	0.0399	753.624	1706.958	953.334	5.2653	8.0583
70	33.11706	524.8	26.36	0.001905	0.0379	764.928	1705.284	940.355	5.2963	8.0370

Table 3-24 Properties of Saturated Ethane (C₂H₆)

Table 3-24 Properties of Saturated Ethane (C_2H_6)

Temperature	Pressure	Density		Specific volume		Specific enthalpy		Heat of vaporization	Specific entropy	
		Liquid	Vapor	Liquid	Vapor	Liquid	Vapor		Liquid	Vapor
t	p	ρ'	ρ''	v'	v''	h'	h''	r	s'	s''
°C	bar	kg/m³	kg/m³	m³/kg	m³/kg	kJ/kg	kJ/kg	kJ/kg	kJ/(kg K)	kJ/(kg K)
−100	0.52505	558.9	1.123	0.001789	0.8888	148.715	649.247	500.532	2.9915	5.8820
−95	0.70892	553.1	1.486	0.001808	0.6731	160.857	654.774	493.917	3.0606	5.8330
−90	0.94105	547.9	1.932	0.001825	0.5177	173.208	660.216	487.009	3.1284	5.7874
−85	1.22681	542.2	2.470	0.001844	0.4048	185.601	665.534	479.933	3.1954	5.7460
−80	1.57495	536.7	3.116	0.001863	0.3209	197.826	670.683	472.857	3.2594	5.7074
−75	1.99761	530.9	3.819	0.001884	0.2570	210.219	675.708	465.488	3.3218	5.6710
−70	2.49972	525.0	4.798	0.001905	0.2084	222.612	680.606	457.994	3.3834	5.6379
−65	3.09302	519.0	5.862	0.001927	0.1706	234.963	685.295	450.332	3.4428	5.6061
−60	3.78635	512.5	7.097	0.001951	0.1409	247.482	689.817	442.335	3.5018	5.5768
−55	4.59147	506.0	8.525	0.001976	0.1173	260.084	694.130	434.046	3.5588	5.5488
−50	5.51722	499.3	10.17	0.002003	0.09832	272.477	698.191	425.714	3.6149	5.5224
−45	6.57438	492.1	12.05	0.002032	0.08301	285.330	702.084	416.754	3.6706	5.4973
−40	7.77569	485.0	14.19	0.002062	0.07046	298.519	705.643	407.124	3.7267	5.4730
−35	9.12901	477.8	16.63	0.002093	0.06013	312.168	708.951	396.783	3.7836	5.4495
−30	10.65002	470.0	19.41	0.002128	0.05152	326.277	711.965	385.688	3.8406	5.4269
−25	12.33677	461.5	22.54	0.002167	0.04437	340.471	714.645	374.174	3.8992	5.4068
−20	14.22945	452.6	26.11	0.002209	0.03830	355.376	716.948	361.572	3.9549	5.3830
−15	16.30846	443.5	30.16	0.002255	0.03316	370.909	718.874	347.965	4.0135	5.3612
−10	18.59341	433.9	34.73	0.002305	0.03879	386.316	720.381	334.065	4.0708	5.3403
−5	21.10391	423.0	39.97	0.002364	0.02502	402.226	751.428	319.202	4.1286	5.3189
0	23.84977	411.7	45.98	0.002429	0.02175	418.680	721.972	303.292	4.1868	5.2971
5	26.86041	399.5	53.19	0.002503	0.01880	435.801	720.841	285.037	4.2463	5.2712
10	30.15545	386.5	62.00	0.002587	0.01613	454.058	718.246	264.187	4.3082	5.2415
15	33.76430	369.5	73.21	0.002706	0.01366	473.569	712.593	239.024	4.3769	5.2025
20	37.74580	350.2	87.49	0.002856	0.01143	494.880	705.099	210.219	4.4422	5.1594
25	42.14898	326.0	106.7	0.00307	0.00937	518.535	693.502	174.966	4.5180	4.1050
30	47.07192	286.0	142.0	0.00349	0.00704	553.034	668.674	113.085	4.6273	5.0003
31	48.15065	271.0	156.0	0.00369	0.00641	565.218	658.584	89.556	4.6662	4.9605
32.1 (crit)	49.32745	213.0	213.0	0.00470	0.00470	610.226	610.226	0	4.8123	4.8123

Table 3-25 Properties of Saturated Methyl Chloride (CH₃CL)

Tempera-ture	Pressure	Density		Specific volume		Specific enthalpy		Heat of vaporization	Specific entropy	
		Liquid	Vapor	Liquid	Vapor	Liquid	Vapor		Liquid	Vapor
t	p	ρ'	ρ''	v'	v''	h'	h''	r	s'	s''
°C	bar	kg/m³	kg/m³	m³/kg	m³/kg	kJ/kg	kJ/kg	kJ/kg	kJ/(kg K)	kJ/(kg K)
−60	0.15593	1068	0.448	0.000936	2.235	328.538	789.044	460.506	3.8142	5.9750
−55	0.21182	1059	0.595	0.000944	1.680	335.656	792.184	456.529	3.8481	5.9407
−50	0.28047	1050	0.772	0.000953	1.295	343.066	795.283	452.216	3.8812	5.9080
−45	0.36775	1041	0.992	0.000961	1.008	350.393	798.297	447.904	3.9142	5.8770
−40	0.47464	1031	1.259	0.000970	0.794	357.762	801.395	443.633	3.9461	5.8485
−37.5	0.53740	1027	1.414	0.000974	0.707	361.488	802.903	441.414	3.9620	5.8347
−35	0.60703	1023	1.583	0.000978	0.632	365.215	804.368	439.153	3.9775	5.8213
−32.5	0.68352	1018	1.768	0.000982	0.566	368.983	805.833	436.851	3.9934	5.8083
−30	0.76786	1014	1.969	0.000986	0.508	372.751	807.341	434.590	4.0089	5.7958
−27.5	0.86004	1010	2.188	0.000991	0.457	376.477	808.764	433.287	4.0239	5.7836
−25	0.96007	1005	2.425	0.000995	0.412	380.203	810.188	429.984	4.0394	5.7719
−22.5	1.06892	1001	2.682	0.000999	0.373	384.013	811.653	427.640	4.0545	5.7606
−20	1.18857	997	2.959	0.001003	0.338	387.865	813.118	425.253	4.0696	5.7493
−17.5	1.31801	992	3.260	0.001008	0.307	391.675	814.542	422.867	4.0846	5.7388
−15	1.45825	988	3.582	0.001013	0.279	395.485	815.965	420.480	4.0997	5.7284
−12.5	1.60927	983	3.927	0.001017	0.255	399.295	817.347	418.052	4.1144	5.7179
−10	1.77304	979	4.299	0.001022	0.233	403.147	818.687	415.540	4.1290	5.7079
−7.5	1.94956	974	4.698	0.001027	0.213	407.041	819.985	412.944	4.1437	5.6978
−5	2.13785	970	5.125	0.001032	0.195	410.893	821.241	410.348	4.1579	5.6882
−2.5	2.34085	965	5.582	0.001037	0.179	414.786	822.497	407.711	4.1726	5.6790
0	3.55855	960	6.066	0.001042	0.1648	418.680	823.753	405.073	4.1868	5.6698
2.5	2.79097	955	6.584	0.001047	0.1519	422.616	824.967	402.351	4.2010	5.6606
5	3.03908	950	7.134	0.001053	0.1402	426.551	826.139	399.588	4.2153	5.6518
7.5	3.30288	945	7.719	0.001058	0.1296	430.487	827.312	396.825	4.2295	5.6434
10	3.58433	940	8.342	0.001064	0.1198	434.381	828.442	394.062	4.2433	5.6350
12.5	3.88441	935	9.004	0.001069	0.1111	438.316	829.531	391.215	4.2571	5.6266
15	4.20117	930	9.704	0.001075	0.1031	442.252	830.619	388.368	4.2710	5.6187
17.5	4.53852	925	10.44	0.001081	0.0958	446.229	831.708	385.479	4.2848	5.6107
20	4.89646	921	11.22	0.001086	0.0891	450.248	832.755	382.506	4.2986	5.6032
23.5	5.27402	916	12.06	0.001092	0.0829	454.268	833.759	379.492	4.3120	5.5957
25	5.67119	911	12.93	0.001098	0.0774	458.287	834.764	376.477	4.3254	5.5881
27.5	6.08895	906	13.85	0.001104	0.0722	462.306	835.685	373.379	4.3388	5.5806
30	6.52927	901	14.82	0.001110	0.0675	466.326	836.606	370.281	4.3522	5.5735
32.5	6.99214	896	15.85	0.001116	0.0631	470.387	837.486	367.099	4.3656	5.5664
35	7.47757	891	16.92	0.001123	0.0591	474.448	838.323	363.875	4.3790	5.5592
37.5	7.98850	886	18.05	0.001129	0.0554	478.509	839.160	360.651	4.3920	5.5525
40	8.52198	881	19.22	0.001135	0.0520	482.612	839.998	357.385	4.4049	5.5463
42.5	9.08292	876	20.45	0.001142	0.0489	486.716	840.793	354.078	4.4179	5.5396
45	9.67034	870	21.75	0.001149	0.0460	490.819	841.547	350.728	4.4309	5.5329
47.5	10.27737	865	23.11	0.001156	0.0433	494.922	842.259	347.337	4.4439	5.5270
50	10.91480	859	24.51	0.001164	0.0408	499.067	842.970	343.904	4.4568	5.5211
52.5	11.59146	853	26.00	0.001172	0.0385	503.170	843.598	340.429	4.4698	5.5153
55	13.28773	848	27.55	0.001180	0.0363	507.315	844.226	336.912	4.4824	5.5090
57.5	13.00362	842	29.18	0.001188	0.0343	511.501	842.342	330.841	4.5075	5.5031
60	13.75873	837	30.87	0.001196	0.0324	515.688	845.441	329.752	4.5075	5.4973

Table 3-26   Properties of Saturated Propane (C_3H_8)

Tempera-ture	Pressure	Density		Specific volume		Specific enthalpy		Heat of vaporization	Specific entropy	
		Liquid	Vapor	Liquid	Vapor	Liquid	Vapor		Liquid	Vapor
t	p	ρ'	ρ''	v'	v''	h'	h''	r	s'	s''
°C	bar	kg/m³	kg/m³	m³/kg	m³/kg	kJ/kg	kJ/kg	kJ/kg	kJ/(kg K)	kJ/(kg K)
−80	0.13141	624.0	0.367	0.001603	2.724	233.665	688.770	455.105	3.3800	5.7380
−75	0.18044	618.6	0.497	0.001616	2.012	346.351	698.693	451.923	3.4420	5.7225
−70	0.24419	613.4	0.648	0.001630	1.544	258.284	706.481	448.197	3.5039	5.7095
−65	0.32558	608.0	0.852	0.001644	1.173	270.174	714.142	443.968	3.5609	5.6945
−60	0.42659	602.5	1.098	0.001659	0.911	281.939	721.762	439.823	3.6161	5.6794
−55	0.55211	597.1	1.389	0.001674	0.720	293.369	729.006	435.637	3.6685	5.6652
−50	0.70706	591.0	1.725	0.001690	0.580	304.464	736.333	431.450	3.7208	5.6543
−45	0.89044	585.3	2.141	0.001707	0.467	315.308	742.362	427.054	3.7706	5.6421
−40	1.11502	579.3	2.630	0.001725	0.380	326.487	748.935	422.448	3.8192	5.6312
−35	1.37881	573.5	3.145	0.001743	0.318	337.917	756.471	418.554	3.8673	5.6245
−30	1.67203	568.0	3.845	0.001761	0.260	349.263	763.505	414.242	3.9151	5.6187
−25	2.01723	561.7	4.651	0.001780	0.215	360.651	769.785	409.134	3.9632	5.6116
−20	2.42322	555.5	5.495	0.001799	0.182	371.955	775.353	403.398	4.0101	5.6032
−15	2.88904	549.3	6.427	0.001820	0.1556	383.260	781.215	397.955	4.0545	5.5932
−10	3.40487	543.0	7.595	0.001842	0.1318	394.773	787.077	392.302	4.0989	4.5894
−5	4.01484	536.7	8.826	0.001864	0.1133	406.496	792.101	385.604	4.1428	5.5810
0	4.68366	530.0	10.28	0.001887	0.0974	418.680	797.334	378.654	4.1868	5.5730
5	5.45348	523.0	11.82	0.001911	0.0846	430.905	802.275	371.369	4.2295	5.5668
10	6.33902	516.0	13.69	0.001935	0.0731	442.922	807.089	364.168	4.2722	5.5584
15	7.29811	509.0	15.65	0.001963	0.0639	455.273	811.904	356.632	4.3149	5.5530
20	8.33369	501.5	17.80	0.001992	0.0561	468.670	816.175	348.551	4.3576	5.5467
25	9.48891	494.0	20.20	0.002023	0.0495	480.393	830.487	340.178	4.4007	5.5416
30	10.80693	486.0	22.98	0.002055	0.0435	493.373	824.423	331.050	4.4439	5.5366
35	12.21909	477.7	25.97	0.002095	0.0385	507.147	828.233	321.086	4.4866	5.5283
40	13.73912	469.0	29.95	0.002135	0.0339	520.880	831.708	310.828	4.5289	5.5211
45	15.45528	459.5	33.11	0.002178	0.0302	535.408	835.602	300.194	4.5720	5.5153
50	17.26951	450.0	37.33	0.002222	0.0268	549.476	838.867	289.392	4.6151	5.5102

Table 3-27 Properties of Saturated Sulfur(IV)-Dioxide (SO_2)

Tempera-ture	Pressure	Density		Specific volume		Specific enthalpy		Heat of vaporization	Specific entropy	
		Liquid	Vapor	Liquid	Vapor	Liquid	Vapor		Liquid	Vapor
t	p	ρ'	ρ''	v'	v''	h'	h''	r	s'	s''
°C	bar	kg/m³	kg/m³	m³/kg	m³/kg	kJ/kg	kJ/kg	kJ/kg	kJ/(kg K)	kJ/(kg K)
−50	0.11572	1557	0.4015	0.0006423	2.4907	350.393	774.181	423.788	3.9109	5.8100
−47.5	0.13631	1551	0.4682	0.0006448	2.1359	353.826	775.563	421.736	3.9264	5.7954
−45	0.15985	1545	0.5424	0.0006472	1.8436	357.302	776.903	419.601	3.9406	5.7811
−42.5	0.18633	1539	0.6270	0.0006498	1.5950	360.609	778.284	417.675	3.9561	5.7669
−40	0.21575	1533	0.7209	0.0006523	1.3872	364.252	779.624	415.372	3.9712	5.7527
−37.5	0.25105	1527	0.8275	0.0006549	1.2085	367.434	780.964	413.530	3.9854	5.7101
−35	0.28832	1521	0.9446	0.0006575	1.0586	371.118	782.304	411.186	4.0009	5.7275
−32.5	0.33245	1515	1.0771	0.0006601	0.9284	374.258	783.601	409.313	4.0143	5.7154
−30	0.38050	1509	1.2220	0.0006627	0.8183	377.942	784.899	406.957	4.0294	5.7028
−27.5	0.43443	1503	1.3843	0.0006653	0.7224	381.083	786.197	405.073	4.0424	5.6915
−25	0.49426	1497	1.5610	0.0006680	0.6406	384.767	787.495	402.728	4.0571	5.6802
−22.5	0.56192	1490	1.7578	0.0006710	0.5689	387.907	788.793	400.886	4.0696	5.6689
−20	0.63547	1484	1.9720	0.0006739	0.5071	391.591	790.049	398.458	4.0842	5.6580
−17.5	0.71785	1477	2.2085	0.0006769	0.4528	394.773	791.305	396.532	4.0972	5.6480
−15	0.80709	1471	2.4643	0.0006798	0.4058	398.374	792.561	394.187	4.1110	5.6379
−12.5	0.90613	1464	2.7465	0.0006829	0.3641	401.598	793.775	392.178	4.1232	5.6279
−10	1.01401	1458	3.0488	0.0006859	0.3280	405.115	795.031	389.917	4.1361	5.6178
−7.5	1.13267	1452	3.3829	0.0006888	0.2956	408.422	796.204	387.781	4.1491	5.6086
−5	1.26114	1446	3.7383	0.0006916	0.2675	411.939	797.418	385.479	4.1625	5.5998
−2.5	1.40235	1440	4.1305	0.0006945	0.2421	415.247	798.590	383.343	4.1742	5.5906
0	1.55435	1434	4.5455	0.0006974	0.2200	418.680	799.763	381.083	4.1868	5.5818
2.5	1.72107	1428	5.000	0.0007005	0.2000	422.071	800.893	378.822	4.1994	5.5735
5	1.89857	1422	5.482	0.0007035	0.1824	425.504	802.065	376.561	4.2119	5.5655
7.5	2.09372	1415	6.010	0.0007066	0.1664	428.854	803.154	374.300	4.2236	5.5571
10	2.30162	1409	6.566	0.0007097	0.1523	432.203	804.245	372.039	4.2349	5.5488
12.5	2.52717	1403	7.168	0.0007130	0.1395	435.637	805.331	369.694	4.2471	5.5412
15	5.76842	1396	7.812	0.0007163	0.1280	438.986	806.420	367.434	4.2592	5.5341
17.5	3.02829	1389	8.496	0.0007197	0.1177	442.419	807.424	365.047	4.2705	5.5266
20	3.30484	1383	9.225	0.0007231	0.1084	445.685	808.471	362.786	4.2818	5.5195
22.5	3.60296	1376	10.01	0.0007266	0.0999	418.992	809.350	360.358	4.2936	5.5123
25	3.91972	1370	10.83	0.0007301	0.0923	453.133	810.230	358.097	4.3049	5.5056
27.5	4.25903	1363	11.73	0.0007338	0.0853	455.691	811.318	355.627	4.3158	5.4985
30	4.61893	1356	12.66	0.0007375	0.0790	459.083	812.407	353.324	4.3262	5.4918
32.5	5.00433	1349	13.66	0.0007414	0.0732	462.516	813.370	350.854	4.3375	5.4855
35	5.41131	1342	14.70	0.0007453	0.0680	465.823	814.291	348.467	4.3484	5.4793
37.5	5.84476	1334	15.82	0.0007495	0.0632	469.173	815.170	346.039	4.3593	5.4730
40	6.30273	1327	17.01	0.0007536	0.0588	472.397	816.091	343.694	4.3685	5.4667
42.5	6.78914	1319	18.28	0.0007578	0.0547	475.704	816.928	341.224	4.3798	5.4608
45	7.30301	1311	19.57	0.0007622	0.0511	479.012	817.766	338.754	4.3903	5.4550
47.5	7.84630	1303	20.96	0.0007666	0.0477	482.361	818.603	336.242	4.4007	5.4491
50	8.41705	1295	22.43	0.0007712	0.0446	485.711	819.440	333.730	4.4104	5.4433
52.5	9.02114	1289	23.92	0.0007759	0.0418	488.893	820.194	331.301	4.4204	5.4336
55	9.65759	1281	25.58	0.0007808	0.0391	492.535	820.990	328.454	4.4313	5.4320
57.5	10.32640	1273	57.24	0.0007857	0.0367	495.843	821.743	325.901	4.4409	5.4265
60	11.03248	1264	29.07	0.0007909	0.0344	499.192	822.455	353.263	4.4510	5.4215

Table 3-28 Properties of Saturated Carbon(IV)-Dioxide (CO_2) Solid-Vapor

Tempera-ture	Pressure	Density		Specific volume		Specific enthalpy		Heat of vaporization	Specific entropy	
		Liquid	Vapor	Liquid	Vapor	Liquid	Vapor		Liquid	Vapor
t	p	ρ'	ρ''	v'	v''	h'	h''	r	s'	s''
°C	bar	kg/m³	kg/m³	m³/kg	m³/kg	kJ/kg	kJ/kg	kJ/kg	kJ/(kg K)	kJ/(kg K)
−100	0.13925	1594	0.428	0.000627	2.336	45.636	630.951	585.315	2.5104	5.8908
−95	0.23144	1590	0.694	0.000629	1.442	51.079	633.882	582.803	2.5431	5.8150
−90	0.37167	1582	1.03	0.000632	0.920	56.940	637.231	580.290	2.5749	5.7435
−85	0.58448	1574	1.67	0.000635	0.598	62.802	640.162	577.360	2.6059	5.6748
−80	0.89633	1566	2.51	0.000639	0.398	68.664	642.674	574.010	2.6373	5.6095
−78.9	0.98067	1566	2.74	0.000639	0.36512	70.045	643.176	573.131	2.6435	5.5948
−75	1.34351	1556	3.72	0.000642	0.2694	74.944	645.186	570.242	2.6695	5.5467
−70	1.98094	1546	5.39	0.000647	0.1854	82.061	646.861	564.799	3.7043	5.4860
−65	2.87335	1534	7.73	0.000652	0.1593	90.016	648.535	558.519	2.7428	5.4261
−60	4.09918	1522	11.0	0.000657	0.0912	99.227	649.373	550.146	2.7863	5.3671
−56.6	51.7791	1513	13.9	0.000661	0.0722	105.507	649.373	543.865	2.8156	5.3273

Table 3-29 Properties of Saturated Carbon(IV)-Dioxide (CO_2) Liquid-Vapor

Temperature	Pressure	Density		Specific volume		Specific enthalpy		Heat of vaporization	Specific entropy	
		Liquid	Vapor	Liquid	Vapor	Liquid	Vapor		Liquid	Vapor
t	p	ρ'	ρ''	v'	v''	h'	h''	r	s'	s''
°C	bar	kg/m³	kg/m³	m³/kg	m³/kg	kJ/kg	kJ/kg	kJ/kg	kJ/(kg K)	kJ/(kg K)
−56.6	5.17791	1178.0	13.9	0.000849	0.0722	301.450	649.373	347.923	3.7200	5.3273
−55	5.55056	1172.0	14.8	0.000853	0.0676	304.380	649.791	345.411	3.7334	5.3172
−50	6.83524	1153.5	18.1	0.000867	0.055407	314.052	651.340	337.289	3.7765	2.2883
−47.5	7.52170	1144.4	19.9	0.000873	0.050250	318.950	652.010	333.060	3.7974	5.2745
−45	8.32585	1134.5	21.8	0.000881	0.045809	323.640	652.680	329.041	3.8184	5.2607
−42.5	9.14960	1125.0	23.9	0.000889	0.041780	328.329	653.266	324.938	3.8393	5.2477
−40	10.05182	1115.0	26.2	0.000897	0.038164	333.227	653.853	320.625	3.8594	5.2348
−37.5	10.98345	1105.0	28.7	0.000905	0.034900	337.958	654.313	316.355	3.8795	5.2222
−35	12.02295	1094.9	31.2	0.000913	0.032008	342.480	655.774	311.958	3.8996	5.2096
−32.5	13.09188	1084.5	33.9	0.000922	0.029480	347.546	655.150	307.604	3.9197	5.1975
−30	14.26868	1074.2	37.0	0.000931	0.027001	352.487	655.485	302.999	3.9389	5.1854
−27.5	15.45528	1063.6	40.2	0.000940	0.024850	357.343	655.737	298.393	3.9607	5.1728
−25	16.80860	1052.6	43.8	0.000950	0.022885	362.284	655.946	293.662	3.9779	5.1615
−22.5	18.31882	1041.7	47.5	0.000960	0.021070	367.308	656.072	288.764	3.9984	5.1489
−20	19.67214	1029.9	51.4	0.000971	0.019466	372.322	656.407	283.823	4.0168	5.1380
−17.5	21.29024	1018.5	55.7	0.000982	0.017950	377.566	656.155	278.590	4.0377	5.1259
−15	22.88872	1006.1	60.2	0.000994	0.016609	382.841	656.072	273.231	4.0570	5.1154
−12.5	24.61469	993.8	65.3	0.001006	0.015320	388.326	655.862	267.537	4.0779	5.1029
−10	26.46815	980.8	70.5	0.001019	0.014194	393.936	655.653	261.717	4.0976	5.0924
−7.5	28.43929	968.0	76.2	0.001033	0.013120	399.756	655.276	225.520	4.1177	5.0807
−5	30.44965	953.8	82.4	0.001048	0.012141	405.743	654.857	249.115	4.1407	5.0698
−2.5	32.56788	940.0	89.0	0.001063	0.011230	411.897	654.271	242.374	4.1625	5.0585
0	34.85283	924.8	96.3	0.001081	0.010383	418.680	653.685	235.005	4.1868	5.0472
2.5	37.12624	910.0	104.3	0.001100	0.009584	426.384	652.387	226.003	4.2077	5.0334
5	39.71693	893.1	113.0	0.001120	0.008850	431.659	650.838	219.179	4.2299	2.0179
7.5	42.36473	876.0	122.3	0.001142	0.008175	438.693	649.289	210.596	4.2517	5.0041
10	45.06156	858.0	133.0	0.001166	0.007519	445.894	647.237	201.343	4.2781	4.9894
12.5	47.88587	838.5	144.7	0.001193	0.006910	453.012	644.558	191.546	4.3015	4.9718
15	50.92593	817.9	158.0	0.001223	0.006323	460.967	641.292	180.325	4.3292	4.9551
17.5	54.03464	795.5	173.2	0.001253	0.005774	468.503	637.524	169.021	4.3543	4.9362
20	57.32968	771.1	189.8	0.001297	0.005269	477.295	632.625	155.330	4.3827	4.9128
22.5	60.65413	742.9	210.4	0.001346	0.004753	486.506	625.927	139.420	4.4141	4.8843
25	64.32182	709.5	236.3	0.001409	0.004232	497.392	616.841	119.449	4.4497	4.8504
27.5	68.00912	666.4	271.8	0.001501	0.003679	510.790	605.202	94.412	4.4924	4.8094
30	71.92197	595.1	335.7	0.001680	0.002979	527.118	590.129	63.011	4.5444	4.7524
31 (crit)	73.51065	463.9	463.9	0.002156	0.002156	558.938	558.938	0	4.6465	4.6465

Table 3-30 Properties of Saturated Mercury (Hg)

Pressure	Temperature	Specific volume		Specific enthalpy		Heat of vaporization	Specific entropy	
		Liquid	Vapor	Liquid	Vapor		Liquid	Vapor
p	t	v'	v''	h'	h''	r	s'	s''
bar	°C	m³/kg	m³/kg	kJ/kg	kJ/kg	kJ/kg	kJ/(kg K)	kJ/(kg K)
0.0009807	118.5	0.0000752	165.9	16.580	319.118	302.538	0.0498	0.8202
0.0019613	134.6	0.0000754	86.16	18.631	320.751	302.119	0.0553	0.7963
0.0029420	144.1	0.0000755	58.78	19.929	321.797	301.868	0.0582	0.7817
0.0039227	151.2	0.0000756	44.84	20.850	322.509	301.659	0.0607	0.7716
0.0049033	161.5	0.0000758	30.62	22.232	323.723	301.366	0.0663	0.7570
0.0078453	168.9	0.0000759	23.35	23.362	324.979	301.198	0.0662	0.7473
0.0098067	175.0	0.0000760	18.94	24.242	325.272	301.031	0.0678	0.7398
0.0147100	186.6	0.0000761	12.95	25.791	326.487	300.696	0.0716	0.7256
0.0196133	195.0	0.0000762	9.893	26.963	327.408	300.445	0.0745	0.7164
0.0294200	207.6	0.0000764	6.772	28.680	328.789	300.110	0.0779	0.7021
0.0392266	216.9	0.0000765	5.178	29.977	329.836	299.859	0.0808	0.6925
0.0490333	221.5	0.0000766	4.206	31.024	330.673	299.649	0.0829	0.6850
0.0588399	230.9	0.0000767	3.550	31.945	331.427	299.484	0.0846	0.6787
0.0784532	241.0	0.0000769	2.716	33.411	332.599	299.189	0.0871	0.6691
0.0980665	249.6	0.0000770	2.209	34.541	333.520	298.979	0.0892	0.6615
0.1176798	256.7	0.0000771	1.866	32.504	334.274	298.770	0.0913	0.6552
0.1372931	262.7	0.0000772	1.618	36.341	334.944	298.603	0.0929	0.6502
0.1569064	268.0	0.0000772	1.430	37.095	335.530	298.435	0.0942	0.6456
0.1765197	272.9	0.0000773	1.282	37.765	336.074	298.310	0.0955	0.6418
0.1961330	277.3	0.0000774	1.1632	38.351	336.535	298.184	0.0967	0.6385
0.2451663	286.7	0.0000775	0.9464	39.607	337.540	297.933	0.0988	0.6310
0.2941995	294.4	0.0000776	0.7995	40.738	338.461	297.723	0.1009	0.6255
0.3922660	308.0	0.0000779	0.6140	42.622	339.926	297.305	0.1043	0.6159
0.4903325	318.8	0.0000780	0.5003	44.171	341.182	297.012	0.1068	0.6104
0.5883990	328.0	0.0000781	0.4234	45.469	342.229	296.760	0.1089	0.6025
0.6864655	335.9	0.0000783	0.3677	46.557	343.066	296.509	0.1110	0.5979
0.7845320	340.7	0.0000783	0.3253	47.478	343.359	296.300	0.1126	0.5937
0.8825985	349.2	0.0000784	0.2922	48.399	344.532	296.132	0.1139	0.5895
0.980665	355.9	0.0000785	0.2655	49.237	345.202	295.923	0.1151	0.5862
1.176798	365.8	0.0000787	0.2240	50.702	346.081	295.672	0.1172	0.5803
1.372931	374.0	0.0000788	0.1953	52.670	347.253	295.421	0.1193	0.5757
1.569064	381.9	0.0000789	0.1730	52.921	348.091	295.169	0.1214	0.5719
1.765197	389.3	0.0000790	0.1555	54.010	348.970	294.960	0.1231	0.5681
1.961330	395.8	0.0000791	0.1414	54.889	349.640	294.751	0.1243	0.5648
2.157463	401.7	0.0000792	0.1296	55.768	350.351	294.583	0.1256	0.5619
2.353596	407.4	0.0000793	0.1198	56.689	351.105	294.416	0.1269	0.5589
2.549729	412.4	0.0000794	0.1114	57.359	351.607	294.248	0.1277	0.5564
2.745862	417.0	0.0000794	0.1043	58.071	352.152	294.081	0.1285	0.5543
2.941995	422.4	0.0000795	0.09798	58.783	352.738	293.955	0.1294	0.5527
3.432328	432.8	0.0000797	0.08524	60.290	354.120	293.620	0.1319	0.5476
3.922660	442.4	0.0000798	0.07558	61.713	355.041	293.327	0.1336	0.5434
4.412993	451.0	0.0000799	0.06801	62.928	355.962	293.034	0.1352	0.5397
4.903325	458.0	0.0000801	0.06487	64.058	357.050	292.783	0.1369	0.5367
5.393658	466.8	0.0000802	0.05682	65.147	357.888	292.532	0.1386	0.5342
5.883990	472.8	0.0000803	0.05254	66.068	358.348	292.406	0.1398	0.5317
6.864655	485.1	0.0000805	0.04578	67.826	359.688	291.987	0.1419	0.5267
7.845320	496.3	0.0000806	0.04065	69.459	360.902	291.569	0.1440	0.5229
8.825985	506.3	0.0000808	0.03660	70.924	362.033	291.108	0.1461	0.5196
9.80665	515.5	0.0000809	0.03383	72.222	362.996	290.773	0.1491	0.5167
11.76798	532.3	0.0000812	0.02837	74.734	364.880	290.145	0.1507	0.5108

Table 3-30 Properties of Saturated Mercury (Hg) (continued)

Pressure	Temperature	Specific volume		Specific enthalpy		Heat of vaporization	Specific entropy	
		Liquid	Vapor	Liquid	Vapor		Liquid	Vapor
p	t	v'	v''	h'	h''	r	s'	s''
bar	°C	m³/kg	m³/kg	kJ/kg	kJ/kg	kJ/kg	kJ/(kg K)	kJ/(kg K)
13.72931	546.7	0.0000814	0.02476	76.828	366.512	289.559	0.1532	0.5066
15.69064	559.8	0.0000816	0.02200	78.879	367.769	289.015	0.1557	0.5028
17.65197	571.4	0.0000818	0.01933	80.722	369.025	288.512	0.1578	0.4995
19.61330	582.4	0.0000819	0.01806	82.145	370.197	288.052	0.1608	0.4961
24.51663	606.5	0.0000823	0.01487	85.662	372.625	286.963	0.1637	0.4899
29.41995	627.1	0.0000827	0.01268	88.676	374.635	285.958	0.1671	0.4848
34.32328	645.0	0.0000830	0.01109	91.398	376.435	285.037	0.1700	0.4802
39.22660	661.8	0.0000832	0.009873	93.826	377.984	284.158	0.1725	0.4765
44.12993	677.0	0.0000835	0.008923	95.878	379.408	283.321	0.1750	0.4731
49.03325	690.9	0.0000837	0.008148	98.139	380.622	282.483	0.1771	0.4702

Table 3-31 Physical Properties of Diphyl
Mixture: volume fraction of Diphenyl ($C_{12}H_{10}$) 26.5 % and Diphenyloxide ($C_{12}H_{10}O$) 73.5 %

Temperature	Saturation pressure	Density		Specific enthalpy		Heat of vaporization	Specific heat capacity	Thermal conductivity	Thermal deffusivity	Viscosity	Kinematic viscosity
		Liquid	Vapor	Liquid	Vapor		Liquid	Liquid	Liquid	Liquid	Liquid
t	p	ρ'	ρ''	h'	h''	r	c'	λ'	a	η	ν
°C	bar	kg/m³	kg/m³	kJ/kg	kJ/kg	kJ/kg	kJ/(kg K)	W/(m K)	mm²/s	mN s/m²	mm²/s
20		1062		12.14	388.95	376.81	1.591	0.1384	0.08194	4.2855	4.04
30		1055		28.47	401.10	372.63	1.663	0.1372	0.07972	3.0303	2.87
40		1046	0.0011	44.80	414.49	368.44	1.675	0.1361	0.07778	2.5105	2.40
50	0.00044	1038	0.0021	61.96	427.05	364.25	1.717	0.1337	0.07500	2.1771	3.10
60	0.00080	1030	0.0038	79.13	439.61	360.06	1.758	0.1326	0.07333	1.8142	1.76
70	0.00142	1021	0.0066	97.13	452.17	355.88	1.800	0.1314	0.07139	1.6083	1.58
80	0.00236	1013	0.0110	115.14	473.11	355.88	1.842	0.1303	0.06972	1.3533	1.34
90	0.00396	1004	0.0180	133.98	485.67	351.69	1.884	0.1279	0.06778	1.1866	1.18
100	0.00629	996	0.0280	152.82	502.42	347.50	1.926	0.1268	0.06611	1.0493	1.05
110	0.00981	988	0.0450	171.66	514.98	343.32	1.968	0.1256	0.06472	0.9277	0.940
120	0.0147	979	0.069	192.59	531.72	339.13	2.010	0.1244	0.06333	0.8267	0.845
130	0.0226	971	0.104	213.53	548.47	334.94	2.052	0.1221	0.06139	0.7375	0.760
140	0.0333	962	0.150	234.46	565.22	330.76	2.093	0.1210	0.06000	0.6639	0.690
150	0.0481	954	0.216	255.39	586.15	330.76	2.135	0.1198	0.05889	0.6002	0.630
160	0.0686	945	0.300	276.33	602.90	326.57	2.177	0.1186	0.05778	0.5474	0.580
170	0.0961	937	0.410	297.26	619.65	322.38	2.219	0.1163	0.05583	0.4965	0.530
180	0.127	928	0.541	322.38	640.58	318.20	2.261	0.1151	0.05500	0.4590	0.495
190	0.177	920	0.709	343.32	657.33	314.01	2.303	0.1140	0.05389	0.4236	0.460
200	0.245	911	0.943	368.44	678.26	309.82	2.345	0.1116	0.05222	0.3923	0.430
210	0.314	903	1.250	389.37	699.20	309.82	2.386	0.1105[1]	0.05139	0.3609[1]	0.400[1]
220	0.412	894	1.600	414.49	720.13	305.64	2.470	0.1093	0.04944	0.3305	0.370
230	0.530	885	2.12	439.61	736.88	297.26	2.512	0.1082	0.04861	0.3099	0.350
240	0.696	877	2.70	464.73	757.81	293.08	2.534	0.1058	0.04722	0.2893	0.330
230	0.873	868	3.50	489.86	778.74	288.89	2.596	0.1047	0.04639	0.2687	0.310
260	1.128	860	4.41	519.16	803.87	284.70	2.638	0.1035	0.04556	0.2511	0.295
270	1.393	851	5.52	544.28	824.80	280.52	2.680	0.1023	0.04500	0.2383	0.280
280	1.706	842	6.80	569.40	841.35	275.14	2.721	0.1000	0.04361	0.2226	0.265
390	2.079	833	8.33	598.71	866.67	267.96	2.721	0.0989	0.04361	0.2108	0.254
300	2.471	823	10.10	623.83	887.60	263.77	2.763	0.0977	0.04306	0.2001	0.243
310	2.952	813	12.20	653.14	912.72	259.58	2.805	0.0965	0.04222	0.1883	0.232
320	3.481	802	14.49	682.45	937.84	255.39	2.805	0.0942	0.04194	0.1795	0.223
330	4.099	793	17.01	707.57	958.78	247.02	2.805	0.0930	0.04194	0.1697	0.214
340	4.825	783	19.88	736.88	979.71	242.83	2.847	0.0919	0.04111	0.1608	0.206
350	5.580	773	23.20	766.18	1004.8	238.65	2.847	0.0896	0.04056	0.1540	0.200
360	6.463	762	26.88	795.49	1025.8	230.27	2.847	0.0884	0.04056	0.1471	0.193
370	7.453	750	30.60	820.61	1046.7	226.09	2.889	0.0872	0.04028	0.1402	0.187
380	8.532	738	33.59	849.92	1067.6	217.71	2.889	0.0861	0.04028	0.1324	0.180
390	9.718	724	40.65	879.23	1092.8	213.53	2.889	0.0837	0.04000	0.1265	0.175
400	11.111	708	46.30	908.54	1113.7	205.15	2.889	0.0826	0.04000	0.1206	0.170

[1] Above 200 °C determinated by extrapolation

Table 3-32 Dynamic Viscosity η of Refrigerants at Saturation

Substance	Chemical formula	Saturation temperature	Viscosity Liquid	Viscosity Vapor
		t	η	η
		°C	μN s/m^2	μN s/m^2
Ammonia	NH_3	−20	253	10.90
		−10	246	11.30
		0	239	11.80
		10	230	12.40
		20	219	12.90
Carbon dioxide	CO_2	−20	120.0	—
		−15	115.5	16.50
		−10	111.2	16.70
		0	100.7	17.40
		10	86.9	18.30
		20	70.1	20.30
		30	47.5	23.50
		31	31.6	31.60
Dichlorodifluoromethane (Frigen 12)	CF_2CL_2	−150	973.996	8.924
		−140	904.860	9.022
		−130	840.234	9.130
		−120	779.334	9.248
		−110	722.064	9.375
		−100	668.323	9.512
		−90	617.721	9.660
		−80	570.257	9.836
		−70	525.931	10.013
		−60	484.154	10.219
		−50	444.928	10.444
		−40	409.918	10.650
		−30	373.829	10.964
		−20	341.468	11.278

Substance	Chemical formula	Saturation temperature	Viscosity Liquid	Viscosity Vapor
		t	η	η
		°C	μN s/m^2	μN s/m^2
Dichlorodifluoromethane (Frigen 12)	CF_2CL_2	−10	311.263	11.621
		0	282.824	12.013
		10	256.248	12.454
		20	231.339	12.955
		30	207.901	13.543
		40	185.934	14.220
		50	165.242	15.034
		60	145.639	16.024
		70	127.094	17.250
		80	109.246	18.848
		90	91.761	21.065
		100	73.893	24.585
		110	51.151	33.352
Methyl chloride	CH_3CL	−20	309	10.30
		−10	301	10.80
		0	293	11.40
		10	281	12.10
		20	269	13.00
		30	264	—
Sulphur dioxide	SO_2	−20	485	10.60
		−10	437	11.30
		0	385	12.30
		10	331	13.50
		20	272	15.10
		30	—	16.90
		40	—	18.30

Table 3-33 Dynamic Viscosity η of Ammonia (NH_3) at Various Pressures and Temperatures

Pressure p bar	p kp/cm²	−20 °C η μN s/m²	−10 °C η μN s/m²	0 °C η μN s/m²	10 °C η μN s/m²	20 °C η μN s/m²	45 °C η μN s/m²	80 °C η μN s/m²
0.9807	1	8.630	9.022	9.316	9.709	10.003	10.983	12.160
1.9613	2	252.815	9.611	9.611	9.905	10.199	10.983	12.160
3.9227	4	259.582	250.266	10.689	10.395	10.689	11.082	12.258
5.8840	6	265.172	256.542	244.970	11.768	11.376	11.278	12.356
7.8453	8	269.879	261.543	250.854	236.340	12.454	11.670	12.651
9.8067	10	273.507	275.760	255.659	241.636	223.690	12.062	12.847
11.7680	12	276.548	269.094	259.386	245.951	228.789	12.749	12.227
13.7293	14	278.999	272.135	262.524	249.383	232.614	15.827	13.337
15.6906	16	281.059	274.390	264.976	252.031	235.654	14.612	14.612
17.6520	18	282.922	276.351	267.133	254.286	238.105	—	15.691
19.6133	20	284.589	278.117	268.898	256.248	240.165	—	16.966
21.5746	22	285.962	279.686	270.369	257.915	241.832	—	18.535
23.5360	24	287.139	280.862	271.644	359.386	243.401	—	—
25.4973	26	288.316	282.039	272.821	260.563	244.872	—	—

Values listed above the lines refer to the vapor and those under the line to the liquid.

Table 3-34 Dynamic Viscosity η of Methyl Chloride (CH_3CL) at Various Pressures and Temperatures

Pressure p bar	p kp/cm²	−20 °C η μN s/m²	−10 °C η μN s/m²	0 °C η μN s/m²	10 °C η μN s/m²	20 °C η μN s/m²	30 °C η μN s/m²
0.4903	0.5	8.728	9.414	9.709	10.199	10.689	11.082
0.9807	1.0	9.316	9.709	10.003	10.297	10.787	11.082
1.4710	1.5	311.557	10.297	10.395	10.395	10.787	11.180
1.9613	2.0	315.284	303.124	10.689	10.591	10.885	11.180
2.4517	2.5	318.520	306.360	11.180	10.885	11.082	11.278
2.9420	3.0	321.070	309.400	295.670	11.278	11.278	11.376
3.4323	3.5	323.325	311.851	298.318	11.866	11.572	11.572
3.9227	4.0	325.385	314.107	300.574	283.412	11.964	11.866
4.4130	4.5	327.150	316.068	302.731	285.864	12.454	12.160
4.9033	5.0	328.317	317.735	304.496	287.923	269.977	12.651
5.3937	5.5	330.092	319.108	305.771	289.787	271.840	13.337
5.8840	6.0	331.171	320.383	307.144	291.258	273.311	14.024
6.3743	6.5	331.955	321.462	308.125	292.434	274.390	15.102
6.8647	7.0	332.445	322.050	308.909	293.219	275.175	253.992

Values listed above the lines refer to the vapor and those under the line to the liquid.

Table 3-35 Dynamic Viscosity η of Sulfur(IV)-Dioxide (SO_2) at Various Pressures and Temperatures

Temperature =		−20 °C	−10 °C	0 °C	10 °C	20 °C	30 °C	40 °C
Pressure								
$\frac{p}{\text{bar}}$	$\frac{p}{\text{kp/cm}^2}$	$\frac{\eta}{\mu\text{N s/m}^2}$	$\frac{\eta}{\mu\text{N s/m}^2}$	$\frac{\eta}{\mu\text{N s/m}^2}$	$\frac{\eta}{\mu\text{N s/m}^2}$	$\frac{\eta}{\mu\text{N s/m}^2}$	$\frac{\eta}{\mu\text{N s/m}^2}$	$\frac{\eta}{\mu\text{N s/m}^2}$
0.4903	0.5	10.394	10.885	11.278	11.866	12.356	12.945	13.631
0.9807	1.0	490.333	11.180	11.670	12.160	12.553	13.043	13.729
1.4710	1.5	496.216	443.216	12.160	12.553	12.847	13.141	13.827
1.9613	2.0	502.100	449.635	392.266	13.043	13.337	13.337	14.024
2.4517	2.5	506.317	454.342	397.856	332.936	13.827	13.533	14.220
2.9420	3.0	509.946	458.951	402.563	338.133	14.514	13.925	14.416
3.4323	3.5	512.888	462.874	406.486	342.742	273.998	14.416	14.710
3.9227	4.0	515.339	466.306	410.212	346.665	278.509	15.200	15.102
4.4130	4.5	517.987	469.346	413.154	350.294	282.922	16.279	15.593
4.9033	5.0	519.949	472.190	416.096	353.039	286.746	–	16.181
5.3937	5.5	521.714	474.740	418.744	355.785	289.787	–	16.867
5.8840	6.0	523.185	477.094	420.901	357.943	293.023	–	17.652
6.3743	6.5	524.460	479.055	422.961	360.100	295.376	–	–
6.8647	7.0	525.833	481.016	424.824	361.865	297.828	–	–
7.3550	7.5	527.009	483.978	426.589	363.434	300.083	–	–
7.8453	8.0	528.088	484.841	428.060	365.298	302.045	–	–

Values listed above the lines refer to the vapor and those under the line to the liquid.

Table 3-36 Dynamic Viscosity η of Carbon(IV)-Dioxide (CO_2) at Various Pressures and Temperatures

Temperature =		−15 °C	−10 °C	0 °C	10 °C	20 °C	30 °C	40 °C
Pressure								
$\frac{p}{\text{bar}}$	$\frac{p}{\text{kp/cm}^2}$	$\frac{\eta}{\mu\text{N s/m}^2}$	$\frac{\eta}{\mu\text{N s/m}^2}$	$\frac{\eta}{\mu\text{N s/m}^2}$	$\frac{\eta}{\mu\text{N s/m}^2}$	$\frac{\eta}{\mu\text{N s/m}^2}$	$\frac{\eta}{\mu\text{N s/m}^2}$	$\frac{\eta}{\mu\text{N s/m}^2}$
4.9033	5	13.533	13.729	13.925	14.220	14.612	14.906	15.691
9.8067	10	14.024	14.220	14.220	14.416	14.808	15.102	15.887
14.7100	15	14.710	14.710	14.612	14.514	15.004	15.298	16.083
19.6133	20	15.495	15.298	15.004	14.808	15.200	15.495	16.377
24.5166	25	116.209	16.083	15.396	15.200	15.495	15.887	16.573
29.4200	30	118.072	112.188	15.985	15.593	15.789	16.181	16.867
34.3233	35	120.033	144.346	17.260	15.945	16.181	16.573	17.260
39.2266	40	120.916	116.209	103.558	16.769	16.671	16.966	17.652
44.1299	45	122.289	117.876	106.108	17.946	17.162	17.358	18.142
49.0333	50	123.564	119.249	108.462	89.633	17.848	17.848	18.633
53.9366	55	124.741	120.622	110.521	92.673	18.829	18.437	19.123
58.8399	60	125.721	121.897	112.482	95.419	71.294	18.221	19.711
63.7432	65	126.800	122.975	114.346	98.067	75.119	20.300	20.496
68.6466	70	127.879	124.152	116.013	100.224	78.551	21.967	21.378
73.5499	75	128.761	125.329	117.778	102.479	81.591	49.622	22.555
78.4532	80	129.742	126.506	119.249	104.539	84.337	55.015	24.222
83.3565	85	130.821	127.585	120.426	106.500	86.985	59.624	27.459
88.2599	90	131.801	128.663	121.897	108.462	89.241	63.841	32.558
93.1632	95	132.684	129.742	123.073	110.129	91.496	67.372	39.423
98.0665	100	133.567	130.723	124.250	111.894	93.555	70.706	46.091
102.9698	105	134.547	131.703	125.329	113.463	95.517	73.746	51.681
107.8732	110	135.430	132.684	126.506	114.934	97.380	76.688	56.094
112.7765	115	136.214	133.665	127.585	116.405	99.145	79.238	59.821
117.6798	120	136.999	134.547	128.565	117.778	100.812	81.886	63.155

Values listed above the lines refer to the vapor and those under the line to the liquid.

Table 3-37 Properties of Saturated Moist Air

Temperature t °C	Pressure p Pa	Density ρ kg/m³	at a pressure of 1.013 25 bar (=760 mm Hg) Density ρ' kg/m³	Moisture x' kg/kg	Specific enthalpy $h_{1+x'}$ kJ/kg³	at a pressure of 0.980 655 bar (=735.5 mm Hg) Density ρ' kg/m³	Moisture x' kg/kg	Specific enthalpy $h_{1+x'}$ kJ/kg³
−20	102.970	1.396	1.395	0.00063	−18.548	1.3490	0.000654	−18.485
−19	113.365	1.394	1.393	0.00070	−17.375	1.3436	0.000720	−17.317
−18	124.643	1.385	1.384	0.00077	−16.203	1.3383	0.000792	−16.136
−17	136.091	1.379	1.378	0.00085	−14.989	1.3330	0.000870	−14.934
−16	150.336	1.374	1.373	0.00093	−13.775	1.3278	0.000955	−13.716
−15	164.948	1.368	1.367	0.00101	−12.602	1.3225	0.001048	−12.481
−14	180.835	1.363	1.362	0.00111	−11.346	1.3174	0.001149	−11.225
−13	197.996	1.358	1.357	0.00122	−10.048	1.3132	0.001258	−9.948
−12	216.923	1.353	1.352	0.00134	−8.750	1.3071	0.001379	−8.642
−11	237.321	1.348	1.347	0.00146	−7.453	1.3020	0.001509	−7.310
−10	259.484	1.342	1.341	0.00160	−6.071	1.2969	0.001650	−5.954
−9	283.314	1.337	1.336	0.00172	−4.731	1.2919	0.001802	−4.568
−8	309.498	1.332	1.331	0.00191	−3.008	1.2869	0.001969	−3.144
−7	337.643	1.327	1.323	0.00208	−1.884	1.2819	0.002149	−1.687
−6	368.142	1.322	1.320	0.00227	−0.419	1.2770	0.002344	−0.193
−5	401.092	1.317	1.315	0.00247	1.089	1.2721	0.002554	1.340
−4	436.788	1.312	1.310	0.00269	3.680	1.2672	0.002783	2.918
−3	475.426	1.308	1.306	0.00294	4.522	1.2623	0.003030	4.547
−2	517.203	1.303	1.301	0.00319	5.903	1.2574	0.003298	6.226
−1	562.117	1.298	1.295	0.00347	7.620	1.2526	0.003586	7.955
0	610.758	1.293	1.290	0.00378	9.420	1.2478	0.003898	9.747
1	656.457	1.288	1.285	0.00407	11.137	1.2430	0.004192	11.493
2	705.392	1.284	1.281	0.00437	12.895	1.2382	0.004506	13.293
3	757.368	1.279	1.275	0.00470	14.738	1.2335	0.004841	15.148
4	812.873	1.275	1.271	0.00503	16.580	1.2288	0.005199	17.057
5	871.811	1.270	1.266	0.00540	18.605	1.2241	0.005579	19.025
6	934.574	1.265	1.261	0.00579	20.515	1.2194	0.005985	21.060
7	1001.259	1.261	1.256	0.00621	22.609	1.2148	0.006416	23.161
8	1072.063	1.256	1.251	0.00665	24.702	1.2101	0.006875	25.330
9	1147.280	1.252	1.247	0.00713	26.921	1.2054	0.007363	27.578
10	1227.106	1.248	1.242	0.00763	29.182	1.2008	0.007882	29.902
11	1311.738	1.233	1.237	0.00805	31.527	1.1962	0.008433	32.310
12	1401.468	1.239	1.232	0.00875	34.081	1.1916	0.009018	34.809
13	1496.593	1.235	1.328	0.00935	36.593	1.1817	0.009634	37.396
14	1597.405	1.230	1.223	0.00997	39.188	1.1824	0.010300	40.089
15	1704.004	1.226	1.218	0.0106	41.784	1.1778	0.010999	42.881
16	1816.878	1.222	1.214	0.0114	44.799	1.1732	0.011741	45.783
17	1936.323	1.217	1.208	0.0121	47.730	1.1686	0.012529	48.806
18	2012.238	1.213	1.204	0.0129	50.660	1.1641	0.013362	51.941
19	2195.709	1.209	1.200	0.0138	54.010	1.1595	0.014246	55.216
20	2336.925	1.205	1.195	0.0147	57.778	1.1549	0.015184	58.628
21	2485.005	1.201	1.190	0.0156	61.127	1.1503	0.016171	62.166
22	2641.912	1.197	1.185	0.0166	64.058	1.1457	0.017221	65.842
23	2807.644	1.193	1.181	0.0177	67.826	1.1411	0.018333	69.735
24	2982.202	1.189	1.176	0.0188	72.013	1.1365	0.019508	73.763
25	3166.567	1.185	1.171	0.0200	75.781	1.1319	0.020755	77.979
26	3359.758	1.181	1.166	0.0214	80.387	1.1272	0.022066	82.367
27	3563.737	1.177	1.161	0.0226	84.573	1.1226	0.023456	87.069
28	3778.502	1.173	1.156	0.0240	89.179	1.1179	0.024926	91.758
29	4004.055	1.169	1.151	0.0256	94.203	1.1132	0.026477	96.774
30	4241.367	1.165	1.146	0.0272	99.646	1.1085	0.028118	102.020
31	4491.446	1.161	1.141	0.0288	104.670	1.1038	0.029855	107.521
32	4753.283	1.157	1.136	0.0306	110.113	1.0990	0.031684	113.266
33	5028.850	1.154	1.131	0.0325	115.974	1.0943	0.033620	119.286
34	5318.146	1.150	1.126	0.0344	122.255	1.0895	0.035665	125.600
35	5622.152	1.146	1.121	0.0366	128.953	1.0846	0.037828	132.219
36	5939.888	1.142	1.116	0.0388	135.652	1.0798	0.040104	139.136
37	6274.295	1.139	1.111	0.0411	142.351	1.0749	0.042516	146.412
38	6624.392	1.135	1.107	0.0435	149.469	1.0699	0.045060	154.037
39	6991.161	1.132	1.102	0.0460	157.424	1.0650	0.047746	162.038
40	7374.601	1.128	1.097	0.0488	165.797	1.0599	0.050578	170.457
41	7776.673	1.124	1.091	0.0517	174.171	1.0549	0.053573	179.275
42	8198.359	1.121	1.086	0.0548	182.963	1.0498	0.056743	188.557
43	8638.678	1.117	1.081	0.0580	192.174	1.0446	0.060085	198.291
44	9099.591	1.114	1.076	0.0613	202.222	1.0394	0.063619	208.532
45	9582.078	1.110	1.070	0.0650	212.689	1.0341	0.067357	219.321
46	10085.16	1.107	1.065	0.0689	223.575	1.0288	0.071299	230.647
47	10611.78	1.103	1.059	0.0728	235.298	1.0235	0.075474	242.587
48	11161.93	1.100	1.054	0.0770	247.021	1.0180	0.079889	255.144
49	11735.62	1.096	1.048	0.0815	260.000	1.0125	0.084553	268.412

Table 3-37 Properties of Saturated Moist Air

Temperature t/°C	Pressure p/Pa	Density ρ/kg/m³	at a pressure of 1.013 25 bar (=760 mm Hg) Density ρ'/kg/m³	Moisture x'/kg/kg	Specific enthalpy $h_{1+x'}$/kJ/kg³	at a pressure of 0.980 655 bar (=735.5 mm Hg) Density ρ'/kg/m³	Moisture x'/kg/kg	Specific enthalpy $h_{1+x'}$/kJ/kg³
50	12334.80	1.093	1.043	0.0862	273.398	1.0069	0.089491	282.383
51	12960.47	1.090	1.037	0.0913	287.214	1.0013	0.094722	297.133
52	13612.61	1.086	1.031	0.0966	302.706	0.9956	0.100256	312.691
53	14293.19	1.083	1.025	0.102	317.778	0.9898	0.106124	329.133
54	15002.21	1.080	1.019	0.108	334.944	0.9839	0.112339	346.504
55	15740.65	1.076	1.013	0.114	352.110	0.9779	0.118926	364.867
56	16509.50	1.073	1.007	0.121	370.950	0.9719	0.125910	384.285
57	17311.68	1.070	1.001	0.128	390.210	0.9657	0.133340	404.910
58	18146.23	1.067	0.995	0.136	412.400	0.9595	0.141227	426.723
59	19015.09	1.063	0.987	0.144	435.427	0.9532	0.149616	449.893
60	19917.31	1.060	0.981	0.152	456.361	0.9467	0.158524	474.448
61	20858.74	1.057	0.974	0.161	481.482	0.9402	0.16804	500.628
62	21839.41	1.054	0.968	0.171	506.603	0.9335	0.17821	528.542
63	22849.49	1.051	0.961	0.181	535.910	0.9268	0.18895	558.013
64	23908.61	1.048	0.954	0.192	565.218	0.9199	0.20053	589.715
65	25006.96	1.044	0.946	0.204	598.712	0.9129	0.21296	623.515
66	26144.53	1.041	0.939	0.216	632.207	0.9058	0.22610	659.563
67	27331.13	1.038	0.932	0.230	669.888	0.8985	0.24033	698.346
68	28556.96	1.035	0.924	0.244	707.569	0.8912	0.25554	739.757
69	29831.83	1.032	0.917	0.259	749.437	0.8837	0.27194	784.351
70	31155.73	1.029	0.909	0.276	795.492	0.8760	0.28872	832.432
71	32528.66	1.026	0.901	0.294	845.734	0.8682	0.30872	884.261
72	33960.43	1.023	0.893	0.314	895.975	0.8602	0.32951	940.615
73	35431.43	1.020	0.885	0.335	950.404	0.8522	0.35185	1001.156
74	36961.26	1.017	0.877	0.357	1013.206	0.8439	0.37623	1067.161

Temperature t/°C	Pressure p/Pa	Density ρ/kg/m³	at a pressure of 1.01325 bar (=760 mm Hg) Density ρ'/kg/m³	Moisture x'/kg/kg	Specific enthalpy $h_{1+x'}$/kJ/kg³	at a pressure of 0.980 655 bar (=735.5 mm Hg) Density ρ'/kg/m³	Moisture x'/kg/kg	Specific enthalpy $h_{1+x'}$/kJ/kg³
75	38549.94	1.014	0.868	0.382	1080.194	0.8355	0.40288	1139.228
76	40187.65	1.011	0.859	0.408	1151.370	0.8269	0.43188	1217.622
77	41894.01	1.009	0.851	0.437	1226.732	0.8181	0.46389	1304.084
78	43649.40	1.006	0.842	0.470	1318.842	0.8092	0.49892	1398.651
79	45473.44	1.003	0.833	0.506	1415.138	0.8001	0.53780	1503.538
80	47356.31	1.000	0.823	0.545	1519.808	0.7908	0.58086	1619.701
81	49307.84	0.997	0.813	0.589	1637.039	0.7813	0.62901	1749.463
82	51328.01	0.994	0.803	0.639	1779.390	0.7716	0.68308	1895.134
83	53416.82	0.992	0.794	0.695	1925.928	0.7617	0.74413	2059.558
84	55574.29	0.989	0.783	0.756	2093.400	0.7516	0.81350	2246.289
85	57800.40	0.986	0.773	0.828	2281.806	0.7414	0.89286	2459.862
86	60104.96	0.983	0.762	0.908	2499.520	0.7308	0.98482	2707.281
87	62487.97	0.981	0.751	1.000	2750.728	0.7201	1.09244	2996.731
88	64949.44	0.978	0.740	1.110	3035.430	0.7091	1.21987	3339.383
89	67489.37	0.975	0.729	1.240	3391.308	0.6979	1.37287	3750.682
90	70107.74	0.973	0.718	1.400	3818.362	0.6865	1.55969	4252.868
91	72814.38	0.970	0.706	1.590	4333.338	0.6749	1.7935	4881.265
92	75609.27	0.967	0.694	1.830	4961.358	0.6629	2.0942	5685.716
93	78492.43	0.965	0.681	2.135	5777.784	0.6507	2.4942	6763.985
94	81463.84	0.962	0.669	2.546	6887.286	0.6383	3.0520	8262.231
95	84523.52	0.959	0.656	3.120	8436.402	0.6256	3.8820	10491.911
96	87691.06	0.957	0.643	3.990	10781.010	0.6126	5.2570	14185.297
97	90946.87	0.954	0.630	5.450	14695.668	0.5994	7.9455	21406.397
98	94300.75	0.951	0.616	8.350	22441.248	0.5859	15.576	41900.657
99	97762.49	0.949	0.602	17.000	45677.988	0.5721	200.023	538188.019
100	101322.31	0.947	0.589	—			—		

Table 3-38 Thermal Properties of Water (H₂O) Superheated Steam

Pressure		Temperature	Density	Specific heat capacity[1]	Thermal conductivity	Viscosity	Kinematic viscosity
$\dfrac{p}{\text{bar}}$	$\dfrac{p}{\text{kp/cm}^2}$	$\dfrac{t}{°C}$	$\dfrac{\rho}{\text{kg/m}^3}$	$\dfrac{c_p}{\text{kJ/(kg K)}}$	$\dfrac{\lambda}{\text{W/(m K)}}$	$\dfrac{\eta}{\mu\text{N s/m}^2}$	$\dfrac{\eta}{\mu\text{m/s}^2}$
0.9807	1	100	0.577	2.030	0.0237	12.553	21.8
		120	0.547	1.997	0.0251	13.337	24.4
		140	0.520	1.980	0.0265	14.024	27.0
		160	0.494	1.972	0.0280	14.808	30.0
		180	0.473	1.963	0.0294	15.495	32.8
		200	0.452	1.963	0.0309	16.279	36.0
		220	0.433	1.968	0.0323	16.966	38.2
		240	0.416	1.972	0.0338	17.750	42.7
		260	0.400	1.976	0.0354	18.535	46.4
		280	0.386	1.985	0.0369	19.221	49.8
		300	0.372	1.997	0.0385	20.006	54.8
		320	0.359	2.010	0.0401	20.692	58.7
		340	0.348	2.022	0.0416	21.477	61.2
1.9613	2	120	1.108	2.085	0.0265	13.533	12.2
		140	1.048	2.047	0.0277	14.220	13.6
		160	0.995	2.022	0.0290	15.004	15.1
		180	0.950	2.005	0.0302	15.691	16.5
		200	0.908	1.997	0.0316	16.475	18.1
		220	0.870	1.997	0.0330	17.162	19.7
		240	0.835	1.997	0.0345	17.946	21.5
		260	0.803	2.001	0.0361	18.633	23.2
		280	0.773	2.005	0.0374	19.417	25.2
		300	0.745	2.014	0.0391	20.104	27.0
		320	0.720	2.022	0.0407	20.888	29.0
		340	0.696	2.031	0.0422	21.575	31.0
3.9921	4	160	2.02	2.143	0.0308	15.298	7.57
		180	1.93	2.101	0.0317	15.985	8.29
		200	1.84	2.072	0.0330	16.769	9.11
		220	1.76	2.055	0.0342	17.456	9.91
		240	1.68	2.043	0.0356	18.240	10.9
		260	1.62	2.039	0.0370	18.927	11.7
		280	1.55	2.039	0.0384	19.711	12.7
		300	1.50	2.043	0.0399	20.398	13.5
		320	1.45	2.047	0.0414	21.084	14.5
		340	1.40	2.056	0.0429	21.869	15.6
5.8840	6	160	3.09	2.298	0.0329	15.691	5.08
		180	2.93	2.218	0.0336	16.377	5.59
		200	2.78	2.156	0.0344	17.064	6.14
		220	2.66	2.118	0.0355	17.848	6.71
		240	2.54	2.097	0.0366	18.535	7.30
		260	2.44	2.085	0.0379	19.221	7.87
		280	2.35	2.076	0.0393	20.104	8.55
		300	2.26	2.072	0.0408	20.692	9.06
		320	2.18	2.077	0.0423	21.477	9.86
		340	2.10	2.077	0.0440	22.163	10.05
7.8453	8	180	3.96	2.348	0.0358	16.867	4.26
		200	3.75	2.256	0.0365	17.554	4.68
		220	3.58	2.193	0.0373	18.338	5.12
		240	3.42	2.156	0.0383	19.025	5.56
		260	3.28	2.131	0.0394	19.711	6.01
		280	3.14	2.114	0.0406	20.398	6.49
		300	3.03	2.106	0.0420	21.182	6.99
		320	2.92	2.101	0.0435	21.869	7.49
		340	2.82	2.101	0.0450	22.555	8.00
9.8067	10	180	5.04	2.537	0.0407	17.652	3.50
		200	4.76	2.357	0.0399	18.338	3.85
		220	4.52	2.260	0.0401	19.025	4.21
		240	4.31	2.210	0.0408	19.711	4.57
		260	4.12	2.181	0.0418	20.496	4.97
		280	3.95	2.160	0.0429	21.182	5.36
		300	3.80	2.152	0.0444	21.869	5.76
		320	3.67	2.143	0.0458	22.555	6.15
		340	3.54	2.139	0.0473	23.242	6.56

[1] Older name: Specific heat

Table 3-39   Thermal Conductivity λ of Water (H_2O) Steam at Various Pressures

t	$\lambda_{\Delta at}$	λ	λ	λ	λ
Pressure $p =$		0.980 665 bar (=1 at)	19.613 3 bar (=20 at)	39.226 6 bar (=40 at)	58.839 9 bar (=60 at)
Temperature		Thermal conductivity[1]			
°C	mW/(m K)	mW/(m K)	mW/(m K)	mW/(m K)	mW/(m K)
100	24.772	24.772	—	—	—
150	29.540	29.191	—	—	—
200	35.472	33.727	—	—	—
250	45.241	39.775	41.752	45.008	—
300	61.639	45.706	47.683	50.242	53.731
350	112.113	51.288	53.265	55.591	58.150
400	—	57.103	58.964	61.058	63.500
450	—	63.267	65.012	67.105	69.431
500	—	70.013	71.757	73.734	75.828
550	—	76.758	78.386	80.363	82.457
600	—	83.969	85.481	87.225	89.318

Table 3-39   Thermal Conductivity λ of Water (H_2O) Steam at Various Pressures   *(continued)*

t	λ	λ	λ	λ	λ	λ
Pressure $p=$	78.453 bar (=80 at)	98.066 5 bar (=100 at)	147.099 75 bar (=150 at)	196.133 0 bar (=200 at)	245.166 25 bar (=250 at)	249.199 5 bar (=300 at)
Temperature	Thermal conductivity[1]					
°C	mW/(m K)	mW/(m K)	mW/(m K)	mW/(m K)	mW/(m K)	mW/(m K)
350	61.523	65.942	87.574	—	—	—
400	66.175	69.431	80.480	95.948	154.679	—
450	71.525	74.432	82.806	94.552	111.997	142.119
500	78.154	80.596	87.690	96.645	108.508	124.092
550	84.550	87.109	95.599	100.948	110.950	120.719
600	91.528	93.854	99.553	106.763	115.486	123.627

[1] Btu/(ft h °F) = 1.73073 W/(m K)

GASES

Table 4-1 Thermal Properties of Gases

Gas	Chemical formula	Molar mass M kg/kmol	Gas constant R J/(kg K)	At a temperature $t = 0\,°C$ Density at 1.01325 bar (760 mm Hg) ρ kg/m³	Specific heat capacity[1] c_p kJ/(kg K)	c_p / c_V γ	At a pressure $p = 1.013\,25$ bar (= 760 mm Hg) Melting point t_m °C	Heat of fusion q_f kJ/kg
Acetylene	C_2H_2	26.04	319.599	1.1709	1.641	1.23	−81	—
Air	—	28.96	287.041	1.2928	1.227	1.40	—	—
Ammonia	NH_3	17.031	488.175	0.7714	2.060	1.32	−77.7	339.131
Argon	Ar	39.944	208.195	1.7839	0.523	1.67	−189.3	29.308
Arsine (hydrogen arsenide)	H_3As	77.93	106.892	3.48	—	—	−113.5	—
n-Butane	C_4H_{10}	58.12	143.177	2.703	1.918*	1.11	−135	75.362
Carbon dioxide	CO_2	44.01	188.778	1.9768	0.825	1.31	−56	184.219
Carbon monoxide	CO	28.01	296.945	1.2500	1.051	1.40	−205	30.145
Carbonyl sulfide	COS	60.07	139.254	2.72	0.670	—	−138.2	—
Chlorine	Cl_2	70.914	117.288	3.22	0.502	1.34	−103	188.406
Cyanogen	C_2N_2	52.04	162.790	2.32	—	1.16	−34.4	—
Dichlorodifluoromethane	CF_2Cl_2	120.92	68.771	5.083	0.590	1.14	−155	—
Ethane	C_2H_6	30.07	276.744	1.356	1.666	1.22	−183.6	92.947
Ethylene	C_2H_4	28.05	296.651	1.2605	1.465	1.24	−169.4	104.670
Fluorine	F_2	38.000	218.688	1.695	—	—	−220	37.681
Helium	He	4.002	2079.010	0.1785	5.234	1.66	—	5.715
Hydrogen	H_2	2.0156	4121.735	0.08987	14.235	1.41	−259.20	58.615
Hydrogen bromide	HBr	80.924	102.872	3.644	0.343	1.36	−87	30.982
Hydrogen chloride	HCl	36.465	228.005	1.6391	0.812	1.42	−112	56.103
Hydrogen iodide	HJ	127.93	65.116	5.789	0.230	1.40	−51	23.027
Hydrogen sulfide	H_2S	34.08	244.186	1.5392	1.105	1.30	−85.6	69.501
Isobutane	C_4H_{10}	58.12	143.177	2.668	1.633*	—	−145	78.293
Krypton	Kr	83.7	100.322	3.74	0.251*	1.68	−157.2	19.678
Methane	CH_4	16.04	518.772	0.7168	2.177	1.30	−182.5	58.615
Methylamine	CH_5N	31.06	267.722	1.39	—	–	−92.5	—
Methyl chloride	CH_3Cl	50.49	164.752	2.307	0.737	1.20	−91.5	—
Methyl ether	C_2H_6O	46.07	180.442	2.1097	1.521	1.11	−138.5	—
Methyl fluoride	CH_3F	34.03	244.284	1.545	—	—	—	—
Neon	Ne	20.183	411.813	0.8999	1.030	1.67	−248.60	16.747
Nitric oxide	NO	30.008	277.136	1.3402	1.009	1.40	−163.5	77.037
Nitrogen	N_2	28.016	296.749	1.2505	1.043	1.40	−210.10	25.749
Nitrous oxide	N_2O	44.016	188.876	1.9780	0.858	1.31	−90.8	148.631
Nitrosyl chloride	NOCl	65.465	126.800	2.9919	—	—	−61.5	—
Oxygen	O_2	32.000	259.778	1.42895	0.913	1.40	−218.83	13.816
Ozone	O_3	48.000	173.382	2.22	—	1.29	−252	—
Phosphine (hydrogen phosphide)	PH_3	34.04	244.186	1.530	—	—	−133.5	32.866
Propane	C_3H_8	44.09	188.778	2.019	1.550	1.14	−189.9	80.387
Propene	C_3H_6	42.08	197.996	1.915	1.425	—	−185.2	69.920
Sulfur dioxide	SO_2	64.06	129.840	2.9263	0.632	1.40	−75.3	116.812
Xenon	X	131.3	63.841	5.89	0.159*	1.66	−111.9	17.585

[1] Older name: Specific heat.

*) Specific heat capacity at 20 °C.

Table 4-1   Thermal Properties of Gases   (continued)

Gas	Chemical formula	Number of atoms in a molecule	Boiling point 1.01325 bar (760 mm Hg) $\dfrac{t}{°C}$	At the boiling temperature		Critical constants		
				Density $\dfrac{\rho}{kg/m^3}$	Heat of vaporization $\dfrac{r}{kJ/kg}$	Temperature $\dfrac{t_{cr}}{°C}$	Pressure $\dfrac{p_{cr}}{°C}$	Density $\dfrac{\rho_{cr}}{kg/m^3}$
Acetylene	C_2H_2	4	−83.6	613	828.986	35.7	63.44903	231
Air	—	—	−194	875	196.780	−140.7	37.65754	310
Ammonia	NH_3	4	−33.4	680	1369.084	132.4	112.97261	235
Argon	Ar	1	−185.9	1404	157.424	−122.4	48.64098	531
Arsine (hydrogen arsenide)	AsH_3	4	−55	—	—	—	—	—
n-Butane	C_4H_{10}	14	+0.5	600	403.608	153.2	36.48074	—
Carbon dioxide	CO_2	3	−78.48	—	573.592	31.0	73.54988	460
Carbon monoxide	CO	2	−191.5	801	216.039	−140.2	34.91167	301
Carbonyl sulfide	COS	3	−48	1200	—	105	65.99875	—
Chlorine	Cl_2	2	−35.0	1558	259.582	144	76.98220	573
Cyanogen	C_2N_2	4	−21	—	—	128.3	60.80123	—
Dichlorodifluoromethane	CF_2Cl_2	5	−30.0	1486	167.472	111.5	40.10920	555
Ethane	C_2H_6	8	−88.6	546	540.097	35	49.62165	210
Ethylene	C_2H_4	6	−103.5	568	523.350	9.5	51.38685	216
Fluorine	F_2	2	−188	—	159.098	−101	—	—
Helium	He	1	−268.9	125	20.934	−267.9	2.28495	69
Hydrogen	H_2	2	−252.78	70.8	460.548	−239.9	12.94478	31
Hydrogen bromide	HBr	2	−67	—	217.714	90	85.31786	807
Hydrogen chloride	HCl	2	−85	—	443.801	51.4	84.33719	610
Hydrogen iodide	HJ	2	−36	—	154.912	150.8	—	—
Hydrogen sulfide	H_2S	3	−60.4	920	548.471	100.4	90.22118	—
Isobutane	C_4H_{10}	14	−10.2	595	395.234	133.7	36.97107	—
Krypton	Kr	1	−153.2	2160	117.230	−63.8	54.91724	909
Methane	CH_4	5	−161.7	415	548.471	−82.5	46.28739	162
Methylamine	CH_5N	7	−6.5	—	862.481	157	74.53054	—
Methyl chloride	CH_3Cl	5	−24	997	418.680	143.1	66.78329	370
Methyl ether	C_2H_6O	9	−24	720	468.922	127	53.93658	—
Methyl fluoride	CH_3F	5	−78	—	—	44.9	62.86063	—
Neon	Ne	1	−246.1	1207	104.670	−228.7	27.26249	484
Nitric oxide	NO	2	−152.00	—	460.548	−94	64.72389	520
Nitrogen	N_2	2	−195.81	810	199.292	−147.1	33.93101	311
Nitrous oxide	N_2O	3	−88.7	—	376.812	36.5	72.56921	460
Nitrosyl chloride	NOCl	3	−5.5	—	—	−165	93.65351	—
Oxygen	O_2	2	−182.97	1131	213.527	−118.8	50.40618	530
Ozone	O_3	3	−112	—	—	−5	93.55544	540
Phosphine (hydrogen phosphide)	PH_3	4	−87.5	—	—	52	65.41036	—
Propane	C_3H_8	11	−42.6	585	447.988	96.8	42.46279	226
Propene	C_3H_6	9	−47.0	609	456.361	92.0	45.89512	—
Sulfur dioxide	SO_2	3	−10.0	1460	401.933	157.3	78.84547	524
Xenon	X	1	108.0	3060	96.296	16.6	58.93797	1150

Table 4-2 Specific Heat Capacity[1] c_p of Gases at a Constant Pressure p

Temperature t °C	O_2 c_p kJ/(kg K)	H_2 c_p kJ/(kg K)	NO c_p kJ/(kg K)	OH c_p kJ/(kg K)	H_2O c_p kJ/(kg K)	N_2 c_p kJ/(kg K)	Air c_p kJ/(kg K)	CO c_p kJ/(kg K)	CO_2 c_p kJ/(kg K)	N_2O c_p kJ/(kg K)	SO_2 c_p kJ/(kg K)	N_2S c_p kJ/(kg K)	NH_3 c_p kJ/(kg K)
0	0.9148	14.1949	0.9990	1.7635	1.8594	1.0392	1.0036	1.0396	0.8148	0.8508	0.607	0.992	2.056
100	0.9337	14.4482	0.9969	1.7430	1.8903	1.0421	1.0103	1.0446	0.9136	0.9500	0.662	1.026	2.206
200	0.9630	14.5043	1.0107	1.7346	1.9406	1.0517	1.0245	1.0584	0.9927	1.0283	0.712	1.068	2.386
300	0.9948	14.5332	1.0350	1.7342	2.0005	1.0693	1.0446	1.0802	1.0567	1.0932	0.754	1.122	2.575
400	1.0237	14.5809	1.0609	1.7405	2.0645	1.0915	1.0695	1.1057	1.1103	1.1472	0.783	1.172	2.738
500	1.0484	14.6622	1.0861	1.7547	2.1319	1.1154	1.0923	1.1321	1.1547	1.1928	0.808	1.227	2.931
600	1.0689	14.7786	1.1087	1.7739	2.2014	1.1392	1.1149	1.1568	1.1920	1.2313	0.825	1.273	3.098
700	1.0856	14.9301	1.1283	1.7978	2.2730	1.1614	1.1355	1.1790	1.2230	1.2632	0.837	1.319	3.257
800	1.0999	15.1148	1.1455	1.8246	2.3450	1.1815	1.1539	1.1987	1.2493	1.2912	0.850	1.361	3.400
900	1.1120	15.3120	1.1597	1.8522	2.4154	1.1991	1.1702	1.2158	1.2715	1.3151	0.858	1.398	3.534
1000	1.1229	15.5175	1.1719	1.8795	2.4824	1.2150	1.1844	1.2305	1.2900	1.3352	0.867	1.432	3.655
1100	1.1317	15.7357	1.1824	1.9063	2.5456	1.2288	1.1970	1.2435	1.3059	1.3532	0.871	1.461	—
1200	1.1401	15.9496	1.1911	1.9322	2.6042	1.2410	1.2083	1.2544	1.3197	—	0.875	1.482	—
1300	1.1484	16.1657	1.1991	1.9596	2.6586	1.2514	1.2179	1.2644	1.3314	—	0.879	—	—
1400	1.1564	16.3691	1.2062	1.9795	2.7089	1.2606	1.2267	1.2728	1.3415	—	0.883	—	—
1500	1.1639	16.5642	1.2121	2.0009	2.7553	1.2686	1.2347	1.2799	1.3498	1.3624	0.888	1.587	4.099
1600	1.1710	16.7472	1.2171	2.0210	2.7980	1.2761	1.2418	1.2866	1.3574	—	0.888	—	—
1700	1.1786	16.9218	1.2217	2.0398	2.8382	1.2824	1.2485	1.2925	1.3636	—	0.892	—	—
1800	1.1857	17.0855	1.2259	2.0570	2.8742	1.2883	1.2544	1.2979	1.3695	—	0.892	—	—
1900	1.1928	17.2433	1.2301	2.0729	2.9073	1.2933	1.2602	1.3025	1.3741	—	0.892	—	—
2000	1.2004	17.3890	1.2338	2.0875	2.9379	1.2979	1.2653	1.3067	1.3783	1.3737	0.896	1.595	4.354
2100	1.2075	17.5259	1.2368	2.1018	2.9668	1.3021	1.2703	1.3105	1.3816	—	0.896	—	—
2200	1.2142	17.6608	1.2393	2.1148	2.9936	1.3063	1.2749	1.3138	1.3842	—	0.896	—	—
2300	1.2213	17.7834	1.2422	2.1273	3.0178	1.3096	1.2791	1.3172	1.3862	—	0.896	—	—
2400	1.2280	17.9019	1.2447	2.1390	3.0409	1.3130	1.2833	1.3201	1.3875	—	0.896	—	—
2500	1.2343	18.0141	1.2468	2.1508	3.0618	1.3159	1.2870	1.3230	1.3879	1.3879	0.900	1.679	4.505
2600	1.2410	18.1201	1.2493	2.1746	3.0819	1.3209	1.2925						
2700	1.2472	18.2197	1.2514	2.1729	3.1007	1.3239	1.2925						
2800	1.2493	18.3415	1.2535	2.1834	3.1187	1.3272	1.2979						
2900	1.2548	18.4454	1.2556	2.1935	3.1355	1.3285	1.3008						
3000	1.2602	18.5475	1.2577	2.2035	3.1355	1.3314	1.3021	1.3356	1.3942	1.3942	0.900	1.704	4.601

[1] Older name: Specific heat.

Table 4-2 Specific Heat capacity[1] c_p of Gases at a Constant Pressure p *(continued)*

Temperature t °C	CS_2 c_p kJ/(kg K)	COS c_p kJ/(kg K)	CH_4 c_p kJ/(kg K)	C_2H_6 c_p kJ/(kg K)	C_3H_8 c_p kJ/(kg K)	C_2H_4 c_p kJ/(kg K)	C_2H_2 c_p kJ/(kg K)	C_6H_6 c_p kJ/(kg K)	C_3H_6 c_p kJ/(kg K)	C_2H_5OH c_p kJ/(kg K)
0	0.585	0.670	2.1654	1.6471	1.5495	1.4595	1.6097	0.9433	1.4260	1.5211
100	0.641	0.745	2.4484	2.0674	2.0168	1.8267	1.8702	1.3352	1.7999	1.8267
200	0.678	0.800	2.8068	2.4899	2.4581	2.1759	2.0439	1.6760	2.1600	2.1156
300	0.708	0.842	3.1753	2.8696	2.8345	2.4777	2.1741	1.9565	2.4765	2.3714
400	0.729	0.875	3.5295	3.2138	3.1610	2.7357	2.2818	2.1826	2.7532	2.5950
500	0.745	0.896	3.8560	3.5190	3.4487	2.9580	2.3763	2.3693	2.9919	2.7892
600	0.758	0.917	4.1529	3.7870	3.6974	3.1535	2.4612	2.5242	3.2000	2.9605
700	0.766	0.934	4.4213	4.0223	3.9159	3.3252	2.5390	2.6553	3.3821	3.1095
800	0.775	0.950	4.6595	4.2157	4.0926	3.4730	2.6099	2.7571	3.5404	3.2414
900	0.783	0.959	4.8726	4.3890	4.2500	3.6044	2.6746	2.8613	3.6777	3.3566
1000	0.787	0.971	5.0614	4.5481	4.3945	3.7208	2.7331	2.9429	3.7978	3.4566
1100	0.791	0.980	5.2264	4.6930	4.5263	3.8209	2.7860	3.0128	3.9025	3.5433
1200	0.795	0.984	5.3675	4.8236	4.6448	3.9088	2.8333	3.0731	3.9921	3.6191

[1] Older name: Specific heat.

Table 4-3 Specific Heat Capacity[1] c_V of Gases at a Constant Volume V

Temperature t °C	O_2 c_V kJ/(kg K)	H_2 c_V kJ/(kg K)	NO c_V kJ/(kg K)	OH c_V kJ/(kg K)	H_2O c_V kJ/(kg K)	N_2 c_V kJ/(kg K)	Air c_V kJ/(kg K)	CO c_V kJ/(kg K)	CO_2 c_V kJ/(kg K)
0	0.6548	10.0705	0.7218	1.2745	1.3980	0.7423	0.7164	0.7427	0.6259
100	0.6737	10.3238	0.7197	1.2539	1.4290	0.7453	0.7231	0.7478	0.7247
200	0.7030	10.3799	0.7335	1.2456	1.4792	0.7553	0.7373	0.7616	0.8039
300	0.7348	10.4088	0.7578	1.2452	1.5386	0.7725	0.7578	0.7834	0.8679
400	0.7637	10.4565	0.7838	1.2514	1.6027	0.7947	0.7813	0.8089	0.9211
500	0.7674	10.5378	0.8089	1.2657	1.6701	0.8185	0.8051	0.8353	0.9659
600	0.8089	10.6537	0.8315	1.2849	1.7400	0.8424	0.8281	0.8600	1.0027
700	0.8261	10.8053	0.8512	1.3088	1.8116	0.8646	0.8487	0.8822	1.0341
800	0.8403	10.9904	0.8683	1.3356	1.8836	0.8847	0.8671	0.9018	1.0601
900	0.8520	11.1875	0.8826	0.3632	1.9536	0.9027	0.8834	0.9190	1.0823
1000	0.8625	11.3931	0.8947	1.3904	2.0210	0.9182	0.8976	0.9337	1.1011
1100	0.8717	11.6113	0.9064	1.4172	2.0838	0.9320	0.9102	0.9466	1.1170
1200	0.8805	11.8252	0.9140	1.4432	2.1407	0.9441	0.9211	0.9575	1.1304
1300	0.8884	12.0412	0.9219	1.4679	2.1972	0.9546	0.9311	0.9676	1.1422
1400	0.8964	12.2447	0.9291	1.4905	2.2475	0.9638	0.9399	0.9755	1.1522
1500	0.9039	12.4398	0.9349	1.5119	2.2939	0.9722	0.9479	0.9831	1.1610
1600	0.9115	12.6228	0.9399	1.5320	2.3367	0.9793	0.9550	0.9898	1.1685
1700	0.9186	12.7970	0.9445	1.5508	2.3768	0.9856	0.9613	0.9956	1.1748
1800	0.9261	12.9611	0.9491	1.5680	2.4129	0.9914	0.9676	1.0006	1.1807
1900	0.9332	13.1189	0.9529	1.5839	2.4459	0.9965	0.9730	1.0057	1.1853
2000	0.9404	13.2642	0.9567	1.5985	2.4765	1.0011	0.9785	1.0099	1.1891
2100	0.9475	13.4015	0.9596	1.6128	2.5054	1.0053	0.9831	1.0136	1.1924
2200	0.9546	13.5363	0.9625	1.6257	2.5318	1.0094	0.9877	1.0170	1.1953
2300	0.9613	13.6590	0.9651	1.6383	2.5565	1.0128	0.9919	1.0203	1.1974
2400	0.9680	13.7775	0.9676	1.6500	2.5791	1.0161	0.9960	1.0233	1.1987
2500	0.9747	13.8897	0.9701	1.6617	2.6004	1.0191	0.9998	1.0258	1.1991
2600	0.9810	13.9956	0.9722	1.6730	2.6205				
2700	0.9872	14.0953	0.9726	1.6839	2.6394				
2800	—	—	0.9768	1.6944	2.6574				
2900	—	—	0.9789	1.7044	2.6741				
3000	—	—	0.9805	1.7145	—				

[1] Older name: Specific heat.

Table 4-3 Specific Heat Capacity[1] c_V of Gases at a Constant Volume V *(continued)*

Temperature t °C	N_2O c_V kJ/(kg K)	SO_2 c_V kJ/(kg K)	H_2S c_V kJ/(kg K)	CS_2 c_V kJ/(kg K)	COS c_V kJ/(kg K)	CH_4 c_V kJ/(kg K)	C_2H_6 c_V kJ/(kg K)	C_3H_8 c_V kJ/(kg K)	C_2H_4 c_V kJ/(kg K)	C_2H_2 c_V kJ/(kg K)	C_6H_6 c_V kJ/(kg K)	C_3H_6 c_V kJ/(kg K)	C_2H_5OH c_V kJ/(kg K)
0	0.6619	0.477	0.745	0.473	0.532	1.6471	1.3708	1.3607	1.1627	1.2895	0.8365	1.2280	1.3406
100	0.7607	0.532	0.779	0.528	0.607	1.9301	1.7911	1.8280	1.5299	1.5504	1.2284	1.6019	1.6462
200	0.8395	0.582	0.825	0.569	0.662	2.2885	2.2136	2.2692	1.8790	1.7237	1.5696	1.9619	1.9351
300	0.9043	0.624	0.875	0.599	0.703	2.6569	2.5933	2.6452	2.1805	1.8539	1.8497	2.2785	2.1910
400	0.9584	0.653	0.929	0.620	0.733	3.0111	2.9375	2.9718	2.4388	1.9619	2.0758	2.5552	2.4145
500	1.0040	0.678	0.980	0.636	0.758	3.3377	3.2423	3.2598	2.6611	2.0569	2.2625	2.7939	2.6088
600	1.0425	0.695	1.030	0.649	0.779	3.6346	3.5106	3.5085	2.8567	2.1418	2.4175	3.0019	2.7800
700	1.0743	0.708	1.076	0.657	0.795	3.9029	3.7455	3.7267	3.0283	2.2196	2.5489	3.1841	2.9291
800	1.1020	0.720	1.118	0.666	0.812	4.1412	3.9389	3.9034	3.1761	2.2906	2.6603	3.3423	3.0610
900	1.1258	0.729	1.156	0.674	0.821	4.3543	4.1123	4.0612	3.3076	2.3552	2.7545	3.4796	3.1761
1000	1.1463	0.737	1.185	0.678	0.833	4.5431	4.2714	4.2052	3.4240	2.4137	2.8361	3.5998	3.2762
1100	1.1677	0.741	1.214	0.682	0.842	4.7081	4.4162	4.3375	3.5236	2.4667	2.9065	3.7045	3.3628
1200	—	0.745	1.239	0.687	0.846	4.8492	4.5473	4.4560	3.6120	2.5139	2.9663	3.7941	3.4386

[1] Older name: Specific heat.

Table 4-4   Molar Heat Capacity $C_{p,m}$ of Gases at a Constant Pressure p

Temperature t °C	O₂ $C_{p,m}$ J/(mol K)	H₂ $C_{p,m}$ J/(mol K)	NO $C_{p,m}$ J/(mol K)	OH $C_{p,m}$ J/(mol K)	H₂O $C_{p,m}$ J/(mol K)	N₂ $C_{p,m}$ J/(mol K)	Air $C_{p,m}$ J/(mol K)	CO $C_{p,m}$ J/(mol K)	CO₂ $C_{p,m}$ J/(mol K)	N₂O $C_{p,m}$ J/(mol K)	SO₂ $C_{p,m}$ J/(mol K)	N₂S $C_{p,m}$ J/(mol K)	NH₃ $C_{p,m}$ J/(mol K)
0	29.274	28.617	29.977	29.990	33.499	29.115	29.073	29.123	35.860	37.451	38.854	33.787	35.002
100	29.877	29.128	29.919	29.647	34.055	29.199	29.266	29.262	40.206	41.809	42.412	34.918	37.597
200	30.815	29.241	30.333	29.500	34.964	29.471	29.676	29.647	43.689	45.263	45.552	36.425	40.696
300	31.832	29.299	31.058	29.496	36.036	29.952	30.226	30.254	46.515	48.119	48.232	38.184	43.836
400	32.758	29.396	31.832	29.605	37.191	30.576	30.949	30.974	48.860	50.501	50.242	39.984	46.599
500	33.549	29.559	32.590	29.844	38.406	31.250	31.640	31.707	50.815	52.511	51.707	41.742	49.949
600	34.202	29.793	33.268	30.170	39.662	31.920	32.301	32.402	52.452	54.202	52.879	43.417	52.796
700	34.746	30.099	33.859	30.580	40.951	32.540	32.900	33.025	53.826	55.609	53.759	45.008	55.433
800	35.203	30.472	34.369	31.033	42.249	33.101	33.432	33.574	54.977	56.827	54.428	46.390	57.903
900	35.584	30.869	34.796	31.501	43.513	33.599	33.905	34.055	55.952	57.878	55:015	47.646	60.206
1000	35.914	31.284	35.165	31.966	44.723	34.043	34.315	34.470	56.773	58.774	55.433	48.776	62.300
1100	36.216	31.723	35.475	32.423	45.858	34.424	34.679	34.826	57.472	59.561	55.768	49.739	—
1200	36.488	32.155	35.743	32.862	46.913	34.763	35.002	35.140	58.071	—	56.061	50.577	—
1300	36.752	32.590	35.981	33.281	47.897	35.060	35.291	35.412	58.586	—	56.354	—	—
1400	36.999	33.000	36.191	33.666	48.801	35.320	35.546	35.646	59.030	—	56.564	—	—
1500	37.242	33.394	36.371	34.030	49.639	35.546	35.772	35.856	59.411	59.829	56.773	52.502	69.794
1600	37.480	33.762	36.526	34.374	50.409	35.747	35.977	36.040	59.737	—	56.899	—	—
1700	37.715	34.114	36.664	34.692	51.133	35.927	36.170	36.203	60.022	—	57.024	—	—
1800	37.945	34.445	36.794	34.985	51.782	36.090	36.346	36.350	60.269	—	57.150	—	—
1900	38.175	34.763	36.911	35.257	52.377	36.237	36.509	36.480	60.478	—	57.234	—	—
2000	38.406	35.056	37.024	35.508	52.930	36.367	36.655	36.597	60.654	60.457	57.317	54.428	74.148
2100	38.636	35.332	37.116	35.747	53.449	36.484	36.798	36.706	60.801	—	57.359	—	—
2200	38.858	35.605	37.196	35.969	53.930	36.593	36.928	36.802	60.918	—	57.443	—	—
2300	39.080	35.852	37.275	36.178	54.370	36.693	37.053	36.894	61.006	—	57.485	—	—
2400	39.293	36.090	37.350	36.379	54.780	36.785	37.170	36.978	61.060	—	57.527	—	—
2500	39.502	36.316	37.422	36.580	55.161	36.869	37.279	37.053	61.085	61.085	57.610	55.601	76.744
2600	39.708	36.530	37.493	36.773	55.525	37.022	37.430						
2700	39.909	36.731	37.560	36.957	55.864	37.106	37.514						
2800	39.984	36.969	37.623	37.137	56.187	37.189	37.597						
2900	40.152	37.199	37.685	37.309	56.488	37.231	37.681						
3000	40.277	37.388	37.744	37.476	56.522	37.263	37.765	37.388	61.378	61.420	57.736	56.271	78.377
M*	32	2.0156	30.008	17.008	18.020	28.016	28.964	28.010	44.010	44.016	64.04	34.08	17.031

[M*] = kg/kmol.

Table 4-4   Molar Heat Capacity $C_{p,m}$ of Gases at a Constant Pressure p (*continued*)

Temperature t °C	CS₂ $C_{p,m}$ J/(mol K)	COS $C_{p,m}$ J/(mol K)	CH₄ $C_{p,m}$ J/(mol K)	C₂H₆ $C_{p,m}$ J/(mol K)	C₃H₈ $C_{p,m}$ J/(mol K)	C₂H₄ $C_{p,m}$ J/(mol K)	C₂H₂ $C_{p,m}$ J/(mol K)	C₆H₆ $C_{p,m}$ J/(mol K)	C₃H₆ $C_{p,m}$ J/(mol K)	C₂H₅OH $C_{p,m}$ J/(mol K)
0	44.506	40.277	34.738	49.530	68.329	40.947	41.910	73.688	59.997	70.087
100	48.651	44.799	39.281	62.170	88.928	51.246	48.692	104.293	75.739	84.197
200	51.707	48.106	45.029	74.873	108.396	61.044	53.214	130.921	90.895	97.469
300	53.884	50.493	50.941	86.290	124.976	69.501	56.606	152.818	104.209	109.275
400	55.559	52.461	56.622	96.636	139.379	76.744	59.411	170.486	115.849	119.575
500	56.815	53.884	61.856	105.805	152.065	82.982	61.868	185.057	125.897	128.535
600	57.778	55.140	66.620	113.868	163.034	88.467	64.079	197.156	134.647	136.448
700	58.490	56.187	70.929	120.936	172.664	93.282	66.105	207.414	142.309	143.314
800	59.076	57.024	74.747	126.755	180.451	97.427	67.952	216.123	148.966	149.385
900	59.536	57.736	78.168	131.964	187.401	101.111	69.635	223.491	154.744	154.702
1000	59.955	58.322	81.195	136.753	193.765	104.377	71.159	229.855	159.810	159.308
1100	60.290	58.825	83.845	141.108	199.585	107.182	72.536	235.340	164.206	163.285
1200	60.541	59.201	86.106	145.039	204.818	109.652	73.767	240.029	167.974	166.760
M*	76.13	60.07	16.031	30.07	44.06	28.031	26.040	78.108	42.08	46.07

[M*] = kg/kmol.

Table 4-5 Molar Heat Capacity $C_{V,m}$ of Gases at a Constant Volume V

Temperature t °C	O$_2$ $C_{V,m}$ J/(mol K)	H$_2$ $C_{V,m}$ J/(mol K)	NO $C_{V,m}$ J/(mol K)	OH $C_{V,m}$ J/(mol K)	H$_2$O $C_{V,m}$ J/(mol K)	N$_2$ $C_{V,m}$ J/(mol K)	Air $C_{V,m}$ J/(mol K)	CO $C_{V,m}$ J/(mol K)	CO$_2$ $C_{V,m}$ J/(mol K)
0	20.959	20.302	21.663	21.675	25.184	20.800	20.758	20.808	27.545
100	21.562	20.813	21.604	21.332	25.740	20.884	20.951	20.947	31.891
200	22.500	20.926	22.019	21.185	26.649	21.156	21.361	21.332	35.374
300	23.517	20.984	22.743	21.181	27.721	21.637	21.951	21.939	38.200
400	24.443	21.081	23.517	21.290	28.876	22.261	22.634	22.659	40.545
500	25.234	21.244	24.275	21.529	30.091	22.935	23.325	23.392	42.500
600	25.887	21.478	24.953	21.855	31.347	23.605	23.986	24.087	44.137
700	26.431	21.784	25.544	22.265	32.636	24.225	24.585	24.710	45.511
800	26.888	22.157	26.054	22.718	33.934	24.786	25.117	25.259	46.662
900	27.269	22.554	26.482	23.186	35.198	25.284	25.590	25.740	47.637
1000	27.599	22.969	26.850	23.651	36.408	25.724	26.000	26.155	48.458
1100	27.901	23.408	27.202	24.108	37.543	26.109	26.364	26.511	49.157
1200	28.173	23.840	27.428	24.547	38.598	26.448	26.687	26.825	49.756
1300	28.437	24.275	27.666	24.966	39.582	26.745	26.976	27.097	50.271
1400	28.684	24.685	27.876	25.351	40.486	27.005	27.231	27.331	50.715
1500	28.927	25.079	28.056	25.715	41.324	27.231	27.457	27.541	51.096
1600	29.165	25.447	28.211	26.059	42.094	27.432	27.662	27.725	51.422
1700	29.400	25.799	28.349	26.377	42.818	27.612	27.855	27.888	51.707
1800	29.630	26.130	28.479	26.670	43.467	27.775	28.031	28.035	51.954
1900	29.860	26.448	28.596	26.942	44.062	27.922	28.194	28.165	52.163
2000	30.091	26.741	28.709	27.193	44.615	28.052	28.340	28.282	52.339
2100	30.321	27.017	28.801	27.432	45.134	28.169	28.504	28.391	52.486
2200	30.543	27.290	28.881	27.654	45.615	28.278	28.613	28.487	52.603
2300	30.765	27.537	28.960	27.863	46.055	28.378	28.738	28.579	52.691
2400	30.978	27.775	29.035	28.064	46.465	28.470	28.855	28.663	52.745
2500	31.187	28.001	29.107	28.265	46.846	28.554	28.964	28.738	52.770
2600	31.393	28.215	29.178	28.458	47.210				
2700	31.594	28.416	29.245	28.642	47.549				
2800			29.308	28.822	47.872				
2900			29.370	28.994	48.173				
3000			29.429	29.161					
M*	32	2.0156	30.008	17.008	18.020	28.016	28.964	28.010	40.010

[M*] = kg/kmol.

Table 4-5 Molar Heat Capacity $C_{V,m}$ of Gases at a Constant Volume V (continued)

Temperature t °C	N$_2$O $C_{V,m}$ J/(mol K)	SO$_2$ $C_{V,m}$ J/(mol K)	N$_2$S $C_{V,m}$ J/(mol K)	CS$_2$ $C_{V,m}$ J/(mol K)	COS $C_{V,m}$ J/(mol K)	CH$_4$ $C_{V,m}$ J/(mol K)	C$_2$H$_6$ $C_{V,m}$ J/(mol K)	C$_3$H$_8$ $C_{V,m}$ J/(mol K)	C$_2$H$_4$ $C_{V,m}$ J/(mol K)	C$_2$H$_2$ $C_{V,m}$ J/(mol K)	C$_6$H$_6$ $C_{V,m}$ J/(mol K)	C$_3$H$_6$ $C_{V,m}$ J/(mol K)	C$_2$H$_5$OH $C_{V,m}$ J/(mol K)
0	29.136	30.522	25.456	36.174	31.945	26.423	41.215	59.997	32.615	33.578	65.356	51.665	61.755
100	33.494	34.081	26.586	40.319	36.467	30.966	53.855	80.596	42.915	40.361	95.961	67.407	75.865
200	36.949	37.221	28.093	43.375	39.755	36.714	66.558	100.065	52.712	44.882	122.590	82.564	89.137
300	39.804	39.900	29.852	45.552	42.161	42.626	77.975	116.644	61.169	48.274	144.486	95.878	100.944
400	42.186	41.910	31.652	47.227	44.129	48.307	88.321	131.047	68.412	51.079	162.155	107.517	111.243
500	44.196	43.375	33.441	48.483	45.552	53.541	97.490	143.733	74.651	53.553	176.725	117.565	120.203
600	45.887	44.548	35.085	49.446	46.808	58.305	105.553	154.702	80.135	55.764	188.825	126.316	128.116
700	47.294	45.427	36.676	50.158	47.855	62.614	112.621	164.332	84.950	57.790	199.082	133.978	134.982
800	48.512	46.097	38.058	50.744	48.692	66.432	118.440	172.119	89.095	59.637	207.791	140.635	141.053
900	49.563	46.683	39.314	51.205	49.404	69.853	123.649	179.069	92.779	61.320	215.160	146.412	146.371
1000	50.459	47.102	40.444	51.623	49.990	72.880	128.438	185.433	96.045	62.844	221.524	151.478	150.976
1100	51.246	47.436	41.407	51.958	50.493	75.530	132.793	191.253	98.850	64.221	227.008	155.875	154.953
1200	—	47.730	42.245	52.209	50.870	77.791	136.724	196.487	101.321	65.452	231.698	159.643	158.429
M*	44.016	64.06	34.08	76.13	60.07	16.031	30.07	44.06	28.031	26.04	78.108	42.08	46.07

[M*] = kg/kmol.

202

Table 4-6 Mean Specific Heat Capacity[1] $\overline{c}_p$ of Gases at a Constant Pressure p in the Temperature Range Between 0 °C and t

Temperature t °C	H_2 $\overline{c}_p$ kJ/(kg K)	N_2 $\overline{c}_p$ kJ/(kg K)	O_2 $\overline{c}_p$ kJ/(kg K)	CO $\overline{c}_p$ kJ/(kg K)	CO_2 $\overline{c}_p$ kJ/(kg K)	Air $\overline{c}_p$ kJ/(kg K)	H_2O $\overline{c}_p$ kJ/(kg K)	NO $\overline{c}_p$ kJ/(kg K)	OH $\overline{c}_p$ kJ/(kg K)
0	14.195	1.039	0.915	1.040	0.815	1.004	1.859	0.999	1.763
100	14.353	1.040	0.923	1.042	0.866	1.006	1.873	0.996	1.750
200	14.421	1.043	0.935	1.046	0.910	1.012	1.894	1.000	1.743
300	14.446	1.049	0.950	1.054	0.949	1.019	1.919	1.007	1.740
400	14.477	1.057	0.965	1.063	0.983	1.028	1.948	1.017	1.740
500	14.509	1.066	0.979	1.075	1.013	1.039	1.978	1.029	1.740
600	14.542	1.076	0.993	1.086	1.040	1.050	2.009	1.040	1.745
700	14.587	1.087	1.005	1.098	1.064	1.061	2.042	1.051	1.751
800	14.641	1.097	1.016	1.109	1.085	1.071	2.075	1.062	1.758
900	14.706	1.108	1.026	1.120	1.104	1.081	2.110	1.072	1.767
1000	14.776	1.118	1.035	1.130	1.122	1.091	2.144	1.081	1.777
1100	14.853	1.127	1.043	1.140	1.138	1.100	2.177	1.090	1.788
1200	14.934	1.136	1.051	1.149	1.153	1.108	2.211	1.098	1.799
1300	15.023	1.145	1.058	1.158	1.166	1.117	2.243	1.106	1.810
1400	15.113	1.153	1.065	1.166	1.178	1.124	2.274	1.113	1.821
1500	15.202	1.160	1.071	1.173	1.189	1.131	2.305	1.119	1.832
1600	15.294	1.167	1.077	1.180	1.200	1.138	2.335	1.125	1.843
1700	15.383	1.174	1.083	1.187	1:209	1.144	2.363	1.131	1.855
1800	15.472	1.180	1.089	1.192	1.218	1.150	2.391	1.136	1.865
1900	15.561	1.186	1.094	1.198	1.226	1.156	2.417	1.141	1.876
2000	15.649	1.191	1.099	1.203	1.233	1.161	2.442	1.146	1.886
2100	15.736	1.197	1.104	1.208	1.241	1.166	2.466	1.150	1.896
2200	15.819	1.201	1.109	1.213	1.247	1.171	2.489	1.154	1.906
2300	15.902	1.206	1.114	1.218	1.253	1.176	2.512	1.158	1.915
2400	15.983	1.210	1.118	1.222	1.259	1.180	2.533	1.161	1.925
2500	16.064	1.214	1.123	1.226	1.264	1.184	2.554	1.164	1.933
2600	16.141		1.127				2.574	1.168	1.942
2700	16.215		1.131				2.594	1.171	1.951
2800							2.612	1.174	1.959
2900							2.630	1.176	1.967
3000								1.179	1.974

[1] Older name: Mean specific heat.

Table 4-6 Mean Specific Heat Capacity[1] $\overline{c}_p$ of Gases at a Constant Pressure p in the Temperature Range Between 0 °C and t (*continued*)

Temperature t °C	SO_2 $\overline{c}_p$ kJ/(kg K)	CH_4 $\overline{c}_p$ kJ/(kg K)	C_2H_4 $\overline{c}_p$ kJ/(kg K)	C_2H_2 $\overline{c}_p$ kJ/(kg K)	N_2O $\overline{c}_p$ kJ/(kg K)	N_2S $\overline{c}_p$ kJ/(kg K)	CS_2 $\overline{c}_p$ kJ/(kg K)	COS $\overline{c}_p$ kJ/(kg K)	C_2H_6 $\overline{c}_p$ kJ/(kg K)	C_3H_8 $\overline{c}_p$ kJ/(kg K)	C_6H_6 $\overline{c}_p$ kJ/(kg K)	C_3H_6 $\overline{c}_p$ kJ/(kg K)	C_2H_5OH $\overline{c}_p$ kJ/(kg K)
0	0.607	2.165	1.460	1.610	0.851	0.992	0.586	0.670	1.647	1.550	0.943	1.426	1.521
100	0.636	2.294	1.648	1.762	0.886	1.009	0.611	0.708	1.860	1.784	1.146	1.624	1.677
200	0.662	2.458	1.824	1.863	0.947	1.026	0.636	0.741	2.068	2.016	1.326	1.800	1.820
300	0.687	2.635	1.994	1.946	0.985	1.051	0.657	0.770	2.269	2.221	1.492	1.974	1.963
400	0.708	2.816	2.146	2.018	1.019	1.080	0.670	0.791	2.466	2.420	1.637	2.133	2.094
500	0.724	2.991	2.288	2.080	1.049	1.097	0.682	0.808	2.648	2.589	1.765	2.281	2.214
600	0.737	3.159	2.418	2.137	1.077	1.122	0.695	0.825	2.816	2.761	1.880	2.418	2.325
700	0.754	3.321	2.533	2.189	1.101	1.147	0.708	0.842	2.972	2.909	1.981	2.544	2.426
800	0.762	3.485	2.643	2.238	1.124	1.172	0.716	0.854	3.117	3.044	2.072	2.659	2.520
900	0.775	3.636	2.742	2.283	1.143	1.193	0.720	0.862	3.251	3.168	2.155	2.765	2.606
1000	0.783	3.771	2.834	2.325	1.162	1.218	0.729	0.875	3.377	3.285	2.230	2.862	2.684
1100	0.791	3.893	2.921	2.365	1.178	1.239	0.733	0.883	3.491	3.935	2.298	2.951	2.758
1200	0.795	4.000	2.999	2.402	—	1.256	0.737	0.892	3.597	3.498	2.359	3.035	2.826

[1] Older name: Mean specific heat.

203

Table 4-7 Mean Specific Heat Capacity[1] $\overline{c}_V$ of Gases at a Constant Volume V in the Temperature Range Between $0\,°C$ and t

Temperature t °C	H_2 $\overline{c}_V$ kJ/(kg K)	N_2 $\overline{c}_V$ kJ/(kg K)	O_2 $\overline{c}_V$ kJ/(kg K)	CO $\overline{c}_V$ kJ/(kg K)	CO_2 $\overline{c}_V$ kJ/(kg K)	Air $\overline{c}_V$ kJ/(kg K)	H_2O $\overline{c}_V$ kJ/(kg K)	NO $\overline{c}_V$ kJ/(kg K)	OH $\overline{c}_V$ kJ/(kg K)
0	10.071	0.742	0.655	0.743	0.626	0.716	1.398	0.722	1.274
100	10.228	0.744	0.663	0.745	0.677	0.719	1.411	0.719	1.261
200	10.297	0.747	0.675	0.749	0.721	0.724	1.432	0.723	1.254
300	10.322	0.752	0.690	0.757	0.760	0.732	1.457	0.730	1.251
400	10.353	0.760	0.705	0.767	0.794	0.741	1.486	0.740	1.251
500	10.384	0.769	0.719	0.777	0.824	0.752	1.516	0.752	1.251
600	10.417	0.779	0.733	0.789	0.851	0.762	1.547	0.763	1.256
700	10.463	0.790	0.745	0.801	0.875	0.773	1.581	0.774	1.261
800	10.517	0.801	0.756	0.812	0.896	0.784	1.614	0.785	1.269
900	10.581	0.811	0.766	0.823	0.916	0.794	1.648	0.795	1.278
1000	10.652	0.821	0.775	0.834	0.933	0.804	1.682	0.804	1.288
1100	10.729	0.830	0.783	0.843	0.950	0.813	1.716	0.813	1.299
1200	10.809	0.839	0.791	0.857	0.964	0.821	1.749	0.821	1.310
1300	10.899	0.848	0.798	0.861	0.977	0.829	1.781	0.829	1.321
1400	10.988	0.856	0.805	0.869	0.989	0.837	1.813	0.836	1.332
1500	11.077	0.863	0.811	0.876	1.001	0.844	1.843	0.842	1.343
1600	11.169	0.870	0.817	0.883	1.011	0.851	1.873	0.848	1.354
1700	11.258	0.877	0.823	0.889	1.020	0.857	1.902	0.854	1.366
1800	11.347	0.883	0.829	0.896	1.029	0.863	1.929	0.859	1.376
1900	11.437	0.889	0.834	0.901	1.037	0.869	1.955	0.864	1.387
2000	11.524	0.894	0.839	0.906	1.045	0.874	1.980	0.868	1.397
2100	11.611	0.900	0.844	0.911	1.052	0.879	2.005	0.873	1.408
2200	11.694	0.905	0.849	0.916	1.058	0.884	2.028	0.877	1.417
2300	11.798	0.909	0.854	0.921	1.064	0.889	2.050	0.880	1.426
2400	11.858	0.914	0.858	0.925	1.070	0.893	2.072	0.884	1.436
2500	11.939	0.918	0.863	0.929	1.075	0.897	2.093	0.887	1.444
2600	12.016		0.868				2.113	0.891	1.453
2700	12.091		0.872				2.132	0.893	1.462
2800							2.151	0.896	1.470
2900							2.168	0.899	1.478
3000								0.902	1.485

[1] Older name: Mean specific heat.

Table 4-7 Mean Specific Heat Capacity[1] $\overline{c}_V$ of Gases at a Constant Volume V in the Temperature Range Between $0\,°C$ and t *(continued)*

Temperature t °C	SO_2 $\overline{c}_V$ kJ/(kg K)	CH_4 $\overline{c}_V$ kJ/(kg K)	C_2H_4 $\overline{c}_V$ kJ/(kg K)	C_2H_2 $\overline{c}_V$ kJ/(kg K)	N_2O $\overline{c}_V$ kJ/(kg K)	N_2S $\overline{c}_V$ kJ/(kg K)	CS_2 $\overline{c}_V$ kJ/(kg K)	COS $\overline{c}_V$ kJ/(kg K)	C_2H_6 $\overline{c}_V$ kJ/(kg K)	C_3H_8 $\overline{c}_V$ kJ/(kg K)	C_6H_6 $\overline{c}_V$ kJ/(kg K)	C_3H_6 $\overline{c}_V$ kJ/(kg K)	C_2H_5OH $\overline{c}_V$ kJ/(kg K)
0	0.477	1.647	1.163	1.290	0.662	0.745	0.473	0.532	1.371	1.361	0.837	1.228	1.341
100	0.507	1.776	1.351	1.442	0.713	0.762	0.502	0.569	1.583	1.595	1.039	1.426	1.496
200	0.532	1.939	1.527	1.544	0.758	0.783	0.528	0.603	1.792	1.827	1.219	1.602	1.640
300	0.557	2.117	1.697	1.627	0.796	0.804	0.544	0.628	1.992	2.032	1.385	1.776	1.782
400	0.578	2.298	1.849	1.698	0.830	0.829	0.561	0.653	2.190	2.230	1.531	1.935	1.913
500	0.595	2.472	1.991	1.761	0.860	0.854	0.574	0.670	2.372	2.400	1.658	2.083	2.033
600	0.607	2.641	2.121	1.818	0.888	0.879	0.586	0.687	2.440	2.572	1.773	2.220	2.144
700	0.624	2.803	2.236	1.870	0.912	0.904	0.595	0.703	2.695	2.720	1.874	2.346	2.245
800	0.632	2.966	2.346	1.919	0.934	0.929	0.603	0.716	2.840	2.855	1.966	2.461	2.339
900	0.645	3.118	2.445	1.964	0.955	0.950	0.611	0.724	2.975	2.978	2.048	2.567	2.425
1000	0.653	3.253	2.537	2.006	0.973	0.971	0.620	0.737	3.100	3.095	2.123	2.664	2.503
1100	0.662	3.375	2.624	2.045	0.989	0.992	0.624	0.745	3.215	3.205	2.191	2.753	2.578
1200	0.666	3.482	2.701	2.083	—	1.013	0.628	0.754	3.321	3.309	2.252	2.837	2.645

[1] Older name: Mean specific heat.

Table 4-8 Mean Molar Heat Capacity[1] $\overline{C}_{p,m}$ of Gases at a Constant Pressure p in the Temperature Range Between 0 °C and t

Temperature t °C	H_2 $\overline{C}_{p,m}$ J/(mol K)	N_2 $\overline{C}_{p,m}$ J/(mol K)	O_2 $\overline{C}_{p,m}$ J/(mol K)	CO $\overline{C}_{p,m}$ J/(mol K)	CO_2 $\overline{C}_{p,m}$ J/(mol K)	Air $\overline{C}_{p,m}$ J/(mol K)	H_2O $\overline{C}_{p,m}$ J/(mol K)	NO $\overline{C}_{p,m}$ J/(mol K)	OH $\overline{C}_{p,m}$ J/(mol K)	SO_2 $\overline{C}_{p,m}$ J/(mol K)
0	28.617	29.115	29.274	29.123	35.860	29.073	33.499	29.977	29.990	38.854
100	28.935	29.144	29.538	29.178	38.112	29.153	33.741	29.906	29.760	40.654
200	29.073	29.228	29.931	29.303	40.059	29.299	34.118	29.998	29.643	42.329
300	29.123	29.383	30.400	29.517	41.755	29.521	34.575	30.229	20.601	43.878
400	29.186	29.601	30.878	29.789	43.250	29.789	35.090	30.530	29.584	45.217
500	29.249	29.864	31.334	30.099	44.573	30.095	35.630	30.869	29.605	46.390
600	29.316	30.149	31.761	30.425	45.753	30.405	36.195	31.213	29.672	47.353
700	29.408	30.451	32.150	30.752	46.813	30.723	36.789	31.552	29.772	48.232
800	29.517	30.748	32.502	31.070	47.763	31.028	37.392	31.874	29.898	48.944
900	29.647	31.037	32.825	31.376	48.617	31.321	38.008	32.171	30.049	49.614
1000	29.789	31.313	33.118	31.665	49.392	31.598	38.619	32.456	30.220	50.158
1100	29.944	31.577	33.386	31.937	50.099	31.862	39.226	32.716	30.409	50.660
1200	30.107	31.828	33.633	32.192	50.740	32.109	39.825	32.958	30.601	51.079
1300	30.287	32.067	33.863	32.427	51.322	32.343	40.407	33.180	30.790	51.623
1400	30.467	32.293	34.076	32.653	51.858	32.565	40.976	33.390	30.974	51.958
1500	30.647	32.502	34.282	32.858	52.348	32.774	41.525	33.582	31.179	52.251
1600	30.832	32.699	34.474	33.051	52.800	32.967	42.056	33.767	31.355	52.544
1700	31.012	32.883	34.658	33.231	53.218	33.151	42.576	33.934	31.543	52.796
1800	31.192	33.055	34.834	33.402	53.604	33.319	43.070	34.089	31.723	53.047
1900	31.372	33.218	35.006	33.561	53.959	33.482	43.539	34.231	31.899	53.214
2000	31.548	33.373	35.169	33.708	54.290	33.641	43.995	34.369	32.075	53.465
2100	31.723	33.520	35.328	33.850	54.596	33.787	44.435	34.499	32.247	53.633
2200	31.891	33.658	35.483	33.980	54.881	33.926	44.853	34.621	32.414	53.800
2300	32.058	33.787	35.634	34.106	55.144	34.060	45.255	34.734	32.577	53.968
2400	32.222	33.909	35.785	34.223	55.391	34.185	45.644	34.838	32.737	54.135
2500	32.385	34.002	35.927	34.336	55.617	34.307	46.017	34.943	32.887	54.261
2600	32.540	34.206	36.069	34.499	55.852	34.332	46.381	35.039	33.034	54.387
2700	32.691	34.290	36.207	34.583	56.061	34.457	46.729	35.131	33.176	54.512
2800	32.866	34.415	36.341	34.667	56.229	34.541	47.060	35.219	33.314	54.596
2900	33.034	34.499	36.509	34.750	56.438	34.625	47.378	35.303	33.448	54.721
3000	33.159	34.583	36.676	34.834	56.606	34.709	—	35.383	33.578	54.847
M*	2.0156	28.016	32.000	28.010	44.010	28.964	18.020	30.008	17.008	64.06

(M*)=kg/kmol.

Table 4-8 Mean Molar Heat Capacity[1] $\overline{C}_{p,m}$ of Gases at a Constant Pressure p in the Temperature Range Between 0 °C and t *(continued)*

Temperature t °C	CH_4 $\overline{C}_{p,m}$ J/(mol K)	C_2H_4 $\overline{C}_{p,m}$ J/(mol K)	C_2H_2 $\overline{C}_{p,m}$ J/(mol K)	N_2O $\overline{C}_{p,m}$ J/(mol K)	N_2S $\overline{C}_{p,m}$ J/(mol K)	CS_2 $\overline{C}_{p,m}$ J/(mol K)	COS $\overline{C}_{p,m}$ J/(mol K)	C_2H_6 $\overline{C}_{p,m}$ J/(mol K)	C_3H_8 $\overline{C}_{p,m}$ J/(mol K)	C_6H_6 $\overline{C}_{p,m}$ J/(mol K)	C_3H_6 $\overline{C}_{p,m}$ J/(mol K)	C_2H_5OH $\overline{C}_{p,m}$ J/(mol K)
0	34.738	40.947	41.910	37.451	33.787	44.506	40.277	49.530	68.329	73.688	59.997	70.087
100	36.806	46.222	45.871	39.712	34.332	46.683	42.622	55.919	78.670	89.472	68.329	77.288
200	39.427	51.163	48.517	41.675	35.002	48.483	44.589	62.195	88.886	103.540	75.739	83.903
300	42.274	55.936	50.677	43.371	35.755	49.907	46.180	68.232	97.929	116.561	83.066	90.477
400	45.180	60.206	52.536	44.862	36.593	51.121	47.520	74.161	106.680	127.907	89.765	96.464
500	47.977	64.184	54.160	46.185	37.430	52.126	48.651	79.629	114.174	137.871	96.003	101.990
600	50.673	67.826	55.638	47.390	37.309	53.005	49.614	84.674	121.752	146.831	101.739	107.140
700	53.277	71.050	56.999	48.475	39.147	53.759	50.493	89.355	128.284	154.744	107.056	111.788
800	55.902	74.148	58.268	49.454	39.984	54.387	51.246	93.713	134.229	161.862	111.871	116.100
900	58.330	76.912	59.444	50.334	40.738	54.931	51.916	97.766	141.765	168.309	116.351	120.077
1000	60.503	79.507	60.537	51.133	41.491	55.391	52.544	101.526	144.821	174.171	120.412	123.678
1100	62.454	81.936	61.571	51.866	42.203	55.852	53.089	104.984	149.678	179.488	124.170	127.111
1200	64.175	84.113	62.542	—	42.831	56.229	53.591	108.162	154.242	184.261	127.697	130.209
M*	16.031	28.031	26.04	44.016	34.08	76.13	60.07	30.047	44.06	78.108	42.08	46.07

[M*]=kg/kmol.

Table 4-9 Mean Molar Heat Capacity[1] $\overline{C}_{V,m}$ of Gases at a Constant Volume V in the Temperature Range Between $0\,°C$ and t

Temperature t °C	H$_2$ $\overline{C}_{V,m}$ J/(mol K)	N$_2$ $\overline{C}_{V,m}$ J/(mol K)	O$_2$ $\overline{C}_{V,m}$ J/(mol K)	CO $\overline{C}_{V,m}$ J/(mol K)	CO$_2$ $\overline{C}_{V,m}$ J/(mol K)	Air $\overline{C}_{V,m}$ J/(mol K)	H$_2$O $\overline{C}_{V,m}$ J/(mol K)	NO $\overline{C}_{V,m}$ J/(mol K)	OH $\overline{C}_{V,m}$ J/(mol K)
0	20.302	20.800	20.959	20.808	27.545	20.758	25.184	21.663	21.675
100	20.620	20.829	21.223	20.863	29.797	20.838	25.426	21.591	21.445
200	20.758	20.913	21.616	20.988	31.744	20.984	25.803	21.683	21.328
300	20.808	21.068	22.085	21.202	33.440	21.206	26.260	21.914	21.286
400	20.871	21.286	22.563	21.474	34.935	21.474	26.775	22.215	21.269
500	20.934	21.549	23.019	21.784	36.258	21.780	27.315	22.554	21.290
600	21.001	21.834	23.446	22.100	37.438	22.090	27.880	22.898	21.357
700	21.093	22.136	23.835	22.437	38.498	22.408	28.474	23.237	21.457
800	21.202	22.433	24.187	22.755	39.448	22.713	29.077	23.559	21.583
900	21.332	22.722	24.510	23.061	40.302	23.006	29.693	23.856	21.734
1000	21.474	22.998	24.803	23.350	41.077	23.283	30.304	24.141	21.905
1100	21.629	23.262	25.071	23.622	41.784	23.547	30.911	24.401	22.094
1200	21.792	23.513	25.318	23.877	42.425	23.794	31.510	24.644	22.286
1300	21.972	23.752	25.548	24.112	43.007	24.028	32.092	24.865	22.475
1400	22.152	23.978	25.761	24.338	43.543	24.250	32.661	25.075	22.659
1500	22.332	24.187	25.967	24.543	44.033	24.459	33.210	25.267	22.847
1600	22.517	24.384	26.159	24.736	44.485	24.652	33.741	25.452	23.040
1700	22.697	24.568	26.343	24.916	44.903	24.836	34.261	25.619	23.228
1800	22.877	24.740	26.519	25.087	45.289	25.004	34.755	25.774	23.408
1900	23.057	24.903	26.691	25.246	45.644	25.167	35.224	25.916	23.584
2000	23.233	25.058	26.854	25.393	45.975	25.326	35.680	26.054	23.760
2100	23.408	25.205	27.013	25.535	46.281	25.472	36.120	26.184	23.932
2200	23.576	25.343	27.168	25.665	46.566	25.611	36.538	26.306	24.099
2300	23.743	25.472	27.319	25.791	46.829	25.745	36.940	26.419	24.263
2400	23.907	25.594	27.470	25.908	47.076	25.870	37.330	26.523	24.422
2500	24.070	25.707	27.612	26.021	47.302	25.992	37.702	26.628	24.572
2600	24.225		27.754				38.066	26.724	24.719
2700	24.376		27.892				38.414	26.816	24.861
2800							38.745	26.904	24.999
2900							39.063	26.988	25.133
3000								27.068	25.263
M*	2.0156	28.016	32.000	28.010	44.010	28.964	18.020	30.008	17.008

[M*]=kg/mol.

Table 4-9 Mean Molar Heat Capacity[1] $\overline{C}_{V,m}$ of Gases at a Constant Volume V in the Temperature Range Between $0\,°C$ and t *(continued)*

Temperature t °C	SO$_2$ $\overline{C}_{V,m}$ J/(mol K)	CH$_4$ $\overline{C}_{V,m}$ J/(mol K)	C$_2$H$_4$ $\overline{C}_{V,m}$ J/(mol K)	C$_2$H$_2$ $\overline{C}_{V,m}$ J/(mol K)	N$_2$O $\overline{C}_{V,m}$ J/(mol K)	N$_2$S $\overline{C}_{V,m}$ J/(mol K)	CS$_2$ $\overline{C}_{V,m}$ J/(mol K)	COS $\overline{C}_{V,m}$ J/(mol K)	C$_2$H$_6$ $\overline{C}_{V,m}$ J/(mol K)	C$_3$H$_8$ $\overline{C}_{V,m}$ J/(mol K)	C$_6$H$_6$ $\overline{C}_{V,m}$ J/(mol K)	C$_3$H$_6$ $\overline{C}_{V,m}$ J/(mol K)	C$_2$H$_5$OH $\overline{C}_{V,m}$ J/(mol K)
0	30.522	26.423	32.615	33.578	29.136	25.456	36.174	31.945	41.215	59.997	65.356	51.665	61.755
100	32.322	28.491	37.891	37.556	31.397	26.000	38.351	34.290	47.604	70.338	81.140	59.997	68.957
200	33.997	31.112	42.831	40.202	33.360	26.670	40.151	36.258	53.880	80.554	95.208	67.407	75.572
300	35.546	33.959	47.604	42.362	35.056	27.424	41.575	37.849	59.917	89.598	108.229	74.734	82.145
400	36.886	36.865	51.833	44.221	36.547	28.261	42.789	39.188	65.846	98.348	119.575	81.433	88.132
500	38.058	39.662	55.852	45.845	37.870	29.098	43.794	40.319	71.314	105.842	129.540	87.672	93.659
600	39.021	42.358	59.494	47.323	39.075	29.977	44.673	41.282	76.359	113.420	138.499	93.408	98.808
700	39.900	44.962	62.718	48.684	40.160	30.908	45.427	42.161	81.040	119.952	146.412	98.725	103.456
800	40.612	47.587	65.816	49.953	41.139	31.652	46.055	42.915	85.398	125.897	153.530	103.540	107.768
900	41.282	50.016	68.580	51.129	42.019	32.406	46.599	43.585	89.451	131.340	160.103	108.019	112.164
1000	41.826	52.188	71.176	52.222	42.818	33.159	47.060	44.213	93.211	136.490	165.839	112.081	115.346
1100	42.329	54.140	73.604	53.256	43.551	33.871	47.520	44.757	96.669	141.346	171.156	115.849	118.780
1200	42.747	55.860	75.781	54.227	—	34.499	47.897	45.259	99.847	145.910	175.929	119.366	121.878
M*	64.06	16.031	28.031	26.040	44.016	34.08	76.13	60.07	30.47	44.06	78.108	42.08	46.07

[M*]=kg/mol.

Table 4-10   Specific Enhalpy h of Gases

Tempe-rature t °C	H_2 h kJ/kg	N_2 h kJ/kg	O_2 h kJ/kg	CO h kJ/kg	CO_2 h kJ/kg	Air h kJ/kg	NO h kJ/kg	OH h kJ/kg	N_2O h kJ/kg	N_2S h kJ/kg	NH_3 h kJ/kg	H_2O h kJ/kg	SO_2 h kJ/kg
0	0.0	0.00	0.00	0.00	0.00	0.00	0.000	0.00	0.000	0.00	0.00	0.00	0.000
100	1435.2	104.04	92.32	104.17	86.58	100.61	99.646	174.97	90.226	100.90	213.11	187.28	63.47
200	2884.3	208.67	187.07	209.26	182.04	202.31	199.96	348.59	189.33	205.15	442.13	378.74	132.14
300	4333.3	314.64	285.00	316.15	284.62	305.72	302.20	522.09	295.63	315.27	700.03	575.69	205.45
400	5790.3	419.10	386.02	425.38	393.06	411.31	406.96	695.85	407.67	432.08	966.31	779.16	282.32
500	7255.7	532.98	489.44	537.59	506.60	519.58	514.14	870.44	524.61	548.47	1250.2	988.92	362.03
600	8725.3	645.61	595.78	651.47	623.83	629.70	623.83	1046.7	646.02	673.24	1550.8	1205.4	443.38
700	10212	760.74	703.38	768.28	744.83	742.32	736.04	1225.5	770.79	803.03	1868.6	1429.4	527.12
800	11715	877.97	812.66	887.18	868.34	856.62	849.92	1406.3	898.91	937.84	2201.0	1660.5	611.27
900	13234	996.88	923.19	1008.2	993.95	973.43	965.06	1590.1	1029.1	1073.9	2547.7	1898.7	697.10
1000	14775	1117.9	1035.0	1130.4	1122.5	1090.7	1081.5	1776.9	1161.8	1218.4	2919.0	2143.6	782.93
1100	16337	1239.7	1147.6	1253.9	1252.3	1210.0	1199.1	1966.5	1296.2	1363.2	—	2394.9	870.02
1200	17920	1363.2	1261.1	1379.1	1383.7	1329.7	1318.0	2058.7	—	1507.2	—	2652.8	956.68
1300	19531	1488.0	1375.4	1505.2	1516.0	1451.6	1437.3	2353.4	—	—	—	2915.7	—
1400	21156	1613.6	1490.5	1632.0	1649.6	1573.8	1557.9	2549.8	—	—	—	3184.1	—
1500	22801	1740.5	1606.9	1759.7	1784.4	1696.9	1678.9	2748.2	1810.8	2027.7	4906.9	3457.5	1223.4
1600	24468	1867.7	1723.7	1887.8	1919.2	1820.8	1800.7	2949.6	—	—	—	3735.0	—
1700	26151	1995.0	1841.4	2017.2	2055.7	1945.2	1922.6	3153.1	—	—	—	4017.7	—
1800	27851	2123.5	1959.4	2146.2	2192.2	2070.4	2044.4	3357.4	—	—	—	4303.2	—
1900	29567	2252.9	2078.7	2276.8	2329.1	2196.4	2167.9	3563.8	—	—	—	4591.7	—
2000	31296	2382.3	2198.1	2406.6	2466.9	2322.0	2291.0	3771.5	2490.3	2837.8	5756.9	4892.3	1668.9
2100	33046	2512.9	2318.7	2537.6	2605.0	2449.7	2414.5	3981.2	—	—	—	5179.5	—
2200	34801	2642.7	2439.2	2668.2	2743.2	2576.1	2538.5	4191.0	—	—	—	5477.2	—
2300	36576	2773.2	2561.5	2800.1	2882.2	2703.8	2662.8	4404.5	—	—	—	5777.8	—
2400	38359	2904.8	2683.7	2932.0	3020.4	2832.8	2786.2	4618.0	—	—	—	6080.5	—
2500	40160	3035.4	2807.3	3064.7	3158.9	2960.1	2911.1	4835.8	3182.0	3671.8	6686.3	6385.7	2169.6
2600	41952	—	2930.3	—	—	—	3035.8	5049.3	—	—	—	6693.9	—
2700	43794	—	3054.3	—	—	—	3160.6	5267.0	—	—	—	7003.3	—
2800	—	—	—	—	—	—	3285.8	5484.7	—	—	—	—	—
2900	—	—	—	—	—	—	3411.8	5702.4	—	—	—	—	—
3000	49362	3701.1	3434.4	3732.1	3858.6	—	3537.0	5924.3	3878.2	4517.6	7557.2	7829.3	2568.2

[1]) 1 Btu = 1.055 06 kJ

Table 4-10   Specific Enhalpy h of Gases   (continued)

Tempe-rature t °C	CH_4 h kJ/kg	C_2H_4 h kJ/kg	C_2H_2 h kJ/kg	CS_2 h kJ/kg	COS h kJ/kg	C_2H_6 h kJ/kg	C_3H_8 h kJ/kg	C_6H_6 h kJ/kg	C_3H_6 h kJ/kg	C_2H_5OH h kJ/kg
0	0.00	0.00	0.00	0.000	0.000	0.00	0.00	0.00	0.00	0.00
100	229.44 ·	164.79	176.18	61.295	70.966	185.98	178.40	114.55	162.36	167.68
200	491.53	364.75	372.69	127.36	148.46	413.66	403.19	265.11	359.98	364.08
300	790.47	598.29	583.93	196.70	230.61	680.77	666.12	447.57	592.01	588.66
400	1126.7	858.29	807.13	268.63	316.40	986.41	967.99	654.82	853.27	837.36
500	1495.1	1143.8	1040.1	342.27	404.91	1323.9	1294.6	882.58	1140.5	1107.0
600	1895.4	1450.7	1282.2	417.76	495.72	1689.8	1656.7	1127.9	1450.7	1395.0
700	2324.5	1772.7	1532.5	494.04	588.25	2080.4	2036.5	1386.7	1781.1	1698.2
800	2787.6	2114.3	1790.4	571.50	682.45	2493.2	2435.5	1658.0	2126.9	2015.5
900	3272.4	2258.4	2054.8	649.37	777.91	2925.7	2850.8	1939.3	2488.6	2345.4
1000	3771.5	2834.5	2325.1	727.67	874.62	3376.7	3284.5	2229.9	2861.7	2683.7
1100	4283.1	3213.0	2601.3	806.80	972.18	3840.6	3734.2	2528.0	3246.4	3034.2
1200	4802.3	3598.1	2882.6	886.35	1070.6	4316.6	4199.4	2830.7	3641.7	3390.9

[1]) 1 Btu = 1.055 06 kJ

Table 4-11 Molar Enhalpy H_m of Gases

Temperature t °C	H$_2$ H_m J/mol	N$_2$ H_m J/mol	O$_2$ H_m J/mol	CO H_m J/mol	CO$_2$ H_m J/mol	Air H_m J/mol	NO H_m J/mol	OH H_m J/mol	N$_2$O H_m J/mol	N$_2$S H_m J/mol	NH$_3$ H_m J/mol	H$_2$O H_m J/mol	SO$_2$ H_m J/mol
0	0.0	0.0	0.0	0.0	0.0	0.0	0.0	0.0	0.0	0.0	0.0	0.0	0.0
100	2893.5	2914.4	2953.8	2917.8	3811.2	2915.3	2990.6	2976.0	3971.2	3433.2	3642.5	3374.1	4065.4
200	5815.5	5844.8	5987.1	5861.5	8013.5	5861.5	5999.7	5928.5	8335.9	7000.3	7536.2	6824.5	8465.7
300	8737.9	8813.2	9118.9	8855.1	12527	8855.1	9068.6	8880.2	13013	10727	11932	10371	13163
400	11673	11840	12351	11916	17300	11916	12213	11832	17945	14637	16454	14034	18087
500	14624	14934	15667	15052	22286	15047	15433	14805	23094	18715	21311	17815	23195
600	17589	18091	19058	18254	27453	18242	18728	17802	28433	22986	26419	21717	28412
700	20586	21315	22504	21529	32770	21508	22085	20842	33959	27403	31820	25753	33762
800	23614	24597	26000	24857	38209	24824	25498	23919	39565	31987	37472	29915	39155
900	26682	27934	29542	28240	43752	28190	28956	27043	45301	36664	43375	34206	44652
1000	29789	31313	33118	31665	49404	31598	32456	30220	51121	41491	49697	38619	50158
1100	32938	34734	36722	35131	55098	35048	35986	33448	57066	46423	—	43166	55726
1200	36128	38192	40361	38632	60876	38531	39549	36722	—	51397	—	47771	61295
1300	39373	41688	44003	42161	66738	42035	43124	40026	—	—	—	52544	—
1400	42663	45217	47688	45720	72599	45594	46725	43375	—	—	—	57359	—
1500	45971	48734	51414	49279	78503	49153	50367	46725	79674	67073	83610	62300	78377
1600	49321	52335	55140	52879	84490	52754	54010	50158	—	—	—	67282	—
1700	52712	55894	58908	56480	90477	56354	57694	53633	—	—	—	72390	—
1800	56145	59494	62718	60122	96506	59955	61378	57108	—	—	—	77540	—
1900	59620	63095	66528	63765	102535	63597	65021	60625	—	—	—	82731	—
2000	63095	66738	70338	67407	108564	67282	68747	64142	109610	93868	98055	88007	106931
2100	66612	70380	74190	71092	114635	70966	72432	67701	—	—	—	93324	—
2200	70171	74064	78042	74776	120747	74651	76158	71301	—	—	—	98683	—
2300	73730	77707	81936	78461	126818	78335	79884	74944	—	—	—	104084	—
2400	77330	81391	85871	82145	132931	82061	83610	78586	—	—	—	109548	—
2500	80973	85076	89807	85829	139044	85788	87337	82229	140048	121417	113169	115053	139002
2600	84615	—	93784	—	—	—	91105	85871	—	—	—	120622	—
2700	88258	—	97762	—	—	—	94873	89556	—	—	—	126190	—
2800	—	—	—	—	—	—	98599	93282	—	—	—	—	—
2900	—	—	—	—	—	—	102367	97008	—	—	—	—	—
3000	99520	103749	109904	104503	169775	—	106135	100734	170696	149469	128702	141053	164541
M*	2.0156	28.016	32.000	28.010	44.010	28.964	30.008	17.008	44.016	34.08	17.031	18.020	64.04

[M*] = kg/mol.

Table 4-11 Molar Enhalpy H_m of Gases (continued)

Temperature t °C	CH$_4$ H_m J/mol	C$_2$H$_4$ H_m J/mol	C$_2$H$_2$ H_m J/mol	CS$_2$ H_m J/mol	COS H_m J/mol	C$_2$H$_6$ H_m J/mol	C$_3$H$_8$ H_m J/mol	C$_6$H$_6$ H_m J/mol	C$_3$H$_6$ H_m J/mol	C$_2$H$_5$OH H_m J/mol
0	0.0	0.0	0.0	0.0	0.0	0.0	0.0	0.0	0.0	0.0
100	3680.6	4622.2	4587.1	4668.3	4262.2	5593.6	7867.0	8947.2	6832.9	7728.8
200	7883.7	10233	9703.3	9696.6	8917.9	12439	17777	20708	15148	16781
300	12682	16781	15203	14972	13854	20469	29379	34968	24920	27143
400	18070	24082	21014	20448	19008	29663	42663	51163	35906	38586
500	23986	32092	27080	26063	24325	39812	57066	68915	47981	50995
600	30405	40696	33383	31803	29768	50786	73060	88090	61044	64267
700	37292	49739	39899	37671	35345	62551	89807	108313	74944	78251
800	44715	59327	46616	43501	40997	74986	107391	129498	89514	92863
900	52502	69208	53499	49446	46725	88007	125688	151478	104712	108061
1000	60499	79507	60537	55391	52544	101530	144821	174171	120412	123678
1100	68705	90142	67730	61420	58406	115472	164625	197449	136615	139839
1200	76995	100944	75053	67491	64309	129791	185098	221105	153237	156251
M*	16.031	28.031	26.040	76.13	60.07	30.07	44.06	78.108	42.08	46.07

[M*] = kg/mol.

208

Table 4-12 Specific Entropy s of Gases

Tempe-rature t °C	H_2 s kJ/(kg K)	N_2 s kJ/(kg K)	O_2 s kJ/(kg K)	CO s kJ/(kg K)	CO_2 s kJ/(kg K)	Air s kJ/(kg K)	NO s kJ/(kg K)	OH s kJ/(kg K)	N_2O s kJ/(kg K)	N_2S s kJ/(kg K)	NH_3 s kJ/(kg K)	H_2O s kJ/(kg K)	SO_2 s kJ/(kg K)
0	0.000	0.0000	0.0000	0.0000	0.0000	0.0000	0.0000	0.0000	0.0000	0.0000	0.0000	0.0000	0.0000
100	4.388	0.3245	0.2826	0.3249	0.2692	0.3127	0.3107	0.5443	0.2851	0.3098	0.6615	0.5765	0.1959
200	7.838	0.5728	0.5083	0.5744	0.4957	0.5543	0.5489	0.9462	0.5204	0.5568	1.2058	1.0333	0.3601
300	10.622	0.7762	0.6958	0.7792	0.6921	0.7524	0.7453	1.2853	0.7243	0.7662	1.6789	1.4097	0.4999
400	12.962	0.9496	0.8583	0.9550	0.8662	0.9224	0.9136	1.5659	0.9048	0.9504	2.1101	1.7375	0.6234
500	14.985	1.1024	1.0019	1.1099	1.0233	1.0718	1.0622	1.8129	1.0668	1.1179	2.5037	2.0264	0.7339
600	16.777	1.2397	1.1304	1.2489	1.1660	1.2058	1.1958	2.0306	1.2217	1.2686	2.8721	2.2902	0.8332
700	18.388	1.3645	1.2472	1.3758	1.2971	1.3281	1.3172	2.2274	1.3498	1.4068	3.2155	2.5330	0.9236
800	19.858	1.4788	1.3540	1.4918	1.4177	1.4398	1.4290	2.4074	1.4750	1.5407	3.5295	2.7591	1.0065
900	21.210	1.5851	1.4528	1.5994	1.5303	1.5437	1.5315	2.5707	1.5914	1.6622	3.8519	2.9684	1.0823
1000	22.475	1.6835	1.5441	1.6994	1.6349	1.6400	1.6266	2.7214	1.6998	1.7794	4.1449	3.1694	1.1530
1100	23.651	1.7760	1.6295	1.7932	1.7329	1.7300	1.7158	2.8638	1.8016	1.8882	—	3.3620	1.2188
1200	24.765	1.8627	1.7091	1.8807	1.8254	1.8146	1.7995	2.9977	—	1.9887	—	3.5420	1.2803
1300	25.824	1.9448	1.7844	1.9636	1.9125	1.8933	1.8782	3.1234	—	—	—	3.7137	—
1400	26.825	2.0222	1.8556	2.0419	1.9946	1.9695	1.9523	3.2406	—	—	—	3.8770	—
1500	27.779	2.0955	1.9226	2.1160	2.0729	2.0411	2.0226	3.3526	2.2106	2.2860	5.4303	4.0361	1.4654
1600	28.696	2.1654	1.9866	2.1863	2.1470	2.1089	2.0892	3.4625	—	—	—	4.1910	—
1700	29.571	2.2320	2.0478	2.2533	2.2177	2.1872	2.1524	3.5672	—	—	—	4.3375	—
1800	30.409	2.2956	2.1064	2.3174	2.2856	2.2353	2.2127	3.6676	—	—	—	4.4757	—
1900	31.217	2.3563	2.1625	2.3785	2.3501	2.2948	2.2705	3.7681	—	—	—	4.6139	—
2000	31.996	2.4145	2.2161	2.4371	2.4120	2.3517	2.3258	3.8644	2.5456	2.6754	6.4770	4.7478	1.6831
2100	32.749	2.4706	2.2680	2.4937	2.4715	2.4062	2.3789	3.9565	—	—	—	4.8734	—
2200	33.473	2.5242	2.3178	2.5477	2.5284	2.4585	2.4304	4.0444	—	—	—	4.9949	—
2300	34.177	2.5761	2.3664	2.6000	2.5833	2.5251	2.4798	4.1282	—	—	—	5.1121	—
2400	34.859	2.6264	2.4192	2.6502	2.6364	2.5581	2.5272	4.2077	—	—	—	5.2293	—
2500	35.521	2.6745	2.4581	2.6988	2.6871	2.6054	2.5732	4.2873	2.8303	2.9977	7.3646	5.3424	1.8631
2600	36.157	—	2.5020	—	—	—	2.6172	4.3626	—	—	—	5.4470	—
2700	36.781	—	2.5447	—	—	—	2.6599	4.4338	—	—	—	5.5517	—
2800	38.477	2.8763	2.7214	2.9098	2.9266	—	2.7013	4.5008	—	—	—	—	—
2900	—	—	—	—	—	—	2.7415	4.5678	—	—	—	—	—
3000	—	—	—	—	—	—	2.7805	4.6348	3.0522	3.2741	8.1182	5.8197	2.0139

Table 4-12 Specific Entropy s of Gases   *(continued)*

Tempe-rature t °C	CH_4 s kJ/(kg K)	C_2H_4 s kJ/(kg K)	C_2H_2 s kJ/(kg K)	CS_2 s kJ/(kg K)	COS s kJ/(kg K)	C_2H_6 s kJ/(kg K)	C_3H_8 s kJ/(kg K)	C_6H_6 s kJ/(kg K)	C_3H_6 s kJ/(kg K)	C_2H_5OH s kJ/(kg K)
0	0.000	0.0000	0.0000	0.0000	0.0000	0.0000	0.0000	0.0000	0.0000	0.0000
100	0.703	0.515	0.5443	0.1897	0.2211	0.5778	0.5485	0.3559	0.5066	0.5150
200	1.327	0.984	1.0099	0.3471	0.4044	1.1179	1.0802	0.7118	0.9713	0.9839
300	1.901	1.428	1.4147	0.4802	0.5619	1.6287	1.5826	1.0593	1.4151	1.4151
400	2.441	1.846	1.7735	0.5949	0.7005	2.1185	2.0683	1.3942	1.8338	1.8129
500	2.948	2.244	2.0963	0.6979	0.8223	2.5874	2.5246	1.7082	2.2316	2.1855
600	3.437	2.613	2.3911	0.7892	0.9324	3.0312	2.8680	2.0055	2.6126	2.5372
700	3.902	2.964	2.6642	0.8717	1.0329	3.4541	3.3787	2.2860	2.9684	2.8680
800	4.338	3.299	2.9144	0.9471	1.1250	3.8560	3.7639	2.5498	3.3076	3.1778
900	4.760	3.613	3.1501	1.0170	1.2108	4.2370	4.1324	2.8010	3.6258	3.4709
1000	5.162	3.915	3.3716	1.0810	1.2900	4.6055	4.4882	3.0396	3.8895	3.7472
1100	5.560	4.199	3.5801	1.1409	1.3641	4.9614	4.8316	3.2657	4.2245	4.0151
1200	5.937	4.472	3.7782	1.1970	1.4331	5.3005	5.1540	3.4792	4.5008	4.2663

Table 4-13 Molar Entropy S_m of Gases

Temperature t °C	H$_2$ S_m J/(mol K)	N$_2$ S_m J/(mol K)	O$_2$ S_m J/(mol K)	CO S_m J/(mol K)	CO$_2$ S_m J/(mol K)	Air S_m J/(mol K)	NO S_m J/(mol K)	OH S_m J/(mol K)	N$_2$O S_m J/(mol K)	N$_2$S S_m J/(mol K)	NH$_3$ S_m J/(mol K)	H$_2$O S_m J/(mol K)	SO$_2$ S_m J/(mol K)
0	0.000	0.000	0.000	0.000	0.000	0.000	0.000	0.000	0.000	0.000	0.000	0.000	0.000
100	8.843	9.090	9.084	9.102	11.853	9.060	9.332	9.253	12.556	10.509	11.263	10.387	12.560
200	15.805	16.048	16.262	16.086	21.813	16.052	16.479	16.119	22.910	18.966	20.515	18.615	23.069
300	21.411	21.742	22.265	21.826	30.363	21.796	22.370	21.855	31.878	26.084	28.596	25.397	32.029
400	26.134	26.607	27.465	26.745	38.129	26.716	27.419	26.628	39.817	32.364	35.923	31.280	39.942
500	30.212	30.886	32.054	31.087	45.033	31.049	31.878	30.815	46.976	38.058	42.664	36.509	47.018
600	33.821	34.725	36.174	34.985	51.313	34.939	35.885	34.541	53.800	43.250	48.902	41.257	53.382
700	37.074	38.221	39.917	38.531	57.074	38.473	39.536	37.891	59.411	48.023	54.722	45.632	59.201
800	40.034	41.433	43.333	41.788	62.396	41.717	42.885	40.947	64.937	52.503	60.122	49.697	64.477
900	42.764	44.405	46.486	44.803	67.340	44.715	45.967	43.752	70.045	56.689	65.565	53.511	69.333
1000	45.310	47.168	49.413	47.604	71.950	47.508	48.827	46.306	74.818	60.625	70.589	57.116	73.855
1100	47.683	49.760	52.128	50.225	76.271	50.116	51.489	48.693	79.298	64.351	—	60.537	78.084
1200	49.928	52.193	54.692	52.683	80.332	52.565	53.997	50.953	—	67.868	—	63.794	82.019
1300	52.059	54.483	57.100	55.002	84.163	54.851	56.354	53.089	—	—	—	66.905	—
1400	54.081	56.652	59.373	57.192	87.789	57.058	58.578	55.098	—	—	—	69.878	—
1500	56.007	58.707	61.525	59.264	91.226	59.126	60.688	57.024	97.343	77.916	92.528	72.725	93.826
1600	57.849	60.663	63.577	61.236	94.492	61.094	62.689	58.866	—	—	—	75.488	—
1700	59.616	62.530	65.532	63.116	97.607	62.969	64.590	60.667	—	—	—	78.126	—
1800	61.307	64.309	67.399	64.908	100.592	64.761	66.528	62.383	—	—	—	80.680	—
1900	62.936	66.013	69.195	66.625	103.427	66.478	68.132	64.058	—	—	—	83.150	—
2000	64.506	67.646	70.920	68.270	106.152	68.123	69.790	65.691	112.123	91.189	110.364	85.536	107.978
2100	66.022	69.212	72.578	69.848	108.765	69.706	71.389	67.282	—	—	—	87.797	—
2200	67.483	70.723	74.173	71.364	111.277	71.226	72.930	68.789	—	—	—	90.016	—
2300	68.902	72.176	75.718	72.825	113.693	72.695	74.408	70.213	—	—	—	92.151	—
2400	70.275	73.575	77.213	74.232	116.020	74.106	75.836	71.594	—	—	—	94.245	—
2500	71.607	74.927	78.662	75.593	118.265	75.475	77.213	72.934	124.474	102.158	125.478	96.255	119.408
2600	72.896	—	80.060	—	—	—	78.540	—74.190	—	—	—	98.180	—
2700	74.148	—	81.425	—	—	—	79.821	75.404	—	—	—	100.023	—
2800	—	—	—	—	—	—	81.061	76.577	—	—	—	—	—
2900	—	—	—	—	—	—	82.262	77.707	—	—	—	—	—
3000	77.540	80.554	87.044	81.433	128.786	—	83.435	78.796	134.354	111.495	138.248	104.586	129.079
M*	2.0156	28.016	32.000	28.010	44.010	28.964	30.008	17.008	44.016	34.08	17.031	18.020	64.06

[M*] = kg/mol.

Table 4-13 Molar Entropy S_m of Gases *(continued)*

Temperature t °C	CH$_4$ S_m J/(mol K)	C$_2$H$_4$ S_m J/(mol K)	C$_2$H$_2$ S_m J/(mol K)	CS$_2$ S_m J/(mol K)	COS S_m J/(mol K)	C$_2$H$_6$ S_m J/(mol K)	C$_3$H$_8$ S_m J/(mol K)	C$_6$H$_6$ S_m J/(mol K)	C$_3$H$_6$ S_m J/(mol K)	C$_2$H$_5$OH S_m J/(mol K)
0	0.000	0.000	0.000	0.000	0.000	0.000	0.000	0.000	0.000	0.000
100	11.304	14.444	14.168	14.444	13.272	17.375	24.283	27.633	21.102	23.781
200	21.269	27.675	26.293	26.419	24.283	33.578	47.688	55.517	40.821	45.343
300	30.480	40.110	36.835	36.551	33.746	48.944	69.878	82.731	59.453	65.147
400	39.147	51.874	46.176	45.301	42.077	63.681	91.230	108.731	77.163	83.527
500	47.311	62.969	54.579	53.130	49.446	77.791	111.411	133.391	93.868	100.734
600	55.140	73.353	62.249	60.081	56.061	91.147	126.525	156.586	109.778	116.896
700	62.593	83.234	69.312	66.361	62.048	103.916	148.966	178.567	124.809	132.052
800	69.585	92.570	75.877	72.097	67.575	115.932	166.007	199.292	139.044	146.329
900	76.367	101.404	82.015	77.414	72.725	127.446	182.335	218.844	152.525	159.894
1000	82.857	109.820	87.776	82.313	77.498	138.541	197.994	237.433	165.421	172.706
1100	89.179	117.817	93.211	86.876	81.936	149.176	213.024	255.018	177.688	184.931
1200	95.250	125.478	98.360	91.147	86.081	159.391	227.385	271.723	189.369	196.528
M*	16.031	28.031	26.040	76.13	60.07	30.07	44.06	78.108	42.08	46.07

[M*] = kg/mol.

Table 4-14 Viscosity (Dynamic Viscosity) η of Gases

Gas	Chemical formula	Temperature t °C	Viscosity η μN s/m^2	Gas	Chemical formula	Temperature t °C	Viscosity η μN s/m^2
Acetone	C_3H_6O	0	7.25	Argon	Ar	20	22.2
		18	7.80			50	24.2
		100	9.43			100	27.1
		119	9.91			200	32.1
		160	11.01			300	36.7
		190	11.86			440	41.0
		217	12.53			493	44.8
		248	13.34			600	48.7
		279	14.16			714	52.6
		306	14.81			880	55.4
Acetylene	C_2H_2	0	9.43	Benzene	C_6H_6	0	7.0
		20	10.20			20	7.5
		40	10.79			50	8.2
		50	11.13			100	9.5
		60	11.31			150	10.8
		80	11.98			200	12.0
		100	12.54			250	13.2
		120	13.18			300	14.5
Air		−194	5.51	Bromine	Br_2	0	14.60
		−183	6.27			20	15.42
		−150	8.70			25	15.28
		−100	11.80			138	20.97
		−50	14.60			190	23.69
		0	17.19			242	26.26
		50	19.26			316	29.99
		100	21.24			349	31.63
		150	23.19			410	34.76
		200	25.12			535	41.06
		250	27.04			588	43.00
		300	28.86			594	42.92
		350	30.68				
		400	32.45	n-Butane	C_4H_{10}	0	6.80
		450	34.13			20	7.39
		500	35.70			40	7.87
		550	37.20			60	8.39
		600	38.68			80	8.85
		650	40.17			100	9.47
		700	41.62			120	9.98
		750	43.01				
		800	44.32	Carbon dioxide	CO_2	−98	8.96
		850	45.60			−78	9.72
		900	46.88			−60	10.61
		950	48.12			−40	11.55
		1000	49.33			−19	12.60
		1100	51.50			0	13.82
		1200	53.74			22	14.71
		1400	57.86			50	16.20
		1600	61.59			100	18.45
						145	20.41
Ammonia	NH_3	−60	7.1			235	24.15
		−40	7.8			300	26.80
		−20	8.6			417	31.06
		0	9.3			490	33.00
		20	10.0			574	37.63
		50	11.1			685	38.00
		100	13.0			764	40.84
		150	14.8			850	43.58
		200	16.6			1008	47.78
		250	18.4			1052	47.86
		300	20.2				
Argon	Ar	−200	5.2	Carbon disulfide	CS_2	0	9.24
		−150	10.0			114	13.03
		−100	14.2			153	14.34
		−50	17.9			190	15.61
		0	21.2			228	16.92

Table 4-14 Viscosity (Dynamic Viscosity) η **of Gases** *(continued)*

Gas	Chemical formula	Temperature t °C	Viscosity η μN s/m^2
Carbon disulfide	CS$_2$	263	18.30
		310	19.66
Carbon monoxide	CO	−80	12.7
		−60	13.7
		−40	14.7
		−20	15.7
		0	16.6
		20	17.6
		50	18.9
		100	21.0
		150	22.9
		200	24.7
		250	26.4
		300	27.9
Carbon tetrachloride (Tetrachloromethane)	CCl$_4$	0	9.3
		20	9.9
		50	10.8
		100	12.3
		150	13.8
		200	15.3
		250	16.8
		300	18.3
Chlorine	Cl$_2$	0	12.30
		20	13.27
		50	14.96
		100	16.79
		150	18.75
		200	20.85
		250	22.76
		300	25.00
Chloroform	CHCl$_3$	0	9.59
		20	10.01
		100	13.07
		161	14.91
		189	15.79
		250	17.76
		308	19.47
Cyanogen	C$_2$N$_2$	0	9.48
		20	10.70
		100	12.70
Ethane	C$_2$H$_6$	−78	6.44
		0	8.55
		20	9.29
		40	9.86
		60	10.50
		80	11.11
		100	11.67
		120	12.30
		150	12.78
		200	14.09
		250	15.26
Ethyl acetate	C$_4$H$_8$O$_2$	0	6.90
		100	9.55
		128	10.18
		159	10.98
		193	11.95
		218	12.50
		249	13.32
		280	14.09
		314	14.97

Gas	Chemical formula	Temperature t °C	Viscosity η μN s/m^2
Ethyl alcohol	C$_2$H$_6$O	0	8.3
		100	10.9
		150	12.4
		200	13.8
		250	15.2
		300	16.5
Ethyl chloride	C$_2$H$_5$Cl	0	9.4
Ethyl ether	C$_4$H$_{10}$O	0	6.9
		20	7.4
		50	8.2
		100	9.4
		150	10.6
		200	11.8
		250	12.9
		300	14.1
Ethylene	C$_2$H$_4$	−80	6.65
		−60	7.35
		−40	8.05
		−20	8.75
		0	9.40
		20	10.08
		50	11.03
		100	12.57
		150	14.03
		200	15.41
		250	16.66
Helium	He	−250	3.7
		−200	8.0
		−100	13.9
		0	18.6
		50	20.8
		100	22.9
		200	27.0
		300	30.7
		400	34.2
		600	40.7
		800	46.5
n-Heptane	C$_7$H$_{16}$	100	7.17
		150	8.11
		202	9.22
		252	10.80
n-Hexane	C$_6$H$_{14}$	0	5.90
		121	8.66
		161	9.58
		189	10.21
		220	10.88
		248	11.44
		280	12.13
		307	12.65
Hydrogen	H$_2$	−250	1.1
		−200	3.3
		−150	4.8
		−100	6.1
		−50	7.3
		0	8.4
		50	9.4
		100	10.3
		200	12.1
		300	13.9
		400	15.4
		500	16.9

Table 4-14 Viscosity (Dynamic Viscosity) η of Gases

(continued)

Gas	Chemical formula	Temperature t °C	Viscosity η μN s/m^2
Hydrogen	H$_2$	600	18.3
		700	19.6
		800	21.0
Hydrogen arsenide	H$_3$As	15	15.52
Hydrogen bromide	HBr	0	17.10
		100	23.65
Hydrogen chloride	HCl	0	13.32
		23	14.45
		53	15.95
		100	18.37
		151	20.18
		202	23.12
		251	25.34
Hydrogen iodide	HJ	0	17.30
		20	18.55
		50	20.18
		100	23.16
		150	26.27
		200	29.24
		250	31.89
Hydrogen phosphide	PH$_3$	0	10.7
		100	14.5
Hydrogen sulfide	H$_2$S	0	11.75
		20	13.00
		100	16.10
Iodine	J$_2$	0	12.30
		106	17.85
		232	23.19
		279	25.61
		329	27.49
		397	30.65
		438	32.50
		523	36.04
Isoamylene	C$_5$H$_{10}$	22	7.14
		40	7.71
		50	7.93
		60	8.29
		80	8.71
		100	9.15
		120	9.67
Isobutane	C$_4$H$_{10}$	0	6.90
		20	7.44
		40	7.92
		60	8.45
		80	8.88
		100	9.47
		120	9.95
Isopropyl alcohol	C$_3$H$_8$O	0	7.0
		120	10.3
		150	11.1
		200	12.5
		250	13.8
Krypton	Kr	0	23.3
		20	24.6
		100	30.6
Mercury	Hg	218	47.09

Gas	Chemical formula	Temperature t °C	Viscosity η μN s/m^2
Mercury	Hg	281	53.10
		300	55.01
		330	58.31
		421	68.56
		496	76.10
		565	83.43
		610	88.02
Methane	CH$_4$	−80	7.4
		−60	8.1
		−40	8.8
		−20	9.5
		0	10.35
		20	10.87
		50	11.80
		100	13.31
		150	14.71
		200	16.05
		250	17.25
		300	18.60
		380	20.26
		499	22.64
Methyl acetate	C$_3$H$_6$O$_2$	100	10.15
		143	11.39
		178	12.36
		219	13.48
		248	14.29
		278	15.08
		307	15.83
Methyl alcohol	CH$_4$O	0	8.7
		100	12.2
		150	14.0
		200	15.6
		250	17.3
		300	18.9
Methyl bromide	OH$_3$Br	0	10.36
		10	12.77
		20	13.27
		30	13.78
		40	14.16
		50	14.57
		60	15.17
		120	17.97
Methyl chloride	CH$_3$Cl	0	9.80
		20	10.61
		30	11.01
		40	11.40
		50	11.75
		60	12.09
		70	12.50
		80	12.87
		90	13.23
		100	13.57
		110	14.00
		120	14.40
		130	14.71
		219	17.69
		257	18.95
		300	20.44
Methylene chloride	CH$_2$Cl$_2$	0	9.1
		22	9.91
		100	12.67
		219	16.67

Table 4-14   Viscosity (Dynamic Viscosity) η of Gases

Gas	Chemical formula	Temperature t °C	Viscosity η μN s/m²
Methylene chloride	CH_2Cl_2	259	17.98
		309	19.56
Methyl ether	C_2H_6O	0	8.50
		20	9.09
		40	9.84
		60	10.44
		80	11.09
		100	11.67
		120	12.28
Neon	Ne	78	23.67
		0	29.81
		20	31.11
		100	36.46
		200	42.48
		250	45.32
		285	47.08
		429	54.54
		502	58.02
		594	62.30
		686	66.26
		827	72.10
Nitric oxide	NO	0	17.97
		20	18.76
		50	20.36
		100	22.72
		150	24.74
		200	26.82
		250	28.70
Nitrogen	N_2	−150	8.4
		−100	11.4
		−50	14.1
		0	16.6
		50	18.8
		100	20.8
		200	24.6
		400	31.1
		600	36.6
		800	41.3
Nitrous oxide	N_2O	0	13.7
		20	14.6
		50	16.0
		100	18.3
		150	20.4
		200	22.5
		250	24.6
		300	26.5
Oxygen	O_2	−200	5.7
		−150	9.7
		−100	13.2
		−50	16.3
		0	19.2
		50	21.8
		100	24.4
		200	29.0
		400	36.9
		600	43.5
		800	49.3

Gas	Chemical formula	Temperature t °C	Viscosity η μN s/m²
Pentane	C_5H_{12}	0	6.2
		120	9.1
		160	10.0
		219	11.3
		250	11.9
Propane	C_3H_8	0	7.50
		20	8.06
		40	8.73
		60	9.22
		80	9.78
		100	10.29
		120	10.82
		150	11.30
		200	12.50
		250	13.60
Propene	C_3H_6	0	7.80
		20	8.35
		40	8.93
		60	9.59
		80	10.23
		100	10.71
		120	11.22
n-Propyl alcohol	C_3H_8O	0	6.8
		120	10.3
		150	11.0
Sulfur dioxide	SO_2	−75	8.58
		−36	10.12
		−20	10.78
		−6	11.31
		0	11.58
		20	12.54
		40	13.52
		60	14.55
		80	15.40
		100	16.12
		120	17.16
		150	18.31
		200	20.38
		293	24.47
		421	28.89
		490	31.15
		595	34.22
		679	37.01
		823	41.00
Water vapor (steam)	H_2O	100	12.55
		150	14.45
		200	16.35
		250	18.27
		300	20.24
		350	22.18
		400	24.12
		500	26.77
Xenon	X	0	21.1
		20	22.6
		100	28.7

Table 4-15 Thermal Conductivity λ of Gases

Gas	Chemical formula	Temperature t °C	Thermal conductivity λ W/(m K)
Acetone	C_3H_6O	0	0.00977
		20	0.01093
		50	0.01303
		100	0.01686
		150	0.02152
		200	0.02710
Acetylene	C_2H_2	−75	0.01175
		0	0.01872
		100	0.02977
Air	—	−180	0.00879
		−150	0.01549
		−100	0.01633
		−50	0.02052
		−20	0.02256
		0	0.02373
		20	0.02512
		40	0.02652
		50	0.02680
		60	0.02791
		80	0.02931
		100	0.03070
		120	0.03198
		140	0.03326
		160	0.03442
		180	0.03570
		200	0.03698
		250	0.04001
		300	0.04291
		350	0.04571
		400	0.04850
		500	0.05396
		600	0.05815
		800	0.06687
		1000	0.07618
		1200	0.08455
		1400	0.09304
		1600	0.10118
Ammonia	NH_3	−50	0.01721
		0	0.01861
		20	0.02442
		40	0.02559
		60	0.02791
		80	0.03024
		100	0.03256
		200	0.04652
		300	0.05815
Amylamine	$C_5H_{13}N$	6.5	0.01175
Argon	Ar	−180	0.00586
		−150	0.00795
		−100	0.01089
		−50	0.01340
		0	0.01633
		20	0.01758
		50	0.01884
		100	0.02177
Benzene	C_6H_6	0	0.00884
		20	0.01047
		50	0.01291
		100	0.01756
		150	0.02256
		200	0.02838

Gas	Chemical formula	Temperature t °C	Thermal conductivity λ W/(m K)
n-Butane	C_4H_{10}	0	0.01349
		20	0.01547
		100	0.02338
Butyl alcohol	$C_4H_{10}O$	100	0.01977
Butylamine	$C_4H_{11}N$	6.5	0.01256
Carbon dioxide	CO_2	−150	0.00465
		−100	0.00814
		50	0.01163
		0	0.01424
		20	0.01591
		50	0.01779
		100	0.02093
		200	0.02847
		300	0.03517
		496	0.04943
		546	0.05943
Carbon disulfide	CS_2	0	0.00675
Carbon monoxide	CO	−180	0.00795
		−150	0.01089
		−100	0.01507
		−75	0.01710
		−50	0.01926
		−25	0.02117
		0	0.02219
Carbon tetrachloride	CCl_4	0	0.00582
		20	0.00640
		50	0.00721
		100	0.00872
		150	0.01012
		200	0.01151
Chlorine	Cl_2	0	0.00795
Chloroform	$CHCl_3$	0	0.00651
		20	0.00704
		50	0.00802
		100	0.01000
		150	0.01186
		200	0.01396
Cyclohexane	C_6H_{12}	100	0.01349
Deuterium	D_2	0	0.12812
		100	0.15784
Dichlorodifluoromethane	CF_2Cl_2	0	0.00830
		20	0.00941
		50	0.01106
		100	0.01384
		150	0.06175
Diethylamine	$C_4H_{11}N$	6.5	0.01256
Dimethylamine	C_2H_7N	6.5	0.01465
Dipropylamine	$C_6H_{15}N$	6.5	0.01093
Ethane	C_2H_6	−75	0.01140
		−50	0.01326
		−25	0.01547
		0	0.01826

1 Btu/(ft h °F) = 1.730 73 W/(m K)

Table 4-15 Thermal Conductivity λ of Gases

(continued)

Gas	Chemical formula	Temperature t °C	Thermal conductivity λ W/(m K)
Ethane	C_2H_6	20	0.02070
		50	0.02489
		100	0.03280
Ethyl acetate	$C_4H_8O_2$	0	0.00907
		20	0.01047
		50	0.01256
		100	0.01651
		150	0.02093
		200	0.02605
Ethyl alcohol	C_2H_6O	0	0.01384
		20	0.01524
		50	0.01745
		100	0.02128
Ethylamine	C_2H_7N	6.5	0.01337
Ethyl bromide	C_2H_5Br	0	0.00721
Ethyl chloride	C_2H_5Cl	0	0.00948
		20	0.01076
		50	0.01279
		100	0.01640
		150	0.02035
		200	0.02477
Ethylene	C_2H_4	−75	0.01070
		−50	0.01279
		−25	0.01500
		0	0.02745
Ethyl ether	$C_4H_{10}O$	0	0.01326
		20	0.01477
		50	0.01745
		100	0.02256
		150	0.02814
		200	0.03442
Ethyl iodide	C_2H_5J	0	0.00593
Helium	He	−200	0.05908
		−180	0.06827
		−150	0.08164
		−100	0.10316
		−50	0.12386
		0	0.14363
		20	0.15119
		50	0.16049
		100	0.17038
n-Heptane	C_7H_{16}	100	0.01768
		200	0.01942
n-Hexane	C_6H_{14}	0	0.01244
		20	0.01384
n-Hexane	C_6H_{12}	0	0.01041
		20	0.01210
		50	0.01454
		100	0.01872
Hydrogen	H_2	−200	0.05152
		−150	0.09211
		−100	0.11639
		−50	0.14654
		0	0.17543

Gas	Chemical formula	Temperature t °C	Thermal conductivity λ W/(m K)
Hydrogen	H_2	20	0.18631
		40	0.19655
		60	0.20818
		80	0.21864
		100	0.22911
		120	0.23958
		140	6.25005
		160	0.25935
		180	0.26749
		200	0.27563
		220	0.28261
		240	0.28842
		260	0.29911
		280	0.29424
		300	0.30940
		500	0.38379
		1000	0.59313
Hydrogen sulfide	H_2S	0	0.01256
Isobutane	C_4H_{10}	0	0.01384
		100	0.02407
Isopentane	C_5H_{12}	0	0.01244
		20	0.01407
		50	0.01675
		100	0.02186
		150	0.02768
		200	0.03431
Krypton	Kr	0	0.00879
Mercury	Hg	200	0.00754
Methane	CH_4	−150	0.01291
		−100	0.01838
		−75	0.02128
		−50	0.02419
		−25	0.02721
		0	0.03024
		20	0.03315
		50	0.03722
Methyl acetate	$C_2H_6O_2$	0	0.01012
		20	0.01163
Methyl alcohol	CH_4O	0	0.01430
		20	0.01582
		50	0.01814
		100	0.02177
Methylamine	CH_5N	6.5	0.01591
Methyl bromide	CH_3Br	0	0.00628
		20	0.00709
		50	0.00837
		100	0.01058
Methyl chloride	CH_3Cl	0	0.00907
		20	0.01047
		50	0.01256
		100	0.01617
		150	0.01989
		200	0.02407
Methylene chloride	CH_2Cl_2	0	0.00663
		20	0.00733

1 Btu/(ft h °F) = 1.730 73 W/(m K)

Table 4-15   Thermal Conductivity λ of Gases   *(continued)*

Gas	Chemical formula	Temperature t °C	Thermal conductivity λ W/(m K)	Gas	Chemical formula	Temperature t °C	Thermal conductivity λ W/(m K)
Methylene chloride	CH_2Cl_2	50	0.00849	Nitrous oxide	N_2O	0	0.01512
		100	0.01076			100	0.02093
		150	0.01314	Oxygen	O_2	−180	0.00837
		200	0.01570			−150	0.01172
Methyl iodide	CH_3J	0	0.00465			−100	0.01633
		20	0.00523			50	0.02052
		50	0.00616			0	0.02428
		100	0.00756			20	0.02596
Neon	Ne	−180	0.02052			50	0.02847
		−100	0.03433			100	0.03182
		0	0.04564			150	0.03489
		100	0.05568	n-Pentane	C_5H_{12}	0	0.01279
Nitric oxide	NO	−75	0.01745			20	0.01435
		−50	0.01954	Propane	C_3H_8	0	0.01512
		−25	0.02163			20	0.01733
		0	0.02373			100	0.02617
		50	0.02261	Propylamine	C_3H_9N	6.5	0.01256
Nitrogen	N_2	−180	0.00879	Sulfur dioxide	SO_2	0	0.00837
		−150	0.01214			100	0.01198
		−100	0.01633	Triethylamine	$C_6H_{15}N$	6.5	0.01130
		−50	0.02052	Trimethylamine	C_3H_9N	6.5	0.01382
		0	0.02386	Water vapor (steam)	H_2O	100	0.02419
		20	0.02554			200	0.03280
		50	0.02763			300	0.04268
		100	0.03056			400	0.05513
		150	0.03315			500	0.07525
		200	0.03559	Xenon	X	0	0.00502
		250	0.03780				
		300	0.03977				
		500	0.04689				
Nitrous oxide	N_2O	−75	0.01140				
		−50	0.01268				
		−25	0.01396				

1 Btu/(ft h °F) = 1.730 73 W/(m K)

Table 4-16 Thermal Conductivity of Diatomic and Triatomic Gases at Various Temperatures

Temperature t/°C	N_2 λ mW/(m K)	O_2 λ mW/(m K)	CO_2 λ mW/(m K)	H_2O λ mW/(m K)	H_2 λ mW/(m K)
0	24.865	24.714	14.444	16.154	174.450
100	31.506	32.552	22.702	24.644	216.318
200	37.565	39.972	31.052	33.657	258.186
300	43.392	47.264	39.379	45.636	300.054
400	49.358	54.254	47.497	57.057	341.922
500	55.208	60.941	55.359	69.966	383.790
600	60.883	67.128	62.883	83.852	425.658
700	66.384	73.060	70.094	98.483	467.526
800	71.676	78.723	76.898	114.090	509.394
900	76.793	83.736	83.434	130.140	551.262
1000	81.724	88.807	89.667	146.654	593.130
1100	86.399	93.738	95.668	163.402	634.998
1200	90.912	98.390	101.309	180.265	676.866

1 Btu/(ft h °F) = 1.730 73 W/(m K)

Table 4-17 Thermal Conductivity of Flue Gases Containing 13 % CO_2 at Various Temperatures

Tempera-ture t/°C	Water content, per cent (H_2O)				
	5% λ mW/(m K)	10% λ mW/(m K)	15% λ mW/(m K)	20% λ mW/(m K)	25% λ mW/(m K)
0	22.446	23.027	23.144	23.144	23.260
100	30.936	31.634	32.099	32.331	32.564
200	39.193	40.123	40.938	41.635	41.984
300	49.079	50.823	52.219	53.265	54.196
400	54.661	56.871	58.964	60.592	61.755
500	61.872	6.012	67.687	69.896	71.641
600	69.082	73.036	76.409	79.317	81.992
700	75.595	80.596	84.783	88.504	91.644
800	81.875	87.807	93.56	97.808	101.414
900	87.807	95.017	101.297	107.112	111.997
1000	93.970	102.111	109.787	116.300	122.115
1100	99.785	108.973	117.463	125.604	132.582

1 Btu/(ft h °F) = 1.730 73 W/(m K)

Table 4-18 Specific Heat Capacity c_p of Dry Air at a Constant Pressure p

Pressure p =	0.980 665 bar (1 at)	9.806 650 bar (10 at)	19.613 3 bar (20 at)	39.226 6 bar (40 at)	58.839 9 bar (60 at)	68.646 65 bar (70 at)	98.066 5 bar (100 at)	137.293 1 bar (140 at)	176.519 7 bar (180 at)	215.746 3 bar (200 at)
Tempera-ture t/°C	c_p kJ/(kg K)	c_p kJ/(kg K)	c_p kJ/(kg K)	c_p kJ/(kg K)	c_p kJ/(kg K)	c_p kJ/(kg K)	c_p kJ/(kg K)	c_p kJ/(kg K)	c_p kJ/(kg K)	c_p kJ/(kg K)
−140	1.0132	1.7082	2.6712	—	—	1.9217	—	—	—	—
−100	1.0090	1.0802	1.1849	—	—	1.3015	—	—	—	—
−50	1.0048	1.0216	1.0551	1.3942	—	—	1.1723	—	—	—
0	1.0048	—	1.0425	1.1472	1.1137	—	1.1388	1.1807	1.2142	1.2393
50	1.0048	—	1.0383	—	1.0886	—	1.1053	1.1388	1.1681	1.1891
100	1.0090	—	1.0341	—	1.0718	—	1.0886	1.1137	1.1346	1.1514
150	1.0174	—	1.0341	—	1.0593	—	1.0760	1.0886	1.1095	1.1262
200	1.0258	—	1.0341	—	1.0509	—	1.0551	1.0634	1.0760	1.0844
280	1.0425	—	1.0341	—	1.0425	—	—	—	—	—

1) Older name: Specific heat.

Table 4-19 Thermal properties of Dry Air at a Pressure $p = 0.980\ 665$ bar (1 at)

Temperature t °C	Density ρ kg/m³	Specific heat capacity[1] c_p kJ/(kg K)	Thermal conductivity λ W/(m K)	Thermal diffusivity α mm/s²	Dynamic viscosity η μN s/m²	Kinematic viscosity ν mm/s²	Prandtl number Pr
−180	3.72	1.047	0.0076	1.94	6.472	1.75	—
−150	2.78	1.038	0.0116	4.03	8.592	3.14	—
−100	1.948	1.022	0.0163	8.0	11.856	5.96	—
−50	1.534	1.013	0.0198	13.1	14.808	9.65	0.71
−20	1.365	1.005	0.0226	16.8	16.279	12.0	0.71
0	1.252	1.011	0.0237	19.2	17.456	13.9	0.71
10	1.206	1.010	0.0244	20.7	17.848	14.66	0.71
20	1.164	1.012	0.0251	22.0	18.240	15.7	0.71
30	1.127	1.013	0.0258	23.4	18.682	16.58	0.71
40	1.092	1.014	0.0265	24.8	19.123	17.6	0.71
50	1.057	1.016	0.0272	26.2	19.515	18.58	0.71
60	1.025	1.017	0.0279	27.6	19.907	19.4	0.71
70	0.996	1.018	0.0286	29.2	20.398	20.65	0.71
80	0.968	1.019	0.0293	30.6	20.790	21.5	0.71
90	0.942	1.021	0.0300	32.2	21.231	22.82	0.71
100	0.916	1.022	0.0307	33.6	21.673	23.6	0.71
120	0.870	1.025	0.0320	37.0	22.555	25.9	0.71
140	0.827	1.027	0.0333	40.0	23.340	28.2	0.71
150	0.810	1.028	0.0336	41.2	23.732	29.4	0.71
160	0.789	1.030	0.0344	43.3	24.124	30.6	0.71
180	0.755	1.032	0.0357	47.0	24.909	33.0	0.71
200	0.723	1.035	0.0370	49.7	25.693	35.5	0.71
250	0.653	1.043	0.0400	60.0	27.557	42.2	0.71
300	0.596	1.047	0.0429	68.9	39.322	49.2	0.71
350	0.549	1.055	0.0457	80.0	30.989	56.5	0.72
400	0.508	1.059	0.0485	89.4	32.754	64.6	0.72
500	0.442	1.076	0.0540	113.2	35.794	81.0	0.72
600	0.391	1.089	0.0581	133.6	38.638	98.8	0.73
700	0.351	1.101	0.0599	162.0	41.580	118.95	0.73
800	0.318	1.114	0.0669	182	43.640	137	0.73
900	0.291	1.126	0.0673	216	46.876	160	0.74
1000	0.268	1.139	0.0762	240	48.445	181	0.74
1100	0.248	1.156	0.0826	277	51.191	206	0.74
1200	0.232	1.164	0.0845	301	52.662	227	0.74
1400	0.204	1.189	0.0930	370	56.781	278	0.76
1600	0.182	1.218	0.1012	447	60.409	332	0.76
1800	0.165	1.243	0.1093		63.841	387	

[1] Older name: Specific heat.

1 Btu/(ft h °F) = 1.730 73 W/(m K)

Table 4-20 Adiabatic and Polytropic Changes of Condition of Gases
If $(p/p) < 1$ than count with reciprocal values of numbers in the tables

$\dfrac{p_1}{p_2}$	For n = 1.4 (adiabate)	1.3	1.2	1.1	For n = 1.4 (adiabate)	1.3	1.2	1.1
	eat: $(p_1/p_2)^{\frac{1}{n}} = V_2/V_1 =$				eat: $(p_1/p_2)^{\frac{n-1}{n}} = T_2/T_1 =$			
1.1	1.070	1.076	1.083	1.090	1.028	1.022	1.016	1.009
1.2	1.139	1.151	1.164	1.180	1.053	1.043	1.031	1.017
1.3	1.206	1.224	1.244	1.269	1.078	1.062	1.045	1.024
1.4	1.271	1.295	1.323	1.358	1.101	1.081	1.058	1.031
1.5	1.336	1.366	1.401	1.445	1.123	1.098	1.070	1.038
1.6	1.399	1.436	1.479	1.533	1.144	1.115	1.081	1.044
1.7	1.461	1.504	1.557	1.620	1.164	1.130	1.092	1.050
1.8	1.522	1.571	1.633	1.706	1.183	1.145	1.103	1.055
1.9	1.581	1.638	1.706	1.791	1.201	1.160	1.113	1.060
2.0	1.631	1.705	1.782	1.879	1.219	1.174	1.123	1.065
2.5	1.924	2.023	2.145	2.300	1.299	1.235	1.265	1.087
3.0	2.193	2.330	2.498	2.715	1.369	1.289	1.201	1.105
3.5	2.449	2.624	2.842	3.126	1.431	1.336	1.232	1.121
4.0	2.692	2.907	3.177	3.505	1.487	1.378	1.260	1.134
4.5	2.926	3.178	3.500	3.925	1.537	1.415	1.285	1.147
5.0	3.156	3.449	3.824	4.320	1.583	1.449	1.307	1.157
5.5	3.378	3.712	4.142	4.710	1.627	1.482	1.328	1.167
6.0	3.598	3.970	4.447	5.100	1.668	1.512	1.348	1.177
6.5	3.809	4.218	4.760	5.483	1.707	1.540	1.366	1.186
7.0	4.012	4.467	5.058	5.861	1.742	1.566	1.383	1.194
7.5	4.217	4.710	5.360	6.250	1.778	1.591	1.399	1.201
8.0	4.415	4.950	5.650	6.620	1.811	1.616	1.414	1.208
8.5	4.612	5.187	5.590	6.997	1.843	1.639	1.429	1.215
9.0	4.800	5.420	6.240	7.370	1.873	1.660	1.442	1.221
9.5	4.993	5.651	6.528	7.742	1.903	1.681	1.455	1.227
10	5.188	5.885	6.820	8.120	1.931	1.701	1.468	1.233
11	5.544	6.325	7.376	8.845	1.984	1.739	1.491	1.244
12	5.900	6.763	7.931	9.574	2.034	1.774	1.513	1.253
13	6.247	7.193	8.478	10.30	2.081	1.807	1.533	1.263
14	6.587	7.614	9.018	11.01	2.126	1.839	1.549	1.271
15	6.919	8.030	9.551	11.73	2.168	1.868	1.570	1.279
16	7.246	8.438	10.08	12.44	2.208	1.896	1.587	1.287
17	7.566	8.841	10.60	13.14	2.247	1.923	1.604	1.294
18	7.882	9.238	11.12	13.84	2.284	1.948	1.619	1.301
19	8.192	9.631	11.63	14.54	2.319	1.973	1.633	1.307
20	8.498	10.02	12.14	15.23	2.354	1.996	1.648	1.313
21	8.803	10.40	12.64	15.93	2.387	2.019	1.661	1.319
22	9.097	10.78	13.14	16.61	2.418	2.041	1.674	1.324
23	9.390	11.15	13.64	17.30	2.449	2.062	1.688	1.330
24	9.680	11.53	14.13	17.97	2.479	2.082	1.698	1.335
25	9.967	11.89	14.62	18.65	2.508	2.102	1.710	1.340
26	10.25	12.26	15.10	19.34	2.537	2.121	1.721	1.345
27	10.53	12.62	15.58	20.01	2.564	2.140	1.732	1.349
28	10.81	12.98	16.07	20.68	2.591	2.158	1.743	1.354
29	11.08	13.33	16.54	21.36	2.617	2.175	1.753	1.358
30	11.35	13.68	17.02	22.02	2.643	2.192	1.763	1.362
31	11.62	14.03	17.49	22.69	2.667	2.209	1.773	1.366
32	11.89	14.38	17.96	23.35	2.692	3.225	1.782	1.370
33	12.15	14.69	18.43	24.01	2.715	2.241	1.792	1.374
34	12.42	15.06	18.89	24.58	2.739	2.256	1.800	1.378
35	12.67	15.41	19.35	25.34	2.761	2.272	1.809	1.382
36	12.93	15.74	19.81	25.99	2.784	2.287	1.817	1.385
37	13.19	16.07	20.26	26.65	2.806	2.301	1.826	1.389
38	13.44	16.41	20.72	27.30	2.827	2.315	1.834	1.392
39	13.69	16.74	21.18	27.95	2.848	2.329	1.842	1.395
40	13.94	17.07	21.63	28.60	2.869	2.343	1.850	1.398

Table 4-21 Heating Values H_s and H_i of Gases

Gas	Chemical formula	Molar mass M kg/kmol	Density ρ kg/m³	Characteristic σ	Volume of oxygen and air required for combustion of one cubic meter of gas		Heating value			
					Oxygen O_{min} m³	Air L_{min} m³	H_s J/mol	H_i J/mol	H_s kJ/kg	H_i kJ/kg
Acetylene	C_2H_2	26.00	1.171	1.25	2.5	11.9	1310468	1265418	50367	48651
Ammonia	NH_2	27.03	0.7714	—	—	—	380999	313466	22358	18422
Benzene	C_6H_6	78.05	3.490	—	—	—	3278264	3143156	41994	40277
i-Butane	C_4H_{10}	58.08	2.668	—	—	—	2873401	2648235	49488	45594
n-Butane	C_4H_{10}	58.08	2.703	1.625	6.5	31.0	2880100	2654934	49572	45720
Butene	C_2H_8	56.06	2.50	1.50	6	28.6	2729794	2549677	48692	45469
Carbon monoxide	CO	28.00	1.250	0.50	0.5	2.38	283446	283446	10132	10132
Ethane	C_2H_6	30.05	1.356	1.75	3.5	16.7	1560839	1425731	51958	47436
Ethylene	C_2H_4	28.00	1.260	1.50	3	14.3	1423512	1333454	50786	47562
Hydrogen	H_2	2.016	0.08987	—	0.5	2.38	286168	241118	141974	119617
Hydrogen sulfide	H_2S-SO_2	34.08	1.539	—	—	—	569405	524355	16705	15407
	H_2S-SO_3	34.08	1.539	—	—	—	667795	622745	19594	18254
Isobutane	C_4H_{10}	58.08	2.668	—	—	—	2873401	2648235	49488	45594
Methane	CH_4	16.00	0.7168	2.00	2	9.52	890951	800893	55601	49949
Methyl chloride	CH_3Cl	50.48	2.307	—	—	—	711756	644223	14110	12770
Propane	C_3H_8	44.06	2.019	1.666	5	23.8	2221516	2041400	50409	46348
Propene	C_3H_6	42.95	1.915	1.50	4.5	21.4	2072466	1937358	49279	46055

1 Btu = 1.055 06 kJ

Table 4-22 Heating Values H_s and H_i of Some Technical Gaseous Heating Fuels

Gas	Molar mass M kg/kmol	Density ρ kg/m³	Characteristics		Content, (% volume)						Heating value	
			σ	ν	H_2	CO	CH_4	C_2H_4	CO_2	N_2	H_s kJ/m³	H_i kJ/m³
Blast furnace gas	28.2	1.25	0.45	1.67	4	28	—	—	8	60	4061	3977
Blue water gas	26.6	1.19	0.67	1.97	6	23	3	0.2	5	62	5024	4815
Carbonization gas, stone coal	15.7	0.70	1.81	0.024	27	7	48	13	3	2	31945	18973
Coke oven gas	11.85	0.53	2.11	0.149	50	8	29	4	2	7	21562	19259
Dowson gas	25.1	1.12	0.77	1.57	12	28	3	0.2	3	54	6448	6029
Illuminating gas	11.2	0.50	2.11	0.060	51	8	32	4	2	3	22944	20473
Mond's gas	23.7	1.06	0.84	1.32	25	12	4	0.3	16	43	6490	5820
Water gas	15.9	0.71	0.98	0.063	49	42	0.5	—	5	3	11765	10802

1 Btu = 1.055 06 kJ

APPENDICES

Table 5-1 Prefixes Used with SI Units

Prefixes Name	Prefixes Symbols	Multiples and Submultiples	Amount
exa	E	10^{18}	1 000 000 000 000 000 000
peta	P	10^{15}	1 000 000 000 000 000
teta	T	10^{12}	1 000 000 000 000
giga	G	10^{9}	1 000 000 000
mega	M*	10^{6}	1 000 000
kilo	k*	10^{3}	1 000
hecto	h	10^{2}	100
deka	da	10	10
deci	d	10^{-1}	0.1
centi	c	10^{-2}	0.01
milli	m*	10^{-3}	0.001
micro	μ*	10^{-6}	0.000 001
nano	n	10^{-9}	0.000 000 001
pico	p	10^{-12}	0.000 000 000 001
femto	f	10^{-15}	0.000 000 000 000 001
atto	a	10^{-18}	0.000 000 000 000 000 001

*) Most commonly used.

Table 5-2 Powers of Number Ten (10)

10^{25} = 10 000 000 000 000 000 000 000 000	10^{-1} = 0.1
10^{24} = 1 000 000 000 000 000 000 000 000	10^{-2} = 0.01
10^{23} = 100 000 000 000 000 000 000 000	10^{-3} = 0.001
10^{22} = 10 000 000 000 000 000 000 000	10^{-4} = 0.000 1
10^{21} = 1 000 000 000 000 000 000 000	10^{-5} = 0.000 01
10^{20} = 100 000 000 000 000 000 000	10^{-6} = 0.000 001
10^{19} = 10 000 000 000 000 000 000	10^{-7} = 0.000 000 1
10^{18} = 1 000 000 000 000 000 000	10^{-8} = 0.000 000 01
10^{17} = 100 000 000 000 000 000	10^{-9} = 0.000 000 001
10^{16} = 10 000 000 000 000 000	10^{-10} = 0.000 000 000 1
10^{15} = 1 000 000 000 000 000	10^{-11} = 0.000 000 000 01
10^{14} = 100 000 000 000 000	10^{-12} = 0.000 000 000 001
10^{13} = 10 000 000 000 000	10^{-13} = 0.000 000 000 000 1
10^{12} = 1 000 000 000 000	10^{-14} = 0.000 000 000 000 01
10^{11} = 100 000 000 000	10^{-15} = 0.000 000 000 000 001
10^{10} = 10 000 000 000	10^{-16} = 0.000 000 000 000 000 1
10^{9} = 1 000 000 000	10^{-17} = 0.000 000 000 000 000 01
10^{8} = 100 000 000	10^{-18} = 0.000 000 000 000 000 001
10^{7} = 10 000 000	10^{-19} = 0.000 000 000 000 000 000 1
10^{6} = 1 000 000	10^{-20} = 0.000 000 000 000 000 000 01
10^{5} = 100 000	10^{-21} = 0.000 000 000 000 000 000 001
10^{4} = 10 000	10^{-22} = 0.000 000 000 000 000 000 000 1
10^{3} = 1 000	10^{-23} = 0.000 000 000 000 000 000 000 01
10^{2} = 100	10^{-24} = 0.000 000 000 000 000 000 000 001
10^{1} = 10	10^{-25} = 0.000 000 000 000 000 000 000 000 1
10^{0} = 1	

Table 5-3 Quantities and SI Units of Thermodynamics

Physical quantity			SI units		
Name	Symbol	Definition	Name	Symbol	Expression in terms of SI base units
thermodynamic temperature	T, Θ [1]		kelvin	K	K
Celsius temperature	t, ϑ	$t = T - T_0$ [2]	degree Celsius	$°C\ (\equiv K)$	K
difference of temperature	$\Delta T, \Delta t, \Delta \vartheta$	$\Delta T = T_2 - T_1$ $\Delta t = t_2 - t_1$	kelvin	K	K
temperature gradient, thermal gradient	$\mathrm{grad}\ T$	$\mathrm{grad}\ T = dT/dl$	kelvin per meter	K/m	$m^{-1}\ K$
speed of chilling, rate of cooling	$\dot{T}, \dot{\vartheta}$	$\dot{T} = dT/dt$	kelvin per second	K/s	$s^{-1}\ K$
time	t		second	s	s
area	A, S	$A = l\ b$	square meter	m^2	m^2
volume	$V, (v)$	$V = l\ b\ h$	cubic meter	m^3	m^3
mass	m		kilogram	kg	kg
mass density, density	ρ	$\rho = m/V$	kilogram per cubic meter	kg/m^3	$m^{-3}\ kg$
specific volume	v	$v = V/m = 1/\rho$	cubic meter per kilogram	m^3/kg	$m3\ kg^{-1}$
force	F	$\vec{F} = m\ \vec{a}$ [3]	newton	N	$m\ kg\ s^{-2}$
pressure	p	$p = F/A$ [4]	pascal	Pa	$m^{-1}\ kg\ s^{-2}$
linear expansion coefficient	α_l	$\alpha_l = \dfrac{1}{l} \left(\dfrac{\partial l}{\partial T} \right)_P$	reciprocal kelvin, kelvin to the power minus one	1/K	K^{-1}
cubic expansion coefficient	α_V, γ	$\alpha_V = \dfrac{1}{V} \left(\dfrac{\partial V}{\partial T} \right)_P$ [5]	reciprocal kelvin, kelvin to the power minus one	1/K	K^{-1}
relative pressure coefficient	α_p, α	$\alpha_p = \dfrac{1}{p} \left(\dfrac{\partial p}{\partial T} \right)_V$ [6]	reciprocal kelvin, kelvin to the power minus one	1/K	K^{-1}
isothermal compressibility	κ_T, κ	$\kappa_T = -\dfrac{1}{V} \left(\dfrac{\partial V}{\partial p} \right)_T$	reciprocal pascal, pascal to the power minus one	1/Pa	$m\ kg^{-1}\ s^2$
isentropic compressibility	κ_S	$\kappa_S = -\dfrac{1}{V} \left(\dfrac{\partial V}{\partial p} \right)_S$	reciprocal pascal, pascal to the power minus one	1/Pa	$m\ kg^{-1}\ s^2$
pressure coefficient	β	$\beta = \left(\dfrac{\partial p}{\partial T} \right)_V$	pascal per kelvin	Pa/K	$m^{-1}\ kg\ s^{-2}\ K^{-1}$
Joule-Thomson coefficient	μ, μ_T	$\mu = \left(\dfrac{\partial T}{\partial p} \right)_H$	kelvin per pascal	K/Pa	$m\ kg^{-1}\ s^2\ K$
number of entities	N		one	1	
amount of substance	n		mole	mol	mol

[1] Only for ideal gas $pV = nRT$.

[2] When symbols for both time and Celsius temperature are required, t should be used for time and ϑ for temperature, T_0 is fixed by convention to be $T_0 = 273.15$ K.

[3] If $m = $ constant then $\vec{F} = m\ \vec{a}$.

[4] F is the force normal to section A.

[5] For ideal gas $\gamma = 1/T_0$; with $T_0 = 273.15$ K worth $(V/V_0)_p = 1 + \gamma t$.

[6] For ideal gas $\beta = 1/T_0$; with $T_0 = 273.15$ K worth $(p/p_0)_V = 1 + \beta t$.

226

Table 5-3　Quantities and SI Units of Thermodynamics　　　*(continued)*

Physical quantity			SI units		
Name	Symbol	Definition	Name	Symbol	Exspression in terms of SI base units
Avogadro constant	L, N_A	$L = N/n$ [7]	reciprocal mole, mole to the power minus one	1/mol	mol^{-1}
molar mass	M	$M = m/n$ [8]	kilogram per mole	kg/mol	$kg\ mol{-1}$
molar volume	V_m	$V_m = V/n$	cubic meter per mole	m^3/mol	$m^3\ mol^{-1}$
gas constant (molar)	R	$R = pV/nT$ [9]	joule per mole kelvin	J/(mol K)	$\dfrac{m^2\ kg}{s^2\ mol\ K}$
gas constant (of substance X)	$R(X)$	$R(X) = R/M(X)$ [10]	joule per kilogram kelvin	J/(kg K)	$m^2\ s^{-2}\ K^{-1}$
compression factor, (compressibility factor)	Z	$Z = \dfrac{pV_m}{RT}$	one	1	
Boltzmann constant	k	$k = R/L$ [11]	joule per kelvin	J/K	$m^2\ kg\ s^{-2}\ K^{-1}$
energy	E, W		joule	J	$m^2\ kg\ s^{-2}$
work	W, A		joule	J	$m^2\ kg\ s^{-2}$
thermal efficiency	η	$\eta = A/Q$ [12]	one	1	
heat, quantity of heat	Q		joule	J	$m^2\ kg\ s^{-2}$
heat flow rate	$\Phi(q)$	$\Phi = Q/t$ [13]	watt	W	$m^2\ kg\ s^{-3}$
density of heat flow rate	$q, (\varphi)$	$q = \Phi/A$	watt per square meter	W/m^2	$kg\ s^{-3}$
thermal conductivity	$\lambda, (k)$	$q = -\lambda\ grad\ T$	watt per meter kelvin	W/(m K)	$m\ kg\ s^{-3}\ K^{-1}$
surface coefficient of heat transfer	α, h	$\alpha = q/\Delta T_{il}$ [14]	watt per square meter kelvin	$W/(m^2\ K)$	$kg\ s^{-3}\ K^{-1}$
coefficient of heat transfer	k, K	$k = q/\Delta T_{ie}$ [15]	watt per square meter kelvin	$W/(m^2\ K)$	$kg\ s^{-3}\ K^{-1}$
diathermancy	Λ	$\Lambda = \lambda/d$	watt per square meter kelvin	$W/(m^2\ K)$	$kg\ s^{-3}\ K^{-1}$
thermal resistance	R	$R = 1/G = \Delta T/\Phi$	kelvin per watt	K/W	$m^{-2}\ kg^{-1}\ s^3\ K$
thermal conductivity	G	$G = 1/R = \Phi/\Delta T$ [16]	watt per kelvin	W/K	$m^2\ kg\ s^{-3}\ K^{-1}$
thermal insulance, coefficient of thermal insulation	M	$M = \Delta T/q = RA$	square meter kelvin per watt	$m^2\ K/W$	$kg^{-1}\ s^3\ K$
thermal diffusivity	$a, (D)$	$a = \lambda/(\rho c_p)$ [17]	square meter per second	m^2/s	$m^2\ s^{-1}$
thermal resistance	R_λ		meter kelvin per watt	m K/W	$m^{-1}\ kg^{-1}\ s^3\ K$

[7]　$L = 6.022\ 1367\ (36) \times 10^{23}\ mol^{-1}$.
[8]　$M = M_r \times$ g/mol, M_r is the relative molecular mass.
[9]　For ideal gas $pV = nRt$; $R = 8.314\ 510\ (70)$ J/(mol K)
[10]　For ideal gas $P = \rho R(X)T$.
[11]　$k = 1.380\ 658\ (12) \times 10^{23}$ J/K.
[12]　Q represents system input heat; A is the work done by system.
[13]　t represents time.
[14]　ΔT_{il} represents temperature difference between liquids (or gas) and wall.
[15]　ΔT_{ie} represents temperature difference between liquids (gases) near outside of the wall and inside of the wall: for straight wall of the thickness δ worths $1/k = 1/\alpha_i + \delta/\gamma + 1/\alpha_e$.
[16]　ΔT represents difference between opponent sides of the wall, $\Delta T = \Delta t$.
[17]　λ is thermal conductivity, ρ is density, and c_p is specific heat capacity at a constant pressure.

Table 5-3 Quantities and SI Units of Thermodynamics *(continued)*

Physical quantity			SI units		
Name	Symbol	Definition	Name	Symbol	Exspression in terms of SI base units
transfer resistance	R_α	$R_\alpha = 1/\alpha = \Delta T/q$	square meter kelvin per watt	m^2 K/W	$kg^{-1}\, s^3$ K
transmission resistance	R_k	$R_k = 1/k = = \dfrac{1}{\alpha_1} + \sum \dfrac{\delta}{\lambda} + \dfrac{1}{\alpha_2}$	square meter kelvin per watt	m^2 K/W	$kg^{-1}\, s^3$ K
diathermance resistance	R_Λ	$R_\Lambda = 1/\Lambda = = \dfrac{d_1}{\lambda_{p1}} + \dfrac{d_2}{\lambda_{p2}} + \cdots$	square meter kelvin per watt	m^2 K/W	$kg^{-1}\, s^3$ K
heat capacity	C	$C = dQ/dT$ [18]	joule per kelvin	J/K	m^2 kg $s^{-2}\, K^{-1}$
heat capacity at a constant pressure	C_p	$C_p = (\partial Q/\partial T)_p$ [19]	joule per kelvin	J/K	m2 kg $s^{-2}\, K^{-1}$
heat capacity at a constant volume	C_V	$C_V = (\partial U/\partial T)_V$ [20]	joule per kelvin	J/K	m2 kg $s^{-2}\, K^{-1}$
specific heat capacity	c	$c = C/m = \dfrac{1}{m}\,(dQ/dT)$	joule per kilogram kelvin	J/(kg K)	$m^2\, s^{-2}\, K^{-1}$
specific heat capacity at a constant pressure	c_p	$c_p = C_p/m = \dfrac{1}{m}\,(\partial H/\partial T)_p$	joule per kilogram kelvin	J/(kg K)	$m^2\, s^{-2}\, K^{-1}$
specific heat capacity at a constant volume	c_V	$c_V = C_V/m = \dfrac{1}{m}\,(\partial U/\partial T)_V$	joule per kilogram kelvin	J/(kg K)	$m^2\, s^{-2}\, K^{-1}$
specific heat capacity at saturation	c_{sat}		joule per kilogram kelvin	J/(kg K)	$m^2\, s^{-2}\, K^{-1}$
medium specific heat capacity	$\bar{c}$	$\bar{c} = \dfrac{1}{T_2 - T_1}\int c(T)dT$ [21]	joule per kilogram kelvin ·	J/(kg K)	$m^2\, s^{-2}\, K^{-1}$
molar heat capacity	C_m	$C_m = \dfrac{C}{n} = \dfrac{1}{n}\,(dQ/dT)$	joule per mole kelvin	J/(mol K)	$\dfrac{m^2\ kg}{s^2\ mol\ K}$
molar heat capacity at a constant pressure	$C_{m,\,p}$	$C_{m,\,p} = C_p/n$	joule per mole kelvin	J/(mol K)	$\dfrac{m^2\ kg}{s^2\ mol\ K}$
molar heat capacity at a constant volume	$C_{m,\,V}$	$C_{m,\,V} = C_V/n$	joule per mole kelvin	J/(mol K)	$\dfrac{m^2\ kg}{s^2\ mol\ K}$
polytropic exponent	n	$pV^n = $ constant	one	1	
isentropic exponent	κ	$\kappa = \dfrac{\rho}{p}\left(\dfrac{\partial p}{\partial \rho}\right)_S = -\dfrac{V}{p}\left(\dfrac{\partial p}{\partial V}\right)_S$	one	1	
ratio of the specific heat capacities	γ, (k)	$\gamma = c_p/c_v$	one	1	
internal energy	U, (E)	$\Delta U = Q - W$ [23]	joule	J	m^2 kg s^{-2}
specific internal energy	u, (e)	$u = U/m$	joule per kilogram	J/kg	$m^2\, s^{-2}$
molar internal energy	U_m, (E_m)	$U_m = U/n$	joule per mole	J/mol	m^2 kg s^{-2} mol
enthalpy	H, (I)	$H = U + pV$	joule	J	m^2 kg s^{-2}
specific enthalpy	h, (i)	$h = H/m$	joule per kilogram	J/kg	$m^2\, s^{-2}$

[18] When the temperature of a system is increased by dT as a result of the addition of a small quantity of heat dQ, the quantity dQ/dT is the heat capacity.

[19] H represents enthalpy.

[20] U represents internal energy.

[21] In the temperature range between T_1 and T_2.

[22] For ideal gas, γ is equal to κ ($\gamma = \kappa = c_p/c_V$).

[23] ΔU represents system internal energy rise; Q represents input heat; W represents the work done by the system.

Table 5-3   Quantities and SI Units of Thermodynamics   *(continued)*

Physical quantity			SI units		
Name	Symbol	Definition	Name	Symbol	Exspression in terms of SI base units
molar enthalpy	H_m	$H_m = H/n$	joule per mole	J/mol	$m^2\,kg\,s^{-2}\,mol$
entropy	S	$dS = dQ/T$ [24)]	joule per kelvin	J/K	$m^2\,kg\,s^{-2}\,K^{-1}$
specific entropy	s	$s = S/m$	joule per kilogram kelvin	J/(kg K)	$m^2\,s^{-2}\,K^{-1}$
molar entropy	S_m	$S_m = S/n$	joule per mole kelvin	J/(mol K)	$\dfrac{m^2\,kg}{s^2\,mol\,K}$
Helmholtz free energy, Helmholtz function	A, F	$A = U - TS$	joule	J	$m^2\,kg\,s^{-2}$
specific Helmholtz free energy, specific Helmholtz function	a, f	$a = A/m$	joule per kilogram	J/kg	$m^2\,s^{-2}$
molar Helmholtz free energy, molar Helmholtz function	A_m, F_m	$A_m = A/n$	joule per mole	J/mol	$m^2\,kg\,s^{-2}\,mol$
Gibbs free energy, Gibbs function	G	$G = U + pV - TS = H - TS$	joule	J	$m^2\,kg\,s^{-2}$
specific Gibbs free energy, specific Gibbs function	g	$g = G/m$	joule per kilogram	J/kg	$m^2\,s^{-2}$
molar Gibbs free energy, molar Gibbs function	G_m	$G_m = G/n$	joule per mole	J/mol	$m^2\,kg\,s^{-2}\,mol$
Massieu function	J	$J = -A/T$	joule per kelvin	J/K	$m^2\,kg\,s^{-2}\,K^{-1}$
Planck function	Y	$Y = -G/T$	joule per kelvin	J/K	$m^2\,kg\,s^{-2}\,K^{-1}$
humidity, absolute humidity	Φ, a	$\Phi = m_w/V$ [25)]	kilogram per cubic meter	kg/m³	$m^{-3}\,kg$
specific humidity	s, q	$s = m_w/m$ [26)]	one	1	
degree of humidity	u, x	$u = m_w/m_0$ [27)]	one	1	
dryness	A	$A = m_0/m; A = 1 - s$	one	1	
relative humidity	φ	$\varphi = \Phi/\Phi_{max}$ [28)]	one	1	
volume humidity	ψ	$\psi = V_w/V_0$ [29)]	one	1	
degree of saturation	χ	$c = \Phi/\Phi_{max} = x/x_s$	one	1	

[24)] For reversible phenomenon only.

[25)] V is the volume of the humid material; m_w is the water mass in the material.

[26)] m represents humid material mass (solid material, liquid or gas mixture); m_w is the water mass in the material.

[27)] $m_0 = m - m_w$ represents dried (dehydrated) material mass; $u = s/(1 - s)$.

[28)] Φ_{max} is the highest possible value of quantity Φ under the same pressure and temperature. For ideal gas mixture $\varphi = p/p_m$.

[29)] $V_0 = V - V_w$ represents the dried material volume; V_w represents the water quantity volume of the material before drying (dehydration).

Table 5-4   Conversion Factors of Some Units of Different Systems

a) Units of force (F)
   1 J/m = W s/m = N
   1 dyn = 10^{-5} N
   1 kp = 9.806 65 N
   1 pdl = 0.138 255 N
   1 lbf = 4.448 22 N

b) Units of pressure (p)
   1 N/m^2 = pa
   1 bar = 10^5 Pa
   1 kp/m^2 = 9.806 65 Pa
   1 mm H$_2$O = 9.806 65 Pa
   1 kp/cm^2 = 0.980 665 bar = 9.806 65×10^4 Pa
   1 atm = 1.013 25×10^5 Pa
   1 mm Hg = 113.332 Pa
   1 Torr = 113.332 Pa
   1 pdl/ft^2 = 1.448 16 Pa
   1 lbf/ft^2 = 47.880 3 Pa

c) Units of dynamic viscosity (η)
   1 P = 0.1 N s/m^2
   1 kp s/ft^2 = 9.806 65 N s/m^2
   1 pdl s/ft^2 = 1.488 16 N s/m^2
   1 lbf s/ft^2 = 0.478 803 N s/m^2

d) Units of energy, work and heat (E, W, Q)
   1 N m = 1 W s = J
   1 erg = 10^{-7} J
   1 kWh = 3.6×10^6 J
   1 kp m = 9.806 65 J
   1 cal = cal$_{lt}$ = 4.186 8 J
   1 Btu = Btu$_{st}$ = 1 055.06 J
   1 ft pdl = 0.042 1401 J
   1 ft lbf = 1.355 82 J

e) Units of power (P)
   1 J/s = M m/s = W
   1 erg/s = 10^{-7} W
   1 cal/s = 4.186 8 W
   1 kcal/h = 1.163 W
   1 kp m/s = 9.806 65 W
   1 KS = 735.499 W
   1 ft pdl/s = 4.214 01×10^{-2} W
   1 ft lbf/s = 1.355 82 W
   1 Btu/h = 0.293 071 W

f) Units of specific heat capacity (c)
   and specific entropy (s)
   1 cal/(kg K) = 4.186 8 J/(kg K)
   1 kp m/(kg K) = 9.806 65 J/(kg K)
   1 ft lbf/(lb °F) = 5.380 32 J/(kg K)
   1 Btu/(lb °F) = 4186.8 J/(kg K)

g) Units of thermal conductivity (λ)
   1 cal/(cm s K) = 4.186 8 W/(cm K)
   1 kcal/(m h K) = 1.163 W/(cm K)
   1 Btu/(ft h °F) = 1.730 73 W/(cm K)

h) Units of coefficient of heat transfer (α, h, k, K)
   1 cal/(s m^2 K) = 4.186 8 W/(cm K)
   1 kcal/(h m^2 K) = 1.163 W/(cm K)
   1 Btu/(h ft^2 °F) = 5.678 26 W/(cm K)

i) Units of heat capacity (C) and entropy (S)
   1 erg/°C = 10^{-7} J/K
   1 cal/K = 4.186 8 J/K
   1 erg/°C = 1899.11 J/K

Table 5-5   Conversion Factors of Units of the Temperature (T, t)

Unit	Symbol	K	°C	°Ré	°F	°R
1 kelvin	K	**1**	**1**	**4/5 = 0.8**	**9/5 = 1.8**	**9/5 = 1.8**
1 degree Celsius	°C	**1**	**1**	**4/5 = 0.8**	**9/5 = 1.8**	**9/5 = 1.8**
1 degree Réaumur	°Ré	**5/4 = 1.25**	**5/4 = 1.25**	**1**	**9/4 = 2.25**	**9/4 = 2.25**
1 degree Fahrenheit	°F	**5/9 = 0.555 55**	**5/9 = 0.555 55**	**4/9 = 0.444 44**	**1**	**1**
1 degree Rankine	°R	**5/9 = 0.555 55**	**5/9 = 0.555 55**	**4/9 = 0.444 44**	**1**	**1**

Examples: 1 °F = 1 °R = 5/9 K = (5/9) °C = (4/9) °Ré   Exact values are printed in **bold** type to distinguish them from rounded values.

Table 5-6   Some Characteristic Temperature Points

State	Temperature				
	K	°C	°Ré	°F	°R
absolute zero	0	−273.15	−218.52	−459.67	0
freezing point of pure water (H$_2$O)	273.15	0	0	+32	491.67
triple point of pure water (H$_2$O)	273.16	+0.01	+0.008	+32.018 3	491.688
boiling point of pure water (H$_2$O)	373.15	+100	+80	+212	671.67

Table 5-7 Numerical Equations which Link Various Temperature Scales

K	°C	°Ré	°F	°R
1	2	3	4	5
1 $\{T\}_K = \{t\}_{°C} + 273.15$	$\{t\}_{°C} = \{T\}_K - 273.15$	$\{t_R\}_{°Ré} = \frac{4}{5}\left[\{T\}_K - 273.15\right]$	$\{t_F\}_{°F} = \frac{9}{5}\{T\}_K - 459.67$	$\{T_R\}_{°R} = \frac{9}{5}\{t\}_K$
2 $\{T\}_K = \frac{5}{4}\{t_R\}_{°Ré} + 273.15$	$\{t\}_{°C} = \frac{5}{4}\{t_R\}_{°Ré}$	$\{t_R\}_{°Ré} = \frac{4}{5}\{t\}_{°C}$	$\{t_F\}_{°F} = \frac{9}{5}\{t\}_{°C} + 32$	$\{T_R\}_{°R} = \frac{9}{5}\{t\}_{°C} + 491.67$
3 $\{T\}_K = \frac{5}{9}\left[\{t_F\}_{°F} + 459.67\right]$	$\{t\}_{°C} = \frac{5}{9}\left[\{t_F\}_{°F} - 32\right]$	$\{t_R\}_{°Ré} = \frac{4}{9}\left[\{T_F\}_{°F} - 32\right]$	$\{t_F\}_{°F} = \frac{9}{4}\{t_R\}_{°Ré} + 32$	$\{T_R\}_{°R} = \frac{9}{4}\{t_R\}_{°Ré} + 491.67$
4 $\{T\}_K = \frac{5}{9}\{t_R\}_{°R}$	$\{t\}_{°C} = \frac{5}{9}\left[\{T_R\}_{°R} - 491.67\right]$	$\{t_R\}_{°Ré} = \frac{4}{9}\left[\{T_R\}_{°R} - 491.67\right]$	$\{t_F\}_{°F} = \{T_R\}_{°Ré} - 459.67$	$\{T_R\}_{°R} = \{t_F\}_{°F} + 459.67$

The numerical equations link the numerical values $\{T\}_K$, $\{t\}_{°C}$, $\{t_R\}_{°Ré}$, $\{t_F\}_{°F}$, $\{t_R\}_{°R}$, of the quantities T, t, t_R, t_F and T_R expressed in units K, °C, °Ré, °F and °R, i.e. $\{T\}_K = \frac{T}{K}$, $\{t\}_{°C} = \frac{t}{°C}$, $\{t_R\}_{°Ré} = \frac{t_R}{°Ré}$, $\{t_F\}_{°F} = \frac{t_F}{°F}$ and $\{T_R\}_{°R} = \frac{T_R}{°Ré}$, where T is the Kelvin temperature, t is the Celsius temperature, t_R is the Réaumur temperature, t_F is the Fahrenheit temperature and T_R is the Rankin temperature, while K is the unit of the temperature Kelvin, °C is the Celsius degree, °Ré is the Réaumur degree, °F is Fahrenheit degree and °R is Rankin degree.

Example: 1. The calculation of the value of the Fahrenheit temperature which corresponds to the state: t = 50 °C, i.e. the numerical value of: $\{t\}°C = \frac{t}{°C} = 50$.

According to expression 2 in column 4 we obtain the Fahrenheit temperature: $\{t_F\}_{°F} = \frac{9}{5}\{t\}_{°C} + 32 = \frac{9}{5} \cdot 50 + 32 = 9 \cdot 10 + 32 = 90 + 32 = 122$. It means that $\{t_F\}_{°F} = \frac{t_F}{°F} = 122$, from which follows that $t_F = 122$ °F.

Note: In tables 5-5, 5-6 and 5-7 the degree Réaumur is represented by the symbol °Ré in order to differentiate it from the symbol °R which represents the degree Rankin.

Table 5.8   Ratio between Celsius and Fahrenheit Degrees

°C	°F	°C	°F	°C	°F	°C	°F	°C	°F
−20	−4.0	40	104.0	100	212.0	160	320.0	400	752
−19	−2.2	41	105.8	101	213.8	161	321.8	410	770
−18	−0.4	42	107.6	102	215.6	162	323.6	420	788
−17	+1.4	43	109.4	103	217.4	163	325.4	430	806
−16	3.2	44	111.2	104	219.2	164	327.2	440	824
−15	5.0	45	113.0	105	221.0	165	329.0	450	842
−14	6.8	46	114.8	106	222.8	166	330.8	460	860
−13	8.6	47	116.6	107	224.6	167	332.6	470	878
−12	10.4	48	118.4	108	226.4	168	334.4	480	896
−11	12.2	49	120.2	109	228.2	169	336.2	490	914
−10	14.0	50	122.0	110	230.0	170	338.0	500	932
−9	15.8	51	123.8	111	231.8	171	339.8	550	1022
−8	17.6	52	125.6	112	233.6	172	341.6	600	1112
−7	19.4	53	127.4	113	235.4	173	343.4	650	1202
−6	21.2	54	129.2	114	237.2	174	345.2	700	1292
−5	23.0	55	131.0	115	239.0	175	347.0	750	1382
−4	24.8	56	132.8	116	240.8	176	348.8	800	1472
−3	26.6	57	134.6	117	242.6	177	350.6	850	1562
−2	28.4	58	136.4	118	244.4	178	352.4	900	1652
−1	30.2	59	138.2	119	246.2	179	354.2	950	1742
±0	32.0	60	140.0	120	248.0	180	356.0	1000	1832
+1	33.8	61	141.8	121	249.8	181	357.8	1050	1922
2	35.6	62	143.6	122	251.6	182	359.6	1100	2012
3	37.4	63	145.4	123	253.4	183	361.4	1150	2102
4	39.2	64	147.2	124	255.2	184	363.2	1200	2192
5	41.0	65	149.0	125	257.0	185	365.0	1250	2282
6	42.8	66	150.8	126	258.8	186	366.8	1300	2372
7	44.6	67	152.6	127	260.6	187	368.6	1350	2462
8	46.4	68	154.4	128	262.4	188	370.4	1400	2555
9	48.2	69	156.2	129	264.2	189	372.2	1450	2642
10	50.0	70	158.0	130	266.0	190	374.0	1500	2732
11	51.8	71	159.8	131	267.8	191	375.8	1550	2822
12	53.6	72	161.6	132	269.6	192	377.6	1600	2912
13	55.4	73	163.4	133	271.4	193	379.4	1650	3002
14	57.2	74	165.2	134	273.2	194	381.2	1700	3092
15	59.0	75	167.0	135	275.0	195	383.0	1750	3182
16	60.8	76	168.8	136	276.8	196	384.8	1800	3272
17	62.6	77	170.6	137	278.6	197	386.6	1850	3362
18	64.4	78	172.4	138	280.4	198	388.4	1900	3452
19	66.2	79	174.2	139	382.2	199	390.2	1950	3542
20	68.0	80	176.0	140	284.0	200	392	2000	3632
21	69.7	81	177.8	141	285.8	210	410	2050	3722
22	71.6	82	179.6	142	287.6	220	428	2100	3812
23	73.4	83	181.4	143	289.4	230	446	2150	3902
24	75.2	84	183.2	144	291.2	240	464	2200	3992
25	77.0	85	185.0	145	293.0	250	482	2250	4082
26	78.8	86	186.8	146	294.8	260	500	2300	4172
27	80.6	87	188.6	147	296.6	270	518	2350	4262
28	82.4	88	190.4	148	298.4	280	536	2400	4352
29	84.2	89	192.2	149	300.2	290	554	2450	4442
30	86.0	90	194.0	150	302.0	300	572	2500	4532
31	87.8	91	195.8	151	303.8	310	590	2550	4622
32	89.6	92	197.6	152	305.6	320	608	2600	4712
33	91.4	93	199.4	153	307.4	330	626	2650	4802
34	93.2	94	201.2	154	309.2	340	644	2700	4892
35	95.0	95	203.0	155	311.0	350	662	3750	4982
36	96.8	96	204.8	156	312.8	360	680	2800	5072
37	98.6	97	206.6	157	314.6	370	698	2850	5162
38	100.4	98	208.4	158	316.4	380	716	2900	5252
39	102.2	99	210.2	159	318.2	390	734	2950	5342

Example: −15 °C = 5 °F; 450 °C = 842 °F.

Interpolation factor

°C	1	2	3	4	5	6	7	8	9	10	20	30
°F	1.8	3.6	5.4	7.2	9	10.8	12.6	14.4	16.2	18	36	54

°C	40	50	60	70	80	90	100
°F	72	90	108	126	144	162	180

Table 5-9 Ratio between Celsius and Fahrenheit Degrees

°F	°C	°F	°C	°F	°C	°F	°C	°F	°C
-459.67	-273.15	31	-0.56	81	27.22	410	210.00	910	487.78
-400	-240.00	32	±0	82	27.78	420	215.56	920	493.33
-350	-212.22	33	0.56	83	28.33	430	211.11	930	498.89
-328	-200.00	34	1.11	84	28.89	440	226.67	940	504.44
-300	-184.44	35	1.56	85	29.44	450	232.22	950	510.00
-250	-156.67	36	2.22	86	30.00	460	337.78	960	515.56
-200	-128.89	37	2.78	87	30.56	470	243.33	970	521.11
-150	-101.11	38	3.33	88	31.11	480	248.89	980	526.67
-148	-100.00	39	3.89	89	31.67	490	254.44	990	532.22
-100	-73.33	40	4.44	90	32.22	500	260.00	1000	537.78
-90	-67.78	41	5.00	91	32.78	510	265.50	1100	593.33
-80	-62.22	42	5.56	92	33.33	520	271.11	1200	648.89
-70	-56.67	43	6.11	93	33.89	530	276.67	1300	704.44
-60	-51.11	44	6.67	94	34.44	540	282.22	1400	760.00
-50	-45.56	45	7.22	95	35.00	550 ·	287.78	1500	815.56
-40	-40.00	46	7.78	96	35.56	560	293.33	1600	871.11
-30	-34.44	47	8.33	97	36.11	570	298.89	1700	926.67
-20	-28.89	48	8.89	98	36.67	580	304.44	1800	982.22
-10	-23.33	49	9.44	99	37.22	590	310.00	1900	1037.8
-0	-17.78	50	10.00	100	37.78	600	315.56	2000	1093.3
1	-17.22	51	10.56	110	43.33	610	321.11	2100	1148.9
2	-16.67	52	11.11	120	48.89	620	326.67	2200	1204.4
3	-16.11	53	11.67	130	54.44	630	332.22	2300	1260.0
4	-15.56	54	12.22	140	60.00	640	337.78	2400	1315.6
5	-15.00	55	12.78	150	65.56	650	343.33	2500	1371.1
6	-14.44	56	13.33	160	71.11	660	348.89	2600	1426.7
7	-13.89	57	13.89	170	76.67	670	354.44	2700	1482.2
8	-13.33	58	14.44	180	82.22	680	360.00	2800	1537.8
9	-12.78	59	15.00	190	87.78	690	365.56	2900	1593.3
10	-12.22	60	15.56	200	93.33	700	371.11	3000	1648.9
11	-11.67	61	16.11	210	98.89	710	376.67	3100	1704.4
12	-11.11	62	16.67	220	104.44	720	382.32	3200	1760.0
13	-10.56	63	17.22	230	110.00	730	387.78	3300	1815.6
14	-10.00	64	17.78	240	115.56	740	393.33	3400	1871.1
15	-9.44	65	18.33	250	121.11	750	398.89	3500	1926.7
16	-8.89	66	18.89	260	126.67	760	404.44	3600	1982.2
17	-8.33	67	19.44	270	132.22	770	410.00	3700	2037.8
18	-7.78	68	20.00	280	137.78	780	415.56	3800	2093.3
19	-7.22	69	20.56	290	143.33	790	421.11	3900	2148.9
20	-6.67	70	21.11	300	148.89	800	426.67	4000	2204.4
21	-6.11	71	21.67	310	154.44	810	432.22	4100	2260.0
22	-5.56	72	22.22	320	160.00	820	437.78	4200	2315.6
23	-5.00	73	22.78	330	165.56	830	443.33	4300	2371.1
24	-4.44	74	23.33	340	171.11	840	448.89	4400	2426.7
25	-3.89	75	23.89	350	176.67	850	454.44	4500	2482.2
26	-3.30	76	24.44	360	182.22	860	460.00	4600	2537.8
27	-2.78	77	25.00	370	187.78	870	465.56	4700	2593.3
28	-2.22	78	25.56	380	193.33	880	471.11	4800	2648.9
29	-1.67	79	26.11	390	198.89	890	476.67	4900	2704.4
30	-1.11	80	26.67	400	204.44	900	482.22	5000	2760.0

Example: -459.67 °F = -273.15 °C; 60 °F = 15.56 °C.

Interpolation factor

°F	1	2	3	4	5	6	7	8	9	10	20	30
°C	0.56	1.11	1.67	2.22	2.78	3.33	3.89	4.44	5.00	5.56	11.11	16.67

°F	40	50	60	70	80	90	100
°C	22.22	27.78	33.33	38.39	44.44	50.00	55.56

Note: When converting the Celsius temperature to Fahrenheit temperature, and vice verse, the first value (in the given examples 1000 °C and 1000 °F) must be read off from the tables in order to take into account the difference in the temperature scales, while the other values are determined by interpolation, as can be seen in the examples.

Example: 2. The expression of the temperature of the melting point of copper (Cu) $t = 1083$ °C in degrees Fahrenheit (°F).
According to table 5-8: 1000 °C = 1832 °F, and by using interpolation:

80 °C = 144 °F and 3 °C = 5.5 °F
1 083 °C = 1 000 °C + 80 °C + 3 °C = 1 832 °F + 144 °F + 5.4 °F = 1 981.4 °F

Or by calculating by using the numerical equation in table 5-7 line 2, column 4, we obtain the numerical value for the unit °F:

$$\{t_F\}_{°F} = \frac{9}{5}\{t\}_{°C} + 32 = \frac{9}{5} \cdot 1\ 083 + 32 = 1\ 949.4 + 32 = 1\ 981.4$$

Since the numerical value is defined by the general expression $\{t_F\} = \dfrac{t_F}{[t_F]}$, it follows that the temperature of the melting point of copper (Cu) in degrees Fahrenheit (°F) is:

$$t_F = \{t_F\}\,[t_F] = 1\ 981.4\ °F$$

Example: 3. The expression of the temperature of the melting point of copper (Cu) $t_F = 1\ 982$ °F in degrees Celsius (°C).
According to table 5-9: 1000 °F = 537.78 °C, and by using interpolation:

900 °F = 500 °C, 80 °F = 44.44 °C and 12 °F = 1.11 °C
1 982 °F = 1 000 °F + 900 °F + 80 °F + 2 °F = 537.78 °C + 500 °C + 44.44 °C + 1.11 °C = 1 083.33 °C

Or by calculating by using the numerical equation in table 5.7 line 3, column 2, we obtain the numerical value for the unit °C:

$$\{t\}_{°C} = \frac{5}{9}[\{t_F\}_{°F} - 32] = \frac{5}{9} \cdot [1\ 982 - 32] = \frac{5}{9} \cdot 1\ 950 = 1\ 083.33$$

Since the numerical value is defined by the general expression $\{t\} = \dfrac{t}{[t]}$ it follows that the temperature of the melting point of copper (Cu) in degrees Celsius (°C) is:

$$t = \{t\}\,[t] = 1\ 083.33\ °C$$

It is obvious that in both examples (2 and 3) we are dealing with the same state expressed in different units.

Table 5-10 Fourth Power of Absolute Temperature $\left(\dfrac{T}{100}\right)^4$

Temperature t/°C	Temperature T/K	Potential $\left(\dfrac{T}{100}\right)^4$	Temperature t/°C	Temperature T/K	Potential $\left(\dfrac{T}{100}\right)^4$	Temperature t/°C	Temperature T/K	Potential $\left(\dfrac{T}{100}\right)^4$	Temperature t/°C	Temperature T/K	Potential $\left(\dfrac{T}{100}\right)^4$	Temperature t/°C	Temperature T/K	Potential $\left(\dfrac{T}{100}\right)^4$
0.0	273.12	55.627	3.1	276.25	58.196	6.1	279.25	60.766	9.1	282.25	63.240	12.1	285.25	66.160
0.1	273.25	55.709	3.2	276.35	58.280	6.2	279.35	60.853	9.2	282.35	63.510	12.2	285.35	66.253
0.2	273.35	52.790	3.3	276.45	58.365	6.3	279.45	60.940	9.3	282.45	63.600	12.3	285.45	66.346
0.3	273.45	55.872	3.4	276.55	58.449	6.4	279.55	61.028	9.4	282.55	63.691	12.4	285.52	66.439
0.4	273.55	55.945	3.5	276.65	58.534	6.5	279.65	61.115	9.5	282.65	63.781	12.5	285.65	66.532
0.5	273.65	56.036	3.6	276.75	58.619	6.6	279.75	61.202	9.6	282.75	63.871	12.6	285.75	66.625
0.6	273.75	56.118	3.7	276.85	58.704	6.7	279.85	61.290	9.7	282.85	63.961	12.7	285.85	66.719
0.7	273.85	56.200	3.8	276.95	58.789	6.8	279.95	61.378	9.8	282.95	64.052	12.8	285.95	66.812
0.8	273.95	56.282	3.9	277.05	58.874	6.9	280.05	61.466	9.9	283.05	64.142	12.9	286.05	66.906
0.9	274.05	56.364	4.0	277.13	58.959	7.0	280.15	61.553	10.0	283.15	64.233	13.0	286.15	67.000
1.0	274.15	56.446	4.1	277.25	59.044	7.1	280.25	61.641	10.1	283.25	64.324	13.1	286.25	67.094
1.1	274.25	56.529	4.2	277.35	59.129	7.2	280.35	61.729	10.2	283.35	64.415	13.2	286.35	67.187
1.2	274.35	56.611	4.3	277.45	59.214	7.3	280.45	61.818	10.3	283.45	64.506	13.3	286.45	67.281
1.3	274.45	56.694	4.4	277.55	59.300	7.4	280.55	61.906	10.4	283.55	64.597	13.4	286.55	67.375
1.4	274.55	56.777	4.5	277.65	59.385	7.5	280.65	61.994	10.5	283.65	64.688	13.5	286.65	67.469
1.5	274.65	56.860	4.6	277.75	59.471	7.6	280.75	62.082	10.6	283.75	64.779	13.6	286.75	67.563
1.6	274.75	56.942	4.7	277.85	59.556	7.7	280.85	62.171	10.7	283.85	64.871	13.7	286.85	67.658
1.7	274.85	57.025	4.8	277.95	59.642	7.8	280.92	62.260	10.8	283.95	64.962	13.8	286.95	67.753
1.8	274.95	57.108	4.9	278.05	59.728	7.9	281.05	62.348	10.9	284.05	65.054	13.9	287.05	67.847
1.9	275.05	57.192	5.0	278.15	59.814	8.0	281.15	62.437	11.0	284.15	65.145	14.0	287.15	67.941
2.0	275.15	57.275	5.1	278.25	59.900	8.1	281.25	62.526	11.1	284.25	65.237	14.1	287.25	68.036
2.1	275.25	57.358	5.2	278.35	59.986	8.2	281.35	62.615	11.2	284.35	65.329	14.2	287.35	68.131
2.2	275.35	27.441	5.3	278.45	60.072	8.3	281.45	62.704	11.3	284.45	65.421	14.3	287.45	68.226
2.3	275.45	57.525	5.4	278.55	60.159	8.4	281.55	62.793	11.4	284.55	65.513	14.4	287.55	68.321
2.4	275.55	57.609	5.5	278.65	60.245	8.5	281.65	62.883	11.5	284.65	65.606	14.5	287.65	68.416
2.5	275.65	57.692	5.6	278.75	60.332	8.6	281.75	62.972	11.6	284.75	65.689	14.6	287.75	68.511
2.6	275.75	57.776	5.7	778.85	60.419	8.7	281.85	63.061	11.7	284.85	65.790	14.7	287.85	68.607
2.7	275.85	57.860	5.8	278.95	60.505	8.8	281.95	63.151	11.8	284.95	65.882	14.8	287.95	68.702
2.8	275.95	57.944	5.9	279.05	60.592	8.9	282.05	63.241	11.9	285.05	65.975	14.9	288.05	68.798
2.9	276.05	58.028	6.0	279.15	60.679	9.0	282.15	63.330	12.0	285.15	66.067	15.0	288.15	68.893
3.0	276.15	58.112												

Table 5-10 Fourth Power of Absolute Temperature $\left(\dfrac{T}{100}\right)^4$

Temperature $\frac{t}{°C}$	$\frac{T}{K}$	Potential $\left(\frac{T}{100}\right)^4$	Temperature $\frac{t}{°C}$	$\frac{T}{K}$	Potential $\left(\frac{T}{100}\right)^4$	Temperature $\frac{t}{°C}$	$\frac{T}{K}$	Potential $\left(\frac{T}{100}\right)^4$	Temperature $\frac{t}{°C}$	$\frac{T}{K}$	Potential $\left(\frac{T}{100}\right)^4$	Temperature $\frac{t}{°C}$	$\frac{T}{K}$	Potential $\left(\frac{T}{100}\right)^4$
15.1	288.25	68.989	19.1	292.25	72.899	23.1	296.25	76.974	27.1	300.25	81.216	32.0	305.15	86.65
15.2	288.35	69.084	19.2	292.35	72.999	23.2	296.35	77.078	27.2	300.35	81.324	33.0	306.15	87.79
15.3	288.45	69.180	19.3	292.45	73.099	23.3	296.45	77.182	27.3	300.45	81.433	34.0	307.15	88.94
15.4	288.55	69.276	19.4	292.55	73.199	23.4	296.55	77.286	27.4	300.55	81.541	35.0	308.15	90.11
15.5	288.65	69.373	19.5	292.65	73.299	23.5	296.65	77.391	27.5	300.65	81.650	36.0	309.15	91.28
15.6	288.75	69.469	19.6	292.75	73.399	23.6	296.75	77.495	27.6	300.75	81.758	37.0	310.15	92.47
15.7	288.85	69.565	19.7	292.85	73.500	23.7	296.85	77.599	27.7	300.85	81.867	38.0	311.15	93.67
15.8	288.95	69.661	19.8	292.95	73.600	23.8	296.95	77.703	27.8	300.95	81.976	39.0	312.15	94.88
15.9	289.05	69.758	19.9	293.05	73.701	23.9	297.05	77.808	27.9	301.05	82.085	40.0	313.15	96.10
16.0	289.15	69.854	20.0	293.15	73.801	24.0	297.15	77.913	28.0	301.15	82.195	41.0	314.15	97.33
16.1	289.25	69.950	20.1	293.25	73.902	24.1	297.25	78.018	28.1	301.25	82.304	42.0	315.15	98.57
16.2	289.35	70.047	20.2	293.35	74.003	24.2	297.35	78.123	28.2	301.35	82.413	43.0	316.15	99.82
16.3	289.45	70.145	20.3	293.45	74.104	24.3	297.45	78.229	28.3	301.45	82.522	44.0	317.15	101.10
16.4	289.55	70.242	20.4	293.55	74.205	24.4	297.55	78.334	28.4	301.55	82.632	45.0	318.15	102.39
16.5	289.65	70.339	20.5	293.65	74.306	24.5	297.65	78.440	28.5	301.65	82.742	46.0	319.15	103.68
16.6	289.75	70.436	20.6	293.75	74.407	24.6	297.75	78.545	28.6	301.75	82.851	47.0	320.15	104.99
16.7	289.85	70.533	20.7	293.85	74.509	24.7	297.85	78.650	28.7	301.85	82.961	48.0	321.15	106.31
16.8	289.95	70.630	20.8	293.95	74.611	24.8	297.95	78.755	28.8	301.95	83.072	49.0	322.15	107.64
16.9	290.05	70.728	20.9	294.05	74.713	24.9	298.05	78.861	28.9	302.05	83.182	50.0	323.15	108.98
17.0	290.15	70.826	21.0	294.15	74.814	25.0	298.15	78.967	29.0	302.15	83.292			
17.1	290.25	70.924	21.1	294.25	74.916	25.1	298.25	79.073	29.1	302.25	83.402			
17.2	290.35	71.021	21.2	294.35	75.017	25.2	298.35	79.179	29.2	302.35	83.513			
17.3	290.45	71.119	21.3	294.45	75.119	25.3	298.45	79.268	29.3	302.45	83.623			
17.4	290.55	71.217	21.4	294.55	75.221	25.4	298.55	79.392	29.4	302.55	83.734			
17.5	290.65	71.315	21.5	294.65	75.324	25.5	298.65	79.499	29.5	302.65	83.845			
17.6	290.75	71.413	21.6	294.75	75.426	25.6	298.75	79.605	29.6	302.75	83.956			
17.7	290.85	71.512	21.7	294.85	75.529	25.7	298.85	79.712	29.7	302.85	84.067			
17.8	290.95	71.610	21.8	294.95	75.631	25.8	298.95	79.819	29.8	302.95	84.178			
17.9	291.05	71.709	21.9	295.05	75.734	25.9	299.05	79.926	29.9	303.05	84.289			
18.0	291.15	71.807	22.0	295.15	75.836	26.0	299.15	80.033	30.0	303.15	84.401			
18.1	291.25	71.906	22.1	295.25	75.939	26.1	299.25	80.140	30.1	303.25	84.512			
18.2	291.35	72.005	22.2	295.35	76.042	26.2	299.35	80.247	30.2	303.35	84.623			
18.3	291.45	72.104	22.3	295.45	76.146	26.3	299.45	80.354	30.3	303.45	84.735			
18.4	291.55	72.203	22.4	295.55	76.249	26.4	299.55	80.462	30.4	303.55	84.847			
18.5	291.65	72.302	22.5	295.65	76.352	26.5	299.65	80.569	30.5	303.65	84.959			
18.6	291.75	72.401	22.6	295.75	76.455	26.6	299.75	80.677	30.6	303.75	85.071			
18.7	291.85	72.501	22.7	295.85	76.559	26.7	299.85	80.784	30.7	303.85	85.183			
18.8	291.95	72.600	22.8	295.95	76.662	26.8	299.95	80.892	30.8	303.95	85.295			
18.9	292.05	72.700	22.9	296.05	76.766	26.9	300.05	81.000	30.9	304.05	85.407			
19.0	292.15	72.799	23.0	296.15	76.870	27.0	300.15	81.108	31.0	304.15	85.520			

Table 5-11 Equations for Polytropic Changes of Ideal Gas States Omitting Potential and Kinetic Energy

	Isochor	Isobar	Isotherm	Isentrop	Polytrope
n	$\pm\infty$	0	1	x	n
c_n	c_v	c_p	$\pm\infty$	0	$c_v\dfrac{n-x}{n-1}$
$\dfrac{v_1}{v_2}$	1	$\dfrac{T_1}{T_2}$	$\dfrac{p_2}{p_1}$	$\left(\dfrac{p_2}{p_1}\right)^{\frac{1}{x}}=\left(\dfrac{T_2}{T_1}\right)^{\frac{1}{x-1}}$	$\left(\dfrac{p_2}{p_1}\right)^{\frac{1}{n}}=\left(\dfrac{T_2}{T_1}\right)^{\frac{1}{n-1}}$
$\dfrac{p_1}{p_2}$	$\dfrac{T_1}{T_2}$	1	$\dfrac{v_2}{v_1}$	$\left(\dfrac{v_2}{v_1}\right)^{\frac{1}{x}}=\left(\dfrac{T_1}{T_2}\right)^{\frac{x}{x-1}}$	$\left(\dfrac{v_2}{v_1}\right)^{\frac{1}{n}}=\left(\dfrac{T_1}{T_2}\right)^{\frac{n}{n-1}}$
$\dfrac{T_1}{T_2}$	$\dfrac{p_1}{p_2}$	$\dfrac{v_1}{v_2}$	1	$\left(\dfrac{p_1}{p_2}\right)^{\frac{x-1}{x}}=\left(\dfrac{v_2}{v_1}\right)^{x-1}$	$\left(\dfrac{p_1}{p_2}\right)^{\frac{n-1}{n}}=\left(\dfrac{v_2}{v_1}\right)^{n-1}$
w_{12}	0	$-p\,(v_2-v_1)$	$RT\ln\dfrac{p_2}{p_1}$	$\dfrac{RT_1}{x-1}\left[\left(\dfrac{p_2}{p_1}\right)^{\frac{x-1}{x}}-1\right]$	$\dfrac{RT_1}{n-1}\left[\left(\dfrac{p_2}{p_1}\right)^{\frac{n-1}{n}}-1\right]$
q_{12}	$c_v\,(T_2-T_1)$	$c_p\,(T_2-T_1)$	$-w_{12}$	0	$c_n\,(T_2-T_1)$
w_{t12}	$v\,(p_2-p_1)$	0	w_{12}	xw_{12}	nw_{12}
s_2-s_1	$c_v\ln\dfrac{T_2}{T_1}$	$c_p\ln\dfrac{T_2}{T_1}$	$-R\ln\dfrac{p_2}{p_1}$	0	$c_n\ln\dfrac{T_2}{T_1}$

Isochor: $V=$ constant, Isobar: $p=$ constant, Isotherm: $T=$ constant, Isentrop: $S=$ constant, Polytrope: $pV^n=$ constant.

Table 5-12 Dimensionless Parameters

The symbols given here are those recommended in the International Standard ISO 31, Part XII (second edition, 1981). The ISO recommendation is that two-letter dimensionless parameters to be printed in *sloping* type in the same way as single-letter quantities. When such a symbol is a factor in a product it should be separated from other symbols by a thin space, a multiplication sign or brackets. This disagrees with some journals that set two-letter symbols in roman type to distinguish them from ordinary products. In this report *sloping roman* is used to distinguish a two-letter symbol from the product of two *italic* single-letter symbols.

The symbols used in these definitions have the following meanings:
a, thermal diffusivity ($\lambda/\rho c_p$)
c, velocity of sound
c_p, specific heat capacity at a constant pressure
f, a characteristic frequency
g, acceleration of free fall
h, heat transfer coefficient:
heat/(time × cross sectional area × temperature difference)
k, mass transfer coefficient:
mass/(time × cross sectional area × mole fraction difference)
l, a characteristic length
v, a characteristic speed
x, mole fraction
B, magnetic flux density
D, diffusion coefficient
$\beta' = -\rho^{-1}(\partial\rho/\partial x)_{T,p}$
γ, cubic expansion coefficient: $-\rho^{-1}(\partial\rho/\partial T)_p$
η, viscosity
λ, mean free path (par. b); thermal conductivity (par. c)
μ, magnetic permeability
ν, kinematic viscosity: η/ρ
ρ, (mass) density
σ, surface tension; electric conductivity
Δp, pressure difference
Δt, a characteristic time interval
Δx, a characteristic difference of mole fraction
ΔT, a characteristic temperature difference

a. Dimensionless constants of matter

Name	Symbol	Definition	SI units
Prandtl number	Pr	$Pr = \nu/a$	1
Schmidt number	Sc	$Sc = \nu/D$	1
Lewis number	Le	$Le = a/D = Sc/Pr$	1

b. Momentum transport

Name	Symbol	Definition	SI units
Reynolds number	Re	$Re = vl/\nu$	1
Euler number	Eu	$Eu = \Delta p/\rho v^2$	1
Froude number	Fz	$Fz = v(lg)^{-1/2}$	1
Grashof number	Gr	$Gr = l^3 g\gamma\Delta T/\nu^2$	1
Weber number	We	$We = \rho v^2 l/\sigma$	1
Mach number	Ma	$Ma = v/c$	1
Knudsen number	Kn	$Kn = \lambda/l$	1
Strouhal number	Sr	$Sr = lf/v$	1

c. Transport of heat

Name	Symbol	Definition	SI units
Fourier number	Fo	$\mathrm{Fo} = a\Delta t/l^2$	1
Péclet number	Pe	$Pe = vl/a = Re \cdot Pr$	1
Rayleigh number	Ra	$Ra = l^3 g\gamma\Delta T/\nu a = Gr \cdot Pr$	1
Nusselt number	Nu	$Nu = hl/\lambda$	1
Stanton number	St	$St = h/\rho v c_p = Nu/Pe$	1

d. Transport of matter in a binary mixture

Name	Symbol	Definition	SI units
Fourier number for mass transfer	Fo^*	$\mathrm{Fo}^* = D\Delta t/l^2 = Fo/Le$	1
Péclet number for mass transfer	Pe^*	$Pe^* = vl/D = Pe \cdot Le$	1
Grashof number for mass transfer	Gr^*	$Gr^* = l^3 g\beta'\Delta x/\nu^2$	1
Nusselt number for mass transfer	Nu^*	$Nu^* = kl/\rho D$	1
Stanton number for mass transfer	St^*	$St^* = k/\rho v = Nu^*/Pe^*$	1

e. Magnetohydrodynamics

Name	Symbol	Definition	SI units
Magnetic Reynolds number	Rm	$Rm = v\mu\sigma l$	1
Alfvén number	Al	$Al = v(\rho\mu)^{1/2}/B$	1
Hartman number	Ha	$Ha = Bl(\sigma/\rho\nu)^{1/2}$	1
Cowling number (second Cowling number)	Co, Co_2	$Co, Co_2 = B^2/\mu\rho v^2 = Al^{-2}$	1
first Cowling number	Co_1	$Co_1 = B^2 l\sigma/\rho v = {}= Rm \cdot Co_2 = Ha^2/Re$	1

Table 5-13 Standard Atomic Weights of the Elements

Element Name	Symbol	Atomic number, proton number Z	Relative atomic mass (atomic weight) A_r	K	L	M	N	O	P	Q
Hydrogen	H	1	1.0079	1						
Helium	He	2	4.00260	2						
Lithium	Li	3	6.941	2	1					
Beryllium	Be	4	9.012182	2	2					
Boron	B	5	10.81	2	3					
Carbon	C	6	12.011	2	4					
Nitrogen	N	7	14.0067	2	5					
Oxygen	O	8	15.9994	2	6					
Fluorine	F	9	18.99840	2	7					
Neon	Ne	10	20.179	2	8					
Sodium	Na	11	22.98677	2	8	1				
Maghesium	Mg	12	24.305	2	8	2				
Aluminium	Al	13	26.98154	2	8	3				
Silicon	Si	14	28.086	2	8	4				
Phosphorus	P	15	30.97376	2	8	5				
Sulfur	S	16	32.06	2	8	6				
Chlorinė	Cl	17	35.453	2	8	7				
Argon	Ar	18	39.948	2	8	8				
Potassium	K	19	39.098	2	8	8	1			
Calcium	Ca	20	40.08	2	8	8	2			
Scandium	Sc	21	44.9559	2	8	9	2			
Titanium	Ti	22	47.90	2	8	10	2			
Vanadium	V	23	50.9414	2	8	11	2			
Chromium	Cr	24	51.996	2	8	13	1			
Manganese	Mn	25	54.9380	2	8	13	2			
Iron	Fe	26	55.847	2	8	14	2			
Cobalt	Co	27	58.9332	2	8	15	2			
Nickel	Ni	28	58.71	2	8	16	2			
Copper	Cu	29	63.546	2	8	18	1			
Zinc	Zn	30	65.38	2	8	18	2			
Gallium	Ga	31	69.72	2	8	18	3			
Germanium	Ge	32	72.59	2	8	18	4			
Arsenic	As	33	74.9216	2	8	18	5			
Selenium	Se	34	78.96	2	8	18	6			
Bromine	Br	35	79.904	2	8	18	7			
Krypton	Kr	36	83.80	2	8	18	8			
Rubidium	Rb	37	85.4678	2	8	18	8	1		
Strontium	Sr	38	87.62	2	8	18	8	2		
Yttrium	Y	39	88.9059	2	8	18	9	2		
Zirconium	Zr	40	91.22	2	8	18	10	2		
Niobium	Nb	41	92.9064	2	8	18	12	1		
Molybdenum	Mo	42	95.94	2	8	18	13	1		
Technetium	Tc	43	98.9062	2	8	18	14	1		
Ruthenium	Ru	44	101.07	2	8	18	15	1		
Rhodium	Rh	45	102.9055	2	8	18	16	1		
Palladium	Pd	46	106.4	2	8	18	18	0		
Silver	Ag	47	107.868	2	8	18	18	1		
Cadmium	Cd	48	112.40	2	8	18	18	2		
Indium	In	49	114.82	2	8	18	18	3		
Tin	Sn	50	118.69	2	8	18	18	4		
Antimony	Sb	51	121.75	2	8	18	18	5		
Tellurium	Te	52	127.60	2	8	18	18	6		
Iodine	I (J)	53	126.9045	2	8	18	18	7		
Xenon	Xe	54	131.30	2	8	18	18	8		
Caesium	Cs	55	132.9054	2	8	18	18	8	1	
Barium	Ba	56	137.34	2	8	18	18	8	2	
Lanthanum	La	57	138.9055	2	8	18	18	9	2	
Cerium	Ce	58	140.12	2	8	18	19	9	2	
Praseodymium	Pr	59	140.9077	2	8	18	21	8	2	
Neodymium	Nd	60	144.24	2	8	18	22	8	2	
Promethium	Pm	61	145.0	2	8	18	23	8	2	
Samarium	Sm	62	150.45	2	8	18	24	8	2	
Europium	Eu	63	151.96	2	8	18	25	8	2	
Gadolinium	Gd	64	157.25	2	8	18	25	9	2	
Terbium	Tb	65	158.9254	2	8	18	27	8	2	
Dysprosium	Dy	66	162.50	2	8	18	28	8	2	
Holmium	Ho	67	164.9304	2	8	18	29	8	2	

Element		Atomic number, proton number	Relative atomic mass (atomic weight)	Electron distribution by shells (K to Q)						
Name	Symbol	Z	A_r	K	L	M	N	O	P	Q
Erbium	Er	68	167.26	2	8	18	30	8	2	
Thulium	Tm	69	168.9342	2	8	18	31	8	2	
Ytterbium	Yb	70	173.04	2	8	18	32	8	2	
Lutetium	Lu	71	174.97	2	8	18	32	9	2	
Hafnium	Hf	72	178.49	2	8	18	32	10	2	
Tantalum	Ta	73	180.9479	2	8	18	32	11	2	
Tungsten	W	74	183.85	2	8	18	32	12	2	
Rhenium	Re	75	186.2	2	8	18	32	13	2	
Osmium	Os	76	190.2	2	8	18	32	14	2	
Iridium	Ir	77	192.22	2	8	18	32	15	2	
Platinum	Pt	78	195.09	2	8	18	32	17	1	
Gold	Au	79	196.9665	2	8	18	32	18	1	
Mercury	Hg	80	200.59	2	8	18	32	18	2	
Thallium	Tl	81	204.37	2	8	18	32	18	3	
Lead	Pb	82	207.2	2	8	18	32	18	4	
Bismuth	Bi	83	208.9804	2	8	18	32	18	5	
Polonium	Po	84	209.0	2	8	18	32	18	6	
Astatine	At	85	210.0	2	8	18	32	18	7	
Radon	Rn	86	222.0	2	8	18	32	18	8	
Francium	Fr	87	223.0	2	8	18	32	18	8	1
Fadium	Ra	88	226.0254	2	8	18	32	18	8	2
Actinium	Ac	89	227.0	2	8	18	32	18	9	2
Thorium	Th	90	232.038	2	8	18	32	18	10	2
Protactinium	Pa	91	231.0359	2	8	18	32	20	9	2
Uranium	U	92	238.029	2	8	18	32	21	9	2
Nertunium	Np	93	237.0482	2	8	18	32	22	9	2
Plutonium	Pu	94	244	2	8	18	32	24	8	2
Americium	Am	95	243	2	8	18	32	25	8	2
Curium	Cm	96	247	2	8	18	32	25	9	2
Berkelium	Bk	97	247	2	8	18	32	26	9	2
Californium	Cf	98	251	2	8	18	32	28	8	2
Einsteinium	Es	99	254	2	8	18	32	29	8	2
Fermium	Fm	100	257	2	8	18	32	30	8	2
Mendelevium	Md	101	258	2	8	18	32	31	8	2
Nobelium	No	102	255	2	8	18	32	32	8	2
Lawrencium	Lr (Lw)	103	256	2	8	18	32	32	9	2
Unnilquadium	Ku	104	261	2	8	18	32	32	10	2
Unnilpentium		105		2	8	18	32	32	11	2

Ans — Lax: Taschenbuch für Chemiker und Physiker, zweite berichtigte Auflage. Springer Verlag, Berlin, Göttingen, Heidelberg, 1949 (Ger.).

Bošnjaković, F. Nauka o toplini — dio prvi (Thermodynamics), 3rd edition, Tehnička knjiga, Zagreb, 1962 (Serb).

Bošnjaković, F. Nauka o toplini — dio drugi (Thermodynamics). Nakladni zavod Hrvatske, Zagreb, 1950 (Serb).

Brezinšćak, M. Mjere i sistemi jedinica (Measures and Units). Tehnička knjiga, Zagreb, 1961 (Serb).

Brezinšćak, M. Mjerenje i računanje u tehnici i znanosti (Measurement and Evaluation in Science and Technology). Tehnička knjiga, Zagreb, 1971 (Serb).

British standard 350, Conversion Factors and Tables, part 1.

Christian, W. Technische Wärmelehre, Band 1. Bergakademie Freiberg, 1958 (Ger.).

Christian, W. Technische Wärmelehre, Band 2. Bergakademie Freiberg, 1960 (Ger.).

Dampftafeln, Ausgabe: Oktober 1983, Hoechst Aktiengesellschaft Frigen-Informationdienst, Frankfurt am Main (Ger.).

Das Grundwissen des Ingenieurs. Fachbuch Verlag, Leipzig, 1959 (Ger.).

Diphyl, Ein Wärmeübertragungsmittel. Farbenfabriken Bayer AG, Leverkusen, 1961 (Ger.).

Dobrovolny, B. Základy technicke thermodynamiky (Fundamentals of Technical Thermodynamics), 2nd edition. Nakladatel Josef Hokr, Praha, 1947 (Czech).

Dubbel. Taschenbuch für den Maschinenbau , Band I. Springer Verlag, Berlin, Göttingen, Heidelberg, 1955 (Ger.).

Eckert, E. Einführung in den Wärme und Stoffaustausch, zweite überarbeitete Auflage. Springer Verlag, Berlin, Göttingen, Heidelberg, 1959 (Ger.).

Faltin, H. Technische Wärmelehre, 4 erweiterte Auflage. Akademie Verlag, Berlin, 1961 (Ger.).

Filipović-Sabioncello. Laboratorijski Priručnik I dio (Laboratory Handbook), book I. Tehnička knjiga, Zagreb, 1962 (Serb).

Filipović-Sabioncello. Laboratorijski Priručnik I dio (Laboratory Handbook), book II. Tehnička knjiga, Zagreb, 1960 (Serb).

Frigen 12. Fabwerke Hoechst AG, Frankfurt am Main (Ger.).

Frigen 22, Dampftafel. Fabwerke Hoechst AG, Frankfurt am Main, 1961 (Ger.).

Grassmann, P. Physikalische Grundlagen der Chemie-Ingenieur-Technik, Band I. Verlag H.R. Sauerlander Co., Aarau, Frankfurt am Main, 1961 (Ger.).

Gregorig, R. Wärmeaustauscher, Grundlagen der Chemischen Technik, Band IV. Verlag H.R. Sauerlander Co., Aarau, 1959 (Ger.).

Gröber-Erk-Grigull. Grundgesetze der Wärmeübertragung — 3 Auflage. Springer Verlag, Berlin, 1955 (Ger.).

Gustavson, P. Tehnologija gorivih plinova (Technology of Gaseous Fuel). Tehnička knjiga, Zagreb, 1952 (Serb).

Haeder/Gärtner. Die Gesetzlichen Einheiten in der Technik, 2 Auflage. Beuth-Vertrieb GmbH, Berlin, Köln, Frankfurt am Main (Ger.).

Hahnemann, H.W. Die Umstellung auf das Internationale Einheitensystem in Mechanik und Wärmetechnik. VDI Verlag GmbH, Düsseldorf, 1959 (Ger.).

Häussler, W. Das Mollier — IX — Diagramm für Feuchte Luft und Seine Technischen Anwendungen. Verlag von Theodor Steinkopff, Dresden, Leipzig, 1960 (Ger.).

Heid-Kollmar. Die Strahlungsheizung, zweite verbesserte Auflage. Carl Marhold Verlagsbuchhandlung, Halle a.S., 1943 (Ger.).

Henning, F. Wärmetechnische Richtwerte. VDI-Verlag GmbH, Berlin, 1938 (Ger.).

Steam Tables. Hoechst Aktiengeselschaft Frigen-Informationsdienst, Frankfurt am Main, 1983 (Ger.).

Hütte. Inženjerski priručnik, prvi deo (Engineer's Handbook). Gradevinska knjiga, Belgrade, 1954 (Serb).

Justi, F. Spezifische Wärme, Enthalpie, Entropie, Dissoziation, technischer Gasse. Verlag von Julius Springer, Berlin, 1938 (Ger.).

Kältemaschinen Regeln, 5 Auflage herausgegeben von Deutschen Kältetechnischen Verein. Verlag C.F.Müller, Karlsruhe, 1958 (Ger.).

Karpov, V.P. Osnovy tekhnicheskoi termodinamiki (Fundamentals of Technical Thermodynamics). Mashgiz, Moscow, 1948 (Rus.).

Klingelnberg. Tehniči priručnik (Technical Handbook), book I. Tehnička knjiga, Zagreb, 1952 (Serb).

Kolbah, D. Priručnik za hemičare (Chemist's Handbook), 2nd edition. Tehnička knjiga, Zagreb, 1961 (Serb).

Kraut, B. Džepni strojarski priručnik (Handbook of Mechanics), 1st Serbo-Croatian edition. Naklada Duro Dakovic, Lubliana — Slav. Brod, 1956 (Serb).

Kraut, B. Džepni strojarski priručnik (Handbook of Mechanics), 2nd Serbo-Croatian edition. Tehnička knjiga, Zagreb, 1963 (Serb).

Landolt-Börnstein. Physikalisch-Chemische Tabellen, V Auflage, I und II Band. Verlag von Julius Springer, Berlin, 1923 (Ger.).

Landolt-Börnstein. Physikalisch-Chemische Tabellen, erster Ergänzungsband. Verlag von Julius Springer, Berlin, 1927 (Ger.).

Landolt-Börnstein. Physikalisch-Chemische Tabellen, zweiter Ergäanzungsband, I und II Teil. Verlag von Julius Springer, Berlin, 1931 (Ger.).

Landolt-Börnstein. Physikalisch-Chemische Tabellen, dritter Ergänzungsband, I und II Teil. Verlag von Julius Springer, Berlin, 1935 (Ger.).

Landolt-Börnstein. Physikalisch-Chemische Tabellen, dritter Ergänzungsband, III Teil. Verlag von Julius Springer, Berlin, 1936 (Ger.).

Lobscheid, H. Dampf, Bobcock-Handbuch, 2 Auflage. Deutsche Babcock Wilcoh-Dampfkessel-Werke A.G. Oberhausen-RHL, 1952 (Ger.).

Malić, D. Termodinamika i termotehnika (Thermodynamics and Heat Engineering), 3rd edition. Gradevinska knjiga, Belgrade, 1963 (Serb).

Mašinski priručnik (Handbook of Mechanics) 2, Tehničar. Gradevinska knjiga, Belgrade, 1956 (Serb).

Mashinostroeniye, entsiklopedicheskii spravochnik, (Encyclopaedia of Mechanical Engineering), vol. 1. Mashgiz, Moscow, 1947 (Rus.).

Mayer/Schiffner. Technische Thermodynamik. VEB Fachbuchverlag, Leipzig, 1986 (Ger.).

Müller-Grag. Technologie der Brennstoffe, 4 Auflage. Franz Deuticke, Wien, 1955 (Ger.).

Netz, H. Formen der Technik, Band I. Georg Westermann Verlag, Braunschweig, Berlin, Hamburg, München, Kiel, Darmstadt, 1960 (Ger.).

Nuber, F. Wärmetechnische Berechnung der Feuerungs — und Dampfkessel — Anlagen. 14 Auflage. R. Oldenbourg, München, 1962 (Ger.).

Orešnik, M. Termodinamične tabele in diagrami (Thermodynamic Tables in Diagrams). Univerzitetna založba, Lubliana, 1962 (Serb).

Padelf/Laporte. Einheiten und Grötenarten der Naturwissenschaften. VEB Fachbuchverlag, Leipzig, 1967 (Ger.).

Pohlmann, W. Taschenbuch für Kältetechniker, 13 Auflage. Verlag C.F.Müller, Karlsruhe, 1956 (Ger.).

Radošević, N. Priručnik za hemičare i tehnologe (Chemist's and Technologist's Handbook). Tehnička knjiga, Belgrade, 1962 (Serb).

Rant, Z. Termodinamika (Thermodynamics). Univerzitetna založba. Lubliana, 1963 (Serb).

Ražnjević, K. Fizikalne veličine i mjerne jedinice SI (Physical Quantities and SI Units). Nakladni zavod Znanje, 1986 (Serb).

Ražnević, K. Physical Quantities and International Units of Measurement. Hemisphere Publishing Corp., New York, 1990.

Recknagel-Sprenger. Taschenbuch für Heizung, Lüftung und Klimatechnik. R. Oldenbourg, München, 1960 (Ger.).

Rietschel-Raiss. Heiz und Lüftungstechnik. 14 Auflage. Springer Verlag, Berlin, Göttingen, Heidelberg, 1960 (Ger.).

Spravochnik mashinostroitelya (Handbook of Mechanical Engineering), vol. 2. Mashgiz, Moscow, 1952 (Rus.).

Technisches Handbuch, Band II. Erwin Engel Verlag, Wien, 1952 (Ger.).

Uhland, W.H. Uhlands Ingenieur-Kalender. Alfred Kröner Verlag, Stuttgart, 1953 (Ger.).

Vukalovich, M.P. Tablitsi termodinamicheskikh svoistv vody i vodyanogo para (Tables of Thermodynamic Properties of Water and Steam of Water), 7th edition. Gosenergoizdat, Moscow, Leningrad, 1963 (Rus.).

Zeise, H. Thermodynamik, Band III/1 Tabellen. S.Hierzel Verlag, Leipzig, 1954 (Ger.).

Zeise, H. Thermodynamik, Band III/2 graphische Darstellungen und Literatur, S.Hierzel Verlag, Leipzig, 1957 (Ger.).